Transistor
Circuit
Design

Contributors

R. P. Abraham

W. W. Bamsch

I. Berlin

J. R. Biard

H. F. Cooke

R. H. Crawford

R. T. Dean

L. A. Delhom

G. E. Giles

L. L. Glover

R. C. Grimes

D. B. Hall

L. K. Hill

S. W. Holcomb

J. W. Huffhines

T. J. Huffington

G. D. Johnson

J. M. King

J. W. Kronlage

A. G. Lambert

J. S. Lee

G. Luecke

W. T. Matzen

P. M. Norris

F. L. Opp

J. T. Pierce

R. L. Pritchard

J. E. Setliff

L. J. Sevin

W. C. Tatom

J. H. Taylor

W. H. Tulloch

J. P. Vergez

J. A. Walston

R. K. Walters

R. L. Weber

E. C. Wilson

R. T. Windecker

Transistor Circuit Design

Prepared by the Engineering Staff of
Texas Instruments Incorporated

Edited by

Joseph A. Walston
Transistor Applications Manager

John R. Miller
Technical Publications Manager

McGraw-Hill Book Company, Inc.
New York   Toronto   London

TRANSISTOR CIRCUIT DESIGN

Preface

During its first decade as a transistor manufacturer, Texas Instruments Incorporated has received many thousands of requests for assistance with circuit design problems. TI has responded to these queries by means of both personal communications and application bulletins having limited circulation. The pattern of recurring inquiries which has emerged suggested both the need for this book and its content.

"Transistor Circuit Design" was compiled for the practicing circuit design engineer. It offers solutions to a wide range of basic engineering problems. A few of the discussions are addressed to the tyro; most require a considerable degree of engineering sophistication; all have proved to be of interest to our correspondents.

One volume cannot encompass discussions in depth of all design problems. Accordingly, this edition is the first of a series—subject matter will be selected and revised in response to recommendations from our readers and as required by advances in the art. Although engineers throughout the Semiconductor-Components division have contributed to this volume, TI's Transistor Applications branch is responsible for its final form and will welcome suggestions and inquiries.

Information contained in this book is believed to be accurate and reliable. However, responsibility is assumed neither for its use nor for any infringement of patents or rights of others which may result from its use. No license is granted by implication or otherwise under any patent or patent right of Texas Instruments or others.

Texas Instruments Incorporated
Semiconductor–Components Division

Contents

Part **1**

Fundamental Considerations

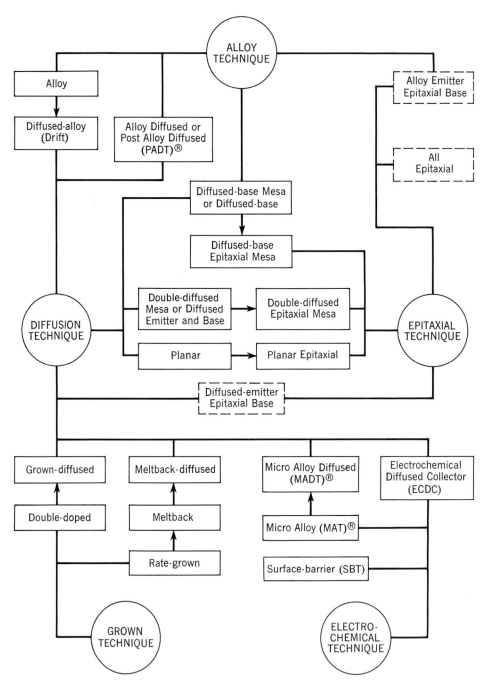

Fig. 1.1. Interrelationship of transistor fabricating techniques and transistor types.

Classification of Junction Transistors

INTRODUCTION

Originally, junction transistors were made by one of two classical methods—the *grown-junction* or the *alloy-junction* technique. During the past few years, however, a number of new types of transistors made by the diffusion technique have become available, with a wide variety of descriptive names such as *mesa* and *planar;* and more recently, the *epitaxial* type of transistor has been introduced. This chapter classifies each of the transistors presently available into one of five major categories, and describes briefly its method of construction.

CLASSICAL TECHNIQUES

The first junction transistors, of 1951, were of the grown-junction type.[1, 2,*] This type comprises a rectangular bar, as shown in Fig. 1.2, cut from a germanium crystal that has been grown from a melt to which suitable impurities have been added. Emitter and collector contacts then are made to the base region, generally located approximately midway between the two ends. Shortly after the grown-junction technique was introduced, the alloy technique was developed;[3] in this technique, small dots of indium are fused, or alloyed, into opposite sides of a germanium wafer of suitable conductivity, as illustrated in Fig. 1.3. Emitter and collector contacts then are made to each of the dots, and the base contact is made to the wafer. Silicon transistors also can be made by each of these two techniques.

Attempts to reduce the dimensions of alloy transistors for high-frequency use subsequently led to the introduction of the electrochemical etching and plating technique, which in turn led to the development of the *surface-barrier* transistor.[4] Physically, the construction of this type of transistor is very similar to that of the alloy transistor, except that depressions are etched into the wafer before the collector and emitter dots are added, and the latter are generally of much smaller size than in the conventional alloy transistor.

* Superscript numbers refer to bibliography entries at end of chapter.

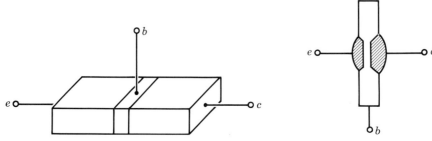

Fig. 1.2. Grown-junction-type transistor.   Fig. 1.3. Alloy-junction-type transistor.

In each of these three classical methods of fabrication, the three regions of the transistor—emitter, base, and collector—generally are of uniform resistivity.

DIFFUSION TECHNIQUE

The introduction of solid-state diffusion techniques has provided an additional method, capable of a high degree of control, of making PN junctions and, hence, of fabricating transistors. Moreover, the use of diffusion techniques makes it possible to provide nonuniform emitter, base, and collector regions in such a manner as to provide better transistor electrical characteristics than are obtainable from the classical designs of uniform-resistivity regions.

Diffusion of impurities can take place from within the crystal,[5] or through the surface from an external source;[6, 7] the latter process generally is termed *gaseous diffusion.* It is also possible to combine diffusion techniques with one of the classical techniques described above. For example, a nonuniform base region can be obtained by diffusion, while the emitter and collector junctions can be made by the alloy technique.[8] Alternatively, one PN junction can be formed by diffusion while the other is formed by one of the classical techniques, or the entire transistor—i.e., the two PN junctions—also can be formed by diffusion.

As a result of this flexibility, transistors made by diffusion may assume any one of several different physical appearances. For example, some diffused transistors are indistinguishable in appearance from corresponding classical structures. On

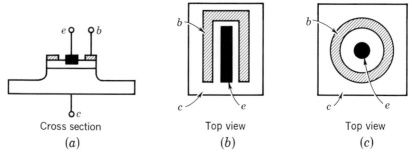

Cross section   Top view   Top view
    (a)   (b)   (c)

Fig. 1.4. Mesa-type construction for diffused-base or double-diffused transistors: (a) cross section; (b) top view; (c) top view.

the other hand, some types of diffusion transistors are of the *mesa* construction, illustrated by Fig. 1.4, in which the semiconductor wafer is etched down in steps so that the base and emitter regions appear as plateaus above the collector region. Both rectangular and circular cross sections have been employed, as illustrated by Fig. 1.4*b* and *c*, respectively.

EPITAXIAL TECHNIQUE

More recently, a new technique—that of epitaxial deposition—has been developed.[9, 10] (Actually, this technique was known in the mid-1950 years, but only since 1960 has it been applied to commercial devices.) In the epitaxial technique as applied to transistors, a film of single-crystal semiconductor material is deposited on a single-crystal substrate. Most of the work in epitaxial films to date has consisted of depositing a layer of a semiconductor material on a substrate of the same material—germanium on germanium or silicon on silicon. However, the deposited epitaxial film may be of a different material from that of the substrate.

Thus far, the epitaxial technique has been used only to develop transistors in which a thin, high-resistivity collector region is deposited on a low-resistivity substrate of the same conductivity type:[10-12] a thin P-type collector region is deposited on a P+ substrate for germanium PNP transistors, or a thin N-type collector region is deposited on an N+ substrate for NPN silicon transistors. This leads to a family of transistors which will be termed here *epitaxial collector,* but known by a variety of names, as, for example, *diffused-base epitaxial mesa transistor.* The chief advantage of this type of transistor is lower saturation resistance and lower collector storage time relative to a comparable nonepitaxial device.

However, the epitaxial technique is considerably more general, and it is possible to deposit multiple layers of different conductivity type, to form epitaxial PN junctions. For example, an N-type epitaxial collector can be deposited on an N+ substrate, followed by a P-type epitaxial-base-layer deposition.[9, 13] The emitter region then may be made by conventional diffusion technique or by the alloying technique. This form of device (which is not yet commercially available) is termed here the *epitaxial-base* transistor. Finally, it should be possible to extend the epitaxial technique further to make a complete *all-epitaxial* transistor by epitaxially depositing collector, base, and emitter layers.[9]

PLANAR TECHNIQUE

The planar technique mentioned often in commercial literature is an auxiliary technique for making junctions by standard diffusion techniques. Strictly speaking, the term planar refers to a device in which each of the junctions—emitter-base and collector-base in a transistor, as shown in Fig. 1.5—is brought to a common plane surface,[14] as distinguished from the mesa structure in which one or more of the PN junctions

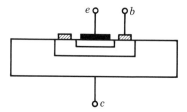

Fig. 1.5. Planar-type double-diffused transistor.

is brought to the surface at the edge of a cylinder comprising the mesa, as shown in Fig. 1.4a. However, the real significance of the planar structure is not that it is planar, per se. Rather, what is important is that, as a result of the technique of diffusion through an oxide mask used in making a planar structure, the junctions are formed *beneath* a protective oxide layer. Hence, many of the surface problems associated with other types of transistors having junctions exposed at the surface are avoided in this type of construction. As a result, the chief advantage of this type of transistor is generally lower reverse currents and improved d-c gain at low currents.

Note, however, that an equivalent structure could be fabricated in which the junctions were formed beneath a protective oxide coating but which were not actually planar.

CLASSIFICATION SCHEME

In this chapter, the transistor types are classified according to five major categories —grown, alloy, electrochemical, diffusion, and epitaxial. The method of classification employed is somewhat arbitrary— e.g., a grown-diffused transistor could be classified as either a grown transistor or a diffused transistor! Accordingly, a cross-referencing scheme is necessary and is provided here by means of the chart fronting this chapter (Fig. 1.1). This chart illustrates the interrelationships among the various techniques for producing different types of transistor structures.

Grown-junction Transistors (Fig. 1.2). DOUBLE-DOPED TRANSISTOR. The original grown-junction transistor, formed by growing a crystal and successively adding P- and N-type impurities to the melt during the course of growing the crystal.[1]

RATE-GROWN OR GRADED-JUNCTION TRANSISTOR. A variation of the double-doped type described above, in which N- and P-type impurities are added to the melt from which the crystal is grown.[15, 16] The growth rate then is varied in a periodic manner while the crystal is drawn from the melt. During one stage of the growth cycle, the crystal contains a predominance of P-type impurities, whereas during the other stage of the cycle, N-type impurities dominate, resulting in a crystal from which NPN transistors can be cut.

MELT-BACK TRANSISTOR. A variation of the *rate-grown* transistor in which the rate growing is performed on a very small physical scale.[17] This results in a lower thermal time constant for the crystal-growing system, so that thinner base regions and, hence, higher-frequency transistors can be obtained.

MELT-QUENCH TRANSISTOR. Very similar to *melt-back* transistor described above.[18]

GROWN-DIFFUSED TRANSISTOR. A transistor made by combining diffusion techniques and the *double-doped* process.[19] In this case, suitable N- and P-type impurities are added simultaneously to the melt during the course of growing the crystal. Subsequently, the base region is formed by diffusion during the continued growth of the crystal.

MELT-BACK DIFFUSED TRANSISTOR. A transistor made by combining diffusion techniques and the *melt-back* process, analogous to the combination of the grown and diffusion techniques described above leading to *grown-diffused* transistors.[20–22] In this case, however, the impurities are added to the transistor bar by the *melt-back* process, and the base region subsequently is formed by diffusion by baking the transistor bar.

Alloy-junction Transistors (Fig. 1.3). ALLOY TRANSISTOR. Previously known also as *fused* transistor, this comprises a wafer of semiconductor material of N- or P-type conductivity with two dots containing P- or N-type impurities, respectively, fused or alloyed into the wafer on opposite sides of the wafer to provide emitter and base junctions, while the base region comprises the original semiconductor wafer.[3, 23, 24]

DRIFT TRANSISTOR.

1. In scientific literature, a *drift* transistor refers to a type of transistor having a nonuniform, or graded, base region so that high-frequency response is improved relative to a similar uniform-base structure.[25]
2. *Drift* transistor, *commercial:* A trade name for a *diffused-alloy* transistor.[8]

DIFFUSED-ALLOY TRANSISTOR. A transistor made by combining diffusion and alloy techniques. The semiconductor wafer first is subjected to a gaseous diffusion to produce the nonuniform base region, and then alloy junctions are formed in exactly the same manner as in a conventional *alloy* transistor.[8] An intrinsic region transistor, e.g., a PNIP unit, can be made by this technique by starting with a semiconductor wafer of essentially intrinsic conductivity.

ALLOY-DIFFUSED TRANSISTOR, OR POST-ALLOY-DIFFUSED TRANSISTOR. Another type of transistor made by combining diffusion and alloy techniques. In this type, the alloy dot material contains *both* N- and P-type impurities. Then the emitter-base junction is formed by the conventional alloy process, while the base region is formed by diffusion from *within* the crystal. (Note that this is the distinction between the diffused-alloy transistor described above and the post-alloy-diffusion technique.) The collector region comprises the original semiconductor wafer.[5, 26, 27] Alternatively, if the original wafer is of the same conductivity type as the base region, then the emitter-base junction and the base region can be formed as described above, while the collector junction can be formed as in a conventional alloy transistor.[28] In this case, as in the diffused-alloy transistor, an intrinsic region can be included between base and collector.

Electrochemically Etched and Plated Transistors (Fig. 1.3). SURFACE-BARRIER TRANSISTOR (SBT). Comprises a wafer of semiconductor material into which depressions have been etched on opposite sides of the wafer by electrochemical techniques.[4] The emitter and collector base *junctions,* or metal-semiconductor contacts, then are formed by electroplating a suitable metal on the semiconductor in the depression areas on opposite sides of the wafer, while the original wafer constitutes the base region.

MICROALLOY TRANSISTOR (MAT). A variation of the *surface-barrier* transistor described above in which suitable N- or P-type impurities are first plated in the etched depressions and then alloyed into the P- or N-type semiconductor wafer.[29]

SILICON-ALLOY TRANSISTOR, OR SURFACE-ALLOY TRANSISTOR (SAT). A variation of the *surface-barrier* transistor described above in which a suitable metal (aluminum) is first evaporated into the etched depressions and then alloyed into the N-type semiconductor wafer.[30-31]

MICROALLOY DIFFUSED TRANSISTOR (MADT).   A transistor made by incorporating diffusion techniques with the *microalloy* transistor construction described above. The semiconductor wafer first is subjected to a gaseous diffusion to provide a nonuniform base region before the electrochemical plating process.[32, 33]

ELECTROCHEMICAL DIFFUSED COLLECTOR (ECDC) TRANSISTOR.[34]   A transistor made by combining diffusion and electrochemical techniques.   A nonuniform base region and the collector-base junction are obtained by gaseous diffusion into a semiconductor wafer that constitutes the collector region.   Then the emitter-base junction is obtained by the use of the electrochemical etch and plating technique, as in the MAT.   The electrochemical technique also is used to place the collector contact close to the collector-base junction.

Diffusion Transistors (Fig. 1.4).   DIFFUSED-BASE TRANSISTOR.   Another type of transistor made by combining diffusion and alloy techniques.   A nonuniform base region and the collector-base junction are formed by gaseous diffusion into a semiconductor wafer that constitutes the collector region.   Then the emitter-base junction is formed by a conventional alloy junction on the base side of the diffused wafer, by evaporation of a metallic stripe, for example, while the remaining portion of the original wafer constitutes the collector region.[6, 35, 36]

DIFFUSED-EMITTER AND BASE OR DOUBLE-DIFFUSED MESA TRANSISTOR.   Comprises a semiconductor wafer which has been subjected to gaseous diffusion of both N- and P-type impurities to form two PN junctions in the original semiconductor material.[7, 37-39]   The active area of the transistor (the area of the collector-base junction) is then defined by etching away the undesired portions of the emitter and base regions to expose a mesa (see Fig. 1.4a).   An intrinsic-region transistor, e.g., PNIP, also can be made by a variation of this process.[40]

TRIPLE-DIFFUSED TRANSISTOR.   A variation of the double-diffused transistor in which the semiconductor wafer first is subjected to a deep diffusion to effectively lower the resistivity of the collector region—e.g., to form an NN+ structure for an NPN transistor.[41-43]   The NN+ wafer is then subjected to gaseous diffusion of both P- and N-type impurities to form emitter-base and collector-base junctions leading to an NPNN+ structure.   Alternatively, this may be considered as an intrinsic-region transistor, for example, NPIN, if the original semiconductor wafer is of very high resistivity.[40]

PLANAR TRANSISTOR.   Comprises a semiconductor wafer which has been subjected to gaseous diffusion of both P- and N-type impurities to form two PN junctions in the original semiconductor material, as in the diffused-emitter and base transistor.   In this case, however, the active area of the device—i.e., the area of the collector-base junction—is defined by oxide masking of the base diffusion, rather than by mesa etching (see Fig. 1.5).[14, 44, 45]

Epitaxial Transistors.   DIFFUSED-BASE EPITAXIAL MESA TRANSISTOR.   One of the epitaxial-collector transistor family.   This transistor is made by combining diffusion, alloy, and epitaxial techniques.   First, a thin collector region is epitaxially deposited upon a low-resistivity substrate.   Then a nonuniform base region and the collector-base junction are formed by gaseous diffusion into the epitaxial collector region.

The emitter-base junction is obtained from a conventional alloy junction on the base side of the diffused wafer.[10, 11]

DOUBLE-DIFFUSED EPITAXIAL MESA TRANSISTOR. Another of the epitaxial-collector transistor family. A thin collector region is epitaxially deposited upon a low-resistivity substrate. Then base and emitter regions are formed as in an ordinary double-diffused mesa transistor, and the collector-base junction area is defined by etching a mesa.[10-12]

PLANAR EPITAXIAL TRANSISTOR. Another of the epitaxial-collector transistor family. A thin collector region is first epitaxially deposited on a low-resistivity substrate. Then base and emitter regions are formed in the same manner as in the conventional planar transistor as described above.

EPITAXIAL-BASE TRANSISTOR. A transistor made by epitaxially depositing a base region of one conductivity type upon a collector region of the opposite conductivity type. The emitter region then can be formed either by alloying or by diffusing, leading, respectively, to an *alloy-emitter epitaxial-base* transistor or a *diffused-emitter epitaxial-base* transistor.[9, 13]

ALL-EPITAXIAL TRANSISTOR. In this case, all three regions of the transistor are obtained by epitaxial deposition.[9]

ACKNOWLEDGMENT

The material presented here by no means describes original work. A number of other semiconductor-device workers have categorized transistors in schemes similar to that described above. In this connection, R. N. Hall,[46] G. C. Dacey and C. D. Thurmond,[47] and P. Kaufmann and G. Freedman[48] have written excellent survey papers describing the methods used to fabricate transistors, in terms of the metallurgy of PN junctions, in considerably more detail than is presented here. The concept of the chart shown in Fig. 1.1 originated with Harry L. Owens.

BIBLIOGRAPHY

1. Shockley, W., M. Sparks, and G. K. Teal: p-n Junction Transistors, *Phys. Rev.,* vol. 83, pp. 151–162, July, 1951.
2. Wallace, R. L., Jr., and W. J. Pietenpol: Some Circuit Properties and Applications of n-p-n Transistors, *Bell System Tech. J.,* vol. 30, pp. 530–563, July, 1951. Also *Proc. IRE,* vol. 39, pp. 753–767, July, 1951.
3. Saby, J. S.: Recent Developments in Transistors and Related Devices, *Tele-Tech,* vol. 10, pp. 32–34, 58, December, 1951.
   Saby, J. S.: Fused Impurity p-n-p Junction Transistors, *Proc. IRE,* vol. 40, pp. 1358–1360, November, 1952.
4. Bradley, W. E.: Part I, Principles of the Surface-barrier Transistor, *Proc. IRE,* vol. 41, pp. 1702–1706, December, 1953. Tiley, J. W., and R. A. Williams: Part II, Electrochemical Techniques for Fabrication of Surface-barrier Transistors, *ibid.,* pp. 1706–1708. Angell, J. B., and F. P. Keiper: Part III, Circuit Applications of Surface-barrier Transistors, *ibid.,* pp. 1709–1712.
5. Beale, J. R. A.: Alloy-diffusion: a Process for Making Diffused-base Junction Transistors, *Proc. Phys. Soc.,* vol. 70B, pp. 1087–1089, November, 1957.

6. Lee, C. A.: A High-frequency Diffused-base Germanium Transistor, *Bell System Tech. J.*, vol. 35, pp. 23–24, January, 1956.
7. Tanenbaum, M., and D. E. Thomas: Diffused Emitter and Base Silicon Transistors, *Bell System Tech. J.*, vol. 35, pp. 1–22, January, 1956.
8. Kestenbaum, A. L., and N. H. Ditrick: Design, Construction, and High-frequency Performance of Drift Transistors, *RCA Rev.*, vol. 18, pp. 12–23, March, 1957.
9. O'Rourke, M. J., J. C. Marinace, R. L. Anderson, and W. H. White: Electrical Properties of Vapor-grown Germanium Junctions, *IBM J. Research and Development*, vol. 4, pp. 256–263, July, 1960.
10. Sigler, John, and S. B. Watelski: Epitaxial Techniques in Semiconductor Devices, *Solid-State J.*, vol. 2, pp. 33–37, March, 1961.
11. Theurer, H. C., J. J. Kleimack, H. H. Loar, and H. Christensen: Epitaxial Diffused Transistors, *Proc. IRE*, vol. 48, pp. 1642–1643, September, 1960.
12. Valdes, L. B.: Characteristics of Silicon Epitaxial Transistors, *Solid-State J.*, vol. 2, pp. 33–36, November, 1961.
13. Clifton, J. K., and H. M. Robertson: A Transistor Utilizing an Epitaxially Grown Base and Collector Region, paper presented at Electron Devices Meeting, Washington, D.C., Oct. 26, 1961.
14. Hoerni, J. A.: Planar Silicon Diodes and Transistors, abstract only, *IRE Trans.*, vol. ED-8, p. 178, April, 1961.
15. Hall, R. N.: p-n Junctions Produced by Growth Rate Variation, *Phys. Rev.*, vol. 88, p. 139, October, 1952.
16. Bridgers, H. E., and E. D. Kolb: Rate-grown Germanium Crystals for High-frequency Transistors, *J. Appl. Phys.*, vol. 26, pp. 1188–1189, September, 1955.
17. Hall, R. N.: Unpublished material presented in June, 1955. See also Baker, D. W.: High-frequency Germanium NPN Tetrode, 1956 *IRE Conv. Record*, part III, pp. 143–150.
18. Pankove, J. I.: Transistor Fabrication by the Melt-Quench Process, *Proc. IRE*, vol. 44, pp. 185–188, January, 1956.
19. Cornelison, B., and W. A. Adcock: Transistors by Grown-diffused Technique, 1957 *IRE WESCON Conv. Record*, part III, pp. 22–27.
20. Statz, H., W. Leverton, and J. Spanos: Unpublished material presented in 1955.
21. Lehovec, K., and A. Levitas: Fabrication of Multiple Junctions in Semiconductors by Surface Melt and Diffusion in the Solid State, *J. Appl. Phys.*, vol. 28, pp. 106–109, January, 1957.
22. Phillips, A. B., and A. N. Intrator: A New High-frequency n-p-n Silicon Transistor, 1957 *IRE Conv. Record*, part III, pp. 3–13.
23. Law, R. R., C. W. Mueller, J. I. Pankove, and L. D. Armstrong: A Developmental Germanium P-N-P Junction Transistor, *Proc. IRE*, vol. 40, pp. 1352–1357, November, 1952.
24. Mueller, C. W., and J. I. Pankove: A p-n-p Triode Alloy-junction Transistor for Radio-frequency Amplification, *RCA Rev.*, vol. 14, pp. 586–598, December, 1953. Also *Proc. IRE*, vol. 42, pp. 386–391, February, 1954.
25. Krömer, H.: Zur Theorie des Diffusions- und des Drift-transistors, parts I, II and III, *Arch. Elekt. Übertr.*, vol. 8, pp. 223–228, 363–369, 499–504, May, August, November, 1954.
    Krömer, H.: The Drift Transistor, "Transistors I," pp. 202–220, RCA Laboratories, Princeton, N.J., 1956.
26. Jochems, T. J. W., O. W. Memelink, and L. J. Tummers: Construction and Electrical Properties of a Germanium Alloy-diffused Transistor, *Proc. IRE*, vol. 46, pp. 1161–1165, June, 1958.

27. Edlinger, W.: High Frequency Transistor by the Alloy-diffusion Technique (in English), *Colloq. intern. sur les dispositifs à semiconducteurs,* vol. 1, pp. 209–215, Editions Chiron, Paris, 1961.

28. Lamming, J. S.: A High-frequency Germanium Drift Transistor by Post Alloy Diffusion, *J. Electronics and Control,* vol. 4, pp. 227–236, March, 1958.

29. Rittmann, A. D., G. C. Messenger, R. A. Williams, and E. Zimmerman: Microalloy Transistor, *IRE Trans.,* vol. ED-5, pp. 49–54, April, 1958.

30. Rittmann, A. D., and T. J. Miles: High Frequency Silicon Alloy Transistor, *IRE Trans.,* vol. ED-3, pp. 78–82, April, 1956.

31. Thornton, C., J. Roshen, and T. Miles: An Improved High-frequency Transistor, *Electronic Inds., Tele-Tech,* vol. 16, pp. 47–49, 124, July, 1957.

32. Thornton, C. G., and J. B. Angell: Technology of Micro-alloy Diffused Transistors, *Proc. IRE,* vol. 46, pp. 1166–1176, June, 1958.

33. McCotter, J. D., M. J. Walker, and M. M. Fortini: A Coaxially Packaged MADT for Microwave Applications, *IRE Trans.,* vol. ED-8, pp. 8–12, January, 1961.

34. Bouchard, J. G. F.: The Electrochemical Diffused-collector Transistor, *Proc. Natl. Electronics Conf.,* vol. 17, pp. 242–249, 1961.

35. Warner, R. M., Jr., G. T. Loman, and J. M. Early: Characteristics, Structure, and Performance of a Diffused-base Germanium Oscillator Transistor, *IRE Trans.,* vol. ED-5, pp. 127–130, July, 1958.

36. Talley, H. E.: A Family of Diffused-base Germanium Transistors, *IRE WESCON Conv. Record,* vol. 2, part III, pp. 115–121, 1958.

37. Wolff, E. A., Jr.: 50 Watt Silicon Diffused Power Transistor, *IRE WESCON Conv. Record,* part III, pp. 40–47, 1957.

38. Aschner, J. F., C. A. Bittman, W. F. J. Hare, and J. J. Kleimack: A Double-diffused Silicon High-frequency Switching Transistor Produced by Oxide Masking Techniques, *J. Electrochem. Soc.,* vol. 106, pp. 413–417, May, 1959.

39. Little, W. A.: A PNP High-frequency Silicon Transistor, *J. Electrochem. Soc.,* vol. 107, pp. 789–791, September, 1960.

40. Iwerson, J. E., J. T. Nelson, and F. Keywell: A Five-watt, Ten-megacycle Transistor, *Proc. IRE,* vol. 46, pp. 1209–1215, June, 1958.

41. Buie, J. F.: A High-frequency Silicon, NPIN, Oscillator Transistor, abstract only, *IRE Trans.,* vol. ED-6, p. 244, April, 1959.

42. Bosenberg, W. A., and A. L. Kestenbaum: A Developmental High-frequency Silicon Transistor, abstract only, *IRE Trans.,* vol. ED-6, p. 244, April, 1959.

43. Roach, W. E.: Designing High-power Transistor Oscillators, *Electronics,* vol. 33, pp. 52–55, Jan. 8, 1960.

44. Allison, D. F., R. H. Beeson, and R. M. Schultz: KMC/s Planar Transistors in Microwatt Logic Circuitry, *Solid State Electronics,* vol. 3, no. 2, pp. 134–141; September, 1961.

45. Grinich, V. H., and J. A. Hoerni: The Planar Transistor Family (in English), *Colloq. intern. sur les dispositifs à semiconducteurs,* vol. 1, pp. 132–142, Editions Chiron, Paris, 1961.

46. Hall, R. N.: Fabrication Techniques for High-frequency Transistors (in English), *Fortschr. Hochfrequenztechnik,* vol. 4, pp. 129–155, Akademische Verlagsgesellschaft m.b.H., Frankfurt am Main, 1959.

47. Dacey, G. C., and C. D. Thurmond: p-n Junctions in Silicon and Germanium: Principles, Metallurgy, and Applications, *Met. Rev.,* vol. 2, pp. 157–192, June, 1957.

48. Kaufmann, P., and G. Freedman: An Analysis of Impurity Distributions and the Relation to Electrical Behavior of Conventional Transistor Constructions, *Semiconductor Prods.,* vol. 2, part I, pp. 17–23, April, 1959; part II, pp. 26–31, May, 1959.

2

Device and Circuit Symbology

Texas Instruments Incorporated, as a member of both EIA and NEMA, supports and adheres to the standards established by these associations. Accordingly, EIA document RS-245 is reproduced here with the permission of EIA, to assist the reader in interpreting symbols and abbreviations as used by TI in its technical publications.

PURPOSE OF STANDARDS

These standards, adopted and issued jointly by the Electronic Industries Association and the National Electrical Manufacturers Association, were formulated by the JEDEC Semiconductor Device Council of the Joint Electron Device Engineering Councils. The JEDEC Semiconductor Device Council is sponsored by both EIA and NEMA to develop standards, proposals and data dealing with semiconductor devices.

EIA-NEMA Standards are adopted in the public interest and are designed to eliminate misunderstandings between the manufacturer and the purchaser and to assist the purchaser in selecting and obtaining without delay the proper product for his particular need. Existence of such standards does not in any respect preclude any member or non-member of EIA or NEMA from manufacturing or selling products not conforming to the standard.

Published by

ELECTRONIC INDUSTRIES ASSOCIATION

Engineering Department

11 West 42nd Street, New York 36, N. Y.

NATIONAL ELECTRICAL MANUFACTURERS ASSOCIATION

155 East 44th Street, New York 17, N. Y.

(Approved by NEMA as a NEMA Standard on 9/29/60)

Price $.80

Printed in U.S.A.

EIA-NEMA STANDARDS

on

LETTER SYMBOLS AND

ABBREVIATIONS FOR

SEMICONDUCTOR DATA

SHEETS AND SPECIFICATIONS

ELECTRONIC INDUSTRIES ASSOCIATION
STANDARD RS-245

NATIONAL ELECTRICAL MANUFACTURERS ASSOCIATION
PUBLICATION No. SK 53 – 1961

Formulated by

JEDEC Semiconductor Device Council

JEDEC RECOMMENDED LETTER SYMBOLS AND ABBREVIATIONS
FOR SEMICONDUCTOR DATA SHEETS AND SPECIFICATIONS

(This Standard was formulated under the cognizance of JEDEC Committee JS-12 on Military Specifications)

INTRODUCTION

This list of recommended letter symbols and abbreviations is the result of work of JS-12, Committee on Military Specifications. Published standards of the American Standards Association, Institute of Radio Engineers and the American Institute of Electrical Engineers, Military Standards, and common usage were all considered in the preparation. The U. S. delegates to the International Electrotechnical Commission were consulted during the preparation, and the standards adopted by that group are in close agreement with this list.

It is intended that the list be reviewed from time to time for additions, deletions or revisions as progress in the field dictates.

CRITERIA AND CONVENTIONS FOR LETTER SYMBOLS

A letter symbol is a character which is used to designate an electrical or physical quantity or an electrical parameter. This use occurs most frequently in mathematical equations (and specifications). Two or more symbols printed together represent a product (multiplication). Letter symbols are distinguished from abbreviations; the latter are used for the units of measurement of the quantities or parameters. The chart shown below will illustrate this point.

QUANTITY	LETTER SYMBOL	UNIT OF MEASUREMENT	ABBREVIATION
Current	I, i	Ampere	AMP, amp or A, a[1]
Voltage	V, v or E, e	Volt	V, v
Resistance	R, r	Ohm	OHM, ohm or Ω[2]
Capacitance	C, c	Farad	F, f
Inductance	L (upper-case only)	Henry	H, h
Time	t (lower-case only)	Second	SEC, sec
Temperature	T (upper-case only)	Degree	DEG, deg[3]

[1] The abbreviation A or a is used with the metric system of multiplier prefixes, for example, μA or μa for microampere.

[2] Ohm should not be abbreviated in text. The abbreviation "Ω" may be used elsewhere with the metric system of multiplier prefixes.

[3] The abbreviation DEG or deg is not used in combination with the abbreviations for temperature scales. The abbreviation "°" is usually used as the combining form for the word degree, for example, °C for degree Centigrade.

1. Letter Symbols for Electrical or Physical Quantities or Electrical Parameters

a. Primary symbol: The letter symbol used to designate a quantity or parameter shall be a single letter. This single letter, referred to as the primary symbol, may be modified by subscripts or superscripts.

EXCEPTIONS:

The symbol BV for breakdown voltage, which has become accepted through long usage, has been continued.

Symbols for frequency cutoff parameters, such as f_{hfe} for small-signal short-circuit forward current transfer ratio cutoff frequency (common emitter), have been formed to provide a consistent method of establishing frequency cutoff symbols for other parameters, such as the y's and z's.

b. Secondary symbol: A subscript or superscript, referred to as the secondary symbol, may be used to modify the primary symbol. The secondary symbol is used to designate special values of states, points, parts, times, etc. An abbreviation may be used as a subscript (secondary symbol).

c. A letter symbol containing both primary and secondary letters has a unique meaning. This meaning is not necessarily the meaning associated with the primary symbol alone, the secondary symbol alone, or a combination meaning formed from both.

14

d. Descriptive information concerning a letter symbol may be added in parentheses after the secondary symbol but on the same level as the primary symbol. Examples: h_{ie} (real) and r_{CE} (sat). The abbreviations rms, max, dc and avg are excluded from the above as this type of information is to be presented as part of the secondary symbol without parentheses. (See paragraph 1f below)

e. Principles of application:

PRIMARY SYMBOLS	
Use lower-case letters for:	Use upper-case letters for:
1. Instantaneous value of current, voltage, and power which vary with time. Example: i, v, p. (See Figure 1.)	1. RMS, maximum, and average (dc) values of current, voltage, and power. Examples: I, V, P. (See Figure 1.)
2. Values of four-pole matrix parameters (ratios of terminal electrical quantities), or other resistances, impedances, admittances, etc., *inherent in the device.* Examples: h_{IB}, r_b, z_{fb}, y_{ic}.	2. Values of four-pole matrix parameters (ratios of terminal electrical quantities), or other resistances, impedances, admittances, etc., *in the external circuits.* Examples: R_c, Z_i, Y_o.

SECONDARY SYMBOLS	
Use lower-case letters for:	Use upper-case letters for:
1. Instantaneous varying component values and rms or effective varying component values. Examples: i_c, I_c.	1. Instantaneous total values, maximum values, and average (dc) values. Examples: i_C, I_{CMAX}, I_C.
2. Small signal values of parameters: Examples: r_b, y_c, h_{ib}, z_{ob}, h_{fb}.	2. Static values and large signal values of parameters. Examples: r_B, h_{IB}, h_{FB}.

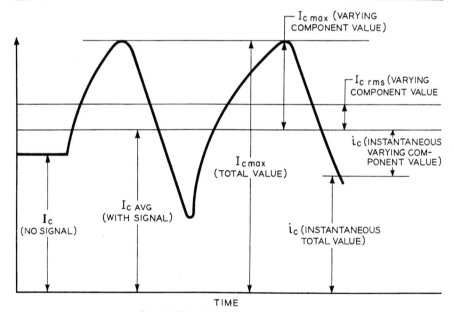

Figure 1. Chart of Collector Current Versus Time

f. Additional conventions for secondary symbols:

(1) If necessary to distinguish between maximum, average, or root-mean-square values, the appropriate abbreviation may be used as a subscript. Examples: I_{cmax}, I_{CAVG}, I_{crms}.

(2) Electrode abbreviations used as subscripts shall be as shown below:

$$E, e = \text{emitter electrode}$$
$$B, b = \text{base electrode}$$
$$C, c = \text{collector electrode}$$
$$\mathbf{J, j} = \text{electrode, general}$$

The use of upper-case letters and lower-case letters for electrode abbreviations shall conform to the following chart:

SYMBOL	SIGNIFICANCE	ELECTRODE ABBR FOR USE AS SUBSCRIPT
i, v, p	Instantaneous varying component value	e, b, c, j
i, v, p	Instantaneous total value	E, B, C, J
I, V, P	RMS or effective varying component value	e, b, c, j
I, V, P	Maximum or average (dc) value	E, B, C, J

(3) The first subscript or subscript pair in matrix notation, identifies the element of the four-pole matrix:

$$i \text{ or } 11 = \text{input}$$
$$o \text{ or } 22 = \text{output}$$
$$f \text{ or } 21 = \text{forward transfer}$$
$$r \text{ or } 12 = \text{reverse transfer}$$

(4) The second subscript or the subscript following the numeric pair identifies the circuit configuration:

$$e = \text{common emitter}$$
$$b = \text{common base}$$
$$c = \text{common collector}$$
$$j = \text{common electrode, general}$$

2. Type Face

a. In textbooks and technical magazines, the use of italic type is recommended for letter symbols and letter subscripts, whether upper or lower case. Numerals appearing as subscripts shall be printed in roman type.

b. In specifications and technical reports prepared on a typewriter and intended for reproduction by a photo-offset process, the use of conventional typewriter type faces is recommended for letter symbols and letter subscripts, whether upper or lower case, and for numerals appearing as subscripts.

CRITERIA AND CONVENTIONS FOR ABBREVIATIONS

An abbreviation is a shortened form of a word or word combination. Abbreviations do not encompass letter symbols or graphical symbols.

1. **Short Words.** Short words are not usually abbreviated unless their abbreviations have been established by long practice.

2. **Spacing.** An abbreviation is usually written with no spaces left between the letters of the abbreviation. The use of hyphens and slant bars is avoided where practicable.

3. **Use of Periods.** Periods are used only to avoid misinterpretation of an abbreviation.

4. **Lettering.** Upper-case or lower-case letters may be used as appropriate except where the use of a particular case has been established by long practice. A multiletter abbreviation will not be a mixture of upper-case and lower-case letters.

5. **Subscripts and Superscripts.** Subscripts and superscripts are not used in abbreviations.

6. **Clarity.** Abbreviations shall be used only when their meanings are unquestionably clear. WHEN IN DOUBT, SPELL IT OUT.

7. **Word Combinations.** Abbreviations or word combinations shall be used as such and shall not be separated for use singly.

8. **Tense and Number.** The same abbreviation shall be used for all tenses, and the singular and plural forms of a given word.

9. **Type Face.** Abbreviations and numerals shall be printed in roman type.

SYMBOLS AND ABBREVIATIONS FOR SEMICONDUCTOR DEVICES

B, b   base electrode

b_n when multiple base electrodes are present, each is numbered in sequence (b1, b2 . . .)

BV_{CBO} breakdown voltage, collector to base, emitter open

BV_{CEO} breakdown voltage, collector to emitter, base open

BV_{CER} breakdown voltage, collector to emitter, with specified resistance between base and emitter

BV_{CES} breakdown voltage, collector to emitter, with base short-circuited to emitter

BV_{EBO} breakdown voltage, emitter to base, collector open

BV_R breakdown voltage, reverse

C, c   collector electrode

C_{ib} input capacitance (common base)

C_{ic} input capacitance (common collector)

C_{ie} input capacitance (common emitter)

C_{ob} output capacitance (common base)

C_{oc} output capacitance (common collector)

C_{oe} output capacitance (common emitter)

E, e   emitter electrode

f_{hfb} small-signal short-circuit forward current transfer ratio cutoff frequency (common base)

f_{hfc} small-signal short-circuit forward current transfer ratio cutoff frequency (common collector)

f_{hfe} small-signal short-circuit forward current transfer ratio cutoff frequency (common emitter)

f_{max} maximum frequency of oscillation

G_{PB} large-signal average power gain (common base)

G_{pb} small-signal average power gain (common base)

G_{PC} large-signal average power gain (common collector)

G_{pc} small-signal average power gain (common collector)

G_{PE} large-signal average power gain (common emitter)

G_{pe} small-signal average power gain (common emitter)

h_{FB} static value of the forward current transfer ratio (common base)

h_{fb} small-signal short-circuit forward current transfer ratio (common base)

h_{FC} static value of the forward current transfer ratio (common collector)

h_{fc} small-signal short-circuit forward current transfer ratio (common collector)

h_{FE} static value of the forward current transfer ratio (common emitter)

h_{fe} small-signal short-circuit forward current transfer ratio (common emitter)

h_{IB} static value of the input resistance (common base)

h_{ib} small-signal value of the short-circuit input impedance (common base)

h_{IC} static value of the input resistance (common collector)

h_{ic} small-signal value of the short-circuit input impedance (common collector)

h_{IE} static value of the input resistance (common emitter)

h_{ie}	small-signal value of the short-circuit input impedance (common emitter)
$h_{ie}(\text{real})$	real part of the small-signal value of the short-circuit input impedance (common emitter)
h_{OB}	static value of the open-circuit output conductance (common base)
h_{ob}	small-signal value of the open-circuit output admittance (common base)
h_{OC}	static value of the open-circuit output conductance (common collector)
h_{oc}	small-signal value of the open-circuit output admittance (common collector)
h_{OE}	static value of the open-circuit output conductance (common emitter)
h_{oe}	small-signal value of the open-circuit output admittance (common emitter)
h_{rb}	small-signal value of the open-circuit reverse voltage transfer ratio (common base)
h_{rc}	small-signal value of the open-circuit reverse voltage transfer ratio (common collector)
h_{re}	small-signal value of the open-circuit reverse voltage transfer ratio (common emitter)
I, i	region of a device which is intrinsic and in which neither holes nor electrons predominate
I_B	base current (dc)
I_b	base current (rms)
i_b	base current (instantaneous)
I_C	collector current (dc)
I_c	collector current (rms)
i_c	collector current (instantaneous)
I_{CBO}	collector cutoff current (dc), emitter open
I_{CEO}	collector cutoff current (dc), base open
I_{CER}	collector cutoff current (dc), with specified resistance between base and emitter
I_{CEX}	collector current (dc), with specified circuit between base and emitter
I_{CES}	collector cutoff current (dc), with base short-circuited to emitter
I_E	emitter current (dc)
I_e	emitter current (rms)
i_e	emitter current (instantaneous)
I_{EBO}	emitter cutoff current (dc), collector open
I_F	forward current (dc)
i_F	forward current (instantaneous)
I_O	average output (rectified) current
I_R	reverse current (dc)
i_R	reverse current (instantaneous)
K_θ	thermal derating factor
L_c	conversion loss
N, n	region of a device where electrons are the majority carriers
NF	noise figure
P, p	region of a device where holes are the majority carriers
P_{BE}	total power input (dc or average) to the base electrode with respect to the emitter electrode
p_{BE}	total power input (instantaneous) to the base electrode with respect to the emitter electrode
P_{CB}	total power input (dc or average) to the collector electrode with respect to the base electrode

p_{CB}	total power input (instantaneous) to the collector electrode with respect to the base electrode
P_{CE}	total power input (dc or average) to the collector electrode with respect to the emitter electrode
p_{CE}	total power input (instantaneous) to the collector electrode with respect to the emitter electrode
P_{EB}	total power input (dc or average) to the emitter electrode with respect to the base electrode
p_{EB}	total power input (instantaneous) to the emitter electrode with respect to the base electrode
P_{IB}	large-signal input power (common base)
P_{Ib}	small-signal input power (common base)
P_{IC}	large-signal input power (common collector)
P_{Ic}	small-signal input power (common collector)
P_{IE}	large-signal input power (common emitter)
P_{Ie}	small-signal input power (common emitter)
P_{OB}	large-signal output power (common base)
P_{ob}	small-signal output power (common base)
P_{OC}	large-signal output power (common collector)
P_{oc}	small-signal output power (common collector)
P_{OE}	large-signal output power (common emitter)
P_{oe}	small-signal output power (common emitter)
P_T	total power input (dc or average) to all electrodes
p_T	total power input (instantaneous) to all electrodes
R_B	external base resistance
R_C	external collector resistance
$r_{CE}(\text{sat})$	collector to emitter saturation resistance
R_E	external emitter resistance
R_L	load resistance
T	temperature
T_A	ambient temperature
T_C	case temperature
t_d	delay time
t_f	fall time
t_{fr}	forward recovery time
T_J	junction temperature
T_{opr}	operating temperature
t_p	pulse time
t_r	rise time
t_{rr}	reverse recovery time
t_s	storage time
T_{stg}	storage temperature

t_w	pulse average time
θ	thermal resistance
θ_{J-A}	thermal resistance, junction to ambient
θ_{J-C}	thermal resistance, junction to case
V_{BB}	base supply voltage (dc)
V_{BC}	base to collector voltage (dc)
V_{bc}	base to collector voltage (rms)
v_{bc}	base to collector voltage (instantaneous)
V_{BE}	base to emitter voltage (dc)
V_{be}	base to emitter voltage (rms)
v_{be}	base to emitter voltage (instantaneous)
V_{CB}	collector to base voltage (dc)
V_{cb}	collector to base voltage (rms)
v_{cb}	collector to base voltage (instantaneous)
V_{CC}	collector supply voltage (dc)
V_{CE}	collector to emitter voltage (dc)
V_{ce}	collector to emitter voltage (rms)
v_{ce}	collector to emitter voltage (instantaneous)
$V_{CE}(sat)$	collector to emitter saturation voltage
V_{EB}	emitter to base voltage (dc)
V_{eb}	emitter to base voltage (rms)
v_{eb}	emitter to base voltage (instantaneous)
V_{EC}	emitter to collector voltage (dc)
V_{ec}	emitter to collector voltage (rms)
v_{ec}	emitter to collector voltage (instantaneous)
V_{EE}	emitter supply voltage (dc)
V_F	forward voltage (dc)
v_F	forward voltage (instantaneous)
V_{CBF}	dc open-circuit voltage (floating potential) between the collector and base, with the emitter biased in the reverse direction with respect to the base
V_{ECF}	dc open-circuit voltage (floating potential) between the emitter and collector, with the base biased in the reverse direction with respect to the collector
V_{RT}	reach through voltage
V_R	reverse voltage (dc)
v_R	reverse voltage (instantaneous)

3

Transistor Specifications

3.1. THE DATA SHEET

The transistor circuit designer must rely heavily upon the manufacturer's data sheets for device information. It is therefore the manufacturer's responsibility to present extensive design data in the simplest possible form.

Considerable thought goes into the layout of today's well-prepared, informative data sheet. This section presents a general discussion of Texas Instruments data sheets, detailing the information normally given and where it may be found. In Chaps. 4, 5, and 6, each parameter normally found on a data sheet is discussed in detail. IRE symbol notation for transistors and their associated circuitry is also presented.

Data sheets published by Texas Instruments normally consist of eight sections. A brief description of the device is given, followed by sections on environmental tests, mechanical data, absolute ratings, electrical characteristics, and typical characteristic curves. Typical application data and parameter measurement information are usually included.

A typical Texas Instruments data sheet is reproduced here. Its numbered parts are analyzed as follows:

N-P-N TYPES 2N1302, 2N1304, 2N1306, AND 2N1308
P-N-P TYPES 2N1303, 2N1305, 2N1307, AND 2N1309
COMPLEMENTARY ALLOY-JUNCTION GERMANIUM TRANSISTORS

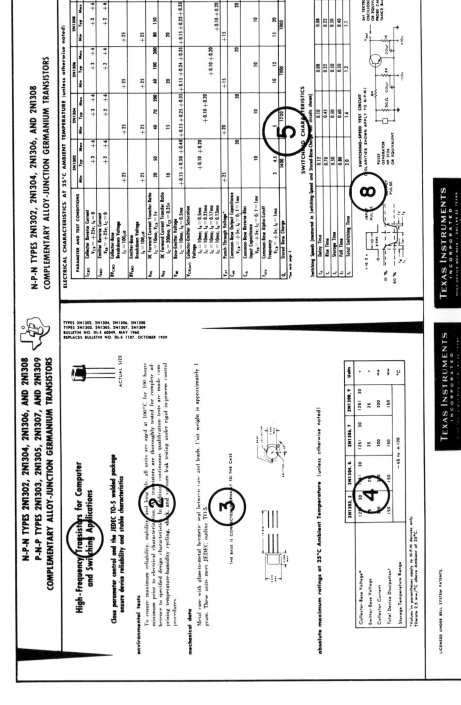

High-Frequency Transistors for Computer and Switching Applications

Close parameter control and the JEDEC TO-5 welded package ensure device reliability and stable characteristics

environmental tests

To ensure maximum reliability, stability and long life, etc. all units are aged at 100°C for 100 hours minimum prior to electrical characterization. Transistors are thoroughly tested for complete additionment to specified design characteristics. In addition continuous qualification tests are made comprising temperature-humidity cycling, shock, and vacuum leak testing under rigid improvens control procedures.

mechanical data

Metal case with glass-to-metal hermetic seal between case and leads. Unit weight is approximately 1 gram. These units meet JEDEC outline TO-5.

THE BASE IS CONNECTED TO THE CASE

absolute maximum ratings at 25°C Ambient Temperature (unless otherwise noted)

	2N1302, 3	2N1304, 5	2N1306, 7	2N1308, 9	Units
Collector-Base Voltage*	(2) 30	(2) 30	(25) 30	(25) 30	v
Emitter-Base Voltage	25	25	25	25	v
Collector Current	300	300	300	300	ma
Total Device Dissipation†	150	150	150	150	mw
Storage Temperature Range	−65 to +100				°C

*Values in parentheses apply to N-P-N devices only.
†Derate 2.5 mw/°C above Ambient of 25°C.

TYPES 2N1302, 2N1304, 2N1306, 2N1308
TYPES 2N1303, 2N1305, 2N1307, 2N1309
BULLETIN NO. DL-S 60349, MAY 1960
REPLACES BULLETIN NO. DL-S 1187, OCTOBER 1959

ACTUAL SIZE

N-P-N TYPES 2N1302, 2N1304, 2N1306, AND 2N1308
COMPLEMENTARY ALLOY-JUNCTION GERMANIUM TRANSISTORS

ELECTRICAL CHARACTERISTICS AT 25°C AMBIENT TEMPERATURE (unless otherwise noted)

PARAMETER AND TEST CONDITIONS	2N1302 Min	Typ	Max	2N1304 Min	Typ	Max	2N1306 Min	Typ	Max	2N1308 Min	Typ	Max	Unit
I_{CBO} Collector Reverse Current $V_{CB} = +25v, I_E = 0$		+3	+6		+3	+6		+3	+6		+3	+6	µa
I_{EBO} Emitter Reverse Current $V_{EB} = +25v, I_C = 0$		+2	+6		+2	+6		+2	+6		+2	+6	µa
BV_{CBO} Collector-Base Breakdown Voltage $I_C = 100µa$	+25			+25			+25			+25			v
BV_{EBO} Emitter-Base Breakdown Voltage $I_E = 100µa$	+25			+25			+25			+25			v
h_{FE} DC Forward Current Transfer Ratio $I_C = 10ma; V_{CB} = 1v$	20	50		40	70		60	100	300	80	150		
h_{FE} DC Forward Current Transfer Ratio $I_C = 200ma; V_{CB} = 0.35v$	10			15			20			20			
V_{BE} Base-Emitter Voltage $I_C = 10ma; I_B = 0.5ma$	+0.15	+0.30	+0.40	+0.15	+0.25	+0.35	+0.15	+0.24	+0.35	+0.15	+0.23	+0.35	v
$V_{CE(sat)}$ Collector-Emitter Saturation Voltage $I_C = 10ma, I_B = 0.5ma$		+0.10	+0.20		+0.10	+0.20		+0.10	+0.20		+0.10	+0.20	v
$V_{CE(sat)}$ $I_C = 10ma, I_B = 0.25ma$													v
$V_{CE(sat)}$ $I_C = 10ma, I_B = 0.17ma$													v
$V_{CE(sat)}$ $I_C = 10ma, I_B = 0.13ma$													v
V_{pt} Punch-Through Voltage*	+25			+20			+15			+15			v
C_{ob} Common-Base Output Capacitance $V_{CB} = +5v, I_E = 0, f = 1mc$		10	20		10	20		10			10	20	µµf
C_{ib} Common-Base Reverse-Bias Input Capacitance $V_{EB} = +5v, I_C = 0, f = 1mc$		10			10			10			10		µµf
f_{hfb} Common-Base Alpha-Cutoff Frequency $V_{CB} = +5v, I_E = 1ma$	3	4.5		5	10	12		10		15	20		mc
Q_s Stored Base Charge		1400			1200			1000			1000			µµas

*See note page 3

SWITCHING CHARACTERISTICS

Switching Speeds (measured in Switching-Speed and Stored-Base-Charge test circuits shown)

	2N1302	2N1304	2N1306	2N1308	
t_d Delay Time	0.12	0.10	0.08	0.08	µsec
t_r Rise Time	0.70	0.45	0.22	0.22	µsec
t_s Storage Time	0.50	0.50	0.50	0.50	µsec
t_f Fall Time	0.80	0.60	0.40	0.40	µsec
t_T Total Switching Time	2.0	1.6	1.3	1.1	µsec

SWITCHING-SPEED TEST CIRCUIT
(POLARITIES SHOWN APPLY TO N-P-N)

S41 TEKTRONIX OSCILLOSCOPE OR EQUIVALENT PROBE CAPACITANCE 8uuf

TEXAS INSTRUMENTS
INCORPORATED
POST OFFICE BOX 5012 • DALLAS 22, TEXAS

22

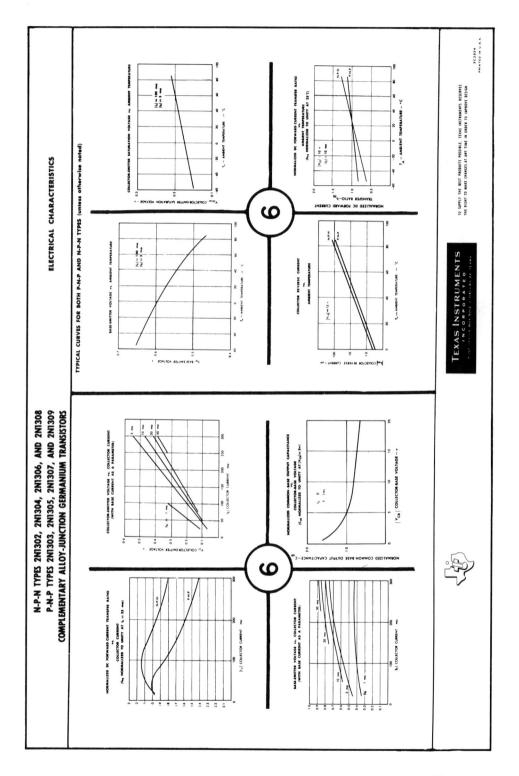

N-P-N TYPES 2N1302, 2N1304, 2N1306, AND 2N1308
P-N-P TYPES 2N1303, 2N1305, 2N1307, AND 2N1309
COMPLEMENTARY ALLOY-JUNCTION GERMANIUM TRANSISTORS

ELECTRICAL CHARACTERISTICS

TYPICAL CURVES FOR BOTH P-N-P AND N-P-N TYPES (unless otherwise noted)

TEXAS INSTRUMENTS
INCORPORATED

TO SUPPLY THE BEST PRODUCTS POSSIBLE, TEXAS INSTRUMENTS RESERVES
THE RIGHT TO MAKE CHANGES AT ANY TIME IN ORDER TO IMPROVE DESIGN

23

P-N-P TYPES 2N1303, 2N1305, 2N1307, AND 2N1309
COMPLEMENTARY ALLOY-JUNCTION GERMANIUM TRANSISTORS

ELECTRICAL CHARACTERISTICS AT 25°C AMBIENT TEMPERATURE (unless otherwise noted)

PARAMETER AND TEST CONDITIONS	2N1303 Min	Typ	Max	2N1305 Min	Typ	Max	2N1307 Min	Typ	Max	2N1309 Min	Typ	Max	Units
I_{CBO} Collector Reverse Current $V_{CB}=-25v$, $I_E=0$		-3	-6		-3	-6		-3	-6		-3	-6	μa
I_{EBO} Emitter Reverse Current $V_{EB}=-25v$, $I_C=0$		-2	-6		-2	-6		-2	-6		-2	-6	μa
BV_{CBO} Collector-Base Breakdown Voltage $I_C=100\mu a$	-30			-30			-30			-30			v
BV_{EBO} Emitter-Base Breakdown Voltage $I_E=100\mu a$	-25			-25			-25			-25			v
h_{FE} DC Forward Current Transfer Ratio $I_C=-10ma$, $V_{CE}=-1v$	20	50		40	70		60	100		80	150		
h_{FE} DC Forward Current Transfer Ratio $I_C=-200ma$, $V_{CE}=-0.35v$	10			15			20			20			
V_{BE} Base-Emitter Voltage $I_C=-10ma$, $I_B=-0.5ma$	-0.15	-0.30	-0.40	-0.15	-0.25	-0.35	-0.15	-0.24	-0.35	-0.15	-0.23	-0.35	v
$V_{CE(sat)}$ Collector-Emitter Saturation Voltage $I_C=-10ma$, $I_B=-0.5ma$ $I_C=-10ma$, $I_B=-0.25ma$ $I_C=-10ma$, $I_B=-0.17ma$ $I_C=-10ma$, $I_B=-0.13ma$		-0.10	-0.20		-0.10	-0.20		-0.10	-0.20		-0.10	-0.20	v
V_{PT} Punch-Through Voltage*	-25			-20			-15			-15			v
C_{ob} Common-Base Output Capacitance $V_{CB}=-5v$, $I_E=0$, $f=1mc$		20			20			20			20		μμf
C_{ib} Common-Base Reverse-Bias Input Capacitance $V_{EB}=-5v$, $I_C=0$, $f=1mc$		7			7			7			7		μμf
f_{hfb} Common-Base Alpha-Cutoff Frequency $V_{CB}=-5v$, $I_E=1ma$	3	4		5			10	12		15	20		mc
Q_B Stored Base Charge		1600			1965			1200			1700		μμc

*See note page 3

SWITCHING CHARACTERISTICS

Switching Speeds (measured in Switching-Speed and Stored-Base-Charge test circuit shown)

	2N1303	2N1305	2N1307	2N1309	Units
t_d Delay Time	0.10	0.08	0.06	0.05	μsec
t_r Rise Time	0.40	0.28	0.20	0.15	μsec
t_s Storage Time	0.90	0.80	0.80	0.70	μsec
t_f Fall Time	0.60	0.45	0.35	0.25	μsec
t_t Total Switching Time	2.0	1.6	1.3	1.1	μsec

CIRCUIT FOR DETERMINING VALUE OF STORED BASE CHARGE
(Polarities shown apply to P-N-P)

CIRCUIT APPLICATIONS

COMPLEMENTARY CURRENT-MODE SWITCHES
(TYPICAL NON-SATURATING SWITCH CASCADE CAPABLE OF OPERATION AT A 3mc RATE)

COMPLEMENTARY EMITTER FOLLOWER
(POSITIVE TRANSISTOR ACTION ON BOTH RISE AND FALL)

COMPLEMENTARY INVERTER
(HIGH-SPEED INVERTER)

*PUNCH-THROUGH MEASUREMENT

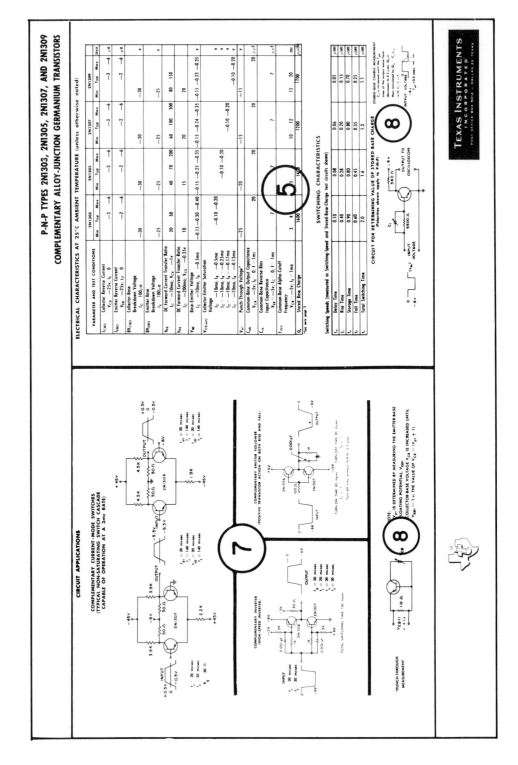

TEXAS INSTRUMENTS
INCORPORATED
POST OFFICE BOX 5012 · DALLAS 22, TEXAS

(1) **Description.** The general classification of the transistor or series is given first. This includes device number, material type, whether NPN or PNP, the basic construction technique used in fabrication, the general purpose for which the device was designed, and its outstanding characteristics. From this description, the designer can quickly determine whether the transistor or transistor series is generally suitable for his application. From this point on, however, the job of selecting a specific transistor for a particular purpose involves consideration of all electrical ratings and characteristics to make sure that the transistor fits the application in every regard.

(2) **Environmental Tests.** The information presented here concerns those tests to which finished devices are subjected before thorough testing for rigid adherence to specified characteristics. The tests most often specified are temperature cycling, aging, stabilization, and mechanical shock testing. In some cases, a particular production process or expected device use dictates additional tests.

Transistors are subjected to these tests to ensure maximum integrity, stability, and long life. The information is presented to indicate to the user the physical ruggedness of the device.

(3) **Mechanical Data.** Mechanical data includes package description as to case type, unit weight, an outline drawing with dimensions, terminal identification, any additional fabrication information, and a statement as to which electrode (if any) is connected to the case.

(4) **Absolute Maximum Ratings.** Absolute maximum ratings are those ratings established by the manufacturer, beyond which degradation of a transistor may occur. These ratings are based on the semiconductor material, manufacturing processes, and internal physical construction. Test conditions are usually not shown for these ratings. Since these ratings represent the extreme capabilities of a transistor, they are not recommended as design conditions. The transistor will not necessarily withstand all maximum rating conditions simultaneously.

(5) **Electrical Characteristics.** This is the portion of the data sheet to which the designer will most often refer. Here he will find the limits to the electrical parameters necessary for a particular circuit design. These limits are guaranteed, and are specified as maximum and/or minimum limits. To prevent any chance of misunderstanding, complete test conditions are specified for every parameter.

In addition to minimum and maximum parameter limits, a typical value is often shown. This value is *not guaranteed,* nor is it required on the data sheet. It merely gives the user an indication of where the mean of a distribution is located when that particular parameter is measured on a very large number of units.

Electrical characteristics are defined as measurable properties of the device which are inherent in its design. Consequently, quantities such as power gain, noise figure, switching times—which are *circuit-dependent*—are not included under Electrical Characteristics, but rather under Operating or Switching Characteristics. Inasmuch as the numerical values of these characteristics are circuit-dependent, a test circuit is included on the data sheet in the section entitled Parameter Measurements Information. In general, these parameters are measured at nominal current and voltage values, since exact values vary slightly with device parameters.

⑥ **Typical Characteristics (Curves).** These curves are usually included, to show the variance of particular parameters with changes in temperature, voltage, and current. The curves are typical, and they conform to information given elsewhere on the data sheet, especially data shown as Electrical, Switching, and Operating Characteristics. Often included are thermal characteristics, which include a dissipation derating curve and possibly curves showing junction temperature response as a function of pulse width and duty cycle.

⑦ **Typical Application Data.** Practical circuit diagrams and typical performance data are usually included on the data sheet. These circuits always correspond to the intended application of the transistor, and are intended to indicate device capabilities as well as to provide the user with practical circuits.

⑧ **Parameter Measurements Information.** This section presents circuits necessary to test the parameters included in the Operating or Switching Characteristics section of the data sheet. Circuit test conditions are specified. Every parameter listed on a data sheet is subject to variation among manufacturers because of difficult test conditions; this information is provided to help minimize correlation problems.

Conclusion. Although much information may be included on a data sheet, it is obvious that the manufacturer must leave much unsaid. Information is included only after a careful appraisal of market requirements, in which cost to the user is the prime consideration. A conscientious manufacturer strives to present those parameters which he knows to be most important to the design engineer, and he strives to present them in the most usable manner.

3.2. TRANSISTOR NUMBERING SYSTEMS

TI Standard Devices. A standard TI device is one that is in production but has not been registered with the Joint Electron Device Engineering Council (JEDEC).

The number assigned to a standard TI device consists of the prefix TI and a sequential number of not more than four digits (e.g., TI 2062).

TI Special Devices. A special device is one that deviates from the product data sheets and/or the JEDEC registration specifications in any detail.

The number assigned to a special device consists of a two-letter prefix and a sequential four- or five-digit number:

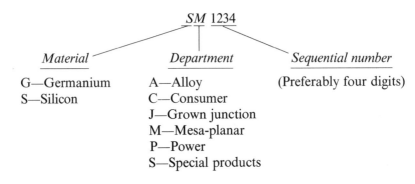

SM 1234

Material	*Department*	*Sequential number*
G—Germanium	A—Alloy	(Preferably four digits)
S—Silicon	C—Consumer	
	J—Grown junction	
	M—Mesa-planar	
	P—Power	
	S—Special products	

TI Development Devices. A development device is one that is in a preproduction stage. The number assigned to a development device consists of TIX and a sequential number of not more than four digits (e.g., TIX 2061). (When a development device becomes a standard TI device, the X is dropped from the prefix.)

JEDEC Type Numbers. A JEDEC type number indicates that a device has been registered with JEDEC. The purpose of registration is to facilitate the purchase and distribution of semiconductor devices by nontechnical individuals, and to provide standardization in the field of electronic devices. Registration procedures are designed to ensure that devices which differ from one another in performance are identified by different type numbers. Type numbers are assigned in numerical sequence as they are requested. 1NXXX numbers usually denote diodes or rectifiers, 2NXXX numbers usually denote triode devices, and 3NXXX numbers usually denote tetrodes.

The semiconductor section of JEDEC is administered by the Semiconductor Device Council, which consists of eight members chosen by the Electronic Industries Association and the National Electrical Manufacturers Association. The council receives policy direction from them. The council formulates the policies and procedures that are followed in assignment of type designations and standardization of electronic devices. The standardization work is carried out in the product committees set up by the council.

One of the essential programs of the Semiconductor Device Council is type registration. The type registration is directed by the type administrator, head of the EIA Standards Laboratory in Newark, N.J. Registration consists of assignment of type numbers, recording of the assignment and the defining data, and releasing of the registration data to the entire electronics industry.

For further information concerning registration, consult *JEDEC Publ.* 15, Type Designation and Registration Procedures for Semiconductor Devices.

Other JEDEC publications particularly useful to design engineers are:

Summary of Registered Crystal Diodes, *JEDEC Publ.* 3.
Summary of Registered Transistors, *JEDEC Publ.* 6.
Summary of Registered Bases and Outlines for Semiconductor Devices, *JEDEC Publ.* 12.

Electronics Industries Association recommended standards, specifications and engineering publications may be obtained from

EIA Engineering Office
Room 2260
11 West 42d Street
New York 36, New York

at the prices indicated in their list.

3.3. MILITARY SPECIFICATIONS

The military services require that transistors they purchase, and those used in equipment they purchase, be of a type they approve procured to specifications they publish. These specifications define the parameters to be measured, the acceptable limits, the environmental and life tests to be performed, and the statistical sampling plan to be used. Government contractors are also directed to use the specifications to specify parts for government equipment. Each of the military services has a branch which issues such specifications.

A transistor procured to these specifications is identified by the letters USA, USN, or USAF stamped on the device. When a transistor type is used by more than one service and the specification has their concurrence, the specifications issued by the Armed Services Electro-Standards Agency and the transistor bear a JAN designation.

Military specifications covering transistors are designated MIL-T- or MIL-S-19500.

Military transistor types differ from regular commercial devices in that they have demonstrated capability of passing many severe environmental tests such as shock, vibration, high G-level centrifuge, temperature cycling, moisture resistance, and usually both storage and operational life tests. These tests are required to assure that the transistor will continue to operate satisfactorily despite severe military service.

Military transistor types may be procured only from qualified suppliers who have demonstrated, by qualification testing, their ability to meet the specification requirements. Furthermore, these military types can be furnished only for use in military equipment; they are not available for commercial uses.

4

Nature of Transistor Quantities
and Parameters

4.1. D-C QUANTITIES AND PARAMETERS

I_{CBO} is the collector current when the collector is biased in the reverse (high resistance) direction with respect to the base, and the emitter is open-circuited. This current is made up of two components, one temperature-dependent and one voltage-dependent. The temperature-dependent component (I_S in Fig. 4.1) is called the saturation current and results from thermal generation of electron-hole pairs, while the voltage-dependent component (I_L) results mainly from surface leakage through the collector-base junction.

I_{CBO} is of primary concern in transistor biasing. Because of its extreme temperature dependence it can become an appreciable part of the base current in low-level applications, and it can cause self-heating and thermal runaway in large-signal applications.

I_{CBO} is generally measured at two voltages, at room temperature and at some elevated temperature. One measurement is made at a voltage low enough so that avalanche multiplication effects are negligible; at this voltage the elevated temperature measurement is also usually made. The temperature is set high enough to ensure that the saturation current is large compared to the leakage current. This allows the designer to use the known temperature dependence of the saturation

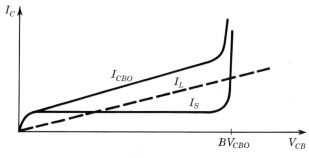

Figure 4.1

29

current to determine the behavior of I_{CBO} at high temperature. Another measurement is made at or near the maximum voltage rating of the collector-base diode, usually at room temperature only.

Variation of I_{CBO} with Junction Temperature. As stated, I_{CBO} is made up of a saturation component (temperature-dependent) and a leakage component (voltage-dependent), expressed as $I_{CBO} = I_S + I_L$. This relationship is shown graphically in Fig. 4.2. At low temperatures, I_{CBO} is mainly the leakage component; at high temperatures, the saturation component becomes dominant. The temperature dependence of I_S derived from Fermi-Dirac statistics has the form[1]

$$I_S = AT^3 \varepsilon^{-N/T} \tag{1}$$

where A and N are dependent on the physical properties of the semiconductor material and T is absolute temperature in degrees Kelvin.

$$\frac{dI_S}{dT} = AT^3 \varepsilon^{-N/T} \frac{1}{T}\left(3 + \frac{N}{T}\right) = \frac{I_S}{T}\left(3 + \frac{N}{T}\right) \tag{2}$$

Rearranging Eq. (2),

$$\frac{dI_S}{I_S} = \left(3 + \frac{N}{T}\right)\frac{dT}{T} \tag{3}$$

It is common to express the I_S temperature dependence in terms of the number of Kelvin degrees (or centigrade degrees) temperature rise that it takes to double I_S. If we set $dI_S/I_S = 1$ in Eq. (3), we arrive at

$$\Delta T = \frac{T^2}{3T + N} \tag{4}$$

This doubling rate is also temperature-dependent; for a transistor that has a large leakage component, however, it has been observed that some constant doubling rate can be used as a conservative approximation over the useful temperature range. For silicon transistors a ΔT of 10 C° has commonly been used, and for germanium transistors a ΔT of 14 C°. However, use of this approximation for transistors that have low leakages (such as planar transistors) can cause the designer trouble, especially at low temperatures. From Eq. (4) we find that $\Delta T = 10$ C° at 130°C

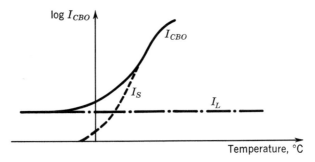

Figure 4.2

for silicon transistors ($N = 14{,}000°$K for silicon). $\Delta T = 10$ C° is a conservative approximation above $130°$C for silicon transistors with low leakage currents, but at $25°$C (room temperature), we find that $\Delta T = 5.97$ C°. It is apparent that applying the $\Delta T = 10$ C° rule of thumb to a value of I_{CBO} measured at room temperature will yield far too optimistic values of I_{CBO} at higher temperatures.

Variation of I_{CBO} with Applied Voltage. At low voltages, the leakage component of I_{CBO} varies almost linearly with applied voltage. At higher voltages, the very strong electric field in the narrow collector-base depletion layer causes a large increase in the kinetic energy of current carriers (holes and electrons) passing through this region; when the carriers *collide* with atoms of the crystal structure, enough energy is released to generate other electron-hole pairs, which in turn are accelerated by the strong electric field and may collide with other atoms, generating still more electron-hole pairs. This process is called avalanche multiplication, and it results in a rapid increase in collector current with collector voltage.

I_{CEO}—The collector current when the collector is biased in the reverse (high resistance) direction with respect to the emitter and the base is d-c open-circuited.

I_{CES}—The collector current when the collector is biased in the reverse (high resistance) direction with respect to the emitter, and the base is shorted to the emitter.

I_{CER}—The collector current when the collector is reverse-biased with respect to the emitter and the base is returned to the emitter through an external resistance.

The relationship among I_{CEO}, I_{CES}, I_{CER}, and I_{CBO} can be found with the aid of the equivalent circuit of Fig. 4.3. The resistor R from base to emitter represents the general termination at this point. For any value of R, $I_C = I_{CER}$ (for $R = \infty$, $I_C = I_{CEO}$). The current generator I_S is the saturation component of I_{CBO}, the leakage component is accounted for by the resistance r_{CL}, and r_B' is the base spreading resistance. For most practical transistors, the current generator I_E is obtained by recognizing that[2]

$$I_E = \frac{-I_{EBO}}{1 - \alpha_N \alpha_I} \epsilon^{\frac{q\phi_E}{KT}} + \frac{1 - \alpha_N}{1 - \alpha_N \alpha_I} I_{EBO} \tag{5}$$

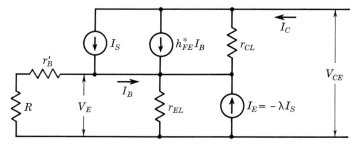

Figure 4.3

where α_N, α_I = normal and inverse common-base current gains of the transistor
$\quad\quad (\alpha_N \cong -h_{FB}^*)$
$\quad\quad I_{EBO}$ = reverse saturation current of the inverted transistor
$\quad\quad \phi_E$ = emitter diode potential
$\quad\quad q$ = electronic charge
$\quad\quad K$ = Boltzmann's constant
$\quad\quad T$ = absolute temperature, °K

If we assume that $KT/q \gg \phi_E$, then Eq. (5) reduces to

$$I_E \cong -\frac{\alpha_N}{1 - \alpha_N \alpha_I} I_{EBO} = \frac{-\alpha_I I_S}{1 - \alpha_N \alpha_I} \tag{6}$$

since $\alpha_N I_{EBO} = \alpha_I I_S$ (see Ref. 2). Then from Fig. 4.3, $\lambda = \alpha_I/(1 - \alpha_N \alpha_I)$. Solving for I_L in Fig. 4.3, we get

$$I_C \cong I_S + h_{FE}^* I_B + \frac{V_{CE}}{r_{CL}} \quad \text{(providing } V_{CE} \gg V_E) \tag{7}$$

and

$$I_B = I_S - \frac{V_E}{r_B' + R} \tag{8}$$

$$V_E = \frac{I_S(1 - \lambda) + h_{FE}^* I_B + V_{CE}/r_{CL}}{(r_B' + R)(r_{CL} + r_{EL}) + r_{CL}r_{EL}} (r_B' + R)r_{CL}r_{EL} \tag{9}$$

Substituting Eq. (9) into Eq. (8) and the result into Eq. (7),

$$I_C = I_{CER} = I_S \left[1 + h_{FE}^* \frac{(r_B' + R)(r_{CL} + r_{EL}) + \lambda r_{CL}r_{EL}}{(r_B' + R)(r_{CL} + r_{EL}) + (1 + h_{FE}^*)r_{CL}r_{EL}} \right]$$
$$+ \frac{V_{CE}}{r_{CL}} \left[1 - \frac{h_{FE}^* r_{EL}r_{CL}}{(r_B' + R)(r_{CL} + r_{EL}) + (1 + h_{FE}^*)r_{EL}r_{CL}} \right] \tag{10}$$

Equation (10) is very cumbersome and the necessary parameters cannot be obtained from a data sheet, but it is useful for qualitative analysis. If we examine Eq. (10) with R set equal to zero and let r_{EL} approach infinity and λ approach zero simultaneously, we find that

$$I_{CER} = I_{CBO} = I_S + \frac{V_{CE}}{r_{CL}}(1 - h_{FB}^*) = I_S + I_L \tag{11}$$

Here our expression reduces to the sum of the thermal saturation current, I_S, and a term representing the collector-base diode leakage current, I_L. Letting R approach infinity in Eq. (10),

$$I_{CER} = I_{CEO} = I_S(1 + h_{FE}^*) + \frac{V_{CE}}{r_{CL}} = (1 + h_{FE}^*)I_{CBO} \tag{12}$$

Finally, setting $R = 0$,

$$I_{CER} = I_{CES} = I_S \left[1 + h_{FE}^* \frac{r_B'(r_{CL} + r_{EL}) + \lambda r_{CL}r_{EL}}{r_B'(r_{CL} + r_{EL}) + (1 + h_{FE}^*)r_{CL}r_{EL}} \right]$$
$$+ \frac{V_{CE}}{r_{CL}} \left[1 - \frac{h_{FE}^* r_{EL}r_{CL}}{r_B'(r_{CL} + r_{EL}) + (1 + h_{FE})r_{CL}r_{EL}} \right] \tag{13}$$

Equation (13) can be reduced to a more familiar expression by making the approximation

$$r'_B \ll r_{CL} \quad \text{and} \quad r'_B \ll r_{EL}$$

which is a good approximation for a practical transistor. With these assumptions, Eq. (13) reduces to

$$I_{CER} = I_S \frac{1}{1 - \alpha_N \alpha_I} + \frac{V_{CE}}{r_{CL}} (1 - h_{FB}^*) \tag{14}$$

In each case we have the sum of a saturation current and a leakage current, which is what we would have intuitively expected before any analysis.

Equation (10) is plotted in Fig. 4.4. This type of plot is sometimes included in data sheets. It should be pointed out that I_{CES} assumes that the collector-to-emitter path is not *punched through,* i.e., that the collector depletion layer does not extend into the emitter.

I_{CEX}—The collector current when the collector is reverse-biased with respect to the base and the base is forward- or reverse-biased with respect to the emitter. This quantity will be approximately equal to I_{CBO} unless the base-emitter junction is reverse-biased by a voltage which exceeds the breakdown rating of this junction.

BV_{CBO}—The breakdown voltage between the collector and base electrodes with the emitter open-circuited.

BV_{CEO}—The breakdown voltage between the collector and emitter with the base open-circuited.

BV_{CES}—The breakdown voltage between the collector and emitter with the base short-circuited to the emitter.

BV_{CER}—The breakdown voltage between the collector and emitter with the base returned to the emitter through an external resistance.

BV_{CEX}—The breakdown voltage between the collector and emitter with a voltage applied between base and emitter.

BV_{EBO}—The breakdown voltage between the emitter and base electrodes with the collector open-circuited.

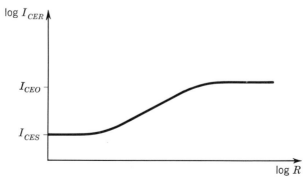

Figure 4.4

The breakdown voltage BV_{CBO} in most transistors is due to the avalanche multiplication of I_{CBO} discussed previously. BV_{CEO} is less than BV_{CBO}, and is quite often less than half of BV_{CBO}. The collector current can be written as

$$I_C = Mh_{FB}I_E \tag{15}$$

M is the multiplication factor that accounts for the rapid rise in I'_{CBO} near BV_{CBO}. An expression for M has been given,[3]

$$M = \frac{1}{1 - (V_{CE}/BV_{CBO})^n} \tag{16}$$

where n is an empirical constant dependent on physical properties of a semiconductor. From Eq. (15) we see that the value of M that will make $I_B = 0$ is $M = -1/h_{FB}$. Substituting this result into Eq. (16),

$$BV_{CEO} = BV_{CBO}\left(\frac{1}{1 + h_{FE}}\right)^{1/n} \tag{17}$$

Equation (17) predicts the voltage at which the total alpha of the transistor equals one. At this voltage, the common-emitter current gain is infinite and the collector current increases unchecked.

It is not possible in practice to measure the true values of these breakdown voltages, since the true value implies that they are measured at infinite collector (or emitter) currents. The values of BV_{CBO}, BV_{CEO}, BV_{CES}, etc., given in a data sheet are measured by applying a constant current to the proper electrodes of the transistor and measuring the voltage between the electrodes. The magnitude of the constant current depends usually on whether the transistor is designed for small-signal, medium-power, or power applications. When the product of the measured current and the breakdown voltage is sufficient to cause heating of the junction, it is customary to make the breakdown voltage measurement with a low duty-cycle pulse (see Pulse Testing, Sec. 5.2). If the junction temperature increases, the measured breakdown voltage decreases because the saturation current increases. This is illustrated in Fig. 4.5.

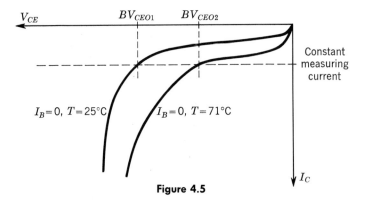

Figure 4.5

V_{PT}—Punch-through voltage—the voltage between the collector and emitter electrodes at which the collector depletion layer extends into the emitter.

BV_{CES}—Breakdown voltage, usually limited by the avalanche breakdown effect previously described rather than by V_{PT}.

V_{EBF}—The d-c open-circuit voltage (floating potential) between the emitter and base electrodes with the collector reverse-biased. This measurement can determine V_{PT}, for if punch-through occurs,

$$V_{EBF} = V_{CB} - V_{PT} \tag{18}$$

V_{BE}—The voltage between the base and emitter electrodes with the base-emitter junction forward-biased and the collector-base junction reverse-biased. In Fig. 4.6, the voltage represented by the ideal characteristic has a negative temperature coefficient; i.e., it decreases with increasing temperature.[4] However, that part of the actual input characteristic beyond the knee of the curve is due mainly to bulk resistance and has a positive temperature coefficient. It is apparent that variation of V_{BE} with temperature depends on the bias current level, the coefficient being negative (approximately -2.5 mv/°C) at low emitter currents, becoming less negative as I_E increases, and possibly going positive at high values of I_E.

$V_{BE(sat)}$—The voltage between the base and emitter electrodes with both the emitter-base and collector-base junctions forward-biased. This quantity is generally measured with the base current greater than the value needed to saturate the lowest h_{FE} transistor of a given type. The previous discussion of V_{BE} vs. temperature applies here also.

$V_{CE(sat)}$—The voltage between the collector and emitter electrodes with both emitter-base and collector-base diodes forward-biased. $V_{CE(sat)}$ is of particular importance in switching applications. It is the minimum switch contact potential, and is usually measured under the same conditions as $V_{BE(sat)}$. It has a positive temperature coefficient since it is partly due to an ohmic drop across the collector bulk resistance.

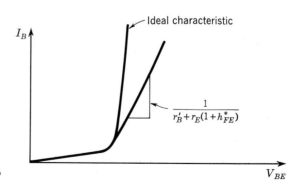

Figure 4.6

Transistor D-C Parameters

h_{FE}—The static value of the common-emitter short-circuit current gain. The short-circuit gain is the most important of the transistor parameters. In circuit analyses where reasonable approximations are made, all parameters can be neglected at one time or another save h_{FE} (or h_{FB}). Since the transistor is a current control device, we would expect the current gain parameter to be important.

h_{FE} **Variation with Emitter Current.** Figure 4.7 shows the variation of h_{FE} with collector current at several junction temperatures for a silicon double-diffused mesa transistor. This graph appears on the data sheet of the TI 2N697. As I_C increases from very small values, h_{FE} increases to a maximum and then decreases at high values of I_C. This can be related to h_{FB} (the static value of the common-base current transfer ratio) variation by recognizing that

$$-h_{FB} = h_{FE}/(1 + h_{FE}) \tag{19}$$

and

$$I_E = I_C/h_{FB} \tag{20}$$

As I_C decreases to some $I_{CBO}(1 + h_{FE}^*)$, I_B approaches zero and $h_{FE} = I_C/I_B$ approaches infinity. But ignoring I_{CBO},[5]

$$|h_{FB}| = \gamma\beta M \tag{21}$$

where $\gamma =$ emitter efficiency, the fraction of the emitter current that is carried by minority carriers in the base side of the base-emitter transition region

$\beta =$ transport factor, the fraction of injected minority carriers in the base that arrive at the collector junction

$M =$ collector multiplication factor, the number of current carriers collected per minority carrier presented at the base side of the collector junction

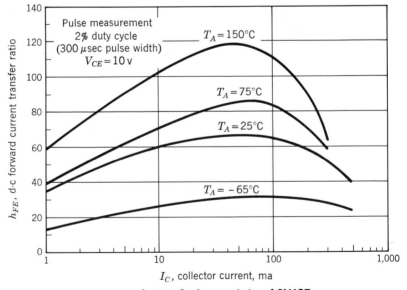

Fig. 4.7. h_{FE} **vs.** I_C **characteristics of 2N697.**

Equation (21) is illustrated by Fig. 4.8, which is the classic one-dimensional current-flow model of an NPN transistor. In the base of an NPN transistor, the majority carriers are holes and the minority carriers are electrons. Three processes have been described[6] to account for the change in h_{FB} with emitter current. Each process dominates at a particular current level. At very low emitter currents, the recombination of electrons and holes in the emitter depletion layer is high compared to the emitter current and lowers emitter efficiency γ. As the emitter current increases, the recombination current in the depletion layer remains constant, causing γ to rise. For still higher emitter currents, an increasing electric field develops in the base region and accelerates the minority electrons toward the collector, increasing β. As the emitter current is increased further, the high minority-carrier density causes an increase in base conductivity, lowering γ. This is known as *conductivity modulation*. Thus, $|h_{FB}|$ will pass through a maximum, then fall off at still higher currents.

The recombination centers in the emitter depletion layer are caused by crystalline defects, both in the bulk of the crystal and at the surface. The recombination current is composed of a volume recombination component and a surface recombination component.[7] In planar transistors, the surface recombination is negligible, owing to the oxide coating over the junction. Planar transistors maintain reasonably high current gains at emitter currents on the order of 1 μa.

The aiding electric field which develops in the base region can be explained with the aid of Fig. 4.9. The charge concentration gradients shown in Fig. 4.9 are valid for step-junction transistors with uniform impurity density in the base.

In diffused transistors, a more complex situation exists; the majority impurity concentration (acceptors) in the base sets up an electric field[8] that retards the minority carriers (electrons) for a short distance from the emitter junction, then accelerates them the remainder of the way to the collector. The field set up by the current flow acts to increase the accelerating field similar to the action in step-junction transistors. Figure 4.9 is used as an illustration because of its simplicity. As electrons are injected into the base, they move toward the collector (by diffusion) and establish a concentration gradient (n_e). In order to maintain space-charge neutrality[9] in the base, an equal hole distribution is established (n_p). It must be remembered that, even though there was an original hole concentration (n_o) due

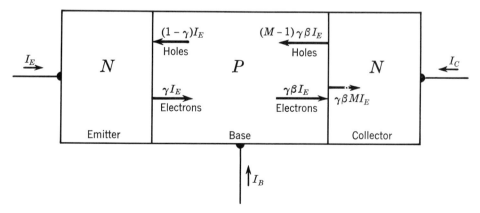

Fig. 4.8.   One-dimensional transistor model.

to the impurity doping, the crystal was electrically neutral, and electrons injected into the base cause an unbalance that must be neutralized by an equal number of holes. (This must not confuse the reader into thinking that the base and emitter currents are equal, for they differ considerably.)

Once the electron and hole distributions are set up in the base, electrons are jerked into the collector region (by the high reverse bias at the collector junction) at a much higher rate than holes can be injected into the emitter by the forward bias on the base-emitter diode. The electrons that are jerked into the collector are balanced by electrons injected into the base from the emitter, while holes that are injected into the emitter from the base are supplied by the generation of electron-hole pairs by the externally applied field at the ohmic (nonrectifying) base contact. The large hole density in the base tends to induce a flow of holes in the same direction as electron flow (toward the collector). This happens until an electric field is set up that prevents further hole movement. An electric field that prevents hole flow in one direction will accelerate electrons in that direction; thus, this field accelerates the minority of electrons toward the collector.

The conductivity modulation referred to previously is caused by the increased number of charge carriers in the base. The conductivity of the base region (σ_b) is given by the formula

$$\sigma_b = q\mu_p(N_a + n_e) \tag{22}$$

where q = electron charge (1.6019×10^{-19} coulomb)
  μ_p = hole mobility
  N_a = acceptor density in the base
  n_e = density of emitted electrons in the base

At low currents the electron density in the P base (for NPN transistors) is negligible compared to the hole density, and the conductivity is relatively independent of emitter current. Increasing emitter currents will eventually cause the electron density to be an appreciable part of the original hole density (n_o). Thus, the increased hole density caused by the equal increased electron density (space-charge

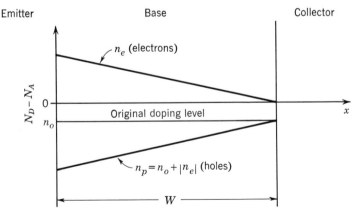

Fig. 4.9. Charge distribution in base.

neutrality requirement) will cause a rapid increase in base conductivity. This increased conductivity will cause the emitter efficiency to decrease according to

$$\gamma = \frac{1}{1 + \sigma_B W / \sigma_E L_{PE}} \tag{23}$$

where W = base width

σ_E = emitter conductivity

L_{PE} = diffusion length for holes in the emitter

In simple terms, the increased hole and electron densities near the emitter junction increase the probability of electrons and holes recombining. This recombination current causes the decrease in γ.

h_{FB} **Variation with Junction Temperature.** It is difficult to arrive at a generalized expression for the temperature dependence of h_{FB}. The three factors (γ, β, M) in h_{FB} are all complex functions of absolute temperature; transistors can be designed so that h_{FB} has almost any desired temperature dependence. As an example, the emitter efficiency, γ, depends[1] on carrier mobility, carrier concentration, and carrier lifetime (among other things). All these quantities are functions of temperature,[10] and the functions depend on the type of material (silicon or germanium), the type of doping, the doping density, and even the type of construction (alloy, mesa, grown junction, etc.). I_{CBO} also plays a part since it contributes to I_C.

All that can be said generally is that the temperature dependence of h_{FB} is not usually a prime consideration in transistor design. It is usual for h_{FB} to fall off at temperatures below room temperature and to increase above room temperature (see Fig. 4.7 for an example).

h_{IE}—The static value of the short-circuit common-emitter input impedance. In Fig. 4.10, h_{IE} is just the slope of the line drawn through the origin and the point of measurement P.

4.2. A-C PARAMETERS

C_{TC}—Collector transition capacitance.

C_{TE}—Emitter transition capacitance.

A transition capacitance is formed by the diffusion mechanism of carriers in an unbiased semiconductor junction. Diffusion creates a region about the junction

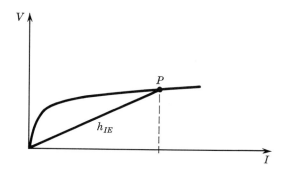

Figure 4.10

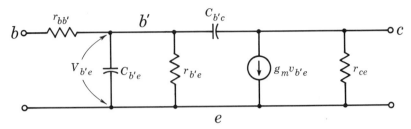

Fig. 4.11. Transcurrent small-signal common-emitter equivalent circuit.

which is depleted of carriers, and an electrostatic potential across this depletion region. If an externally applied voltage forces a change in this junction potential, the charge which is thus added or removed corresponds precisely to that from a capacitor with plates having an area and a separation corresponding to the cross section and thickness of the depletion region and having a dielectric with permittivity equal to that of the semiconductor material.

There are actually two types of capacitance at a semiconductor junction: a transition capacitance, as defined above, which is primarily dependent on junction voltage, and a diffusion capacitance, C_d, which is dependent on junction current. The value of the hybrid-π collector-base junction capacitance C'_{bc} (see Fig. 4.11) is equal to the sum of these components:

$$C'_{bc} = C_{TC} + \frac{C_{cd}}{2} \tag{24}$$

Since C_{TC} is usually much greater than $C_d/2$, for high-frequency work C'_{bc} is approximately equal to C_{TC}. The value of C_{ob}, the common-base parallel output capacitance with input open-circuited, must include header capacitance. The expression for C_{ob}, using the above approximation, is given by Eq. (25) if r'_{bb} is very small.

$$C_{ob} = C_{TC} + C_{header} \tag{25}$$

For the emitter-base junction, the diffusion capacitance is the major component of the hybrid-π emitter-base capacitance, C_{be}; the value of C'_{be} is described by

$$C'_{be} = \frac{1}{\omega_T r'_e} \tag{26}$$

where ω_T is $2\pi f_T$, and $r'_e = 25 \text{ mv}/I_e = 25$ ohms for 1 ma of I_e. Usually this value of C'_{be} is much larger than the value of C_{TE}, except for low currents.

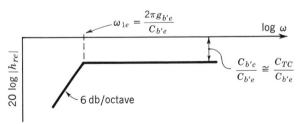

Fig. 4.12. Variation of $|h_{re}|$ with frequency.

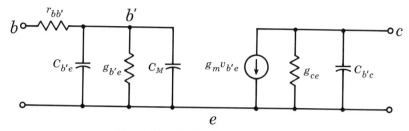

Fig. 4.13.   Modified hybrid-π circuit.

The effect of the collector transition capacitance in circuit design can be demonstrated by the following example.   The reverse voltage transfer ratio, h_{re}, is given by Eq. (27).

$$h_{re} = \frac{SC'_{bc}}{g'_{be} + SC'_{be}} \tag{27}$$

where

$$S = j\omega$$
$$C'_{bc} \cong C_{TC}$$

and

$$g'_{be} = \frac{1 - \alpha_o}{r'_e}$$

This equation is derived from the hybrid-π small-signal equivalent circuit shown in Fig. 4.11.   It is very similar to the Giacolletto equivalent circuit.   Normalizing Eq. (27) yields Eq. (28),

$$h_{re} = \frac{C'_{bc}}{g'_{be}} \frac{S}{1 + SC'_{be}/g'_{be}} \tag{28}$$

The value of h_{re} approaches asymptotically the value C'_{bc}/C'_{be} as indicated in Fig. 4.12, which shows the plot of $|h_{re}|$ vs. frequency.   Therefore, it is evident that a low value of C_{TC} minimizes the high-frequency feedback voltage ratio.

A variation to the equivalent circuit of Fig. 4.11 yields the equivalent circuit in Fig. 4.13, where C_M is the familiar Miller capacity and is given by Eq. (29),

$$C_M = C'_{bc}(1 + A'_{bc}) \tag{29}$$

where A'_{bc} is the ratio $|V_{ce}/V'_{be}|$.   Here again, it is evident that minimizing C'_{bc} minimizes the effective capacity in the input circuit.

As a more elementary example of the effect of C_{TC} on the design of high-frequency circuits, it can be shown that the effects of this capacitance may be neutralized by the circuit in Fig. 4.14.   This is identical with Fig. 4.15 for a simple internal feedback element, C_c, where C_c is the collector capacity, and is defined as

$$C_c = C_{TC} + C_{cd} \tag{30}$$

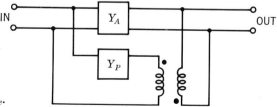

Fig. 4.14.   A neutralizing circuit for y_{re}.

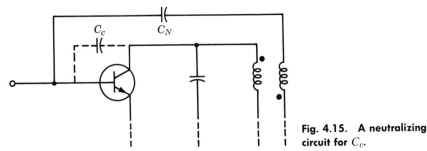

Fig. 4.15. A neutralizing circuit for C_c.

Since the collector junction capacity is usually much larger than the diffusion capacity that parallels it, we may say that

$$C_c \cong C_{TC} \tag{31}$$

Therefore, the capacitance needed to neutralize the effect of C_c is given by

$$C_N = \left(\frac{N_1}{N_2}\right) C_{TC} \qquad (\text{if } C_{cd} \ll C_{TC})$$

C_{ob}, as defined earlier, is the common-base parallel output capacitance, with the input open-circuited ($I_E = 0$). $C_{ob} = C_c + C_{header}$ is the expression for the total capacitance between the collector terminal and the base terminal. Header capacitance naturally varies with the type of header. For the TO-5 and TO-18 (3-lead) package, they are as shown in Table 4.1.

Typical curves of C_{ob} vs. voltage are shown in Figs. 4.16 and 4.17. Notice in Fig. 4.17 that since $C_{cd} \ll C_{TC}$ and $C_{ed} \ll C_{TE}$, the values of C_{TC} and C_{TE} are very nearly equal to C_{ob} and C_{ib}, respectively.

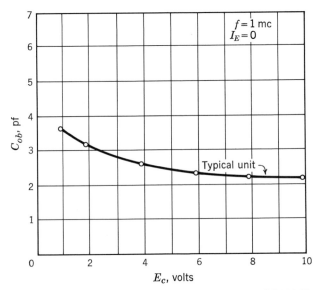

Fig. 4.16. C_{ob} vs. E_C: types 2N1141, 2N1142, and 2N1143.

Table 4.1. Typical Header Capacitances

Capacitance	Picofarads	
	TO-5	TO-18
C_{cb}	0.6	0.75
C_{eb}	0.3	0.05
C_{ce}	0.6	0.75

c_{ies}—Equivalent short-circuit common-emitter series input capacitance.
r_{ies}—Equivalent short-circuit common-emitter series input resistance.
c_{iep}—Equivalent short-circuit common-emitter parallel input capacitance.
r_{iep}—Equivalent short-circuit common-emitter parallel resistance.

r_{iep} and c_{iep} are the measured equivalent input shunt resistance and capacitance of the device with its output short-circuited. Chapter 5 discusses the test jigs and instruments used to measure these parameters. The conversion to the series components r_{ies} and c_{ies} yields the form for h_{ie}. That is to say, Re $(h_{ie}) = r_{ies}$ and Im $(h_{ie}) = 1/\omega c_{ies}$. Figure 4.18 shows the typical variation of the equivalent parallel input values of resistance and capacitance vs. frequency for a germanium transistor biased as indicated. Notice also in Fig. 4.18 that the input has gone inductive at $\cong 110$ mc. Figure 4.19 shows the variation of r_{iep} with bias conditions for a typical VHF germanium transistor.

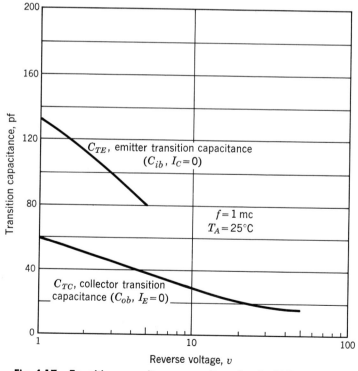

Fig. 4.17. Transition capacitance vs. voltage for the 2N1714 series.

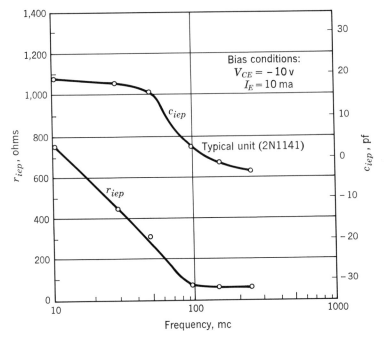

Fig. 4.18. c_{iep} **and** r_{iep} **vs. frequency: type 2N1141.**

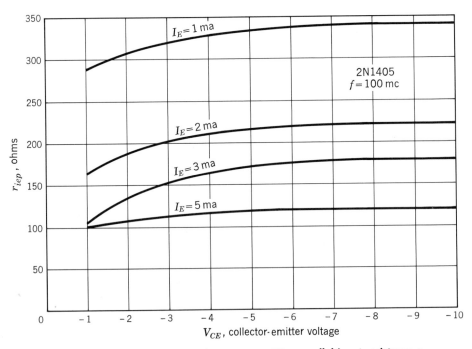

Fig. 4.19. Equivalent short-circuit common-emitter parallel input resistance r_{iep}.

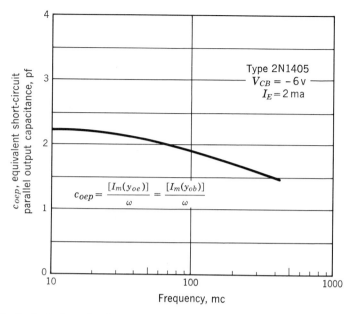

Fig. 4.20. Equivalent short-circuit common-emitter (or common-base) parallel output capacitance vs. frequency.

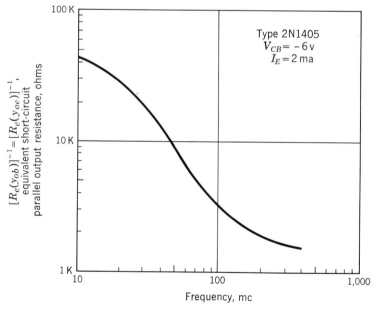

Fig. 4.21. Equivalent short-circuit common-emitter (or common-base) parallel output resistance vs. frequency.

c_{oep}—Equivalent short-circuit common-emitter parallel output capacitance.

r_{oep}—Equivalent short-circuit common-emitter parallel output resistance.

r_{oep} and c_{oep} are the measured equivalent output shunt resistance and capacitance with the input short-circuited. Figures 4.20 and 4.21 show the variation of c_{oep} and r_{oep} with frequency at a given bias point. Figure 4.22 shows the variation in r_{oep} with bias conditions for a typical VHF germanium transistor.

The application of c_{iep}, c_{oep} and r_{iep}, r_{oep} is demonstrated in Sec. 5.4. It is generally more convenient to use shunt impedances than series impedances for interstage design. However, if a strict h-parameter analysis is used, the c_{iep} and r_{iep} would have to be converted to h_{ie} as mentioned earlier and the output admittances would have to be measured with the input open-circuited. r_{ies} is also useful in the calculation of unilateralized power gain and impedance gain. It is for this reason that r_{ies} and r_{oep} are often specified on the data sheet at the optimum small-signal operating point and at a frequency most applicable for optimum device performance. The equations are:

$$\text{Power gain} = 20 \log |h_{fe}| + 10 \log \frac{r_{oep}}{4r_{ies}} \tag{32}$$

and

$$\text{Impedance gain} = 10 \log \frac{r_{oep}}{4r_{ies}} \tag{33}$$

y_{fe}—Equivalent common-emitter forward transmittance with output short-circuited.

y_{ie}—Equivalent common-emitter input admittance with output short-circuited.

h_{fe}—Equivalent common-emitter forward current transfer ratio with output short-circuited.

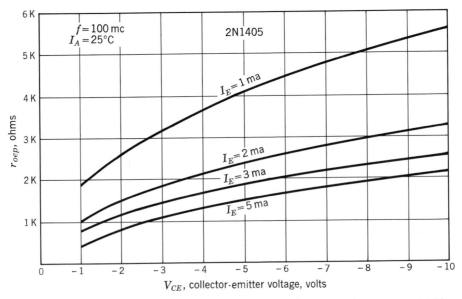

Fig. 4.22. Equivalent short-circuit common-emitter parallel output resistance r_{oep} at 100 mc.

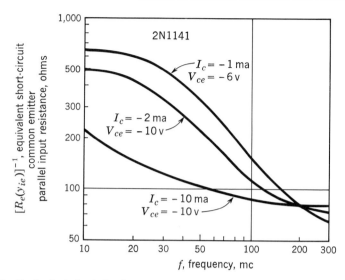

Fig. 4.23. Equivalent short-circuit common-emitter parallel input resistance vs. frequency.

A comprehensive discussion of y_{ie}, y_{fe}, and h_{fe} vs. frequency is presented in Sec. 19.2, which deals with the design of wideband feedback amplifiers. The present discussion, therefore, is limited to showing how the header capacitance affects the measurement of h_{fe}, and presents curves to show the variation of these parameters with bias.

There is usually a discrepancy between VHF measurements of h_{fe} on the General Radio transfer-function bridge and on h_{fe} test jigs, because the header capacitance is usually tuned out when measuring h_{fe} in test jigs, whereas the effect of header capacitance may not be excluded when the transfer-function bridge is set up to measure h_{fe} directly. However, h_{fe} may be calculated ($h_{fe} = y_{fe}/y_{ie}$) by measuring y_{fe} and y_{ie} on the transfer bridge and subtracting the known header capacitance from y_{ie}. This procedure yields very good correlation with readings made on the h_{fe} test jig.

Variation of $[\mathrm{Re}\,(y_{ie})]^{-1}$ for three bias conditions can be seen in Fig. 4.23. The general variation of y_{fe} with bias is presented in Fig. 4.24. Figure 4.25 shows the variation of $|h_{fe}|$ with bias for the 2N1405.

f_{hfb}—Frequency at which $|h_{fb}| = 0.707h_{fbo}$.
f_b—Frequency equivalent of the $r_b'C_c$ time constant.
f_c—Frequency at which $|h_{fb}|$ is minimum.
f_T—Frequency at which $|h_{fe}| = 1$, or is extrapolated to equal unity.

The characteristic frequencies f_{hfb}, f_b, f_c, and f_T are shown in Fig. 4.26. f_{hfb} is described by

$$\frac{1}{f_{hfb}} = \frac{1}{f_a} + \frac{2(1 + a_o m)}{f_b} \tag{34}$$

As this equation shows, f_{hfb} is related to two other frequencies, f_a and f_b. The first,

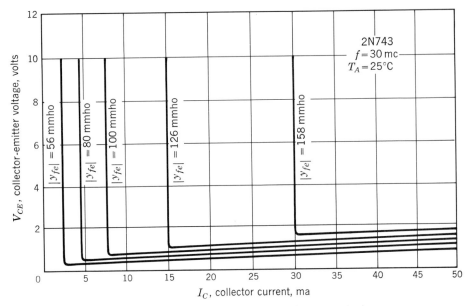

Fig. 4.24.   Contours of constant transadmittance, $|y_{fe}|$.

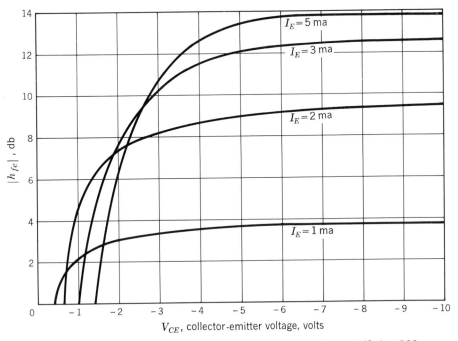

Fig. 4.25.   Short-circuit common-emitter forward current transfer ratio $|h_{fe}|$ at 100 mc.

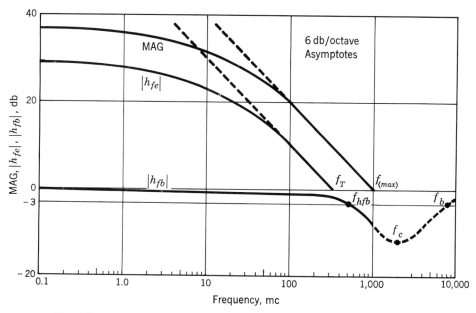

Fig. 4.26.   Variation of MAG, $|h_{fe}|$, and $|h_{fb}|$ with frequency: type 2N1405.

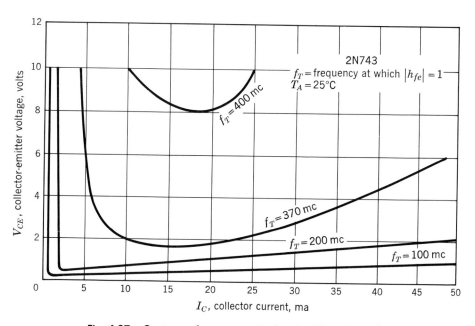

Fig. 4.27.   Contours of constant-gain–bandwidth product, f_T.

f_a, is simply the frequency at which the current multiplication factor a is equal to $0.707 \, |a_o|$; it is related to f_T and m by

$$f_a = f_T(1 + a_o m) \tag{35}$$

Actually, a is equal to h_{fb} (or α) only if the common-base equivalent-T base resistance, r_b, is zero. If r_b is not 0, then a is related to h_{fb} by the expression

$$h_{fb} = \frac{a + r_b/r_c}{1 + r_b/r_c} \tag{36}$$

where r_c is the collector resistance in the common-base T-equivalent circuit.

The quantity f_b is the frequency equivalent of the $r_b'C_c$ time constant and is modified by a constant, $2(1 + a_o m)$, where a_o is the low-frequency value of a, and m is the excess phase term (whose value is somewhere between 0.5 and 0.8 for the 2N1405 germanium transistor).

The frequency f_c is the point at which $|h_{fb}|$ is a minimum. It is shown in Fig. 4.26 as being 2 Gc for the 2N1405 transistor; f_c is given by

$$f_c = \sqrt{f_a f_b} \tag{37}$$

The frequency f_T is the frequency where $|h_{fe}| = 0$ db, or can be extrapolated to equal 0 db. To obtain f_T, the $|h_{fe}|$ response with frequency is usually extrapolated at 6 db/octave to $|h_{fe}| = 1$ from a measurement at which $|h_{fe}| = 2$. The product $f|h_{fe}|$ has been referred to as the gain-bandwidth product, and is equal to f_T. Figure 4.26 shows f_T as 330 mc for the 2N1405. Figure 4.27 shows the variation of f_T with bias.

  MAG—Maximum available gain.

  $f_{(max)}$—Frequency at which MAG is unity.

The parameters $f_{(max)}$ and maximum available gain MAG are best treated together. The following equations and discussion will detail the interrelation of these parameters with the previously defined parameters.

Maximum available gain for transistors is given by the expression

$$\text{MAG} = \frac{|h_f|^2 r_{op}}{4 r_{is}} \tag{38}$$

At very high frequencies, MAG decreases 6 db/octave increase in frequency. Since a gain slightly greater than 0 db is necessary to establish oscillation, the frequency at which MAG = 0 db is labeled $f_{(max)}$, the maximum frequency of oscillation.

Equation (38) permits the calculation of gain from measurements of input and output resistance and current gain. Below 100 mc, these measurements can be made with a Boonton RX meter and relatively simple test circuits. Above 100 mc, the General Radio 1607 A bridge should be used.

Another method of computing gain, which is simpler but somewhat less accurate, is to determine $f_{(max)}$ from its relationship to f_T and f_b. This method proceeds as follows. From Eq. (38), using the common-emitter configuration,

$$\frac{|h_{fe}|^2 r_{oep}}{4 r_{ies}} f = f_{(max)} = 1 \tag{39}$$

The following relationships are valid at frequencies approaching $f_{(max)}$:

$$|h_{fe}|^2 = \left(\frac{f_T}{f}\right)^2 \tag{40}$$

$$r_{ies} = r_b' \quad \text{(true only for germanium)} \tag{41}$$

and

$$r_{oep} = \frac{1}{2\pi f_T C_c} \tag{42}$$

Substituting Eqs. (40) to (42) into (39) gives

$$\frac{(f_T/f_{(max)})^2}{8\pi r_b' C_c f_T} = 1 \tag{43}$$

which simplifies to

$$\frac{f_T}{4f_{(max)}^2} f_b = 1 \tag{44}$$

where

$$f_b = \frac{1}{2\pi r_b' C_c} \quad \text{(defined earlier)}$$

Therefore, $f_{(max)}$ may be found from Eq. (44):

$$f_{(max)} = \sqrt{\frac{f_T f_b}{4}} \tag{45}$$

or

$$f_{(max)} = \sqrt{\frac{f_T}{8\pi r_b' C_c}} \tag{46}$$

Thus, $f_{(max)}$ can be computed from measurements of f_T and $r_b' C_c$. The measurements of f_T and $r_b' C_c$ are discussed in Chap. 5. MAG at high frequencies is then determined from

$$\text{MAG} = 20 \log \frac{f_{(max)}}{f} \tag{47}$$

4.3. SWITCHING CHARACTERISTICS

Definition of I_{B1} and I_{B2}. I_{B1} is defined as turn-on base current as shown in Fig. 4.28. I_{B2} is the turn-off base current and is a transient current with its maximum amplitude occurring at the beginning of the turn-off interval. After the

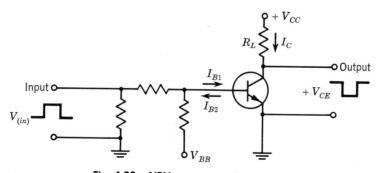

Fig. 4.28. NPN common-emitter switch.

stored base charge has been removed, the transistor turns off, and I_{B2} approaches I_{CBO}.

Overdrive Factor.   Overdrive factor for a particular transistor operating under a given set of conditions is defined as follows:

$$\text{O.F.} = \frac{I_{B1}}{I_{B1(sat)}} = \frac{I_{B1}h_{FE}}{I_{C(sat)}} \tag{48}$$

where I_{B1} = the turn-on base current

  $I_{B1(sat)}$ = the base current required to just saturate the transistor ($I_{C(sat)}/h_{FE}$)

  h_{FE} = the current gain at the specified ON conditions

For a particular group of transistors having a given h_{FE} spread, the overdrive factor is calculated using the minimum h_{FE} specified for the group at the specified operating conditions.   Thus, for reliable operation the circuit must be designed using the inequality

$$\text{O.F.} > \frac{I_{B1}h_{FE(min)}}{I_{C(sat)}} \tag{49}$$

The minimum overdrive factor must be greater than one.

Transistor Switching Times.   The switching time definitions are shown graphically in Fig. 4.29.

t_d = *delay time* = time interval between the 10% point of the increasing circuit input voltage waveform and the 10% point of the increasing collector current waveform (refer to Fig. 4.29).

The delay time is mainly due to two factors:

1. Since a transistor switch should be reverse-biased to hold it OFF, the base-emitter junction capacitance will have a voltage across it.   It takes time to discharge this capacitor and charge it to the forward voltage.   The larger the reverse bias, the longer the delay.
2. Time is required for the emitter current to diffuse across the base region.   This is represented by a base charge which must be supplied by the input circuit.

t_r = *rise time* = time interval between the 10 and 90% points of the increasing collector current waveform.

The rise time, which indicates the frequency response of the transistor, is a function of the alpha-cutoff frequency.   It is also a function of the amount of turn-on current.   The higher the turn-on current, the shorter the rise time.

t_s = *storage time* = time interval between the 90% point of the decreasing circuit input voltage waveform and the 90% point of the decreasing collector current waveform (refer to Fig. 4.29).

Storage time is a function of h_{FE} and the turn-on and turn-off currents.   By definition, the collector current is saturated when the collector voltage falls below the base voltage and thereby applies a forward bias to the collector-base junction. This causes the collector to inject a charge into the base region.   The collector current cannot decrease until these stored charges are swept out.   The higher the h_{FE} and the larger the turn-on drive, I_{B1}, the longer the storage time.   The larger the turn-off drive, I_{B2}, the shorter the storage time.

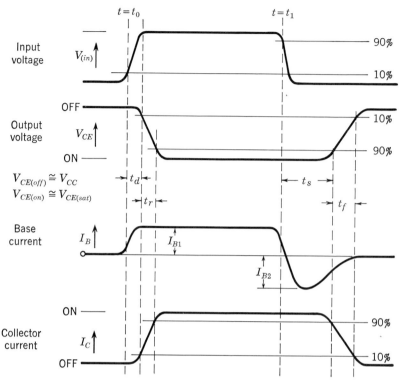

Fig. 4.29. Waveforms associated with switching circuit shown in Fig. 4.28.

$t_f = fall\ time =$ time interval between the 90 and 10% points of the decreasing collector current waveform (refer to Fig. 4.29).

The fall time is also indicative of the frequency response of the device. It is, like t_r, a function of overdrive—in this case, a turn-off drive. The larger the turn-off drive, the shorter the fall time.

$T_T = total\ switching\ time = t_d + t_r + t_s + t_f$.

Propagation Time. The time required for a discrete logic level to pass (propagate) through a single logic stage is referred to as propagation time. This time is measured from the 50% point of the incoming waveform to the 50% point of the outgoing waveform. Since there is some finite difference between turn-on time ($t_{ON} = t_d + t_r$) and turn-off time ($t_{OFF} = t_s + t_f$), the propagation time varies depending on whether the logic stage is turning ON or turning OFF. Therefore, a propagation measurement is normally made across an even number of logic stages as is shown in Fig. 4.30, and the measured time is divided by the number of stages.

If the incremental switching times (t_d, t_r, t_s, and t_f) are known, a close approximation of t_p can be obtained by using

$$t_p = \frac{t_d + t_r/2 + t_s + t_f/2}{2} \tag{50}$$

Switching measurements often indicate that

$$t_r \gg t_d \quad \text{and} \quad t_s \gg t_f$$

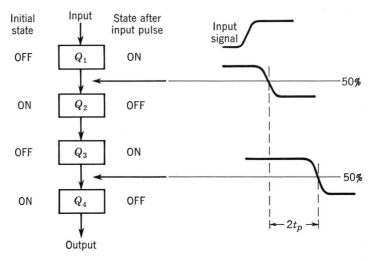

Fig. 4.30. Block diagram showing propagation time.

If this is true, then

$$t_p = \frac{t_r}{4} + \frac{t_s}{2} \quad \text{or} \quad t_p = \frac{t_{ON}}{4} + \frac{t_{OFF}}{2}$$

Importance of Propagation Time. The importance of propagation time is illustrated by Fig. 4.31, where four identical transistor switches are placed in cascade.

Stages 1 and 3 are OFF; stages 2 and 4 are ON. If the input changes stage 1 to ON, the other stages are also changed. The output from 4 will not occur until a time equal to $2T_T$ after the input is applied to stage 1. If the output of stage 4 were to be coincident in a gate with the input to stage 1, the gate must be held ON to accommodate the large time difference of $2T_T$. Thus, the speed at which information can be propagated is limited by T_T.

Definition of Q_B

$$Q_B = total\ stored\ base\ charge = Q_S + Q_{SX}$$

where Q_S = stored base charge at the edge of saturation, and Q_{SX} = excess stored base charge due to saturation.

In general, an approximation of Q_S and Q_{SX} for alloy transistors can be found from the following equations:

$$Q_S = \frac{I_{C(sat)}}{\alpha_N \omega_N} \qquad Q_{SX} = I_{BX} \frac{\omega_N + \omega_I}{\omega_N \omega_I (1 - \alpha_N \alpha_I)}$$

where α_N = small-signal common-base low-frequency forward current transfer ratio
ω_N = small-signal common-base short-circuit current gain radian cutoff frequency

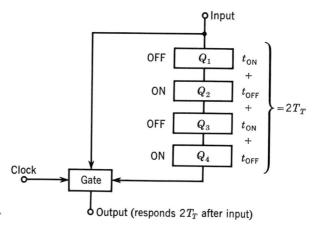

Fig. 4.31. Propagation time.

Output (responds $2T_T$ after input)

α_I = inverted alpha (which is the same as α_N except that the collector and emitter terminals are interchanged)

ω_I = inverted-alpha radian cutoff frequency (which is the same as ω_N with the collector and emitter terminals interchanged)

$I_{C(sat)}$ = collector current at the edge of saturation

$$I_{BX} = I_{B1} - \frac{I_{C(sat)}}{h_{FE}} = \text{the excess base current}$$

4.4. THERMAL QUANTITIES

Heat Flow. To understand the flow of heat through a solid, it is helpful to create an analogy between heat power and electric power. In order to produce a flow of electric charge (coulombs) from one point to another, a difference in electrostatic pressure (voltage) must exist. The rate of flow of charge may be given in coulombs per second, or amperes. Whatever impedes this flow is called electrical resistance (R) and is measured in electrical ohms (volts per ampere).

Similarly, in order to produce a flow of heat energy (joules) from one point to another, a difference in heat *pressure* (temperature) must exist. The rate of flow of heat energy may be given in joules per second, or watts. Whatever impedes this flow is called thermal resistance (θ) and is measured in thermal ohms (centigrade degrees per watt).

Figure 4.32 illustrates this analogy as it might be applied to a transistor dissipating a constant power into an air-cooled heat sink. The total thermal resistance, θ_T, is the sum of the individual thermal resistances through which the heat power must flow from its origin to the ambient into which it is finally dissipated. Typically this ambient will be the surrounding air. For transistors without a heat sink, θ_{C-S} and θ_{S-A} merge to form a single θ_{C-A}.

In practice, however, other factors vastly complicate this picture. Physical substances must store or release energy in order to change in temperature. In our analogy, this effect is in some ways similar to electrical capacitance, which must

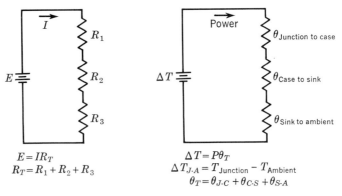

$$E = IR_T$$
$$R_T = R_1 + R_2 + R_3$$

$$\Delta T = P\theta_T$$
$$\Delta T_{J\text{-}A} = T_{\text{Junction}} - T_{\text{Ambient}}$$
$$\theta_T = \theta_{J\text{-}C} + \theta_{C\text{-}S} + \theta_{S\text{-}A}$$

Figure 4.32

store or release charge in order to change in voltage. The product of a thermal capacitance, C_H, and a thermal resistance, θ, forms a thermal time constant. Each separate material through which the heat power must flow will exhibit its own specific heat capacitance and thermal resistance, and will introduce its own thermal time constant.

Table 4.2 summarizes the analogy.

The instantaneous heat power, p_J, generated at the junction consists of some steady-state value, P_J, plus some function of time, $p_J(\tau)$. Therefore, when the instantaneous temperature difference between the junction and the ambient must be found, it is more convenient and accurate to use a circuit similar to Fig. 4.33. Here a generator forces a power flow, p_J, through a network of thermal capacitances and resistances, creating a temperature differential $\Delta T_{J\text{-}A}$.

The thermal circuit of Fig. 4.33 is analogous to an electrical low-pass filter, and the $p_J(\tau)$ portion of p_J may be rapidly attenuated as p_J flows around the loop. If $p_J(\tau)$ contains only frequencies in the upper audio range, C_{HJ} could completely bypass these, and $\Delta T_{J\text{-}C}$ might be computed from $P_{J(max)}$ alone. If lower-frequency components of $p_J(\tau)$ are present, analysis of $\Delta T_{J\text{-}C}$ requires an exact statement of the function p_J and of the junction time constant, $C_{HJ}\theta_{J\text{-}C}$, or τ_{TH}. The thermal capacitances of the case and the sink, C_{HC} and C_{HS}, usually bypass $p_J(\tau)$ even at low audio frequencies.

Of course, Fig. 4.33 is an oversimplification of the physical structures encountered in practice. A better analog would show many time constants and parallel paths

Table 4.2

Electrical term	Thermal term
EMF, volts....................	Temperature differential, centigrade degrees
Charge, coulombs.............	Energy, joules
Current, amperes..............	Power, watts
Resistance, ohms..............	Thermal resistance, θ, centigrade degrees/watt
Capacitance, farads...........	Thermal capacitance, C_H, joules/centigrade degree

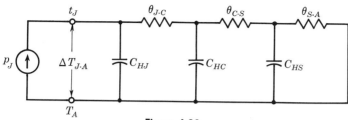

Figure 4.33

for heat power flow, with distributed—rather than lumped—parameters. Also, the parameters would be nonlinear with temperature. For example, the junction-to-case temperature response is shown as resulting from only a single $\theta_{J\text{-}C}$ and a single C_{HJ}: a useful first approximation. Actually, it is the result of several θ's and C_H's within the transistor case, and it seldom follows exactly a simple exponential function approach to asymptote. The true junction-to-case temperature response to a step-function power input tends to lead the value predicted from τ_{TH} at first, and lag behind it later. The only time of perfect agreement will be, of course, when the $\Delta T_{J\text{-}C}$ reaches 63.2% of its ultimate value. Similar considerations apply to $\theta_{C\text{-}S}C_{HC}$ and to $\theta_{S\text{-}A}C_{HS}$. But for most purposes, the effect of power transients on junction temperature may be approximated with this linear thermal circuit using the familiar techniques of electrical transient analysis.

Data Sheet Information. The data sheet may present thermal design information in several ways:

1. A guaranteed value for $\theta_{J\text{-}C}$.
2. A guaranteed value for the junction time constant. This is defined as the time required for the junction temperature to reach 63.2% of its new steady-state value if the case temperature is held constant and the power dissipation is abruptly increased.
3. A maximum junction operating temperature, $T_{J(max)}$. This may be assumed equal to the maximum permissible storage temperature unless the data sheet makes a distinction.
4. A maximum total average power dissipation at a specified case or free-air ambient temperature.
5. Power dissipation vs. temperature derating curves.
6. Other curves, such as junction-to-case temperature drop vs. power pulse duration and repetition rate.

If $\theta_{J\text{-}C}$ is not specifically stated, it may be calculated from items 3 and 4. For example, the 2N389 data sheet gives:

$$\text{Total dissipation at } 100°\text{C case temperature} = 45 \text{ watts}$$
and
$$\text{Maximum junction temperature} = +200°\text{C}$$

Applying the analogy,

$$\Delta T_{J\text{-}C} = 200°\text{C} - 100°\text{C} = 100 \text{ C}°$$

$$\theta_{J\text{-}C} = \frac{100 \text{ C}°}{45 \text{ watts}} = 2.22 \text{ C}°/\text{watt}$$

Also given for the 2N389 is a graph of power dissipation for this unit mounted on a 4- by 4- by ⅛-in. copper heat sink. The derating curve for this mounting has a slope of -0.114 watt/C°. The slope of the derating curve will be the negative of the reciprocal of the thermal impedance. θ_T will thus equal 8.78 C°/watt for this combination. For further thermal considerations, see Chap. 7.

BIBLIOGRAPHY

1. Leighton, R. B.: "Principles of Modern Physics," McGraw-Hill Book Company, Inc., New York, 1959.
2. Ebers, J. J., and J. L. Moll: Large-signal Behavior of Junction Transistors, *Proc. IRE,* vol. 42, pp. 1761–1772, December, 1954.
3. Miller, S. L., and J. J. Ebers: Alloyed Junction Avalanche Transistors, *Bell System Tech. J.,* vol. 34, September, 1955.
4. Linn, H. C., and A. A. Barco: Temperature Effects in Circuits Using Junction Transistors, "Transistors I," RCA Laboratories, Princeton, N.J., 1956.
5. Ryder, R. M.: A Descriptive Summary of the Design Theory of Transistors, "Transistor Technology," vol. 1, p. 217, D. Van Nostrand Company, Inc., Princeton, N.J., 1958.
6. Gärtner, W. W., R. Havel, R. Stampfl, and F. Caruso: The Current Amplification of a Junction Transistor as a Function of Emitter Current and Junction Temperature, *Proc. IRE,* vol. 46, pp. 1875–1876, November, 1958.
7. Webster, W. M.: On the Variation of Junction Transistor Current Amplification Factor with Emitter Current, *Proc. IRE,* vol. 42, pp. 914–920, June, 1954.
8. Tanenbaum, M., and D. E. Thomas: Diffused Emitter and Base Silicon Transistors, *Bell System Tech. J.,* vol. 35, pp. 1–22, January, 1956.
9. Shockley, W.: "Electrons and Holes in Semiconductors," p. 61, D. Van Nostrand Company, Inc., Princeton, N.J., 1950.
10. Gärtner, W. W.: Temperature Dependence of Junction Transistor Parameters, *Proc. IRE,* vol. 45, pp. 662–680, May, 1957.

5

Measurement of Electrical
Quantities and Parameters

5.1. D-C MEASUREMENTS

Breakdown Voltages. Breakdown voltages are measured at a specified current level which is set high enough to be in the constant-voltage region of the breakdown characteristic. Measurements in this region, however, may result in damage to the device from excessive power dissipation. For this reason, breakdown characteristics are usually guaranteed as a leakage current which is measured in the nearly constant current region of the characteristic.

When a guaranteed breakdown voltage at a high current level is required, pulse-testing techniques using a small duty cycle are usually employed. One such pulse-testing technique is discussed in the next section.

Typical breakdown-voltage parameters measured are BV_{CBO} (collector-base breakdown, emitter open) and BV_{EBO} (emitter-base breakdown, collector open). Variations of the collector-emitter breakdown measurement include BV_{CER} (resistive termination between base and emitter), BV_{CEX} (bias applied between base and emitter), and BV_{CES} (emitter-base short-circuited).

Illustrated in Fig. 5.1 are circuits for measuring BV_{CBO} and BV_{CEO}. BV_{CER}, BV_{CEX}, and BV_{CES} can be measured by inserting the proper circuitry between the base and emitter in the BV_{CEO} test circuit. Since the circuit resistance is very high, particularly on the BV_{CBO} tests, the VTVM used should have 100 megohms input impedance. In some cases it will be necessary to use a 100-megohm VTVM on the most sensitive scale (0–1 volt on the Hewlett-Packard 410B) and use external multipliers to avoid loading the test circuit.

Leakage Currents. A leakage current is measured at a specified reverse voltage applied across the appropriate terminals of a transistor. This voltage is usually one-half to two-thirds of the value of the breakdown voltage, BV_{XXX}. Measurement of this sort is often used to guarantee a minimum breakdown voltage. Typical leakage parameters measured are I_{CBO} (collector-base leakage, emitter open), I_{CEO} (collector-emitter leakage, base open), and I_{EBO} (emitter-base leakage, collector open).

Variations of the collector-emitter leakage measurement include I_{CER} (resistive

59

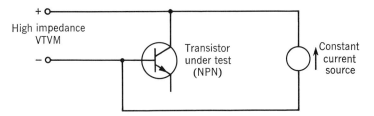

(a) Measurement of BV_{CBO}

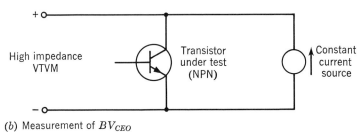

(b) Measurement of BV_{CEO}

Figure 5.1

termination between base and emitter), I_{CEX} (bias applied between base and emitter), and I_{CES} (emitter-base short-circuited).

A typical I_{CBO} measuring circuit is illustrated in Fig. 5.2 for an NPN transistor. (Reverse all polarities for PNP transistor measurement.) The $-V_{CB}$ source should have fairly high resistance so that a shorted unit will not take out the power supply. The purpose of the silicon diode and 8.2-kilohm resistor (plus the 4-kilohm meter resistance) is to shunt the meter at approximately a 2:1 overload. The push-button "Diode Out" switch provides a quick check on the shunting effect of the diode for a critical measurement. A microammeter or electrometer is used to read the leakage current.

5.2. PULSE TESTING

Pulse testing is used to minimize heating effects that might change the parameter being measured. Parameters normally measured by this method are h_{FE}, $V_{CE(sat)}$, V_{BE}, breakdown voltage, and in-production testing of thermal resistance. The

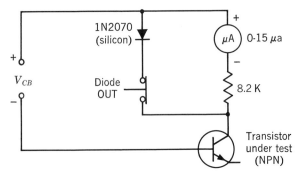

Figure 5.2

following sections discuss the test circuits used to measure the above parameters for the 2N337, 2N497, 2N1047, and 2N389 transistors. This method or a similar method is used to test other transistors.

h_{FE} **Pulse Testing.** In pulse testing for h_{FE}, it is convenient to measure the voltage drop across a resistor in series with the base lead. This determines the base current, I_B, at a specified collector current, I_C, and collector-to-emitter voltage, V_{CE}. From this information, h_{FE} can be computed from I_C/I_B. Figure 5.3 shows a typical collector characteristic for the common-emitter configuration.

In the quiescent state, the transistor under test is held at point 1 in Fig. 5.3. During the testing cycle, the collector current is pulsed ON, driving the transistor to point 2. The unit under test is held at this point for 300 μsec, and then returned to point 1 where it remains for a period of 14 msec. This means that the transistor is under test conditions only 2% of the time. A pulse width of 300 μsec was chosen so that the rise and fall time of the unit under test would not be an appreciable portion of the test cycle. This pulse width is short enough to allow a minimum of junction heating. The measurement of h_{FE} is made while the transistor is at point 2. A block diagram of the h_{FE} pulse test set is shown in Fig. 5.4.

The pulse generator produces a negative pulse which operates the switch, allowing the collector current to flow into the unit under test. During the remaining portion of the pulse period, the collector current is shunted to ground through the switch. The pulse amplitude is not particularly critical but must be sufficient to operate the switch and allow the full collector current to flow. The driving amplifier uses a differential input with the transistor under test in the feedback loop. Point B is the summing junction of the operational amplifier and is forced to assume the same potential as the other input (ground) during the ON time of the pulse. This will cause the collector of the transistor under test to be at ground. When this occurs, the required V_{CE} is supplied by the constant voltage supply.

The readout method shown in Fig. 5.4 permits the use of a peak-to-peak VTVM, measuring the voltage drop across R. A differential amplifier is connected across R and the VTVM is connected between the output of the amplifier and ground. For a fixed value of collector current, the meter can be calibrated directly in terms of h_{FE}.

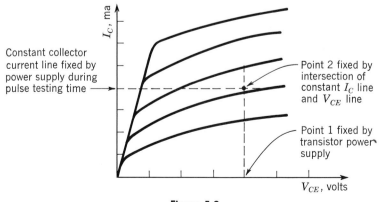

Figure 5.3

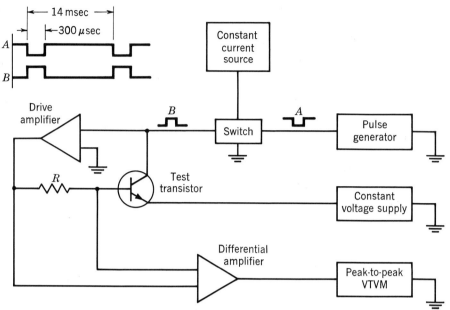

Fig. 5.4.   Voltage waveshapes as a function of time.

The foregoing circuit is used for different transistors merely by changing the constant-current and constant-voltage sources to the appropriate values for the types being tested.

$V_{CE(sat)}$, R_{CS} **Pulse Testing.**   In pulse testing for R_{CS}, it is convenient merely to measure the collector saturation voltage $V_{CE(sat)}$ at a specified collector current I_C. If necessary, R_{CS} can then be computed from $V_{CE(sat)}/I_C$. For a given I_C value, $V_{CE(sat)}$ is defined as the collector-to-emitter voltage that exists when an increase in base current produces no change in V_{CE}. To ensure that even the lowest beta unit is driven into saturation, an excess of base current should be used. Figure 5.5 shows both the $V_{CE(sat)}$ point (for a particular I_C value) and the R_{CS} line on a typical collector characteristic for the common-emitter connection.

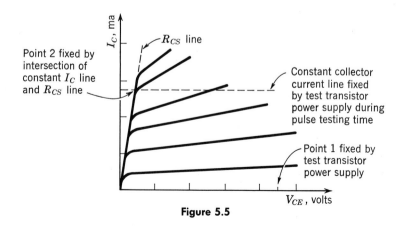

Figure 5.5

In the quiescent state, the transistor under test is held at point 1 in Fig. 5.5. During the testing cycle, the base current is pulsed ON, driving the transistor to point 2. The unit under test is held at this point for 300 μsec and then returned to point 1 where it remains for a period of 14 msec. This means that the transistor is under test conditions only 2% of the time. The measurement of $V_{CE(sat)}$ is made while the transistor is at point 2. A block diagram of the $V_{CE(sat)}$ pulse test set is shown in Fig. 5.6.

The pulse generator produces a negative pulse which operates switch 1 and allows the driving current to flow into the base of the transistor under test. During the remaining portion of the pulse period, the base current is shunted to ground through switch 1. The pulse amplitude is not particularly critical, but it must be sufficient to operate switch 1 and allow the base current supply to drive the transistor under test into saturation. The pulse observed at the collector of the unit under test is shown in waveform C.

A readout method as shown in Fig. 5.6 enables one to use a peak-to-peak VTVM and directly measure the $V_{CE(sat)}$ voltage. The pulse from the pulse generator is integrated, and the slowly rising leading edge is used to trigger a one-shot multivibrator whose pulse width is set at something less than 300 μsec (in particular, the

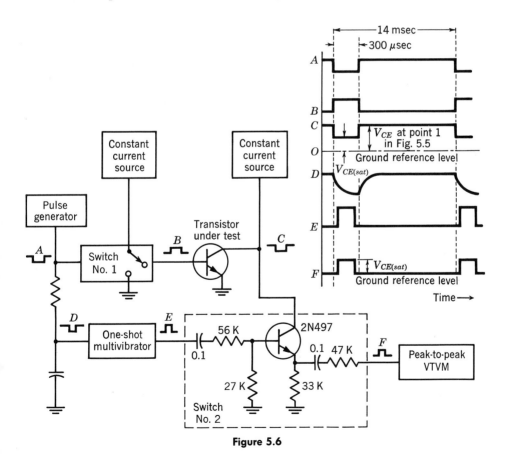

Figure 5.6

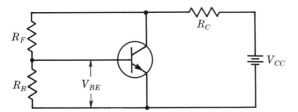

Figure 5.7

multivibrator pulse must terminate before the 300-μsec pulse ends). The multivibrator turns ON switch 2 (one 2N497), which forces the emitter of the 2N497 to assume nearly the same voltage as its collector, which in turn is the same voltage as the collector of the transistor under test. So long as $V_{CE(sat)}$ for the 2N497 is very small compared to $V_{CE(sat)}$ for the transistor under test, the peak-to-peak VTVM will read the desired pulse amplitude.

The foregoing circuit is used for different transistors merely by changing the constant-current sources to the appropriate values for the types being tested.

Definition of $V_{BE(sat)}$. V_{BE} is the d-c voltage that appears between the base and emitter of a transistor when it is operating. If the transistor is operating in a common-emitter circuit, V_{BE} will be the voltage that appears on the base as shown in Fig. 5.7. V_{BE} will be positive for NPN transistors and negative for PNP transistors.

If the ratio of the collector current I_C to the base I_B is less than the $h_{FE}(\beta)$ of the transistor, it is said to be saturated. That is, for standard conditions,

$$\frac{I_C}{I_B} < h_{FE} \tag{1}$$

When the transistor is saturated, the voltage that appears on the base is called the saturated V_{BE}, or $V_{BE(sat)}$.

Measurements of $V_{BE(sat)}$ are made by driving a constant collector current I_C into the collector and a constant base current I_B into the base. A block diagram for measuring $V_{BE(sat)}$ is shown in Fig. 5.8.

In general, the V_{BE} of an unsaturated transistor has a negative temperature coefficient. That is, if the temperature of the transistor goes up, the V_{BE} will go down.

At Texas Instruments, the pulse-testing technique is used to minimize transistor junction heating due to power dissipation during the test. To make such a test, a pulse generator is used to drive the collector and base current sources. This generator generates a positive pulse of approximately 300 μsec duration and an OFF

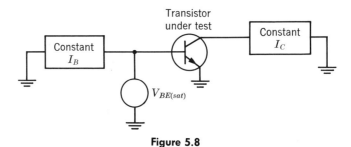

Figure 5.8

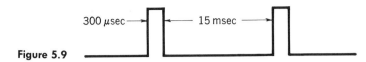

Figure 5.9

time of approximately 15 msec. The waveform from this pulse generator is shown in Fig. 5.9.

The duty cycle of this type of wave is approximately 2%. Rise and fall times of the pulses are kept between 10 and 20 μsec so that high-frequency harmonics will be negligible.

The pulse generator used at Texas Instruments has a high output impedance; it is used therefore to drive a pulse amplifier. This pulse amplifier uses two transistors in a Darlington connection as an emitter follower (shown in Fig. 5.10).

The input impedance of this amplifier is equal to the h_{FE} of the Darlington-connected transistors multiplied by R_L. That is,

$$Z_{(in)} \cong R_L(h_{FE\,Q1})(h_{FE\,Q2}) \tag{2}$$

The output impedance of the Darlington pair is equal to the generator impedance R_G divided by $(h_{FE\,Q1})(h_{FE\,Q2})$. That is,

$$Z_{(out)} \cong \frac{R_G}{(h_{FE\,Q1})(h_{FE\,Q2})} \tag{3}$$

In order to drive a constant current into the collector and base of the transistor under test, it is necessary to use a constant-current regulator that will regulate with a load voltage variation from zero to 10 volts. A simple current generator is shown in Fig. 5.11.

This current regulator is basically an emitter-follower. The resistor R_1 and the reference diode D form a voltage divider between the power supply and ground. The reference diode will keep the voltage constant between the base of the transistor and the power supply. The V_{BE} of a transistor is nearly constant over its operating range. The voltage drop across R_2 will be equal to the reference voltage of the zener diode V_Z minus the V_{BE} of the transistor,

$$V_{R2} = V_Z - V_{BE} \tag{4}$$

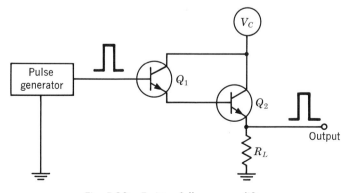

Fig. 5.10. Emitter-follower amplifier.

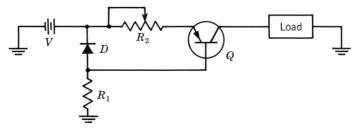

Fig. 5.11. Current regulator.

The current that flows through the resistor R_2 to give this voltage drop is equal to the base and collector currents of the transistor,

$$I_{R2} = I_B + I_C \tag{5}$$

I_C, being the load current, is equal to I_B times the h_{FE} of the transistor,

$$I_C = I_B h_{FE} \tag{6}$$

Solving these equations for I_C in terms of V_Z, V_{BE}, h_{FE}, and R_2, we have

$$I_C = \frac{(V_Z - V_{BE})h_{FE}}{(1 + B)R_2} \tag{7}$$

If the h_{FE} of the transistor is large with respect to 1, this equation will reduce to

$$I_C = \frac{V_Z - V_{BE}}{R_2} \tag{8}$$

The voltage drop across the load cannot exceed the voltage of the power supply minus V_Z. R_1 is chosen to give a good operating current through the diode.

Since there is no capacity in this current regulator, its response is very fast. Driven with a pulse source, it will produce an output of constant-current pulses.

Peak voltage can be read using a rectifier, filter capacitor, amplifiers, and d-c meter as shown in Fig. 5.12.

In this circuit, the input pulse is amplified by the first amplifier A_1. The gain of A_1 must be a known constant value. The diode D rectifies these pulses and charges the capacitor C. The reverse resistance of the diode and the input resistance of the amplifier are about 100 megohms each. This gives a parallel combined resistance of approximately 50 megohms through which the capacitor must discharge. A small capacitor will, therefore, give a large time constant. The amplifier A_2 has a gain of one and will have the same voltage as the capacitor at its output. The readout meter M is a 20,000-ohm/volt d-c meter.

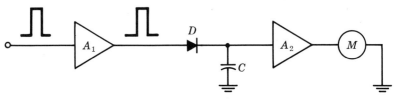

Figure 5.12

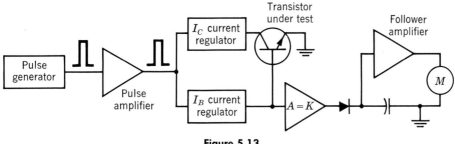

Figure 5.13

The pulse test circuit used at Texas Instruments is built up using the above described circuit elements. Figure 5.13 shows a simplified drawing of the complete pulse V_{BE} test circuit.

In this test circuit, the pulses from the pulse generator are amplified by the pulse amplifier. The output from the pulse amplifier drives the collector (I_C) and base (I_B) current regulators. The current pulses drive the collector and base of the transistor under test. The peak-reading amplifier circuit is used to read the $V_{BE(sat)}$ voltage pulses that appear on the base of the transistor under test.

Breakdown Voltage Pulse Testing. Although the following pulse measurement discussion covers a particular breakdown voltage, BV_{CER}, all breakdown voltage measurements can be made using similar pulse-testing procedures. Only slight changes of the transistor connection in the pulse circuit will be required.

BV_{CER} is defined as the breakdown voltage from collector to emitter with a turn-off resistor connected between the base and emitter of the transistor. This breakdown voltage is found to be considerably smaller for large currents than for small currents. BV_{CER} is, therefore, measured at current values near the maximum operating range.

Figure 5.14 shows a circuit that can be used to measure the BV_{CER} of transistors.

This circuit uses a constant-current generator to drive a predetermined I_C into the collector, and a meter to measure the breakdown voltage. The resistor R is used to turn the transistor OFF. This circuit will measure BV_{CER}, but it may damage the transistor because of excessive power dissipation. This power dissipation is equal to BV_{CER} times I_C. Typical values may be

$$BV_{CER} = 100 \text{ volts}$$
$$I_C = 100 \text{ ma}$$
$$\text{Power} = (100)(0.10) = 10 \text{ watts}$$

Thus 10 watts might be dissipated in a 1-watt transistor.

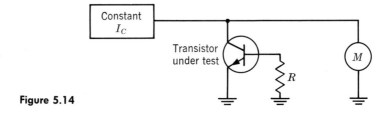

Figure 5.14

In order to reduce this power dissipation, Texas Instruments uses the pulse-testing technique. To make this test, a pulse generator is used to drive the collector current source. This generator has a positive pulse output of approximately 300 μsec duration and an OFF time of approximately 15 msec. The resultant waveform is shown in Fig. 5.9.

The duty cycle of this wave is about 2%. The power dissipated in the transistor using the pulse technique will be 2% of 10 watts, or 0.2 watt. This power should not damage a 1-watt transistor.

To obtain a pulse source with enough power to drive a BV_{CER} test set, a pulse generator is used to drive an emitter-follower amplifier. The amplifier uses two transistors in a Darlington connection as an emitter-follower (shown in Fig. 5.10). The pulse output from the amplifier is used to drive a constant-current regulator (Fig. 5.11).

Peak voltage can be read using a rectifier, filter capacitor, follower amplifier, and d-c meter (Fig. 5.12). Amplifier A_1 is not required for large breakdown voltage measurements.

The BV_{CER} test circuit used at Texas Instruments is composed of the above-described circuit elements; a block diagram of this test set is shown in Fig. 5.15.

In this test circuit, the pulses from the pulse generator are amplified and used to drive the current regulator. These current pulses are driven into the collector of the transistor under test. The amplitude of the voltage pulses that appear on the collector is equal to BV_{CER}. These pulses are integrated by R_1C_1 and then read on the meter with the peak-reading network. The meter reads directly in BV_{CER} volts.

Thermal Resistance Test Set. The forward voltage drop of a silicon diode at 25°C will range from 0.5 to 1.0 volt at low currents. This voltage drop reduces as a linear function of temperature until the drop is about 0.2 volt for most diodes. That is:

$$\frac{\Delta V}{\Delta T} = K$$

This phenomenon can be used to measure the change in collector junction temperature of silicon transistors. A similar phenomenon exists for germanium transistors and is used in the same manner.

The thermal resistance from junction to case of the transistor, θ_{J-C}, is defined as the collector junction to case temperature differential, ΔT_{J-C}, per watt of dissipation in the transistor.

$$\theta_{J-C} = \frac{\Delta T_{J-C}}{P}$$

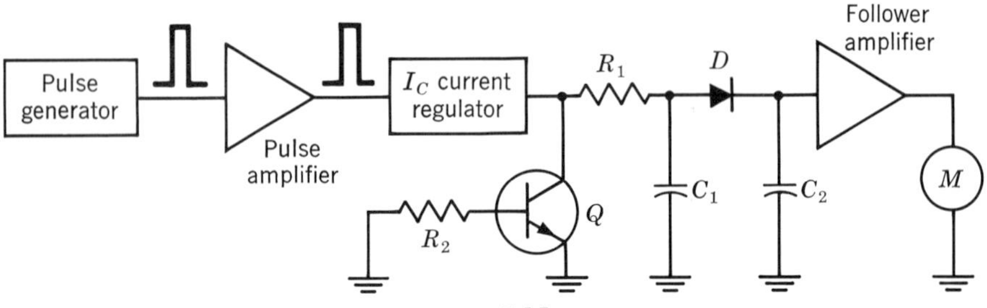

Figure 5.15

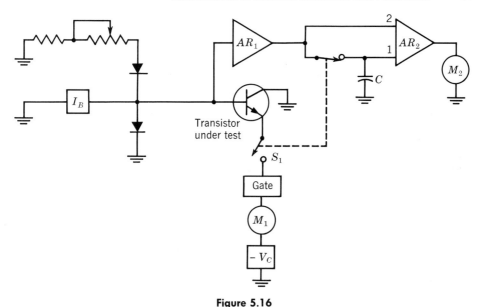

Figure 5.16

A block diagram of a thermal resistance test set is shown in Fig. 5.16.

This test set uses the pulse technique. It uses about 2% of the test time to drive current through the base-collector diode in the forward direction, measuring the change in the forward voltage drop as the transistor is heated; 98% of the test time is used to dissipate power in the transistor.

I_B is adjusted to about 100 μa. V_C is adjusted to the specified V_{CE} of the transistor under test. AR_1 is a peak-reading amplifier. It will detect pulses on its input and give an output d-c voltage level that is equal to the peaks of the input pulses. AR_2 is a differential amplifier. The gate opens the emitter of the transistor under test 2% of the time and shorts it to the V_C power supply 98% of the time.

To start the test of a transistor, switch S_1 is put in the position shown. The transistor is inserted and the amplifier AR_1 will have an output equal to the forward voltage drop of the base-collector diode. This voltage is stored on the capacitor C and will remain there during the remainder of the test. S_1 is then switched to the other position. R is adjusted until the proper current flows through the transistor. The power dissipation in the transistor will be indicated on the wattmeter M_1. The change in voltage drop across the base-collector diode will be indicated on the voltmeter M_2, which can be calibrated in degrees centigrade.

To obtain the thermal resistance of a transistor, the power must be left on the transistor long enough for it to reach an equilibrium temperature.

5.3. SMALL-SIGNAL PARAMETER MEASUREMENTS AND TEST CIRCUITS

The subject of h parameters is exhaustively covered in the literature. The intention here is not to discuss these parameters, but rather to show the basic test circuits for the four h parameters currently being used by Texas Instruments in an attempt to achieve a higher degree of correlation between company and customer. A brief

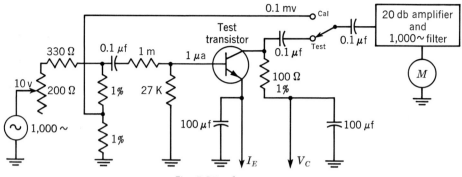

Fig. 5.17. h_{fe} **test set.**

discussion of these parameters may be found in the Equivalent Circuits section of this manual, Chap. 6.

Definition of h_{fe}. The parameter h_{fe} is used at Texas Instruments since it appears to be a more universally accepted and more useful measurement than h_{fb}. Values of h_{fb} can be derived from h_{fe} by using the following formula:

$$h_{fb} \cong \frac{-h_{fe}}{1 + h_{fe}}$$

The basic test circuit for h_{fe} is shown in Fig. 5.17. A similar circuit can be derived for measuring h_{fb}.

The ratio h_{fe} is defined as the small-signal short-circuit forward current transfer ratio.

$$h_{fe} = \frac{di_c}{di_b} \qquad \text{at } v_{ce} = \text{constant} \tag{9}$$

Holding I_b to a fixed value of 1 μa alternating current will result in a test set capable of reading directly in h_{fe}. A calibration level of 10 mv was chosen so that direct readings of h_{fe} from 10 to 100 can be obtained on the 10-mv scale. If readings higher than 100 or lower than 10 are required, these may be obtained by changing to a higher or lower range.

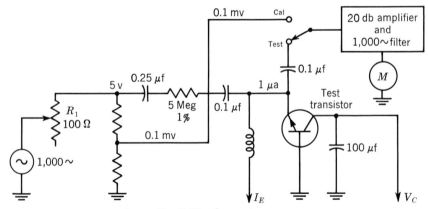

Fig. 5.18. h_{ib} **test set.**

Definition of h_{ib}.   The basic test circuit for h_{ib} is shown in Fig. 5.18.   This parameter is defined as the short-circuit input resistance.

$$h_{ib} = \frac{dv_{eb}}{di_e} \qquad \text{at } v_{cb} = \text{constant} \tag{10}$$

As with h_{fe}, if a fixed value of input current is used, the output meter will give a direct reading of h_{ib}.   The calibration level of 10 mv remains so that direct readings of h_{ib} from 10 to 100 ohms are obtained on the 10-mv scale.

Definition of h_{ob}.   Figure 5.19 shows the basic test circuit for h_{ob}, the small-signal value of the open-circuit output admittance.

$$h_{ob} = \frac{di_c}{dv_{cb}} \qquad \text{at } i_e = \text{constant} \tag{11}$$

In this measurement the input voltage is held constant at 1 volt, and the current is read as the voltage drop across the 1-kilohm resistor.

$$h_{ob} = \frac{\text{output reading, volts/1 kilohm}}{1 \text{ volt}} \tag{12}$$

h_{ob} = output reading, mv, and will be a direct reading in μmhos

Thus, a value of h_{ob} from 0.1 to 1 μmho is read directly on the 10-mv scale.   The calibration level for this parameter is the same as the previous ones, 10 mv.

Definition of h_{rb}.   The basic test circuit for h_{rb} is shown in Fig. 5.20.   The ratio h_{rb} is defined as the small-signal value of the open-circuit reverse voltage transfer ratio.

$$h_{rb} = \frac{dv_{eb}}{dv_{cb}} \qquad \text{at } i_e = \text{constant} \tag{13}$$

The output voltage is held constant in this measurement, so that variations of input voltage will give a direct reading of h_{rb} on the output meter.   Direct readings of h_{rb} from 100 to 1,000 ($\times 10^{-6}$) are read on the 10-mv scale.

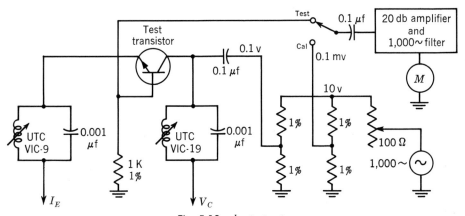

Fig. 5.19. h_{ob} test set.

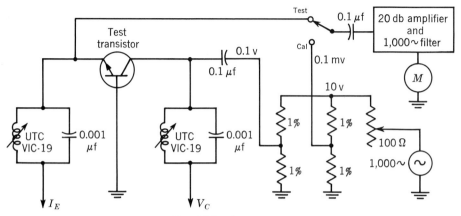

Fig. 5.20. h_{rb} **test set.**

These test circuits should give good correlation since the basic test circuit is the same as that used by Texas Instruments for production testing. The recommended readout meter is a Ballantine 310A or equivalent. The 1,000-cycle filter used is a UTC BMI-1000. Use of the 20-db amplifier will allow direct reading of all parameters on one meter scale. The noise level of the amplifier should be low in comparison to the readings observed on the meter. The recommended signal generator is a Hewlett-Packard 200CD.

5.4. HIGH-FREQUENCY MEASUREMENTS

Measurements Using Commercial Test Equipment. Measurements of small-signal a-c transistor parameters in the high-frequency range ($>$ 1 mc) are usually made using commercially available test equipment. However, this test equipment is not often designed for testing production quantities. Texas Instruments has found four items of commercial test equipment which are convenient for quantity testing. The following list indicates the parameters measured and the frequency range used with each piece of test equipment:

1. Wayne-Kerr, model B601:
   Frequency range: 15 kc to 5 mc.
   Parameters measured: y_{ib}, y_{ob}, y_{ie}, y_{fe}, and h_{fb} (requires standard adapters).
   Also used to measure C_{ob}, C_{ib}, and C_{TE} at 1 mc.
   Measurement range: Capacitance 0.01 to 20,000 pf.
   Resistance 10 ohms to 10 megohms.
2. Wayne-Kerr, model B801:
   Frequency range: 1 to 100 mc.
   Parameters measured: y_{ib}, y_{ob}, y_{ie}, and y_{oe} (requires the building of adapters).
   Measurement range: Capacitance 0 to 235 pf.
   Conductance 99.9 to 0.1 mmho.
3. General Radio transfer function and immittance bridge, type 1607-A:
   Frequency range: 25 to 1,500 mc with reduced accuracy above 1,000 mc.

Parameters measured: y_i, y_o, y_r, y_f, z_i, z_o, z_r, z_f, h_i, h_o, h_r, and h_f for all configurations (common emitter, etc.).

Measurement range:

Voltage and current ratios	0–30 ohms
Transimpedances Z_r	0–1,500 ohms
Transadmittance Y_r	0–600 mmhos
Impedance Z_i	0–1,000 ohms
Admittance Y_i	0–400 mmhos

4. Boonton RX meter:

Frequency range: 0.5 to 250 mc.

Parameters measured: admittances such as y_i, y_o, and h_o.

Commonly used to obtain parallel input and output resistance and capacitance (r_p, C_p). Requires printed circuit board adapters.

Measurement range: Capacitance $+25$ to -100 pf.*

Resistance 15 ohms to ∞.

$|h_{fe}|$**Measurement.**   The measurement of $|h_{fe}|$ at some higher frequency than 1,000 cps is useful for two purposes: A design engineer using the devices in the common-emitter configuration in a high-frequency application needs this information for proper design, and the information obtained is useful in the calculation of power gain.   The formula used in calculating power gain, assuming a conjugate match loss less neutralization, is

$$A_P = |h_{fe}| \text{ db} + 10 \log\left(\frac{r_o}{4r_{ies}}\right) \tag{14}$$

where r_o is the parallel output resistance with the input shorted and r_{ies} is the series input resistance with the output shorted.

If $|h_{fe}|$ is read directly in decibels, then the calculations of power gain are considerably simpler.   If required, $|h_{fe}|$ can be converted to a numerical value by applying the following formula:

$$|h_{fe}|_{numeric} = \text{antilog}\left(\frac{|h_{fe}| \text{ db}}{20}\right) \tag{15}$$

A first approximation of the gain-bandwidth product, f_T, is often obtained by measuring $|h_{fe}|$ at some frequency well above the frequency at which $|h_{fe}|$ has fallen 3 db (f_{hfe}), and extrapolating to $|h_{fe}| = 0$ db at the rate of 6 db/octave or 20 db/decade.   For greatest accuracy, the test frequency should lie about halfway between f_{hfe} and the expected f_T. f_T can also be obtained by multiplying the numerical measured gain by the test-point frequency if this frequency is well above the upper corner frequency (f_{hfe}).

The measurement of $|h_{fe}|$ at frequencies above 30 mc and below 1,500 mc is often made using a General Radio transfer function and immittance bridge, type 1607-A.   For measurements up to and including 100 mc, the basic measuring circuit shown in Fig. 5.21 can be used; however, extreme care in the circuit layout is required if measurements are to be made above 30 mc.   This circuit should

---

* Negative reading indicates inductance.

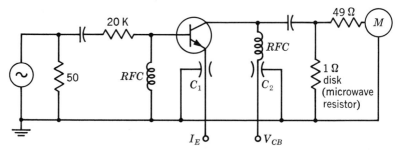

Fig. 5.21. High-frequency h_{fe} test set.

be built in a metal box, preferably brass. At frequencies above 20 mc the use of feed-through capacitors C_{FT} in addition to the bypass capacitors C_1 and C_2 is recommended. All leads should be kept as short as possible, and shielding between input and output is essential. The chokes L_1 and L_2 are chosen so that they will be self-resonant at or slightly above the measuring frequency.

To calibrate the test set, a short circuit is inserted between collector and base, and the signal generator output is adjusted until a convenient reference level is obtained on the output meter. The input signal level is kept low enough to avoid exceeding true small-signal conditions.

The readout meter should have a 50-ohm termination and a direct-reading decibel scale, and should be capable of operating over the desired frequency range. It is desirable to use at least one range higher than the lowest range of the meter, since this will allow a $-$ db reading.

C_{ob} **Measurement.** The capacitance between the collector and base (C_{ob}) consists of two parameters, a collector transition capacitance and a collector diffusion capacitance. The collector transition capacitance C_{TC} is due to the space-charge region at the collector-base junction. Neglecting a small ohmic drop, the entire reverse bias applied between the collector and base appears across this junction. Since a high electric field is maintained here, all free charge carriers are swept out of a narrow region, leaving only the nuclei and bound electrons. This

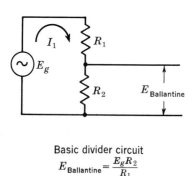

Basic divider circuit

$$E_{\text{Ballantine}} = \frac{E_g R_2}{R_1}$$

where $R_2 \ll R_1$

Figure 5.22

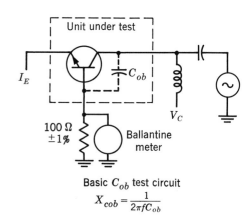

Basic C_{ob} test circuit

$$X_{cob} = \frac{1}{2\pi f C_{ob}}$$

Figure 5.23

space-charge region has a charge per unit volume which is equal to the impurity concentration times the electronic charge q. This collector junction capacitance shunts the output circuit, and in this respect it is very similar to the plate-to-grid capacitance of a vacuum tube, and limits high-frequency gain in exactly the same manner. Collector diffusion capacitance C_{dc} varies directly as the collector current, and effectively parallels C_{TC} so that $C_{ob} = C_{TC} + C_{dc}$.

The capacitance between the emitter and collector leads can be neglected since it is reduced by $1/(h_{fe} + 1)$ at the collector-base terminals.

The capacitance between the collector and base of a transistor can be determined by applying a high-frequency signal to the collector and measuring the current passed by the C_{ob} at the transistor. This measurement is valid provided the following requirements are met: The signal is a high-frequency low-level source, the emitter circuit is open to the a-c signal, and the reactive component X_{ob} is approximately equal to the impedance Z_{ob} of the transistor.

Figure 5.22 shows the basic voltage-divider circuit of the C_{ob} test. If R_2 is negligible ($\cong 100$ ohms) compared to R_1 ($\cong 10$ kilohms), then I_1 is proportional to E_g/R_1 and $E_{Ballantine} = E_g R_2/R_1$.

Texas Instruments recommends the use of a circuit similar to the one shown in Fig. 5.23, or a Wayne-Kerr bridge model B601, for measuring C_{ob}. In the circuit of Fig. 5.23, a 1-mc signal is fed across the divider network C_{ob} of the transistor and the 100-ohm resistor. The Ballantine meter reads the alternating current across the 100-ohm resistor. The recommended readout is a 310 Ballantine or equivalent. The test set should be wired to minimize stray capacitance. A test socket made of Teflon® is desirable.

r_{iep}, c_{iep}, r_{oep}, **and** c_{oep} **Measurement.** Measurement of input and output resistance at some frequency other than 1,000 cps is desirable in a good many cases. If a designer plans to use the devices in the megacycle ranges, this information is necessary for the proper design of IF strips, high-frequency tuned amplifiers, and other applications of this type. The easiest way to make these measurements is with the Boonton RX meter and printed circuit test boards.

Figure 5.24 shows the circuit used with the RX meter to measure r_{oep} and c_{oep}, the parallel output resistance, common emitter, and the parallel output capacitance, common emitter. These two values are read directly from the dials of the RX meter in terms of resistance and capacitance.

Figure 5.25 shows the circuit used to measure r_{iep} and c_{iep}. r_{iep} is the parallel input resistance, common emitter, while c_{iep} is the input capacitance, common

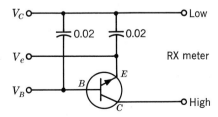

Fig. 5.24. $r_{oep}c_{oep}$.

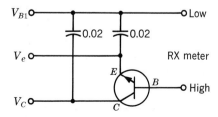

Fig. 5.25. $r_{iep}c_{iep}$.

emitter. These parameters are read directly from the RX meters. In design of IF strips, these parameters are far more useful than the equivalent series parameters, but for the calculation of power gain, the series input resistance is easier to use.

Formulas for converting the parallel measurements to series resistance and series capacitance are:

$$r_{ies} = \frac{r_{iep}}{1 + (\omega c_{iep} r_{iep})^2} \qquad c_{ies} = \frac{1 + (\omega c_{iep} r_{iep})^2}{\omega^2 c_{iep} r_{iep}^2}$$

Parallel input and output impedance can also be measured in the common-base configuration. Also, these parameters can be measured with desired input or output terminations.

The RX meter circuit board details are shown in Figs. 5.26 and 5.27.

5.5. SWITCHING TIME MEASUREMENTS

The Complete System. Transistor switching times are usually measured in a system as shown in Fig. 5.28.

The resultant waveforms for an NPN transistor in this system are shown in Fig. 5.29.

The accuracy of switching time measurements is affected by the rise time of the test system. Since the transistor is connected between the pulse source and the oscilloscope, the response of these test instruments will cause an increase in the measured transistor response time.

Equation (16) can be used to determine the transistor rise time if the system rise time is known.

$$\left(\begin{array}{c}\text{Rise}\\\text{time}\\\text{measured}\end{array}\right)^2 = \left(\begin{array}{c}\text{rise}\\\text{time of}\\\text{transistor}\end{array}\right)^2 + \left(\begin{array}{c}\text{rise}\\\text{time of}\\\text{test system}\end{array}\right)^2 \qquad (16)$$

The system rise time can be observed by removing the transistor and shorting the base-to-collector terminals on the test setup. Then by using the system rise time and the measured rise time of the transistor, the per cent error can be computed, using

$$\% \text{ error} = 100 \left[\frac{t_{r\,measured}}{\sqrt{(t_{r\,measured})^2 - (t_{r\,system})^2}} - 1 \right] \qquad (17)$$

If $t_{r\,system} \leqq \frac{1}{2} t_{r\,measured}$, then

$$\% \text{ error} \cong 50 \left(\frac{t_{r\,system}}{t_{r\,measured}} \right)^2 \qquad (18)$$

This relationship is shown graphically in Fig. 5.30. From this we see that to have an error of less than 5% the equipment must be at least three times faster than what is being measured.

Coaxial Line Generators. A pulse generated by a coaxial line pulse generator is dependent upon the electric charge stored in a coaxial cable. The length of the

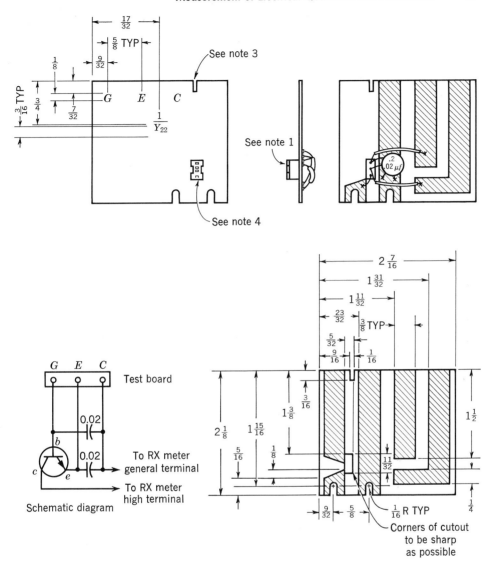

Test board

Schematic diagram

To RX meter general terminal

To RX meter high terminal

Corners of cutout to be sharp as possible

Fig. 5.26. RX meter $r_{oep}c_{oep}$.

Notes:
(1) Mount bottom of subminiature socket flush with copper side of board. Cement in place.
(2) Leads of capacitor to be short as possible. Solder in place as near to RX meter ground terminal as possible without interference.
(3) Symbolize board as shown with approximate size of characters shown. Decals permissible.
(4) Mark collector end of socket red.
(5) Shaded portion indicates copper.

Note:
(A) Bottom view shown.
(B) Shaded portion indicates copper.

Material:
Grade FF-91 Phenolic $\frac{1}{16}$ thick with 2 oz copper one side.

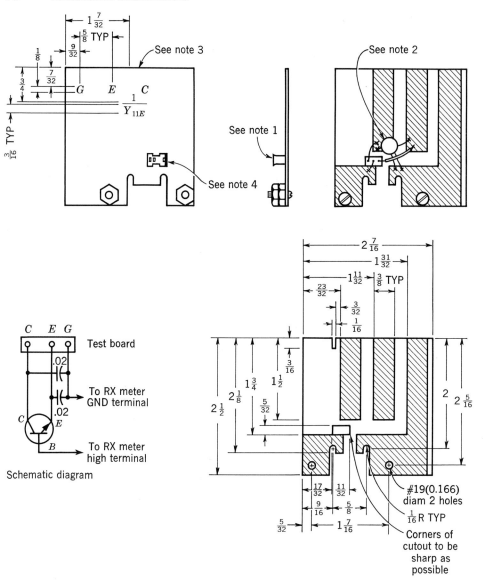

Notes:
(1) Mount bottom of subminiature socket flush with copper side of board. Cement in place.
(2) Leads of capacitor to be short as possible. Solder in place as near to RX meter ground terminal as possible without interference.
(3) Symbolize board as shown with approximate size of characters shown. Decals permissible.
(4) Mark collector end of socket red.
(5) Shaded portion indicates copper.

Note:
(*A*) Bottom view shown.
(*B*) Shaded portion indicates copper.

Material:
Grade FF-91 Phenolic $\frac{1}{16}$ thick with 2 oz copper one side.

Fig. 5.27. RX meter $r_{iep}c_{iep}$.

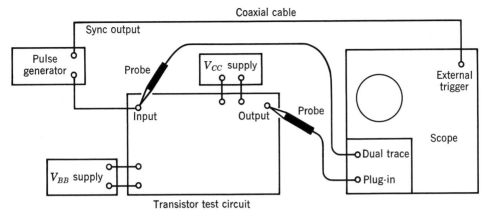

Fig. 5.28. Typical switching time test setup.

cable determines the pulse width, and the amount of charge determines the pulse amplitude. A circuit diagram of a typical coaxial generator is shown in Fig. 5.31.

A very fast rise pulse is generated using this method, by the closing of the relay contacts. The trailing edge of the pulse, however, must propagate to the open end of the cable and back. This length of cable attenuates the high-frequency components of the pulse, causing a long fall time for wide pulses. Figure 5.32 shows the relationship among the pulse width, type of pulse-forming cable, cable length, and pulse fall time.

Transistor Circuit Termination. It is important that the test circuit properly terminate the input pulse from the generator. The terminating resistor R_o in Fig. 5.33 must be located as close as possible to the output end (*not* the signal generator

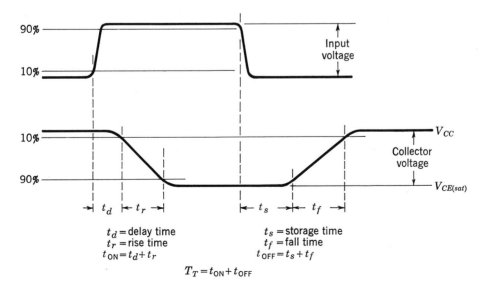

Fig. 5.29. Switching time definitions.

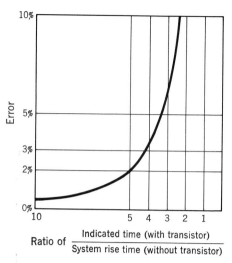

Ratio of $\dfrac{\text{Indicated time (with transistor)}}{\text{System rise time (without transistor)}}$ **Fig. 5.30. Test system error.**

end) of the cable, to keep the signal at a constant impedance level throughout its path, to prevent reflections. As a further precaution against reflections, the lead length from the cable termination to the transistor input should be as short as possible.

Figure 5.33 shows how the proper termination resistance can be maintained when the base-driving resistance is low.

Coupling Capacitor. When the d-c level of the transistor test circuit must be isolated from the pulse generator, the coupling capacitor must be chosen to eliminate droop (see Fig. 5.34). The per cent droop may be determined from

$$\% \, D = 100 \, (1 - \epsilon^{-t/RC}) \tag{19}$$

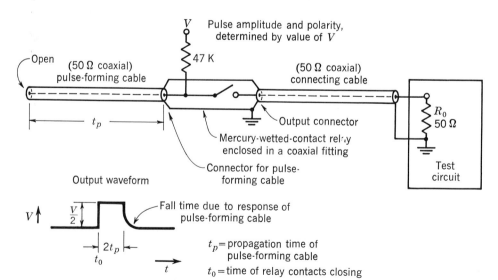

Fig. 5.31. Coaxial pulse generator.

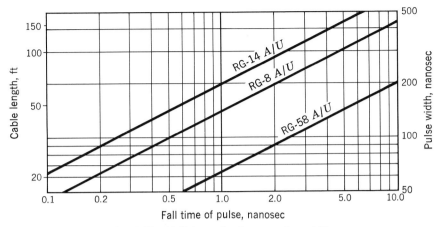

Fig. 5.32. **Fall time of pulse vs. pulse width.**

Problem:

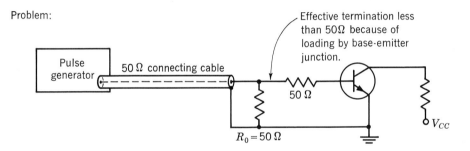

Effective termination less
than 50Ω because of
loading by base-emitter
junction.

Solution:

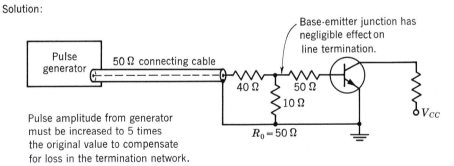

Base-emitter junction has
negligible effect on
line termination.

Pulse amplitude from generator
must be increased to 5 times
the original value to compensate
for loss in the termination network.

Fig. 5.33. **Termination resistance.**

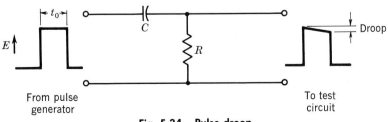

Fig. 5.34. **Pulse droop.**

where C = capacitance, μf
$\quad R$ = total loading effect, ohms (including transistor)
$\quad t$ = pulse width, μsec
$\quad \% D$ = % droop at end of pulse

If $t \leqq \frac{1}{20}RC$, then

$$\% D \cong 100 \frac{t}{RC}$$

Therefore, to maintain less than 1% droop,

$$C \geqq \frac{100t}{R} \tag{20}$$

Figure 5.35 shows some typical values of R and C used in test circuits.

Even though the value of the coupling capacitor is large enough to eliminate droop, there remains the problem of d-c level shift due to the charging of the coupling capacitor (see Fig. 5.36). When

$$t_p + t' \ll RC$$

this level shift is proportional to the duty cycle of the input pulse,

$$S = E_p t_p f_p$$

where S = d-c level shift
$\quad E_p$ = pulse amplitude
$\quad t_p$ = pulse width, sec
$\quad f_p$ = pulse repetition rate, pulses/sec

From this we see that it is best to use a duty cycle of less than 5%.

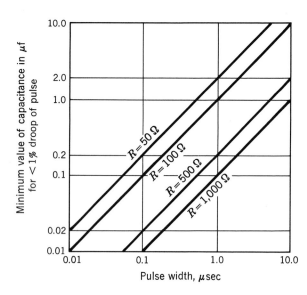

Fig. 5.35. Minimum value for coupling capacitor.

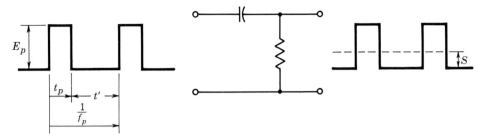

Fig. 5.36. D-c shift with capacitor coupling.

Bypass Capacitors. Even though power supplies with good regulation are used for V_{BB} and V_{CC} in Fig. 5.37, their recovery time and lead inductance may prevent the voltage from remaining constant at the test circuit. Therefore, C_2 and C_3 must be used to provide adequate high-frequency bypassing at the V_{BB} and V_{CC} terminals of the test set.

All leads should be kept as short as possible to keep inductance low. Even so, some larger capacitors, especially paper and electrolytic types, will cause ringing, owing to their series inductance. A low-inductance mica or ceramic capacitor may be used in parallel with the larger one to reduce ringing. Sometimes the combination of capacitors will resonate and make the ringing worse. In this case several combinations should be tried while the point to be bypassed is monitored with a scope.

Emitter-Base Breakdown Protection. The emitter-base breakdown voltage rating should not be exceeded in the test circuit. One solution is to keep V_{BB} low enough to prevent emitter-base breakdown, but a low value of V_{BB} will cause variations of the turn-off current with variations in $V_{BE(on)}$.

Assume that a high value of V_{BB} (10 volts) is used in Fig. 5.38a to maintain a constant turn-off base current with variations of $V_{BE(on)}$ of different test transistors. The turn-off current from the base is a transient current and will cease when the charge is removed from the base region. Therefore, the voltage at the base tends to rise toward the value

$$V_{BE(off)} = \frac{V_{BB}(R_1 + R_0)}{R_1 + R_2 + R_0}$$

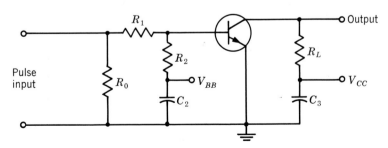

Fig. 5.37. Bypass capacitors.

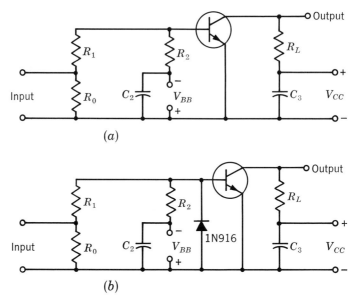

(a)

(b)

Fig. 5.38. BV_{EBO} **protection circuit.**

If $|V_{BE(off)}| > |BV_{EBO}|$, a fast computer diode may be used to clamp the voltage at the base to a value lower than BV_{EBO} of the test transistor. Figure 5.38b shows a 1N916 diode used for this purpose. For a PNP transistor, the diode polarity would be reversed.

Scope Probe Adjustment. Most scopes require the use of probes to reduce the capacitive loading on the circuit and increase the input resistance. The probes must be adjusted so that the RC product of the probe is equal to the RC product of the scope input circuit (see Fig. 5.39).

When properly adjusted, the phase shift is at a minimum and the frequency response is flat (within the passband of the scope). Figure 5.40 shows the effect of this adjustment on a pulse.

It is important to have a nearly perfect pulse for making this adjustment. Instructions are furnished in the operating manual for the particular scope probe used.

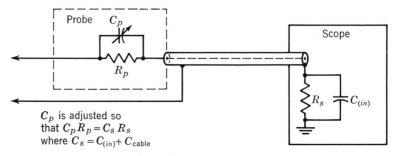

C_p is adjusted so that $C_p R_p = C_s R_s$ where $C_s = C_{(in)} + C_{cable}$

Fig. 5.39. Probe compensation circuit.

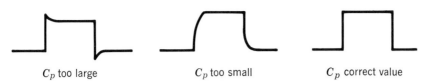

C_p too large C_p too small C_p correct value

Fig. 5.40. Scope probe compensation.

Grounding of Scope Probe. With fast rise pulses it is important to have a ground at the scope probe, in addition to any other grounds to the scope chassis. Figure 5.41 shows the results of a probe used with and without a ground connection near the signal test point. Short ground and signal leads are necessary throughout the circuit to prevent this type of ringing.

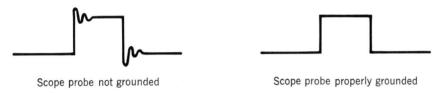

Scope probe not grounded   Scope probe properly grounded

Fig. 5.41. Scope waveforms.

6

Equivalent Circuits and Parameter Interrelationships

One of the first steps in analyzing and designing transistor circuits is to represent the transistor by a satisfactory equivalent circuit. Many equivalent circuits are in use. Each is used to represent a different type of transistor at different operating conditions. In general, equivalent circuits may be divided into two types: those which regard the transistor as a black box upon which measurements are made, and those which regard the transistor as being made up of physically realizable active and passive components. The following discussion illustrates several of the more common equivalent circuits used in transistor circuit design.

The equivalent circuits in this chapter represent the a-c or incremental equivalent circuits, as opposed to the d-c or static representation. All the small-signal parameter symbols with which we are dealing will be given in lower case to distinguish them from static parameter symbols, given in upper case.

The Two-terminal Network. Consider a two-terminal black box. At one frequency, the behavior of a linear device may be specified in terms of two measurements: one an open-circuit voltage, the other a short-circuit current. Equivalent circuits, good at the frequency of measurement, may then be drawn for the device (as shown in Fig. 6.1).

v_{oc}—Open-circuit voltage.
i_{sc}—Short-circuit current.

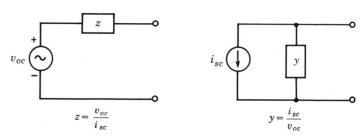

$$z = \frac{v_{oc}}{i_{sc}}$$

$$y = \frac{i_{sc}}{v_{oc}}$$

Fig. 6.1. Two-terminal network.

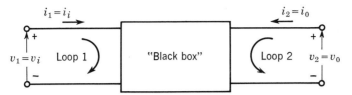

Fig. 6.2. Four-terminal network.

The Four-terminal Network.   A set of measurements may be made on a linear four-terminal device similar to those made on the two-terminal device. The three-terminal transistor is considered a special case of a four-terminal device, with two terminals common to both input and output. Consider the black box of Fig. 6.2. It is possible, by making appropriate measurements of the various voltages and currents, to arrive at a useful equivalent circuit for any linear device, active or passive. The voltages and currents are shown to establish the measurement convention.

Figure 6.3 is shown to illustrate that a three-terminal network is just a special case of the four-terminal network of Fig. 6.2.

Two statements may be made concerning Figs. 6.2 and 6.3:

1. There are only two independent voltages and two independent currents.
2. If any two quantities are fixed by external means, then the other two are fixed by the black-box parameters. Note that generally we are not free to specify any two quantities arbitrarily; the quantities picked must be compatible with the black-box parameters. Of the six possible circuit representations relating the voltages and currents, three have proved particularly helpful in describing junction transistors: (*a*) open-circuit impedance measurements, (*b*) short-circuit admittance measurements, and (*c*) a combination of the two, *hybrid* parameter measurement.

Open-circuit Impedance Parameters.   Two equations may be used to define the black box as given in Fig. 6.2:

$$v_1 = z_{11}i_1 + z_{12}i_2 \tag{1}$$

$$v_2 = z_{21}i_1 + z_{22}i_2 \tag{2}$$

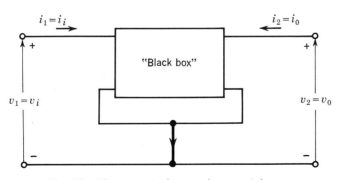

Fig. 6.3. Three-terminal network: a special case.

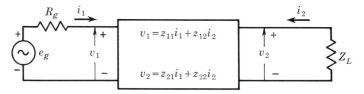

$$v_1 = z_{11}i_1 + z_{12}i_2$$

$$v_2 = z_{21}i_1 + z_{22}i_2$$

Figure 6.4

From Eqs. (1) and (2), if the output is open-circuited or $i_2 = 0$,

$$z_{11} = \frac{v_1}{i_1} \qquad \text{input impedance} \tag{3}$$

$$z_{21} = \frac{v_2}{i_1} \qquad \text{forward transfer impedance} \tag{4}$$

If the input is open-circuited or $i_1 = 0$,

$$z_{12} = \frac{v_1}{i_2} \qquad \text{reverse transfer impedance} \tag{5}$$

$$z_{22} = \frac{v_2}{i_2} \qquad \text{output impedance} \tag{6}$$

i_1 and i_2 are independent variables.

z_{21} may be read as "the voltage in (loop) 2 due to the current in (loop) 1." Each of the other three z parameters may be treated in the same manner. All the electrical properties of Fig. 6.4 may be calculated by using the impedance parameters. Current gain of the black box shown in Fig. 6.4 is given as an example.

$$A_i = \frac{i_2}{i_1}$$

From Fig. 6.4 see

$$v_2 = -i_2 Z_L \tag{7}$$

If Eq. (7) is substituted into Eq. (2),

$$-i_2 Z_L = z_{21}i_1 + z_{22}i_2$$

$$\frac{i_2}{i_1} = -\frac{z_{21}}{z_{22} + Z_L} = A_i \tag{8}$$

Short-circuit Admittance Parameters. The black box of Fig. 6.2 may also be represented by the following two equations:

$$i_1 = y_{11}v_1 + y_{12}v_2 \tag{9}$$

$$i_2 = y_{21}v_1 + y_{22}v_2 \tag{10}$$

These are known as the short-circuit admittance equations with v_1 and v_2 as the independent quantities.

From Eqs. (9) and (10) with the output shorted or $v_2 = 0$,

$$y_{11} = \frac{i_1}{v_1} \qquad \text{input admittance} \qquad (11)$$

$$y_{21} = \frac{i_2}{v_1} \qquad \text{forward transfer admittance} \qquad (12)$$

If the input is shorted or $v_1 = 0$,

$$y_{12} = \frac{i_1}{v_2} \qquad \text{reverse transfer admittance} \qquad (13)$$

$$y_{22} = \frac{i_2}{v_2} \qquad \text{output admittance} \qquad (14)$$

Like the z parameters, all the electrical characteristics of a black box are known if the y parameters are known.

Since z parameters are open-circuit parameters, a network can best be characterized by z parameters whose input and output may easily be open-circuited (e.g., low z circuit). A similar statement can be made about the y parameters. Since y parameters are short-circuit parameters, a network can best be characterized by y parameters whose input and output may easily be short-circuited.

Hybrid Parameters. A third set of very useful parameters combines part of the open-circuit measurements and part of the short-circuit measurements to form a hybrid parameter system.

The hybrid or h parameters may be defined by the following equations:

$$v_1 = h_{11}i_1 + h_{12}v_2 \qquad (15)$$
$$i_2 = h_{21}i_1 + h_{22}v_2 \qquad (16)$$

With the output short-circuited or $v_2 = 0$,

$$h_{11} = \frac{v_1}{i_1} \qquad \text{input impedance} \qquad (17)$$

$$h_{21} = \frac{i_2}{i_1} \qquad \text{forward transfer current ratio} \qquad (18)$$

If the input is open-circuited or $i_1 = 0$,

$$h_{12} = \frac{v_1}{v_2} \qquad \text{reverse transfer voltage ratio} \qquad (19)$$

$$h_{22} = \frac{i_2}{v_2} \qquad \text{output admittance} \qquad (20)$$

The admittance parameter set finds its chief usefulness at very high frequencies, where open-circuit measurement may lead to difficulties. It is almost impossible to avoid stray capacitance between transistor elements, and with open-circuited terminals these may cause regenerative effects which are often very unstable and unpredictable. If only short-circuit parameters are measured, then the stray (or parasitic) capacitances merely act as shunt reactances to ground, and do not enter into the active transistor measurements.

Of the three sets of parameters listed, the h parameters are the most often used in general transistor audio work and low-frequency video.

Comparison of z, y, and h Parameters. Representation by hybrid parameters is the most useful scheme for two reasons. First, the h parameters are easy to measure. It must be remembered that h parameters are measured at some bias point; therefore, the terminals of the device cannot merely be shorted for a short-circuit measurement or opened for an open-circuit measurement. The short and open circuits must take place with regard to the biasing network attached to the transistor. The z and y parameters require either all open-circuit or all short-circuit measurements. Since the input impedance is rather low and the output impedance is rather high for a transistor (common base and common emitter), one type of measurement for both input and output is difficult. The z_{11} and z_{21} measurements require the output to be open-circuited, which is difficult to do, particularly at high frequencies; it is equally difficult to short the input circuit for the y_{12} and y_{22} measurements. With the hybrid parameters, however, it is necessary only to short-circuit the output or open-circuit the input; this is easily accomplished at both low and high frequencies.

The second advantage of h parameters is that the input impedance, output admittance, and current gain of the device as used in a circuit approximate h_{11}, h_{22}, and h_{21}, respectively, if certain assumptions are made. As an example: current gain $= h_{21}/(1 + h_{22}R_L)$. If R_L is small compared to $1/h_{22}$, then the current gain of the device in the circuit equals h_{21}.

Representation of Equivalent Circuits. In four-terminal network theory, the small-signal parameters (z, y, and h) are characterized by numerical subscripts; in transistor circuit work, these parameters are usually designated by letter subscripts.

The first subscript designates whether the parameter is input or output, forward or reverse; the second subscript indicates the transistor configuration. The following shows the relationship between the numerical and literal designations.

$11 = i$ . . . . Input parameter
$12 = r$ . . . . Reverse parameter
$21 = f$ . . . . Forward parameter
$22 = o$ . . . . Output parameter
Common-base configuration . . . . b
Common-emitter configuration . . . . e
Common-collector configuration c

Using letter subscripts, h_{oe} would designate the *output h* parameter for the common-emitter configuration.

Representation of Equivalent Circuits. The h-parameter equations having been written and defined, it is necessary to show how an equivalent circuit is derived from the equations.

Common-base Equivalent Circuit. The hybrid equivalent circuit for the h parameters of the common-base configuration (Fig. 6.5a) is shown in Fig. 6.5b.

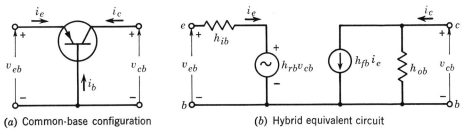

(a) Common-base configuration   (b) Hybrid equivalent circuit

Fig. 6.5. Common-base configuration and hybrid equivalent circuit: (a) common-base configuration; (b) hybrid equivalent circuit.

The reverse voltage transfer ratio, h_{rb}, appears as a voltage generator in the input circuit; the forward current transfer ratio, h_{fb}, appears as a current generator in the output circuit. By calling v_1 and v_2, and i_1 and i_2 of Eqs. (15) and (16), v_{eb} and v_{cb}, and i_e and i_c, respectively, and adding the base subscript b to the h parameters, the equations (for input and output) relating the h parameters for the common-base configuration become

$$v_{eb} = h_{ib}i_e + h_{rb}v_{cb} \qquad (21)$$

$$i_c = h_{fb}i_e + h_{ob}v_{cb} \qquad (22)$$

Common-emitter Equivalent Circuit and Equations. The hybrid equivalent circuit for the h parameters of the common-emitter configuration (Fig. 6.6a) is shown in Fig. 6.6b.

The reverse voltage transfer ratio, h_{re}, appears as a voltage generator in the input circuit; the forward current transfer ratio, h_{fe}, appears as a current generator in the output circuit. By calling v_1 and v_2, and i_1 and i_2 of Eq. (15) and (16), v_{be} and v_{ce}, and i_b and i_c, respectively, and adding the emitter subscript e to the h parameters, the common-emitter equations (for input and output) relating the h parameters for the common-emitter configuration become

$$v_{be} = h_{ie}i_b + h_{re}v_{ce} \qquad (23)$$

$$i_c = h_{fe}i_b + h_{oe}v_{ce} \qquad (24)$$

Common-collector Equivalent Circuit and Equations. The hybrid equivalent

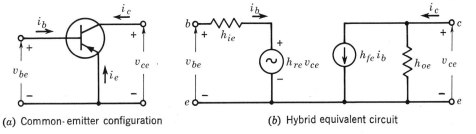

(a) Common-emitter configuration   (b) Hybrid equivalent circuit

Fig. 6.6. Common-emitter configuration and hybrid equivalent circuit: (a) common-emitter configuration; (b) hybrid equivalent circuit.

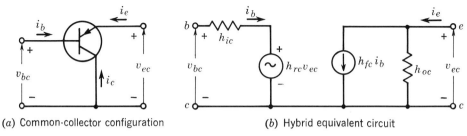

(a) Common-collector configuration   (b) Hybrid equivalent circuit

Fig. 6.7. Common-collector configuration and hybrid equivalent circuit: (a) common-collector configuration; (b) hybrid equivalent circuit.

circuit for the h parameters of the common-collector configuration (Fig. 6.7a) is shown in Fig. 6.7b.

The reverse voltage transfer ratio, h_{rc}, appears as a voltage generator in the input circuit; the forward current transfer ratio, h_{fc}, appears as a current generator in the output circuit. By substituting v_{bc} for v_1, v_{ec} for v_2 and i_b for i_1 in Eq. (15) and by substituting i_b for i_1, i_e for i_2, and v_{ec} for v_2 in Eq. (16), and adding the collector subscript c to the h parameter of Eqs. (15) and (16), the common-collector equations (for input and output) relating the h parameters for the common-collector configuration become

$$v_{bc} = h_{ic}i_b + h_{rc}v_{ec} \qquad (25)$$

$$i_e = h_{fc}i_b + h_{oc}v_{ec} \qquad (26)$$

Electrical properties of the equivalent circuits such as current gain and input impedance are given at the end of this chapter.

Two equivalent circuits will now be shown for the z and y parameters. The first circuit is in terms of voltage generators, while the second has been constructed in terms of current generators. The reader will recall that any two-terminal network may be represented by either a voltage generator in series with an impedance or a current generator in parallel with an impedance.

T-equivalent Circuit. The second main type of equivalent circuit (physical representation) is illustrated by the representation of the T-equivalent circuit. The common-base configuration is given in Fig. 6.10 to define the basic component values

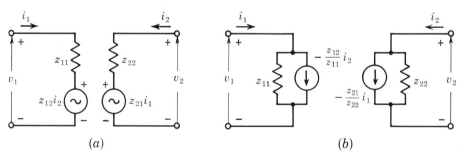

(a)   (b)

Fig. 6.8. z-parameter equivalent circuit.

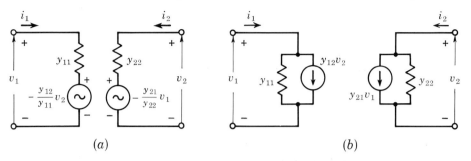

(a) (b)

Fig. 6.9. y-parameter equivalent circuit.

of the equivalent circuit.   The common-base parameters are related to the common-emitter configuration in Fig. 6.11.

α = the fraction of emitter current that becomes collector current. α ranges typically from 0.90 to 0.999.

r_b = ohmic resistance of the base contact and of the base region.   This component can range from tens of ohms to several hundred ohms.

r_c = incremental value of resistance of the collector junction, which is a reverse-biased diode.   Its value ranges typically from one to several megohms.

r_e = incremental resistance of the forward-biased emitter-base diode.   Its resistance is a function of the emitter current and is given approximately by

$$r_e \cong \frac{KT}{qI_E}$$

where K = Boltzmann's constant
T = temperature, $^\circ$K
q = electronic charge

Substituting values for K, T, and q (at room temperature KT/q = 26 mv),

$$r_e \cong \frac{26}{I_E} \qquad (27)$$

where I_E is given in milliamperes, and r_e is given in ohms.

The common-emitter configuration is given in Fig. 6.11.

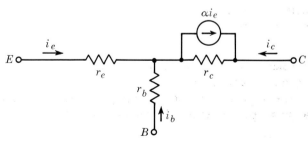

Fig. 6.10.   T-equivalent circuit, common base.

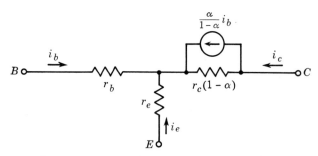

Fig. 6.11.   T-equivalent circuit, common emitter.

Parameter Conversion Tables.   Figures 6.5 (hybrid equivalent circuit) and 6.10 (T-equivalent circuit) give two basic equivalent circuits.   By using these equivalent circuits and standard network theory, analyses of transistor circuits may be made.   Tables 6.1 to 6.8 give the electrical properties of the equivalent circuits. Conversion tables between sets of equivalent circuits are also given.   Manufacturer's data sheets on particular transistors usually present the *h*-parameter values for the *CB* configuration or the *CE* configuration, or a portion of each.   These data sheets seldom provide all the needed values in a form suitable for direct substitution into the equations of the configuration being analyzed; therefore, it becomes necessary to convert the *h*-parameter values given for one configuration to the values suitable for another configuration.

The relations given in these tables are exact; in cases where an approximate form is also given, it is designated by $\cong$.   Refer to Fig. 6.2 for the definition of the basic voltages and currents listed.

The following information is given in Tables 6.1 through 6.8:

Table 6.1:

a. Common-base *h* parameters in terms of common-emitter, common-collector, and T parameters.

b. Common-collector *h* parameters in terms of common-emitter, common-base, and T parameters.

Table 6.2:

a. Common-emitter *h* parameters in terms of common-base, common-collector, and T parameters.

b. T parameters in terms of common-emitter, common-base, and common-collector parameters.

Table 6.3:

a. Input impedance, output impedance, current gain, and voltage gain in terms of *h* and T parameters.

b. Insertion power gain, transducer power gain, available power gain, and operating power gain in terms of *h* parameters.

Table 6.4:

a. *z* parameters in terms of *h* parameters.

b. *y* parameters in terms of *h* parameters.

Table 6.5:

a. Common-emitter z parameters in terms of common-collector and common-base z parameters and T parameters.

b. Common-emitter y parameters in terms of common-collector and common-base y parameters and T parameters.

Table 6.6:

a. Common-base z parameters in terms of common-emitter and common-collector z parameters and T parameters.

b. Common-base y parameters in terms of common-emitter and common-collector y parameters and T parameters.

Table 6.7:

a. Common-collector z parameters in terms of common-emitter and common-base z parameters and T parameters.

b. Common-collector y parameters in terms of common-emitter and common-base y parameters and T parameters.

Table 6.8:

Input impedance, output impedance, voltage gain, and current gain in terms of z and y parameters.

Table 6.1

h parameter	Common-emitter	Common-collector	T-equivalent circuit
h_{ib}	$\dfrac{h_{ie}}{(1+h_{fe})(1-h_{re})+h_{ie}h_{oe}} \cong \dfrac{h_{ie}}{1+h_{fe}}$	$\dfrac{h_{ic}}{h_{ic}h_{oc}-h_{fc}h_{rc}} \cong -\dfrac{h_{ic}}{h_{fc}}$	$r_e+(1-\alpha)r_b$
h_{rb}	$\dfrac{h_{ie}h_{oe}-h_{re}(1+h_{fe})}{(1+h_{fe})(1-h_{re})+h_{ie}h_{oe}} \cong \dfrac{h_{ie}h_{oe}}{1+h_{fe}}-h_{re}$	$\dfrac{h_{fc}(1-h_{rc})+h_{ic}h_{oc}}{h_{ic}h_{oc}-h_{fc}h_{rc}} \cong h_{re}-1-\dfrac{h_{ic}h_{oc}}{h_{fc}}$	$\dfrac{r_b}{r_c+r_b} \cong \dfrac{r_b}{r_c}$
h_{fb}	$\dfrac{-h_{fe}(1-h_{re})-h_{ie}h_{oe}}{(1+h_{fe})(1-h_{re})+h_{ie}h_{oe}} \cong -\dfrac{h_{fe}}{1+h_{fe}}$	$\dfrac{h_{rc}(1+h_{fc})-h_{ic}h_{oc}}{h_{ic}h_{oc}-h_{fc}h_{rc}} \cong -\dfrac{1+h_{fc}}{h_{fc}}$	$-\alpha$
h_{ob}	$\dfrac{h_{oe}}{(1+h_{fe})(1-h_{re})+h_{ie}h_{oe}} \cong \dfrac{h_{oe}}{1+h_{fe}}$	$\dfrac{h_{oc}}{h_{ic}h_{oc}-h_{fc}h_{rc}} \cong \dfrac{h_{oc}}{h_{fc}}$	$\dfrac{1}{r_c+r_b} \cong \dfrac{1}{r_c}$

h parameter	Common-emitter	Common-base	T-equivalent circuit
h_{ic}	h_{ie}	$\dfrac{h_{ib}}{(1+h_{fb})(1-h_{rb})+h_{ob}h_{ib}} \cong \dfrac{h_{ib}}{1+h_{fb}}$	$r_b+\dfrac{r_e r_c}{r_e+r_c-\alpha r_c} \cong r_b+\dfrac{r_e}{1-\alpha}$
h_{rc}	$1-h_{re}$	$\dfrac{1+h_{fb}}{(1+h_{fb})(1-h_{rb})+h_{ob}h_{ib}} \cong 1$	$\dfrac{r_c-\alpha r_c}{r_e+r_c-\alpha r_c} \cong 1-\dfrac{r_e}{(1-\alpha)r_c}$
h_{fc}	$-(1+h_{fe})$	$\dfrac{h_{rb}-1}{(1+h_{fb})(1-h_{rb})+h_{ob}h_{ib}} \cong -\dfrac{1}{1+h_{fb}}$	$-\dfrac{r_c}{r_e+r_c-\alpha r_c} \cong \dfrac{-1}{1-\alpha}$
h_{oc}	h_{oe}	$\dfrac{h_{ob}}{(1+h_{fb})(1-h_{rb})+h_{ob}h_{ib}} \cong \dfrac{h_{ob}}{1+h_{fb}}$	$\dfrac{1}{r_e+r_c-\alpha r_c} \cong \dfrac{1}{(1-\alpha)r_c}$

Table 6.2

h parameter	Common-base	Common-collector	T-equivalent circuit
h_{ie}	$\dfrac{h_{ib}}{(1+h_{fb})(1-h_{rb})+h_{ob}h_{ib}} \cong \dfrac{h_{ib}}{1+h_{fb}}$	h_{ic}	$r_b + \dfrac{r_e r_c}{r_e + r_c - ar_c} \cong r_b + \dfrac{r_e}{1-\alpha}$
h_{re}	$\dfrac{h_{ib}h_{ob}-h_{rb}(1+h_{fb})}{(1+h_{fb})(1-h_{rb})+h_{ob}h_{ib}} \cong \dfrac{h_{ib}h_{ob}}{1+h_{fb}}-h_{rb}$	$1-h_{rc}$	$\dfrac{r_e}{r_e+r_c-ar_c} \cong \dfrac{r_e}{(1-\alpha)r_c}$
h_{fe}	$\dfrac{-h_{fb}(1-h_{rb})-h_{ob}h_{ib}}{(1+h_{fb})(1-h_{rb})+h_{ob}h_{ib}} \cong \dfrac{-h_{fb}}{1+h_{fb}}$	$-(1+h_{fc})$	$\dfrac{ar_c-r_e}{r_e+r_c-ar_c} \cong \dfrac{\alpha}{1-\alpha}$
h_{oe}	$\dfrac{h_{ob}}{(1+h_{fb})(1-h_{rb})+h_{ob}h_{ib}} \cong \dfrac{h_{ob}}{1+h_{fb}}$	h_{oc}	$\dfrac{1}{r_e+r_c-ar_c} \cong \dfrac{1}{(1-\alpha)r_c}$

T parameter	Common-emitter	Common-base	Common-collector
α	$\dfrac{h_{fe}(1-h_{re})+h_{ie}h_{oe}}{(1+h_{fe})(1-h_{re})+h_{ie}h_{oe}} \cong \dfrac{h_{fe}}{1+h_{fe}}$	$-h_{fb}$	$\dfrac{h_{ic}h_{oc}-h_{rc}(1+h_{fc})}{h_{ic}h_{oc}-h_{fc}h_{rc}} \cong \dfrac{1+h_{fc}}{h_{fc}}$
r_c	$\dfrac{h_{fe}+1}{h_{oe}}$	$\dfrac{1-h_{rb}}{h_{ob}}$	$-\dfrac{h_{fc}}{h_{oc}}$
r_e	$\dfrac{h_{re}}{h_{oe}}$	$h_{ib}-(1+h_{fb})\dfrac{h_{rb}}{h_{ob}}$	$\dfrac{1-h_{rc}}{h_{oc}}$
r_b	$h_{ie}-\dfrac{h_{re}(1+h_{fe})}{h_{oe}}$	$\dfrac{h_{rb}}{h_{ob}}$	$h_{ic}+\dfrac{h_{fc}(1-h_{rc})}{h_{oc}}$
a	$\dfrac{h_{fe}+h_{re}}{1+h_{fe}}$	$-\dfrac{h_{fb}+h_{rb}}{1-h_{rb}}$	$\dfrac{h_{fc}+h_{rc}}{h_{fc}}$

Table 6.3

	Input impedance	Output impedance
h parameter	$Z_i = \dfrac{v_i}{i_i} = h_i - \dfrac{h_f h_r Z_L}{1 + h_o Z_L}$	$Z_o = \dfrac{v_o}{i_o} = \dfrac{1}{h_o - \dfrac{h_f h_r}{h_i + Z_g}}$
Common-base T-equivalent circuit	$r_e + r_b\left(\dfrac{r_c - ar_c + R_L}{r_c + r_b + R_L}\right) \cong r_e + r_b(1 - \alpha)$	$r_c + r_b\left(1 - \dfrac{ar_c + r_b}{r_e + r_b + R_g}\right) \cong r_c$
Common-emitter T-equivalent circuit	$r_b + \dfrac{r_e(r_c + R_L)}{r_c - ar_c + r_e + R_L} \cong r_b + \dfrac{r_e}{1-\alpha}$	$r_c - ar_c + r_e\left(1 + \dfrac{ar_c - r_e}{r_e + r_b + R_g}\right) \cong \dfrac{r_c}{1-\alpha}$
Common-collector T-equivalent circuit	$r_b + \dfrac{r_c(r_e + R_L)}{r_c - ar_c + r_e + R_L} \cong r_b + \dfrac{r_e + R_L}{1-\alpha}$	$r_e + (r_b + R_g)\dfrac{r_c - ar_c}{r_c + r_b + R_g}$
	Insertion power gain $\left(\dfrac{\text{power into load}}{\text{power generator would deliver directly}}\right)$	Transducer power gain $\left(\dfrac{\text{power into load}}{\text{maximum available generator power}}\right)$
h parameter where Z_g and Z_L are pure resistance	$G_i = \dfrac{h_f^2(R_g + R_L)^2}{[(h_i + R_g)(1 + h_o R_L) - h_f h_r R_L]^2}$	$G_t = \dfrac{4h_f^2 R_g R_L}{[(h_i + R_g)(1 + h_o R_L) - h_f h_r R_L]^2}$

	Current gain	Voltage gain
h parameter	$A_i = \dfrac{i_o}{i_i} = \dfrac{h_f}{1 + h_o Z_L}$	$A_v = \dfrac{v_o}{v_i} = \dfrac{1}{h_r - \dfrac{h_i}{Z_L}\left(\dfrac{1 + h_o Z_L}{h_f}\right)}$
Common-base T-equivalent circuit	$\dfrac{ar_c + r_b}{r_c + r_b + R_L} \cong \alpha$	$\dfrac{(ar_c + r_b)R_L}{r_e(r_c + r_b + R_L) + r_b(r_c - ar_c + R_L)} \cong \dfrac{\alpha R_L}{r_e + r_b(1 - \alpha)}$
Common-emitter T-equivalent circuit	$\dfrac{-(ar_c - r_e)}{r_c - ar_c + r_e + R_L} \cong \dfrac{\alpha}{1 - \alpha}$	$\dfrac{-(ar_c - r_e)R_L}{r_e(r_e + R_L) + r_b(r_c - ar_c + r_e + R_L)} \cong -\dfrac{\alpha R_L}{r_e + r_b(1 - \alpha)}$
Common-collector T-equivalent circuit	$\dfrac{r_c}{r_c - ar_c + r_e + R_L} \cong \dfrac{1}{1 - \alpha}$	$\dfrac{r_c R_L}{r_c(r_e + R_L) + r_b(r_c - ar_c + r_e + R_L)} \cong \dfrac{1}{1 + r_e + r_b\dfrac{1 - \alpha}{R_L}}$
	Available power gain $\left(\dfrac{\text{maximum available output power}}{\text{maximum available generator power}}\right)$	Operating power gain $\left(\dfrac{\text{power into load}}{\text{power into transistor}}\right)$
h parameter where Z_g and Z_L are pure resistance	$G_a = \dfrac{h_f^2 R_g}{(h_i + R_g)[h_o(h_i + R_g) - h_f h_r]}$	$G_1 = A_v A_i = \dfrac{v_o i_o}{v_i i_i} = \left(\dfrac{h_f}{1 + h_o R_L}\right)h_r - \dfrac{h_i}{R_L}\left(\dfrac{1 + h_o R_L}{h_f}\right)$

Table 6.4

	Common-emitter	Common-base	Common-collector
z_{11b}	$\dfrac{\Delta h}{h_{oe}}$	$\dfrac{\Delta h}{h_{ob}}$	$\dfrac{1}{h_{oc}}$
z_{12b}	$\dfrac{\Delta h - h_{re}}{h_{oe}}$	$\dfrac{h_{rb}}{h_{ob}}$	$\dfrac{1 + h_{fc}}{h_{oc}}$
z_{21b}	$\dfrac{\Delta h + h_{fe}}{h_{oe}}$	$\dfrac{-h_{fb}}{h_{ob}}$	$\dfrac{1 - h_{rc}}{h_{oc}}$
z_{22b}	$\dfrac{d}{h_{oe}}$	$\dfrac{1}{h_{ob}}$	$\dfrac{d}{h_{oc}}$
y_{11b}	$\dfrac{d}{h_{ie}}$	$\dfrac{1}{h_{ib}}$	$\dfrac{d}{h_{ic}}$
y_{12b}	$\dfrac{h_{re} - \Delta h}{h_{ie}}$	$-\dfrac{h_{rb}}{h_{ib}}$	$-\dfrac{1 + h_{fe}}{h_{ic}}$
y_{21b}	$-\dfrac{\Delta h + h_{fe}}{h_{ie}}$	$\dfrac{h_{fb}}{h_{ib}}$	$\dfrac{h_{rc} - 1}{h_{ic}}$
y_{22b}	$\dfrac{\Delta h}{h_{ie}}$	$\dfrac{\Delta h}{h_{ib}}$	$\dfrac{1}{h_{ic}}$

$$\Delta h = h_i h_o - h_r h_f$$
$$d = (1 + h_f)(1 - h_r) + h_i h_o \cong 1 + h_f$$

Table 6.5

z parameter	Common-collector	Common-base	T-equivalent circuit
z_{11e}	$z_{11} - z_{12} - z_{21} + z_{22}$	z_{11}	$r_e + r_b$
z_{12e}	$z_{22} - z_{12}$	$z_{11} - z_{12}$	r_e
z_{21e}	$z_{22} - z_{21}$	$z_{11} - z_{21}$	$r_e - a r_c$
z_{22e}	z_{22}	$z_{11} - z_{12} - z_{21} + z_{22}$	$r_e + r_c(1 - a)$
y parameter	Common-collector	Common-base	T-equivalent circuit
y_{11e}	y_{11}	$y_{11} + y_{12} + y_{21} + y_{22}$	$\dfrac{r_e + r_c(1 - a)}{\Delta}$
y_{12e}	$-(y_{11} + y_{12})$	$-(y_{12} + y_{22})$	$-\dfrac{r_e}{\Delta}$
y_{21e}	$-(y_{11} + y_{21})$	$-(y_{21} + y_{22})$	$-\dfrac{r_e - a r_c}{\Delta}$
y_{22e}	$y_{11} + y_{12} + y_{21} + y_{22}$	y_{22}	$\dfrac{r_e + r_b}{\Delta}$

$$\Delta = r_e r_b + r_c[r_e + r_b(1 - a)]$$

Table 6.6

z parameter	Common-emitter	Common-collector	T-equivalent circuit
z_{11b}	z_{11}	$z_{11} - z_{12} - z_{21} + z_{22}$	$r_e + r_b$
z_{12b}	$z_{11} - z_{12}$	$z_{11} - z_{21}$	r_b
z_{21b}	$z_{11} - z_{21}$	$z_{11} - z_{12}$	$r_b + a r_c$
z_{22b}	$z_{11} - z_{12} - z_{21} + z_{22}$	z_{11}	$r_b + r_c$
y parameter	Common-emitter	Common-collector	T-equivalent circuit
y_{11b}	$y_{11} + y_{12} + y_{21} + y_{22}$	y_{22}	$\dfrac{r_b + r_c}{\Delta}$
y_{12b}	$-(y_{12} + y_{22})$	$-(y_{21} + y_{22})$	$-\dfrac{r_b}{\Delta}$
y_{21b}	$-(y_{21} + y_{22})$	$-(y_{12} + y_{22})$	$-\dfrac{r_b + a r_c}{\Delta}$
y_{22b}	y_{22}	$y_{11} + y_{12} + y_{21} + y_{22}$	$\dfrac{r_e + r_b}{\Delta}$

$$\Delta = r_e r_b + r_c[r_e + r_b(1 - a)]$$

Table 6.7

z parameter	Common-emitter	Common-base	T-equivalent circuit
z_{11c}	$z_{11} - z_{12} - z_{21} + z_{22}$	z_{22}	$r_b + r_c$
z_{12c}	$z_{22} - z_{12}$	$z_{22} - z_{21}$	$r_c(1 - a)$
z_{21c}	$z_{22} - z_{21}$	$z_{22} - z_{12}$	r_c
z_{22c}	z_{22}	$z_{11} - z_{12} - z_{21} + z_{22}$	$r_e + r_c(1 - a)$
y parameter	Common-emitter	Common-base	T-equivalent circuit
y_{11c}	y_{11}	$y_{11} + y_{12} + y_{21} + y_{22}$	$\dfrac{r_e + r_c(1 - a)}{\Delta}$
y_{12c}	$-(y_{11} + y_{12})$	$-(y_{11} + y_{21})$	$\dfrac{-r_c(1 - a)}{\Delta}$
y_{21c}	$-(y_{11} + y_{21})$	$-(y_{11} + y_{12})$	$-\dfrac{r_c}{\Delta}$
y_{22c}	$y_{11} + y_{12} + y_{21} + y_{22}$	y_{11}	$\dfrac{r_b + r_c}{\Delta}$

$$\Delta = r_e r_b + r_c[r_e + r_b(1 - a)]$$

Table 6.8

Parameter	Input impedance	Output impedance	Voltage gain	Current gain
z	$\dfrac{\Delta z + z_{11}Z_L}{z_{22} + Z_L}$	$\dfrac{\Delta z + z_{22}Z_g}{z_{11} + Z_g}$	$\dfrac{z_{21}Z_L}{\Delta z + z_{11}Z_L}$	$\dfrac{-z_{21}}{z_{22} + Z_L}$
y	$\dfrac{y_{22} + Y_L}{\Delta y + y_{11}Y_L}$	$\dfrac{y_{11} + Y_g}{\Delta y + y_{22}Y_g}$	$-\dfrac{y_{21}}{y_{22} + Y_L}$	$\dfrac{y_{21}Y_L}{\Delta y + y_{11}Y_L}$

$\Delta z = z_{11}z_{22} - z_{12}z_{21}$
$\Delta y = y_{11}y_{22} - y_{12}y_{21}$

Part **2**

D-C and Low-frequency Designs

7

Transistor Biasing

7.1. ESTABLISHING THE QUIESCENT OPERATING POINT

The Meaning of Bias. In a vacuum-tube amplifier, bias refers to the d-c voltage applied to the grid of the tube to establish its operating point on the dynamic characteristic curve. In a transistor amplifier, bias can be considered to be the direct current applied to the input terminal of the transistor (base or emitter) to establish an operating point on the load line of the output characteristic curve.

In these discussions we refer to the output (collector) current and the output voltage (V_{CE} or V_{CB}) as the *bias point*. When setting the bias, we are interested in maintaining control of the collector current rather than the base or emitter current; hence our interest is in the stability of the bias point and not the actual bias current.

For vacuum-tube amplifiers it is relatively simple to draw a load line on a set of common-cathode characteristic curves (I_B vs. V_B), select an operating point, and establish it by either a fixed grid bias supply voltage or a resistor in series with the cathode. A similar approach is possible with transistors: One can draw a load line on a set of common-emitter characteristic curves (I_C vs. V_{CE}), select a desirable value of quiescent collector current, and calculate the proper value of base resistance

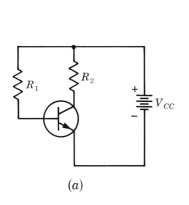

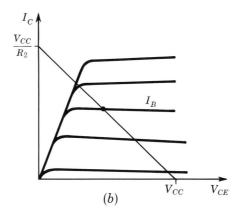

(a) (b)

Figure 7.1

105

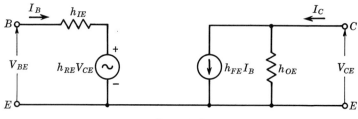

Figure 7.2

to establish the required base current. This approach leads logically to a circuit like that in Fig. 7.1. The base resistance, R_1, is chosen by assuming that the base-to-emitter voltage (V_{BE}) of the transistor is zero: i.e., $R_1 = V_{CC}/I_B$. Designs of this type have both simplicity and a charming element of unpredictability. If R_1 (and hence, I_B) is fixed, there is nothing to prevent I_C from varying in accordance with the current gain, h_{FE}, of the transistor. This type of biasing is very roughly analogous to fixed-bias vacuum-tube amplifiers; but while there are many advantageous applications for fixed-bias vacuum-tube amplifiers, a similarly biased transistor stage should not be used in any application. Generally, a graphical approach to bias network design is of little use in transistor circuitry for the following reasons: (1) There is a wide variation in common-emitter characteristics between devices; (2) the characteristics of each device vary widely with temperature; and (3) the common-base characteristics do not quite describe the transistor in a practical circuit. It is more useful to do an analytical bias design, using equivalent circuits for both the transistor and the external circuit.

Transistor Equivalent Circuit.   The equivalent circuit shown in Fig. 7.2 is modeled after the general hybrid two-port network used to represent the small-signal behavior of the transistor. The common-emitter d-c h parameters are shown. However, only three of these can be independent at a time, so that the circuit is seldom useful for matrix analysis. Better insight is provided by the model shown in Fig. 7.3. Here a diode simulates the base-emitter input characteristics, and a new parameter, defined by $h_{FE}^* = (I_C - I_{CBO})/(I_B + I_{CBO})$, represents the internal current gain mechanism.

External Circuit.   Any network connected external to the three terminals of the transistor can be reduced to a T equivalent as in Fig. 7.4. As an illustration of this, take the general bias circuit of Fig. 7.5 and reduce it to the T network of Fig. 7.4. If these two circuits are to be equivalent, then we can apply Thévenin's

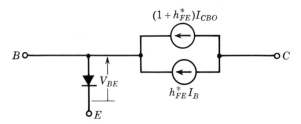

Figure 7.3

theorem to each pair of terminals. Considering only the external circuit, the resistance between the base and emitter terminals with all external voltage sources reduced to zero is

$$RB + RE = R_1 + R_2 + \frac{R_7(R_4 + R_5 + R_6)}{R_4 + R_5 + R_6 + R_7} \tag{1}$$

Between base and collector terminals,

$$RB + RC = R_1 + R_3 + \frac{R_6(R_4 + R_5 + R_7)}{R_4 + R_5 + R_6 + R_7} \tag{2}$$

and between emitter and collector,

$$RE + RC = R_2 + R_3 + \frac{(R_4 + R_5)(R_6 + R_7)}{R_4 + R_5 + R_6 + R_7} \tag{3}$$

Solving Eqs. (1), (2), and (3) simultaneously,

$$RE = R_2 + \frac{R_7(R_4 + R_5)}{R_4 + R_5 + R_6 + R_7} \tag{4}$$

$$RC = R_3 + \frac{R_6(R_4 + R_5)}{R_4 + R_5 + R_6 + R_7} \tag{5}$$

and

$$RB = R_1 + \frac{R_6 R_7}{R_4 + R_5 + R_6 + R_7} \tag{6}$$

Examining each pair of terminals for open-circuit voltages, we find that

$$V'_{BB} = V_{CC}\frac{R_7}{R_4 + R_5 + R_6 + R_7} \tag{7}$$

and

$$V'_{CC} = V_{CC}\frac{R_6 + R_7}{R_4 + R_5 + R_6 + R_7} \tag{8}$$

The circuit of Fig. 7.5 is perfectly general in that the equivalent of any single-stage bias network can be obtained from Eqs. (4) through (8) by setting the appropriate resistors equal to zero or infinity.

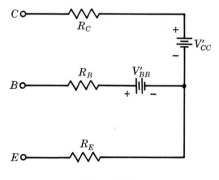

Figure 7.4

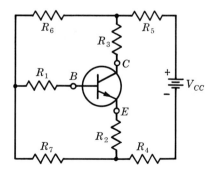

Figure 7.5

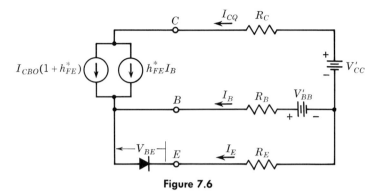

Figure 7.6

Setting the Bias.   By combining the internal and external equivalent circuits as in Fig. 7.6, an expression for the bias-point collector current, I_{CQ}, can be obtained. From Fig. 7.6,

$$I_{CQ} = h_{FE}^* I_B + (1 + h_{FE}^*) I_{CBO} \tag{9}$$

$$I_B = \frac{V_{BB}' - V_{BE} - I_{CBO}(1 + h_{FE}^*) R_E}{R_R + (1 + h_{FE}^*) R_E} \tag{10}$$

Combining Eqs. (9) and (10),

$$I_{CQ} = \frac{h_{FE}^*(V_{BB}' - V_{BE}) + (1 + h_{FE}^*) I_{CBO}(R_B + R_E)}{R_B + (1 + h_{FE}^*) R_E} \tag{11}$$

Equation (11) by itself does not yield the necessary information to bias a transistor in any given application; there are too many variables which must be arbitrarily chosen.   However, the apparently arbitrary choice of I_{CQ} and R_B or R_E is often restricted by the particular application.   For example, if a low-noise amplifier is desired, a value of I_{CQ} would be chosen such that I_{CQ}/h_{FB}^* is at or near the optimum value of emitter current recommended by the data sheet for minimum noise figure. R_B would also be chosen such that it is large compared to the recommended optimum signal source resistance, so that it does not appreciably affect the source resistance.   The problem is then to solve Eq. (11) for the necessary value of emitter resistance.   But this is no small problem, since we would also like a value of emitter resistance that would keep I_{CQ} within certain reasonable limits.

The parameters h_{FE}^*, V_{BE}, and I_{CBO} are all extremely temperature-dependent, and we must investigate Eq. (11) to see what happens to I_{CQ} at the highest and lowest operating-junction temperatures.   Inspection of Eq. (11) shows that minimum I_{CQ} will occur when V_{BE}, R_B, and R_E are at a maximum and I_{CBO}, h_{FE}^*, and V_{BB} are at a minimum.   If minimum $I_{CBO} = 0$, then $h_{FE}^* = h_{FE}$.   Using overlines to indicate maximum (most positive) values and underlines to indicate minimum (most negative) values,

$$\underline{I_{CQ}} \gtreqqless \frac{h_{FE}(\underline{V_{BB}'} - \overline{V_{BE}})}{\overline{R_B} + \overline{R_E}(1 + h_{FE})} \tag{12}$$

This condition generally occurs at the lowest junction temperature.

Similar reasoning shows that maximum I_{CQ} occurs with minimum V_{BE} and R_E and with maximum I_{CBO}, h_{FE}^*, V_{BB}', and R_B. Assuming h_{FE}^* approaches infinity as a maximum,

$$\overline{I}_{CQ} \lessgtr \frac{\overline{V}_{BB}' - \underline{V}_{BE} + \overline{I}_{CBO}(\overline{R}_B + \underline{R}_E)}{\underline{R}_E} \tag{13}$$

This condition generally occurs at the highest junction temperature. Notice that the sign convention of these equations is correct for NPN transistors. The variations in R_B, R_E, and V_{BB} are due to resistance and power-supply tolerances and are of concern where such circuits are to be mass-produced.

If I_{CQ} is to be held within the bounds of a given $\overline{I}_{CQ}$ and $\underline{I}_{CQ}$, Eqs. (12) and (13) may be combined to specify an R_E.

$$R_E \geqq \frac{\underline{h}_{FE}[\overline{V}_{BE}(1 + C) - \underline{V}_{BE}(1 - D) + \overline{I}_{CBO}\overline{R}_B(1 - D)] + \underline{I}_{CQ}\overline{R}_B(1 + C)}{\underline{h}_{FE}(\overline{I}_{CQ} - \overline{I}_{CBO})(1 - B)(1 - D) - \underline{I}_{CQ}(1 + \underline{h}_{FE})(1 + A)(1 + C)} \tag{14}$$

where

$$\overline{R}_E = R_E(1 + A) \tag{15}$$

$$\underline{R}_E = R_E(1 - B) \tag{16}$$

$$\overline{V}_{BB}' = V_{BB}'(1 + C) \tag{17}$$

and

$$\underline{V}_{BB}' = V_{BB}'(1 - D) \tag{18}$$

A and C are the tolerance limits on R_E and V_{BB}' at the highest ambient temperature, and B and D are the limits at the lowest temperature. It is interesting to note that for Eq. (14) to have any meaning, the denominator must be positive and greater than zero. This imposes the condition

$$\overline{I}_{CQ} > \frac{(1 + A)(1 + C)}{(1 - B)(1 - D)}\left(1 + \frac{1}{\underline{h}_{FE}}\right)\underline{I}_{CQ} + \overline{I}_{CBO} \tag{19}$$

Equation (19) gives the minimum variation within which I_{CQ} can be held under specified temperature extremes and resistance tolerances. This provides a quick check on whether a given set of limits on I_{CQ} is possible, but says nothing about the practicality of such limits.

7.2. HEAT DISSIPATION

Two thermal requirements must be met for satisfactory transistor operation:

1. The greatest instantaneous heat released at the junction must flow through the thermal impedance to the highest ambient temperature ever encountered without raising the junction above its maximum rated temperature. In other words, for Fig. 7.7,

$$T_{junction(max)} = T_{ambient(max)} + \Delta T_{J-A(max)}$$

2. The circuit must be stabilized against thermal runaway.

The instantaneous power released at the junction depends upon the instantaneous

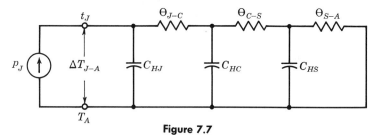

Figure 7.7

values of i_C, v_{CE}, i_B, and v_{BE}. For the general case, it consists of a steady-state component P_J and a time-varying component $p_J(\tau)$. The lowest frequency present in the electrical signal will usually be the fundamental frequency of the Fourier expansion of $p_J(\tau)$.

$$p_J = P_J + p_J(\tau) \tag{20}$$

In many designs the transistor carries only d-c and/or audio-frequency signals, and the power-transient peaks do not exceed about one-tenth second. From Sec. 4.4, since a conservative design results from taking $C_{HJ} = 0$, a good rule of thumb for transistors operating within these limits is

$$\Delta T_{J\text{-}A(max)} = \theta_{J\text{-}C} p_{J(peak)} + \theta_{C\text{-}A} P_{J(max)} \tag{21}$$

This expression would apply to the power stages of most audio amplifiers. It is also useful for estimating the peak t_J encountered in voltage-regulator designs. For the latter purpose, $P_{J(max)}$ is taken to be the maximum steady-state $V_{CE}I_C$ product to be met in normal operation, while $p_{J(peak)}$ is the peak instantaneous $v_{CE}i_C$ product that might be imposed by a transient condition. For the estimate to be conservative, the transistor case temperature must not change appreciably during the transient.

7.3. THERMAL STABILITY

Thermal Runaway. The second requirement for satisfactory operation concerns thermal stability. A rise in junction temperature alters the transistor parameters in a direction that increases collector current. This increased current, in turn, may cause increased dissipation and higher junction temperature. If a transistor is to avoid thermal *runaway,* the rate at which heat released at the junction increases with a rise in junction temperature must not exceed the rate at which the amount of power which can be dissipated changes as the temperature changes. We may derive this criterion in the following way:

Thermal runaway consists of a repetition of three physical processes:

1. A change in i_C results in a change in $p_{J(released)}$.
2. A change in $p_{J(released)}$ results in a change in t_J.
3. A change in t_J results in a change in i_C.

Each process may be considered as a *black box* defined by an input, an output, and a transfer function. This is diagrammed in Fig. 7.8.

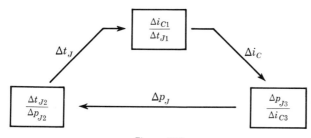

Figure 7.8

If the *loop gain* around this network is unity or greater at any frequency, that is, if

$$\frac{\Delta i_{C1}}{\Delta t_{J1}} \frac{\Delta t_{J2}}{\Delta p_{J2}} \frac{\Delta p_{J3}}{\Delta i_{C3}} \geqq 1 \tag{22}$$

then thermal runaway is possible.

It will be convenient to evaluate each term of Eq. (22) as a derivative, and write the stability criterion as

$$\frac{d i_{C1}}{d t_{J1}} \frac{d t_{J2}}{d p_{J2}} \frac{d p_{J3}}{d i_{C3}} < 1 \tag{23}$$

Equations (22) and (23) assume that the transistor is not subject to thermal feedback from another heat source dependent upon the transistor currents: e.g., two transistors in Darlington connection mounted upon the same heat sink. For these cases, Fig. 7.7 is no longer sufficient. The expression for $(\Delta t_{J2}/\Delta p_{J2})(\Delta p_{J3}/i\Delta_{C3})$ becomes quite complicated and will not be presented here. Approximations which circumvent this problem can usually be made for individual cases.

At any instant in its operation, the transistor must be in one of three conditions:

1. The transistor is ON and is not in saturation: i.e., the emitter diode is forward-biased, the collector diode is reverse-biased, and transistor action is taking place.
2. The transistor is ON and is in saturation: i.e., the emitter and collector diodes are both forward-biased.
3. The transistor is OFF: i.e., the collector diode is reverse-biased, the emitter diode is reverse-biased or unbiased, and no appreciable transistor action is occurring.

Thermal stability is of importance only in the first and, occasionally, the last cases. Before discussing the application of Eq. (22), it will be helpful to examine in detail the form of its constituent derivatives.

Description of dt_{J2}/dp_{J2}. Since t_J is a function of both p_J and the definite integral of p_J with respect to time, dt_{J2}/dp_{J2} will also contain time-dependent terms. In other words, at any instant of time, $\tau = x$,

$$\left. \frac{dt_{J2}}{dp_{J2}} \right|_{\tau=x} = \frac{dt_{J2}/d\tau}{dp_{J2}/d\tau} \tag{24}$$

If the thermal impedance can be considered to be purely resistive, these time-dependent terms vanish and

$$\frac{dt_{J2}}{dp_{J2}} = \theta_T \tag{25}$$

$(dp_{J3}/di_{C3})(di_{C1}/dt_{J1})$ **for an OFF Transistor.** For a transistor in the OFF condition,

$$\frac{dp_{J3}}{di_{C3}} \frac{di_{C1}}{dt_{J1}} = v_{CB} \frac{dI_{CBX}}{dt_J} + v_{EB} \frac{dI_{EBX}}{dt_J} \tag{26}$$

This assumes that the IR drops caused by I_{CBX} and by I_{EBX} are too small to affect the values of v_{CB} and v_{EB}.

di_{C1}/dt_{J1} **for an ON Transistor.** As far as the transistor is concerned, all circuitry external to it may almost always be reduced to one of the three-terminal networks shown in Figs. 7.9 and 7.10. These circuits are simply extensions of the network of Fig. 7.4.

Z_{BB}, Z_{CC}, and K are used principally to describe active external circuit elements linking i_C to i_B: e.g., amplifier feedback loops. If the stage is isolated or if only passive elements are present, these terms may vanish.

These network parameters strongly influence the thermal stability of the stage. If the transistor is directly affected by active elements in the external circuitry—as for example, a stage in a direct-coupled amplifier with an overall feedback loop—then the parameters of Figs. 7.9 and 7.10 may become both complex and negative. Such a feedback loop may keep the stage thermally stable until an overload elsewhere in the amplifier opens the loop. Then the sudden shift of values may cause quick runaway.

The choice between Figs. 7.9 and 7.10 depends upon the base supply impedance. For a low impedance, Fig. 7.9 is usually preferred; for a high impedance, Fig. 7.10 may be more convenient. When the network representation of Fig. 7.9 is feasible, di_{C1}/dt_{J1} may be evaluated in a convenient and useful form for an ON transistor by separating the circuit elements as shown in Fig. 7.11.

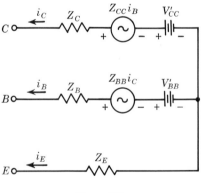

Figure 7.9

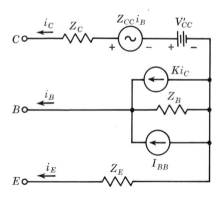

Figure 7.10

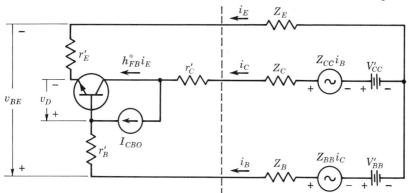

Figure 7.11

In Fig. 7.11, the entire circuit external to the transistor is represented on the right of the dashed line as an equivalent-T network: three impedances, Z_E, Z_C, and Z_B, and four supply voltages, V'_{CC}, V'_{BB}, $Z_{CC}i_B$, and $Z_{BB}i_C$. On the left is an equivalent circuit for the transistor itself, in which the principal temperature-sensitive parameters have been isolated. The basic equations are:

$$i_C = h^*_{FB}i_E + I_{CBO} \tag{27}$$

$$i_B + i_E + i_C = 0 \tag{28}$$

$$v_D = i_E(Z_E + r'_E) - i_B(Z_B + r'_B) + V'_{BB} + Z_{BB}i_C \tag{29}$$

$$i_C = \frac{h^*_{FB}(v_D - V'_{BB}) + I_{CBO}(Z_B + r'_B + Z_E + r'_E)}{(1 + h^*_{FB})(Z_B + r'_B) + Z_E + r'_E + h^*_{FB}Z_{BB}} \tag{30}$$

We may now solve for di_{C1}/dt_{J1}:

$$\frac{di_{C1}}{dt_{J1}} = S\left(\frac{dI_{CBO}}{dt_J} + i_E\frac{dh^*_{FB}}{dt_J}\right) + \left[\frac{h^*_{FB}}{(Z_B + r'_B)(1 + h^*_{FB}) + Z_E + r'_E + h^*_{FB}Z_{BB}}\right]$$
$$\left[\frac{dv_D}{dt_J} + i_B\frac{dr'_B}{dt_J} - i_E\frac{dr'_E}{dt_J}\right] \tag{31}$$

where S, the current stability factor, is defined by

$$S \equiv \frac{\delta i_C}{\delta I_{CBO}} = \frac{Z_B + r'_B + Z_E + r'_E}{(1 + h^*_{FB})(Z_B + r'_B) + Z_E + r'_E + h^*_{FB}Z_{BB}} \tag{32}$$

The network in Fig. 7.10 may also be used to derive di_{C1}/dt_{J1}. The circuit is shown in Fig. 7.12, and the basic equations are:

$$i_C = h^*_{FB}i_E + I_{CBO} \tag{33}$$

$$i_C + i_B + i_E = 0 \tag{34}$$

$$I_{BB} + Ki_C = i_B + i_{ZB} \tag{35}$$

$$V_D = i_E(r'_E + Z_E) + Z_B i_{ZB} - i_B r'_B \tag{36}$$

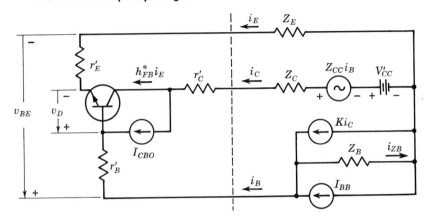

Figure 7.12

and
$$i_C = \frac{h_{FB}^*(v_D - Z_B I_{BB}) + I_{CBO}(Z_B + r_B' + Z_E + r_E')}{(1 + h_{FB}^*)(Z_B + r_B') + Z_B K h_{FB}^* + Z_E + r_E'} \tag{37}$$

Then,

$$\frac{di_{C1}}{dt_{J1}} = S\left(\frac{dI_{CBO}}{dt_J} + i_E \frac{dh_{FB}^*}{dt_J}\right)$$

$$+ \left[\frac{h_{FB}^*}{(1 + h_{FB}^*)(Z_B + r_B') + Z_B K h_{FB}^* + Z_E + r_E'}\right]\left[\frac{dv_D}{dt_J} + i_B \frac{dr_B'}{dt_J} - i_E \frac{dr_E'}{dt_J}\right] \tag{38}$$

where
$$S \equiv \frac{di_C}{dI_{CBO}} = \frac{Z_B + r_B' + Z_E + r_E'}{(1 + h_{FB}^*)(Z_B + r_B') + Z_B K h_{FB}^* + Z_E + r_E'} \tag{39}$$

If the base is driven from a constant-current source (i.e., if $Z_B = \infty$),

$$S = \frac{1}{1 + h_{FB}^*(1 + K)} \tag{40}$$

and
$$\frac{di_{C1}}{dt_{J1}} = S\left(\frac{dI_{CBO}}{dt_J} + i_E \frac{dh_{FB}^*}{dt_J}\right) \tag{41}$$

Simplifying Assumptions. At the expense of a conservative design, several simplifying assumptions may be made:

1. At high junction temperatures,

$$h_{FB}^* \cong -1 \tag{42}$$

A conservative design results when this substitution is made in the numerator of the fraction in the first pair of brackets in Eqs. (31) and (38). It may also be possible to assume

$$h_{FB}^* Z_{BB} \cong -Z_{BB} \tag{43}$$

and
$$h_{FB}^* Z_B K \cong -Z_B K \tag{44}$$

without serious loss of accuracy.

2. I_{CBO} consists of at least two components: an ohmic leakage between collector and base, and the diode saturation current. For a reasonably clean junction, the saturation current usually dominates at high temperatures, and over a small Δt_J can be approximated by

$$I_{CBO} \cong N\epsilon^{(Bt_J)} \tag{45}$$

$$\frac{dI_{CBO}}{dt_J} \cong BI_{CBO} \tag{46}$$

$$B = \frac{\ln 2}{\Delta T_0} \tag{47}$$

where ΔT_0 is the number of centigrade degrees rise in junction required for I_{CBO} to double. ΔT_0 is a complex function of temperature, but for silicon transistors operating near their upper temperature limits, $\Delta T_0 \cong 10\ C°$. If I_{CBO} doubles every 10 C° rise, then

$$\frac{dI_{CBO}}{dt_J} = 0.0693 I_{CBO} \tag{48}$$

For germanium transistors, $\Delta T_0 \cong 14\ C°$, and

$$\frac{dI_{CBO}}{dt_J} \cong 0.0495 I_{CBO} \tag{49}$$

These approximations must be used with some caution, since surface states at the junction can produce erratic I_{CBO} at elevated temperatures. Also, I_{CBO} may be strongly dependent on v_{CB} at voltages near avalanche breakdown.

3. Since the first pairs of brackets in Eqs (31) and (38) enclose negative quantities, $|di_{C1}/dt_{J1}|$ maximizes for an NPN transistor when the sum in the second pair of brackets reaches its most negative value. Theoretical considerations of the transistor suggest that

$$\frac{dv_D}{dt_J} \cong -0.0025\ \text{volt/C°} \tag{50}$$

For a PNP device, the sign of this quantity is positive. The two other quantities in the second brackets are often either of opposing sign or so small that they can safely be ignored.

4. The conservative minimum limit of r_E' is, of course, zero. (The evaluation of r_B' and of dh_{FB}^*/dt_J will be discussed at the end of this chapter.)

Thus, for NPN silicon transistors, Eq. (31) may be reduced to

$$\frac{di_{C1}}{dt_{J1}} = S\left(0.0693 I_{CBO} + i_E \frac{dh_{FB}^*}{dt_J}\right) + \frac{0.0025}{(1 + h_{FB}^*)(Z_B + r_B') + Z_E + h_{FB}^* Z_{BB}} \tag{51}$$

Equation (38) becomes

$$\frac{di_{C1}}{dt_{J1}} = S\left(0.0693 I_{CBO} + i_E \frac{dh_{FB}^*}{dt_J}\right) + \frac{0.0025}{(1 + h_{FB}^*)(Z_B + r_B') + Z_E + K Z_B h_{FB}^*} \tag{52}$$

Notice that Eq. (38) differs from Eq. (31) only in that the quantity KZ_B has been substituted for Z_{BB}. To avoid duplication, the derivations which follow will be based only on Eq. (31). The corresponding results from Eq. (38) may be obtained by replacing Z_{BB} with KZ_B. Also, the equations will show only the constants for NPN silicon transistors.

dp_{J3}/di_{C3} **for an ON Transistor.** The power dissipated in an ON transistor can be found from Fig. 7.9 or 7.10:

$$p_J = i_C(V'_{CC} + i_B Z_{CC} - i_C Z_C + i_E Z_E) + v_{BE} i_B \tag{53}$$

$$\frac{dp_{J3}}{di_{C3}} = V'_{CC} + Z_{CC}\left(i_C \frac{di_B}{di_C} + i_B\right) - 2Z_C i_C + Z_E\left(i_E + i_C \frac{di_E}{di_C}\right) + i_B \frac{dv_{BE}}{di_C} + v_{BE} \frac{di_B}{di_C} \tag{54}$$

Substituting,

$$\frac{dp_{J3}}{di_{C3}} = V'_{CC} + v_{BE} \frac{di_B}{di_C}$$

$$- i_C\left[2Z_C - Z_{CC}\left(\frac{1}{h_{FE}} + \frac{di_B}{di_C}\right) - Z_E\left(\frac{1}{h_{FB}} + \frac{di_E}{di_C}\right) - \frac{1}{h_{FE}} \frac{dv_{BE}}{di_C}\right] \tag{55}$$

At the high junction temperatures which aggravate runaway, current gains are usually large, and

$$\frac{dp_{J3}}{di_{C3}} \cong V'_{CC} - 2i_C(Z_C + Z_E) \tag{56}$$

If no inductance is present in Z_C or Z_E, then for the NPN case

$$\frac{dp_{J3}}{di_{C3}} \leq V'_{CC} \tag{57}$$

This is a very useful *worst case* approximation.

Complex Impedances. Complex electrical and thermal impedances can strongly affect thermal stability. Figure 7.13 gives two such examples. Both circuits may be quite stable if the electrical reactances are ignored. But it is intuitively obvious that if L is made large enough in the first circuit, the rate at which i_B can change with time will become so slow that the transistor could run

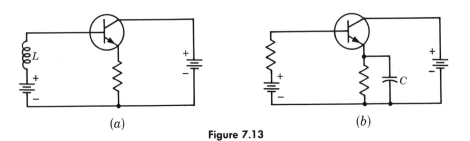

(a)   (b)

Figure 7.13

away in the meanwhile. Similarly, as C becomes infinite in the second circuit, Z_E approaches zero and S may become large enough for instability. The fact that runaway does not occur instantaneously for small values of L or C is due, in part, to the complex nature of the thermal impedance: as the rate of change of p_J with time increases, $\Delta t_{J2}/\Delta p_{J2}$ usually decreases.

It has been customary for both the literature and the design engineer to ignore these reactive effects. The temptation is strong: an exact analysis is virtually impossible. The success of this philosophy may have resulted from three things: (1) A design which is conservative on the basis of a resistive analysis alone is usually safe from reactive troubles; (2) a fast thermal runaway may not be recognized for what it is; and (3) reactive thermal runaways are sometimes oscillatory, and the blame gets placed on an unknown electrical feedback path. As transistor circuit design becomes more sophisticated, these problems may become more serious.

Quiescent Stability. The first requirement for any circuit is that thermal runaway will not occur at an infinitely slow rate. Equation (22) must be satisfied for the zero-frequency, or quiescent, condition. This is a simple mode to evaluate, since all capacitive and inductive reactances are effectively open and short circuits, respectively. The thermal circuit has the simplicity of Fig. 7.7, and if the network of Fig. 7.9 were used with a silicon transistor, Eq. (22) would become approximately

$$\frac{1}{\theta_T} > \frac{V'_{CC} - 2I_{CQ}(R_C + R_E)}{(1 + h^*_{FB})(R_B + r'_B) + R_E - Z_{BB}}$$
$$\left[(R_B + r'_B + R_E)\left(0.0693I_{CBO} + I_{EQ}\frac{dh^*_{FB}}{dt_J}\right) + 0.0025\right] \quad (58)$$

where I_{CQ} and I_{EQ} are quiescent currents.

If this expression is solved for R_E, a rather unmanageable quadratic results. But if Z_E is neglected in Eq. (56), then

$$R_E > \frac{\theta_T\left(V'_{CC} - 2I_{CQ}R_C\right)\left[(R_B + r'_B)\left(0.0693I_{CBO} + I_{EQ}\frac{dh^*_{FB}}{dt_J}\right) + 0.0025\right]}{1 - \theta_T\left(V'_{CC} - 2I_{CQ}R_C\right)\left(0.0693I_{CBO} + I_{EQ}\frac{dh^*_{FB}}{dt_J}\right)} \quad (59)$$

Of course, these inequalities—and the ones which follow—must be evaluated for the peak junction temperature that might be reached during any signal conditions in order to assure stability while the transistor cools down afterward.

Now let us expand the application of Eq. (58).

Dynamic Stability. Since a stage restricted to quiescent operation has rather limited application, some study must be made of the effects of a signal. At very low signal frequencies, the problem approaches the quiescent stability case. Now, however, I_{CQ} is actually the slowly varying instantaneous value of the collector current. But if i_C is changing, at what magnitude will it impose the most stringent stability requirement?

Equation (58) can be put in the form

$$\frac{1}{\theta_T} > (V'_{CC} - 2i_C R_T)(M + N i_E) \tag{60}$$

where $R_T = R_E + R_C$ $\tag{61}$

$$M = 0.0693 S I_{CBO} + \frac{0.0025}{(1 + h^*_{FB})(R_B + r'_B) + h^*_{FB} Z_{BB} + R_E} \tag{62}$$

and $N = S \dfrac{dh^*_{FB}}{dt_J}$ $\tag{63}$

If $-i_E = i_C$, the right-hand side of Eq. (60) maximizes with respect to i_C when

$$i_C \text{ (worst case)} = \frac{V'_{CC}}{4R_T} + \frac{M}{2N} = \frac{V'_{CC}}{4R_T} + \frac{0.0693 I_{CBO} + 0.0025/(R_B + r'_B + R_E)}{dh^*_{FB}/dt_J} \tag{64}$$

providing that $N \neq f(i_C)$, $M \neq f(i_C)$ and $R_T \neq f(i_C)$. The first two conditions do not often exist; nevertheless, they offer a useful first approximation. If $\infty > i_C \geq 0$, Eq. (64) may be substituted into Eq. (60) to give

$$\frac{1}{\theta_T} > \frac{(V'_{CC} N - 2M R_T)^2}{-8 N R_T} \tag{65}$$

In an actual circuit, of course, i_C may never reach this worst-case value. If Eq. (64) gives $i_C < 0$, the actual worst instability will occur when $i_C = 0$. This is often the case for class B stages. Note that the inequality signs restricting i_C must be reversed for PNP transistors.

Equation (65) will often serve for the analysis of the power stage of a voltage regulator. The equivalent circuit of the regulator, however, is more likely to be that of Fig. 7.10.

At high frequencies, the fluctuations of p_J become so rapid that they are completely averaged out by even the shortest junction time constant. For the a-c component of p_J, the thermal impedance is effectively zero and the concept of an instantaneous stability varying with the instantaneous operating point becomes useless. Instead, the problem may be analyzed as a special case of quiescent stability, where I_{CQ} is then the average value of the collector current.

It can be shown that for a distortionless class A stage carrying a sine- or square-wave signal, the average value of $(V'_{CC} - 2i_C R_T)(M - i_C N)$ over one full cycle increases as the signal level falls. This is to be expected, since P_J decreases with increasing signal level while the average collector current remains constant. Thus, for a particular I_{CQ}, the no-signal state imposes a more stringent stability requirement than do high-frequency signals.

For class B operation, however, the average collector current increases with signal level. Also, because of the nature of the push-pull action, the reflected load impedance must be included in R_C for a dynamic analysis. For a resistive load, the collector current waveform which will produce maximum instability for the maximum time is a square wave of amplitude I_{WC}, where

$$I_{WC} = \frac{V'_{CC}}{4(R_E + R_C)} + \frac{M}{2N} \qquad (66)$$

This equation is subjected to the same restrictions as Eq. (64). And again, for the half-cycle that the transistor is ON, Eq. (65) describes the worst stability conditions. However, at these frequencies, the observed stability will be some average of the instantaneous stability throughout the signal cycle. A conservative approximation might be

$$\frac{1}{\theta_T} > \frac{1}{2} \left[(V'_{CC} - 2I_{WC}R_T)(M - I_{WC}N) + (2V'_{CC})(0.0693I_{CBX}) \right.$$
$$\left. + 0.0693I_{EBX}V_{EB(off\ max)} \right] \qquad (67)$$

or, making the required substitution,

$$\frac{1}{\theta_T} > \frac{(V'_{CC}N - 2R_T M)^2}{-16NR_T} + 0.0693V'_{CC}I_{CBX} + 0.0347V_{EB(off\ max)}I_{EBX} \qquad (68)$$

Rapid Runaway. Thus far we have explored the behavior of Eq. (22) at very slow rates of thermal runaway. But a complete analysis would seem to require that we examine Eq. (22) for every possible combination of values of i_C, $di_C/d\tau$, and $\int_{\tau=0}^{\tau=x} i_C\, d\tau$. This would be a formidable task, practicable only with an electronic computer. Sometimes such herculean effort can be avoided. Inspection often reveals that the problem may be reduced to a small number of worst-case situations treating only resistive components. If each of these is stable at peak junction temperature, the circuit should be unconditionally stable. Selection and validity of these worst-case situations will depend upon the electrical and thermal time constants of the circuit. The magnitude of these will suggest the values of $dp_J/d\tau$ and $di_C/d\tau$ which should be explored. For particular values, equivalent resistive networks may be substituted for each complex impedance; the analysis proceeds along the line of Eq. (65).

To illustrate this approach, consider the transformer-coupled audio amplifier of Fig. 7.14. The magnitudes of the transformer inductances and the bypass capacitor

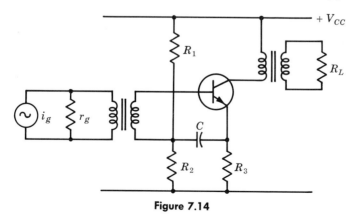

Figure 7.14

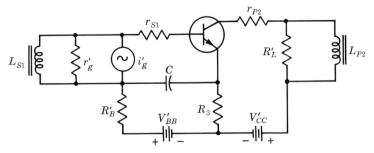

Figure 7.15

are assumed to be satisfactory down to perhaps 20 cps. For our purposes this circuit may be rearranged as in Fig. 7.15. Here,

L_{S1} = inductance of the driver transformer secondary
r_{S1} = d-c resistance of the driver transformer secondary
L_{P2} = inductance of the output transformer primary
r_{P2} = d-c resistance of the output transformer primary
$R_B' = R_1 R_2/(R_1 + R_2)$

To predict very slow rates of thermal runaway, Eq. (58) will be satisfactory if

$$\theta = \theta_T$$
$$R_C = r_{P2}$$
$$R_B = r_{S1} + R_B'$$
$$R_E = R_3$$
and
$$V_{CC}' = V_{CC}$$

It is intuitively obvious that if runaway is sufficiently rapid, because of the quick change of currents L_{S1} and L_{P2} will present high impedances compared to r_g' and R_L', while C will present a low impedance compared to $(R_3 + R_B')$. To predict instabilities of this type, Eqs. (64) and (65) might be used. Now, however,

$$\theta \leqq \theta_{J\text{-}C}$$

$$R_C = r_{P2} + R_L' + \frac{R_B' R_3}{R_B' + R_3}$$

$$R_B = r_{S1} + r_g'$$

$$R_E = 0$$

and
$$V_{CC}' = V_{CC} + I_{CQ}\left[R_L' - R_3\left(1 + \frac{1}{h_{FE}}\right) + \frac{R_B' R_3}{R_B' + R_3}\right]$$

Runaway at faster rates is still less likely, because while R_B has already reached a maximum, the effective value of θ will continue to decrease as $di_C/d\tau$ increases. Slower rates, however, may be possible. The shift of R_E from R_3 to zero will decrease stability, and the change of R_B from $(r_{S1} + R_B')$ to $(r_{S1} + r_g')$ will do so if $r_g' > R_B'$. Stability should be checked for the rates of $di_C/d\tau$ at which these impedance shifts occur. One way this may be done is to note the frequencies, f_o, at which $X_{LS1} = r_g'$ and $X_C = R_3 + R_B'$. A suitable value for θ is found for each frequency, using a thermal circuit similar to Fig. 7.7 and letting $p_J = P_o \sin 2\pi f_o \tau$. Conservative resistive equivalents of each electrical impedance may be selected in a similar way. Stability can then be evaluated for each of these sets of quantities.

This crude approximation will serve to indicate whether or not a detailed analysis is needed. It is often easier, however, to stop at this point, build the circuit, and test it.

Evaluation of dh^*_{FB}/dt_J. For many transistors, the approximation $1 + h_{FB} \cong 1/(1 + h_{FE})$ is valid. This allows a simple estimate of dh^*_{FB}/dt_J:

$$\frac{dh^*_{FB}}{dt_J} \cong \frac{\Delta h_{FB}}{\Delta t_J} = \frac{h_{FB2} - h_{FB1}}{t_{J2} - t_{J1}} \cong \frac{1/(1 + h_{FE2}) - 1/(1 + h_{FE1})}{t_{J2} - t_{J1}} \qquad (69)$$

In general, the lower the average value of h_{FE} over a given Δt_J, the greater the absolute magnitude of dh^*_{FB}/dt_J. Thus, Eq. (69) should be evaluated from low h_{FE} transistors over a narrow temperature range just below the expected maximum junction temperature. Figure 7.16 will allow a quick estimate of Δh_{FB}.

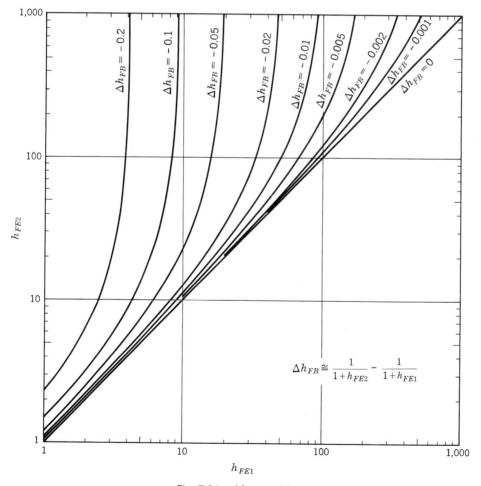

$$\Delta h_{FB} \cong \frac{1}{1 + h_{FE2}} - \frac{1}{1 + h_{FE1}}$$

Fig. 7.16. Δh_{FB} **vs.** Δh_{FE}.

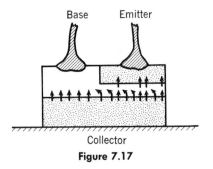

Base   Emitter

Collector

Figure 7.17

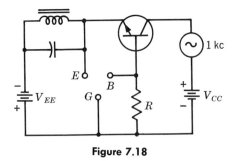

Figure 7.18

Evaluation of r_B'. The term r_B' as used in this chapter is not exactly the familiar ohmic resistance term of transistor equivalent circuits. The best definition of this quantity is an explanation of how it arises.

Figure 7.17 shows a cross section of an idealized double-diffused mesa transistor. Leakage currents flowing from the collector into the base region on the left side of the wafer meet with little resistance between the collector junction and the base lead. Currents on the right side, however, must move some distance horizontally through the base to reach the lead, meeting a comparatively large resistance. For lumped-parameter representation, it is convenient to define an average effective value, r_B', of this bulk resistance.

Precise measurement of r_B' is probably impossible, but for many transistor geometries the simple test circuit shown in Fig. 7.18 can give an approximation. V_{CC} and V_{EE} are adjusted to bias the transistor to its usual d-c operating conditions. A small 1-kc alternating current flow into the collector and out of the base is superimposed upon the direct currents. The high-Q LC pair in the emitter lead prevents any a-c flow out of this terminal. Under these conditions, the emitter will acquire a floating a-c potential which is an average of the collector junction-to-base IR drops. The signal current, i_s, can be found from

$$i_s = \frac{v_{BG}}{R} \tag{70}$$

Then a very simple one-dimensional current flow in the base leads to

$$r_B' \cong \frac{3v_{EB}}{i_s} = \frac{3v_{EB}R}{v_{BG}} \tag{71}$$

BIBLIOGRAPHY

Articles

Benedict, Robert P.: Transient Heat Flow, *Electro-Technol.* pp. 93–112, December, 1961.
Kraus, Allan D.: Heat Flow Theory, *Elec. Mfg.*, pp. 123–142, April, 1959.
Kraus, Allan D.: Extended Surfaces for Heat Transfer, *Electro-Technol.* This is an excellent series of articles beginning February, 1961, and extending at least through July, 1961.
Luft, Werner: Taking the Heat off Semiconductor Devices, *Electronics*, pp. 53–56, June 12, 1959.

Walston, Joseph A.: Thermal Considerations in Transistor Circuit Design, TI Application Report, 1962.

Webber, K. L.: Temperature Stabilization of Transistors in Class B Amplifiers, *Proc. IRE Australia,* pp. 726–733, December, 1959.

Books

Brown, A. I., and S. M. Marco: "Introduction to Heat Transfer," 3d ed., McGraw-Hill Book Company, Inc., New York, 1958.

Eckert, E. R. G., and R. M. Drake, Jr.: "Heat and Mass Transfer," 2d ed., McGraw-Hill Book Company, Inc., New York, 1959.

Jakob, Max: "Heat Transfer," 2 vols., John Wiley & Sons, Inc., New York, 1949, 1957.

Lin, H. C., and A. A. Barco: Temperature Effects in Circuits Using Junction Transistors, "Transistors I," RCA Laboratories, Princeton, N.J., 1956.

McAdams, W. H.: "Heat Transmission," 3d ed., McGraw-Hill Book Company, Inc., New York, 1954.

Schneider, P. J.: "Heat Conduction," Addison-Wesley Publishing Company, Inc., Reading, Mass., 1956.

8

Direct-coupled Amplifiers

This chapter provides detailed information on the nature of the sources of drift in transistors, and presents techniques for the design of low-drift circuits for use in the input stages of direct-coupled amplifiers. Although only the common-emitter configuration is considered, the approach is applicable to any circuit in which drift may affect circuit performance.

The minimum detectable signal of an amplifier is determined by the spurious signals originating within the amplifier. Noise and/or pickup define this limit for a-c amplifiers; d-c drift is usually the determining factor for direct-coupled amplifiers. It is customary to specify drift in terms of the change of input voltage or current required to maintain constant output conditions when the parameters of the amplifier vary. If several stages are cascaded, the equivalent input drift for the amplifier will be determined by the input stage, providing that stage has moderate gain.

8.1. SOURCES OF DRIFT

The major sources of drift in a transistor are changes in the d-c properties of the collector-base and emitter-base diodes and the d-c transfer ratio. Figure 8.1 is a T-equivalent circuit which has been modified to include both the d-c and small-signal a-c characteristics of a transistor.

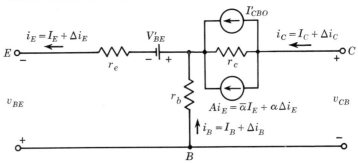

Fig. 8.1. Equivalent circuit for direct current and low-frequency alternating current (NPN).

The small-signal elements r_e, r_c, r_b, and α are the conventional T parameters evaluated at the desired operating point. The V'_{BE} battery, I'_{CO} current generator, and d-c transfer ratio, $\overline{\alpha}$, are included to provide the proper direct currents and voltages at the operating point.

The total instantaneous currents i_C, i_B, and i_E are made up of two components. The design quiescent currents are denoted by I_C, I_B, and I_E while the incremental deviations from the quiescent values are denoted by Δi_C, Δi_B, and Δi_E.

Emitter-Base Diode. Figure 8.2 shows the VI characteristic of a typical forward-biased emitter-base diode. In the equivalent circuit, the base-to-emitter terminal voltage is approximated by

$$V_{BE} = V'_{BE} + I_B r_b + I_E r_e \tag{1}$$

The ideal diode incremental resistance, r''_e, given by

$$r''_e = \frac{kT}{qI_E} \tag{2}$$

is included in r_e.

Collector-Base Diode. The reverse-biased collector-base diode is represented by the true saturation-current generator I'_{CBO}, and the small-signal collector resistance r_c. The current in r_c when d-c bias is applied to the collector includes the diode leakage current. The symbol I_{CBO} denotes total passive reverse current and is given by

$$I_{CBO} = I'_{CBO} + V_{CB} g_c \tag{3}$$

where

$$g_c = \frac{1}{r_c}$$

Current Transfer Ratio. Figure 8.3 shows an exaggerated static plot of the collector current generator transfer ratio, A. Over a range of values of i_E near the

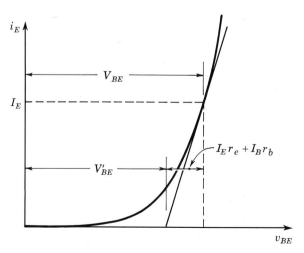

Fig. 8.2. Emitter-base diode forward characteristic.

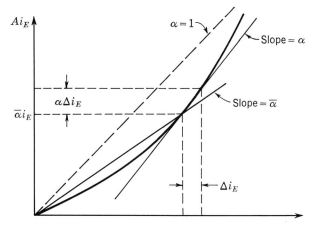

Fig. 8.3.   Collector current generator static characteristic.

design operating point, the Ai_E current generator of Fig. 8.1 may be approximated by

$$Ai_E = \bar{\alpha}I_E + \alpha\,\Delta i_E \tag{4}$$

where $\bar{\alpha}$ is the static or d-c value of the transfer ratio at the operating point and α is the conventional small-signal T parameter.

Temperature Effects.   Figure 8.4 shows the collector current generator static characteristic for two temperatures.   For constant emitter current, the change in the collector current generator may be attributed to a change in value of the d-c transfer ratio, $\bar{\alpha}$.

$$\Delta(Ai_E) = (\bar{\alpha}_2 - \bar{\alpha}_1)I_E = \Delta\bar{\alpha}I_E \tag{5}$$

where the subscripts refer to the two temperatures.   In the emitter circuit, a change in temperature causes a change in the V'_{BE} battery and also a voltage change, due

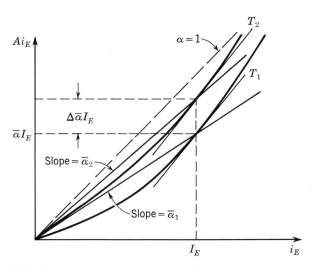

Fig. 8.4.   Effect of temperature on collector current generator.

to shifts in r_e and r_b. For constant-emitter current, the change in base-emitter voltage is

$$\Delta V_{BE} = \Delta V'_{BE} + I_E\,\Delta r_e + I_B\,\Delta r_b \qquad (6)$$

For constant collector-base voltage, changes in the passive component of collector current due to variations of I'_{CBO} and g_c may be expressed by

$$\Delta I_{CBO} = \Delta I'_{CBO} + V_{CB}\Delta g_c \qquad (7)$$

8.2. DRIFT* EQUIVALENT CIRCUIT

The input drift of a transistor stage may be calculated using the equivalent circuit of Fig. 8.1 by taking into account the changes in the various parameters as indicated by Eqs. (5) to (7). However, such a calculation is cumbersome, owing to the presence of the terms representing the reference-temperature operating point.

The small-signal equivalent circuit of Fig. 8.5 follows directly from Fig. 8.1 by the removal of the currents and voltages which define the operating point. The ΔV_{BE} battery in the emitter circuit is defined by Eq. (6), the ΔI_{CBO} current generator by Eq. (7), and the $\Delta\bar{\alpha}I_E$ current generator by Eq. (5) and Fig. 8.4.

Since the drift produced by changes in r_e, r_b, and r_c is included in ΔV_{BE} and ΔI_{CBO}, the explicit dependence of these parameters on temperature has been omitted from this circuit. The variation of small-signal gain due to changes in these elements and in α may be considered separately if necessary. This equivalent circuit may be used directly to calculate the small-signal gain of a transistor stage at frequencies down to and including d-c, and to predict shifts from the design operating point due to changes in temperature.

8.3. SINGLE-ENDED STAGE

Analysis. The single-ended common-emitter stage of Fig. 8.6a may be analyzed for equivalent input drift by using the circuit in Fig. 8.6b. Input current and voltage drift are, respectively, the values of Δi_B and Δv_1 required to maintain Δi_C at zero as the parameters of the circuit vary.

* The term *drift* as used refers to shifts in the d-c operating point of an amplifier due to changes in the circuit parameters, and has no connection with the terms drift field or drift transistor. None of the transistors considered are drift transistors.

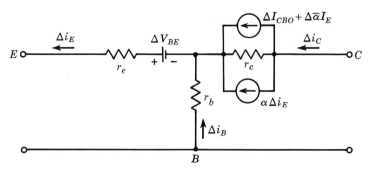

Fig. 8.5. Equivalent circuit for drift and low-frequency alternating current (NPN).

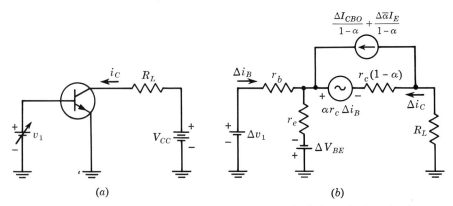

Fig. 8.6. (a) Single-ended common-emitter stage; (b) drift equivalent circuit.

The input voltage drift is given by

$$\Delta v_1 = -\frac{\alpha r_c + r_b}{\alpha r_c - r_e} \Delta V_{BE} - \frac{r_b r_c + r_e r_c}{\alpha r_c - r_e} (\Delta \bar{\alpha} I_E + \Delta I_{CBO}) \tag{8}$$

and the input current drift is

$$\Delta i_B = -\frac{\Delta V_{BE}}{\alpha r_c - r_e} - \frac{r_c}{\alpha r_c - r_e} (\Delta \alpha I_E + \Delta I_{CBO}) \tag{9}$$

For most transistors, the current transfer ratio increases with rising temperature. Thus, $\Delta \bar{\alpha} I_E$ in Eq. (9) is normally positive and adds to ΔI_{CBO} along with $\Delta V_{BE}/r_c$. In most cases r_c is large enough so that $\Delta V_{BE}/r_c$ may be neglected. As would be expected from the definition of equivalent input drift, Eqs. (8) and (9) are independent of the collector load resistor, R_L. Also, since

$$\alpha r_c \gg r_e, r_b \tag{10}$$

Eqs. (8) and (9) are insensitive to variations in the small-signal parameters r_c, r_b, and r_e.

As a good approximation, the expressions for equivalent input voltage drift and equivalent input current drift may be written, respectively, as

$$\Delta v_1 \cong -\Delta V_{BE} - (r_b + r_e) \left(\frac{\Delta I_{CBO}}{\alpha} + \frac{\Delta \bar{\alpha}}{\alpha} I_E \right) \tag{11}$$

and

$$\Delta i_B \cong -\frac{1}{\alpha} (\Delta \bar{\alpha} I_E + \Delta I_{CBO}) \tag{12}$$

For high-gain transistors, α is very near unity, and changes only a few per cent over the useful temperature range of the device; it may, therefore, be considered a constant.

Input Voltage Drift. Figures 8.7 and 8.8 show static plots of v_1 vs. temperature for various constant values of i_C; Fig. 8.7 is for a silicon grown-junction transistor and Fig. 8.8 is for a germanium alloy transistor. The slope of these curves is predominantly due to $\Delta V_{BE}/\Delta T$. The departure from a straight line in the germanium unit is due to the ΔI_{CBO} term in Eq. (11).

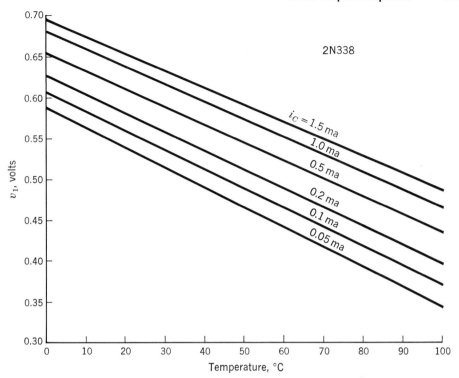

Fig. 8.7.   Equivalent input voltage drift, single-ended stage silicon transistor.

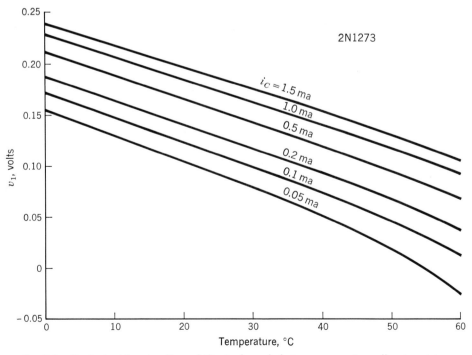

Fig. 8.8.   Equivalent input voltage drift, single-ended stage germanium alloy transistor.

For transistors with no body resistance, and holding i_E constant, the expression for the change in V_{BE} with temperature is

$$\frac{\Delta V_{BE}}{\Delta T} = -\frac{E_g - V_{BE}}{T} + \frac{5}{2}\frac{k}{q} \tag{13}$$

where E_g is the energy gap, and both E_g and V_{BE} are functions of temperature. Typical values of this coefficient lie between 2.0 and 3.0 mv/C° for both germanium and silicon; for a germanium transistor at room temperature and $V_{BE} = 0.1$ volt, Eq. (13) predicts a value of 2.3 mv/C°.

Input Current Drift. Figures 8.9 and 8.10 are static plots of i_B vs. temperature for various constant values of i_C. In the silicon transistor (Fig. 8.9), I_{CBO} is negligible at all temperatures considered and the input current drift is due to the variation of $\bar{\alpha}$. For the germanium transistor (Fig. 8.10), Δi_B is principally due to I_{CBO} at moderate and high temperatures, with α being the controlling factor at low temperatures.

The saturation-current temperature characteristic may be approximated by

$$I'_{CBO} = Ne^{BT} \tag{14}$$

where N and B are constants which vary from unit to unit and with material type. For a germanium transistor, leakage current is negligible and $\Delta I_{CBO} \cong \Delta I'_{CBO}$. The temperature coefficient of I_{CBO} for small excursions of temperature is

$$\frac{\Delta I_{CBO}}{\Delta T} = B(I_{CBO})_T \tag{15}$$

where $(I_{CBO})_T$ is the value of I_{CBO} at reference temperature.

For larger temperature increments, the number of degrees required for I_{CBO} to double in magnitude is useful. This coefficient is given by

$$\delta T \cong \frac{0.693}{B} \tag{16}$$

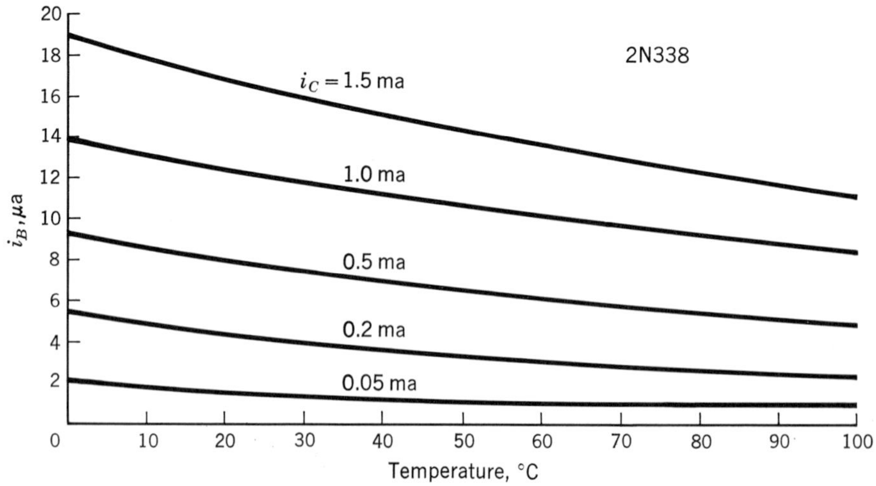

Fig. 8.9. Equivalent input current drift, single-ended stage silicon transistor.

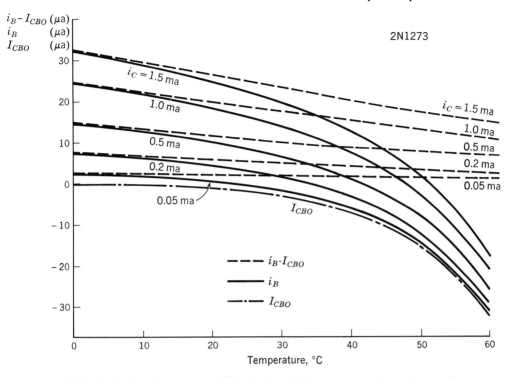

Fig. 8.10. Equivalent input current drift, single-ended stage germanium alloy transistor.

When the transistor is to operate over an extreme temperature range the change in I_{CBO} is approximately equal to the value of I_{CBO} at the highest temperature.

From Figs. 8.9 and 8.10 the temperature dependence of $\bar{\alpha}$ is such that $\Delta\bar{\alpha}I_E$ is approximately a linear function of temperature for both germanium and silicon.

Typical Drift Parameters. Figure 8.11 is a plot of $\Delta V_{BE}/\Delta T$ vs. I_C for typical transistors of each type; typical values of $\Delta\bar{\alpha}I_E/\Delta T$ are plotted vs. I_C in Fig. 8.12. These data were obtained from a sample of 10 randomly selected production transistors of each type listed. The coefficients represent average values over the tem-

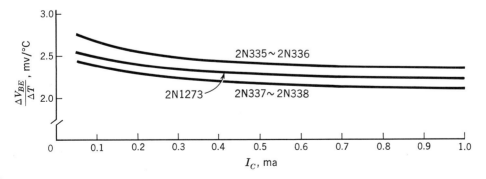

Fig. 8.11. $\Delta V_{BE}/\Delta T$ **vs.** I_C.

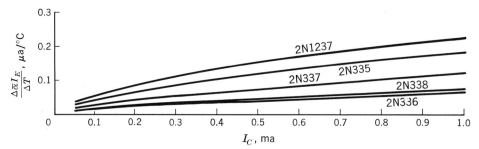

Fig. 8.12. $\Delta\bar{\alpha}I_E/\Delta T$ **vs.** I_C.

perature ranges considered; however, as seen from Fig. 8.7 through 8.10, the coefficients do not vary radically with temperature.

Figure 8.13 is a plot of the temperature, T_{CBO}, at which $\Delta I_{CBO}/\Delta T$ is equal to $\Delta\bar{\alpha}I_E/\Delta T$, as a function of collector current. For a given collector current and below the critical temperature T_{CBO}, the temperature dependence of I_{CBO} may be neglected in predicting circuit performance. For temperatures near T_{CBO} the temperature coefficients of both I_{CBO} and $\bar{\alpha}I_E$ must be considered, while at temperatures above T_{CBO} it is necessary to consider only I_{CBO}. Figure 8.13 also includes a table which lists typical values of $\Delta I_{CBO}/\Delta T(I_{CBO})_T$ and δT for the 2N1273.

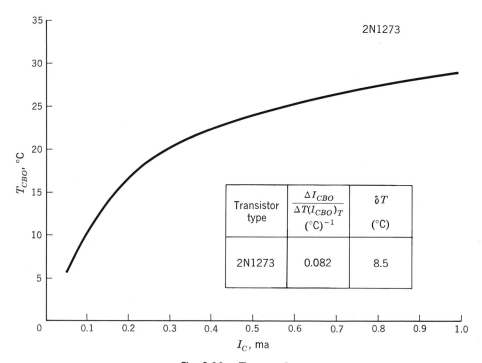

Transistor type	$\dfrac{\Delta I_{CBO}}{\Delta T(I_{CBO})_T}$ $(°C)^{-1}$	δT $(°C)$
2N1273	0.082	8.5

Fig. 8.13. T_{CBO} **vs.** I_C.

8.4. DIFFERENTIAL STAGE

The use of local degeneration in d-c amplifiers to stabilize the operating point invariably reduces the stage gain and degrades the minimum detectable signal of the amplifier. However, drift reduction by compensation does not materially affect gain and, hence, offers a significant improvement in minimum detectable signal. The emitter-coupled differential amplifier is a versatile input stage which offers voltage-drift compensation between similar transistors.

Figure 8.14 is the equivalent circuit of a typical differential d-c amplifier stage. For a pair of transistors which are matched at the operating point but have different thermal coefficients, and for $r_c \gg R_E + r_e$, $R_B + r_b$, the equivalent input voltage drift is

$$\Delta v_1 - \Delta v_2 = -(\Delta V_{BE1} - \Delta V_{BE2}) - \frac{R_B + r_b + R_E + r_e}{\alpha}(\Delta I_{CBO1} - \Delta I_{CBO2})$$

$$- \frac{R_B + r_b + R_E + r_e}{\alpha}(\Delta \bar{\alpha}_1 I_{E1} - \Delta \bar{\alpha} I_{E2}) \quad (17)$$

This expression has the same form as Eq. (11), which is the equivalent input voltage drift for a single-ended stage. However, thermal effects are appreciably reduced in the differential connection since changes in corresponding parameters of the two transistors are subtractive.

The response of a differential amplifier to input signals may be analyzed from the equivalent circuit of Fig. 8.14.

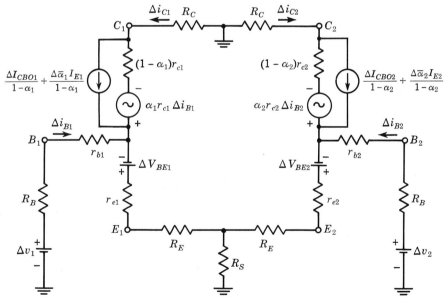

Fig. 8.14. Differential-amplifier equivalent circuit for drift and low-frequency alternating current (NPN).

By properly arranging terms, it is possible to express Δi_{C1} as

$$\Delta i_{C1} = G_D(\Delta v_1 - \Delta v_2) + G_A \frac{\Delta v_1 + \Delta v_2}{2} \tag{18}$$

where G_D and G_A are respectively the transconductances for the differential and average, or common-mode, input signals.

If $(\Delta i_{C1} - \Delta i_{C2})$ is considered as the output in Fig. 8.14, the differential stage transconductance is the same as that of the single-ended stage of Fig. 8.15a. This single-ended stage may be used to predict the differential gain and drift performance of the differential stage. The current and voltage drift generators are the difference between the drift generators of the two transistors as indicated in Eq. (17).

The circuit of Fig. 8.15b has a transconductance equal to G_A and may be used for determining common-mode gain and drift. The drift generators in this case are the average of the corresponding drift generators of the two transistors in the differential stage.

An examination of the expressions for gain and drift of the differential amplifier shows that many of the bias-stabilization techniques normally employed in RC-coupled amplifiers may be used to stabilize the common-level operating point of individual stages without affecting the differential performance.

The common-mode rejection factor of a differential amplifier is defined as

$$M = \frac{G_D}{G_A} \tag{19}$$

It is possible to achieve perfect common-mode rejection in a circuit of this type since G_A [and therefore the denominator of Eq. (19)] vanishes when R_S is equal to the critical value $(R_S)_K$ given by

$$(R_S)_K = \frac{\alpha r_c - R_E - r_e}{2} \tag{20}$$

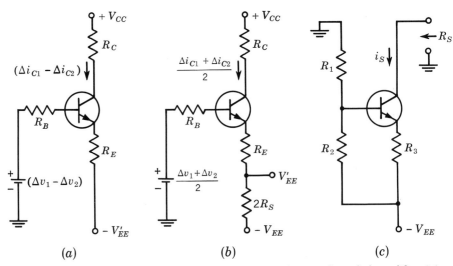

(a)   (b)   (c)

Fig. 8.15. (a) Equivalent differential amplifier; (b) equivalent single-ended amplifier; (c) constant-current source for common-mode rejection.

When high values of R_S are necessary to provide adequate common-mode rejection, supply voltage requirements may be excessive. The transistor constant-current source of Fig. 8.15c provides a high incremental resistance for these applications. When the base and emitter resistors of the constant-current source are properly proportioned, an incremental resistance of $(R_S)_K$ may be realized.

8.5. INPUT STAGE DESIGN

In the design of low-drift input stages for direct-coupled amplifiers, some of the variables which must be considered are source resistance, maximum operating temperature, temperature range, and the desired drift performance.

Choice of Transistor. A knowledge of the maximum operating temperature allows a choice to be made between germanium and silicon transistors. At temperatures below their respective values of T_{CBO}, drift performances of germanium and silicon are quite comparable. As shown in Fig. 8.12, the silicon transistors tend to have lower input current drift than the germanium transistors. From Fig. 8.11 the input voltage drift is essentially the same for all types. Typical values of T_{CBO} for germanium alloy transistors are given in Fig. 8.13; for the silicon transistors considered in this chapter, T_{CBO} is in excess of $100°C$.

The choice of transistor type may also be influenced by the source impedance, range of temperature, and desired performance. For low source resistance, low values of input voltage drift may be obtained at temperatures above T_{CBO}. With high source resistance, the best drift performance occurs at temperatures where I_{CBO} may be neglected. For any given configuration, the drift may be significantly reduced by placing the amplifier in a constant-temperature oven.

Choice of Circuit. In general, the input drift of a differential stage is at least as good as an equivalent single-ended stage using standard transistors. For low source resistances, the differential stage offers an improvement of 10:1 or better in drift, owing to V_{BE}. This improvement may be attributed to the inherent consistency of the $\Delta V_{BE}/\Delta T$ coefficients, which for unmatched transistors of a given type differ by 10% or less. For high-resistance applications in which the voltage drift due to $\Delta i_B/\Delta T$ is greater than $\Delta V_{BE}/\Delta T$, single-ended and differential stages have comparable performance unless transistors with matched $\Delta i_B/\Delta T$ coefficients are used in the differential connection. For unmatched transistors of a given type, $\Delta \bar{\alpha} I_E/\Delta T$ coefficients may differ by 2:1. The $\Delta I_{CBO}/\Delta T$ coefficients in germanium transistors typically differ by 3:1 or less; for matched I_{CBO} at the operating temperature, $\Delta I_{CBO}/\Delta T$ coefficients differ by less than 20%.

Choosing the Operating Point. Figure 8.12 shows that low values of input current drift may be obtained by operating the input transistors at low values of collector current. The input voltage drift is only slightly dependent on collector current; the increase in $\Delta V_{BE}/\Delta T$ as collector current is reduced may usually be neglected. In order to reduce the leakage component of I_{CBO}, the collector-base voltage should be held as low as possible.

Optimizing the low-frequency noise performance also calls for low values of collector current and collector-base voltage. Optimum noise figure normally occurs at source resistances in the order of a few kilohms. In general, the precautions taken to reduce drift also tend to give low noise.

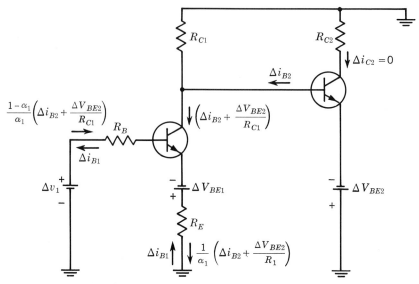

Fig. 8.16.   Input drift due to stages one and two.

As the collector current is reduced to minimize input current drift, the current gain, α, decreases and the internal emitter resistance, r_e, increases.   The gain reduction due to these two effects places a lower limit on the first-stage collector current.

In summary, a typical low drift input stage will be a differential amplifier with collector current between 10 and 200 μa.   The collector voltage should be 6 volts or less to minimize leakage.   At temperatures below T_{CBO}, an equivalent input voltage drift of 400 μv or less per centigrade degree may be realized by using unmatched 2N336 or 2N338 transistors, provided the sum of resistances in the base and emitter leads is less than 8 kilohms.   For more critical applications, further drift reduction may be realized by matching the transistors and/or placing the amplifier in a constant-temperature oven.

In order for the differential amplifier to provide drift cancellation, the transistors must be at the same temperature.   Both transient and steady-state temperature differentials may be minimized by securely mounting both transistors in a common heat sink of large thermal capacity.

8.6.   SECOND-STAGE DRIFT

Figure 8.16 schematically shows the effect of drift in the second stage referred to the input.   For a single-ended amplifier, both the current drift and voltage drift of stage 2 tend to cancel the equivalent input drift due to stage 1; for a differential amplifier, the stage-2 drift may aid or oppose the drift of stage 1.

8.7.   TWO DESIGN EXAMPLES

Figure 8.17 is the schematic of a d-c differential amplifier which makes use of some of the design techniques outlined in this chapter.   The amplifier performs

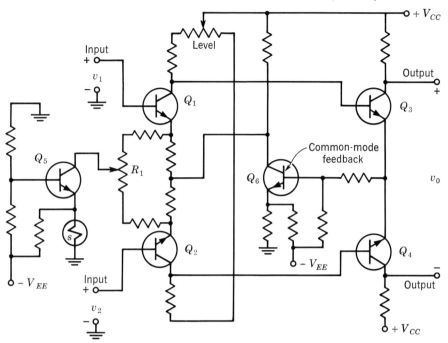

Fig. 8.17. D-c differential amplifier.

best with low-resistance sources such as reference diodes, thermocouples, strain gauges, accelerometers, etc.

Transistors Q_1 and Q_2 are operated at $V_{CE} = 6$ volts, and $I_C = 50$ μa; Q_3 and Q_4 collector currents are 200 μa. The input transistor pair have $\Delta V_{BE}/\Delta T$ coefficients matched to within 60 μv/C°. Since both $\Delta \bar{\alpha} I_E/\Delta T$ and $\Delta V_{BE}/\Delta T$ are constants, the residual input voltage drift is a linear function of temperature and may be compensated by the *sensistor** resistor S, and its associated transistor Q_5. The *sensistor* resistor has a positive temperature coefficient of 0.7% per C°. Potentiometer R_1 may be adjusted such that the *sensistor* resistor correction will cause either output to increase with temperature. When R_1 is in center position, no correction results.

The common-mode feedback transistor Q_6 stabilizes the sum of the first-stage collector currents, and hence gives almost perfect common-mode rejection.

If 2N336 or 2N338 transistors are used in this circuit at temperatures below T_{CBO}, adjustment of R_1 to give minimum drift as the temperature is cycled over the desired range will give drifts of 6 μv or less per centigrade degree over a 15°C temperature range.

A Four-stage Differential Amplifier. The circuit of Fig. 8.18 is designed for maximum open-loop amplification of the differential signal. Series-shunt negative feedback provides a high input impedance and low output impedance. The closed-loop gain is determined by the differential feedback network and can be adjusted by varying R_1. Local shunt feedback in the third stage shapes the frequency response and prevents oscillation under closed-loop conditions.

* Reg. U.S. Pat. Off.

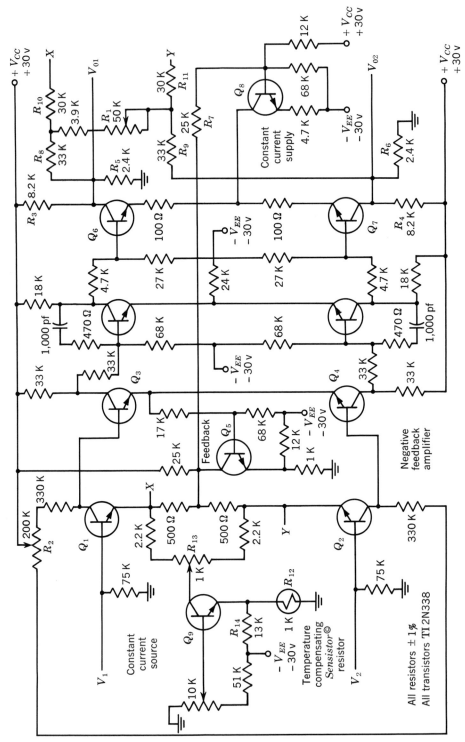

Fig. 8.18. Differential amplifier circuit.

Since all the transistors are NPN, the voltage level is increased at the collector of each stage. Voltage-divider networks in the collector circuits of the second and third stages drop the average output voltage to the desired level. Resistor R_2 provides zero adjustment for the differential output, or a level control for either of the single-ended terminals. No provision is made for adjusting the average output voltage.

The amplifier of Fig. 8.18 responds to a differential signal of 25 μv superimposed on a common level which varies from zero to five volts. An input circuit similar to that of Fig. 8.19, with a high value of R_S, provides sufficient common-mode rejection to operate under these conditions. However, when series feedback is applied to the input, the feedback resistors shunt R_S and reduce the common-mode rejection factor. The values of the feedback resistors determine the change of collector current which results from a specified variation in the common level of the source and, therefore, the minimum quiescent current at which the stage can be operated.

Transistors Q_1 through Q_5 maintain the quiescent emitter currents of the input pair essentially constant at 50 μa for the 5-volt change in the common input level. This circuit acts as a negative feedback amplifier in which the common level of the source is the input, and the potential of the emitters of Q_3 and Q_4 is the output.

Output is fed back to the emitters of Q_1 and Q_2 by the feedback transistor Q_5 in such a direction as to oppose a change of input current. Amplified feedback provides adequate common-mode rejection by maintaining the closed-loop gain of the common-level amplifier at much less than unity. Small common-level changes which occur at the collectors of Q_1 and Q_2 are further rejected by the common-mode rejection of the second, third, and fourth stages.

Input Circuit. The d-c stability of an amplifier is determined primarily by the input stage, since the equivalent input drift due to any subsequent stage is reduced by the preceding gain. This stage is therefore operated at bias conditions which produce minimum drift. Transistors with the best possible d-c characteristics

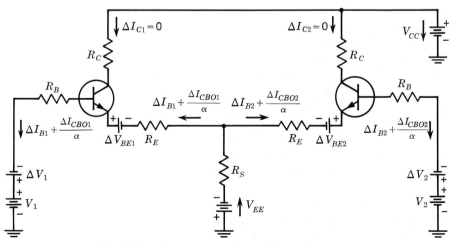

Fig. 8.19. Common-emitter amplifier configuration.

should be used for the input pair. For the circuit in Fig. 8.18, the optimum collector current for the first stage was selected as 50 μa. Operation at lower levels would deteriorate the gain because of a decrease in α and an increase in the emitter diode resistance r_e, thus increasing the drift of the second stage.

Because of the linearity of the V_{BE} temperature characteristic, it is possible to match V_{BE} thermal coefficients for the input pair within 60 μv/C$^\circ$ by measuring V_{BE} at two widely different temperatures. The magnitudes of V_{BE} are also matched to reduce the required range of zero adjustment.

Temperature coefficients for I_{CBO} and α are not considered sufficiently uniform to warrant matching. Effects of I_{CBO} are minimized by selecting units with low I_{CBO} at the operating temperature.

Output Circuit. Output impedance for single-ended loads is determined by the collector supply networks in the final stage. Since the collectors of Q_6 and Q_7 are effectively connected by the low differential output impedance, the output impedance from either terminal to ground is approximately the parallel combination of R_3, R_4, R_5, and R_6.

When a single-ended output is used, drift in the average level of the output must be eliminated as well as differential drifts. The average voltage of the output terminals is made independent of the emitter potentials of Q_6 and Q_7 by Q_8, which acts as a constant-current supply.

Variations of the supply voltage present another source of drift in the single-ended output circuit. An increase, ΔV_{CC}, in the positive supply voltage causes the average output voltage to increase by $\Delta V_o = \Delta V_{CC}/[R_5/(R_3 + R_5)]$. This drift is compensated partially by the constant-current source, since an increase in the positive supply voltage produces an increase in the collector current of Q_8.

Resistor R_7 eliminates coupling of common-mode input voltage variations to the output terminals through the differential feedback network. An increase in the common level of the source causes the average potential at the emitters of the input circuit to rise, thus increasing the current which flows through R_8, R_9, R_{10}, and R_{11}, from the emitters of the input stage to the output collectors. The average potential of the output terminals can remain constant only if the collector currents of Q_6 and Q_7 increase such that the currents in the collector supply networks of the final stage do not change.

The increase in the average emitter potential of the first stage causes the base of Q_8 to increase because of the connection through R_7. Since Q_8 determines the average collector current of the final stage, collector currents of Q_6 and Q_7 are also increased. Resistor R_7 may be adjusted such that the average output level is not affected by common-mode variations of the source.

Thermal Compensator. The residual overall drift of the amplifier is compensated by a special silicon resistor R_{12} which has a positive temperature coefficient. This *sensistor* silicon resistor compensates for thermal variation resulting from V_{BE}, the primary cause of amplifier drift. Temperature characteristics of this element are shown in Fig. 8.20.

A variation of R_{12} with temperature changes the collector current of Q_9 and the current in potentiometer R_{13}. The amount of this change is determined by the bias current which is supplied to the silicon resistor through R_{14}. When R_{13} is moved from its center position, a temperature-dependent potential is produced

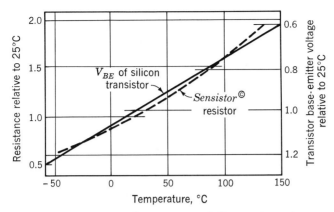

Fig. 8.20. Temperature characteristics of silicon resistor element.

between the emitters of Q_1 and Q_2; this potential may be adjusted for the desired compensation.

A change in the collector current of Q_9 with temperature does not affect the quiescent condition of Q_1 and Q_2, because of the common-mode rejection provided by Q_5. Changes in the average level of the source do not affect the compensation adjustment since, at a fixed temperature, Q_9 is a constant-current source.

Test Results. The amplifier has a voltage gain for a single-ended output which is continuously variable from 100 to 500, and a frequency response flat within one per cent to 1,000 cps. When used with a low-impedance source such as a strain gauge or thermocouple, it has drift characteristics superior to those of its electron-tube counterpart.

The differential input impedance is in excess of 140,000 ohms. The output impedance is less than 1,000 ohms to a single-ended signal, and less than 50 ohms to a differential signal. The common-mode rejection factor is greater than 50,000:1.

Drift was evaluated over a 12-hr period after an initial warmup of 45 min. The equivalent input drift is less than 60 μv from 70 to 80°C. For critical drift applications, the amplifier should be operated under closely controlled temperature conditions.

The input transistor pair and the silicon resistor should be mounted in a common heat sink of high thermal capacity. This procedure reduces transient drifts due to different thermal time constants. Low drift characteristics are dependent upon the stability of the transistor coefficients with time, the accuracy of adjusting the temperature-compensation network, and the degree to which the temperature characteristic of the compensation network matches the drift characteristic of the amplifier.

Size, low power requirements, and low drift make the amplifier desirable for military telemetering systems. Because of its versatility, many other applications will be apparent for industrial and laboratory instrumentation.

The following sections illustrate methods of biasing and calculating the voltage gain and input impedance of differential amplifiers.

A Two-stage Differential Amplifier. The circuit of Fig. 8.21 shows a typical design problem. Q_1, Q_2, Q_3, and Q_4 comprise the actual differential amplifier, while

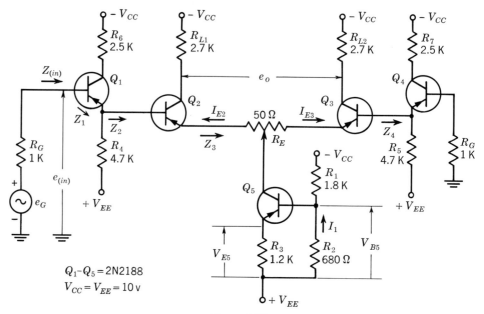

$$Q_1-Q_5 = 2N2188$$
$$V_{CC} = V_{EE} = 10 \text{ v}$$

Figure 8.21

Q_5 is used as a constant-current source. Q_5 supplies bias current to Q_2 and Q_3, appears as a high a-c or incremental impedance to the signal, and requires only a fairly small d-c voltage drop. Two supplies are required for this amplifier so that the input may be set at ground level.

Constant-current Generator. R_1 and R_2 form a voltage divider that sets the emitter voltage of Q_5. With the emitter voltage of Q_5 set at a given level, R_3 determines I_{E5}. From the data sheet, I_{E2} and I_{E3} were selected to equal 2 ma, so that $I_{E5} = 4$ ma.

$$V_{B5} = \frac{(V_{CC} + V_{EE})R_2}{R_1 + R_2} \tag{21}$$

$$V_{B5} \cong V_{E5} \tag{22}$$

$$I_{E5} = \frac{V_{E5}}{R_3} \tag{23}$$

By using Eqs. (21) to (23), the actual values of R_1, R_2, and R_3 can be calculated.

Voltage Gain. Figure 8.22 shows the equivalent circuit used in calculating the voltage gain of Fig. 8.21.

The current gain of the circuit is calculated first, and the voltage gain follows from the relationship

$$A_V = A_I \frac{R_L}{R_{(in)}}$$

In the calculations it is assumed that the voltage gains of the emitter followers, Q_1 and Q_4, are unity.

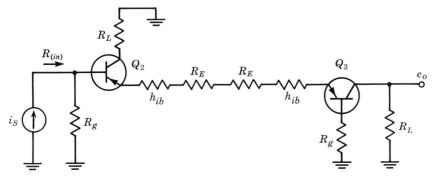

Figure 8.22

$$A_{V\,(collector\text{-}collector)} = \frac{e_O}{e_{(in)}} = \frac{R_L}{[(h_{fe}+1)/h_{fe}](h_{ib}+R_E)+R_g/h_{fe}} \cong \frac{R_L}{h_{ib}+R_E} \quad (24)$$

Circuit values substituted into Eq. (24) give a calculated gain of 60:

$$\frac{2.7 \text{ kilohms}}{20 \text{ ohms} + 25 \text{ ohms}} = 60$$

This agrees closely with the measured values of Table 8.1 (differential amplifier performance).

Input Impedance. To find the input impedance, find Z_4, then Z_3, and work progressively back to find $Z_{(in)}$ (refer to Fig. 8.21 for symbol meanings).

$$Z_{(in)} = h_{ie1} + (h_{fe1}+1)\frac{R_4\left[h_{ie2}+2R_E(h_{fe2}+1)+h_{ib3}(h_{fe2}+1)+\left(\dfrac{h_{fe2}+1}{h_{fe3}+1}\right)Z_4\right]}{R_4+h_{ie2}+2R_E(h_{fe2}+1)+h_{ib3}(h_{fe3}+1)+\left(\dfrac{h_{fe2}+1}{h_{fe3}+1}\right)Z_4} \quad (25)$$

where

$$Z_4 = \frac{R_5 h_{ib4}+R_5 R_g/(h_{fe4}+1)}{R_5+h_{ib4}+R_g/(h_{fe4}+1)}$$

Let $h_{fe} \gg 1$, and let all respective parameters be equal:

$$Z_{(in)} = h_{ie} + \frac{h_{fe}R_4(2h_{ie}+2R_E h_{fe}+Z_4)}{R_4+2h_{ie}+2R_E h_{fe}+Z_4} \quad (26)$$

$Z_{(in)}$ can be reduced to an approximate form:

$$Z_{(in)} \cong h_{fe}\frac{R_4 2h_{ie}+2R_E h_{fe}+h_{ib}+R_g/h_{fe}}{R_4+2h_{ie}+2R_E h_{fe}+h_{ib}+R_g/h_{fe}} \quad (27)$$

Substituting circuit values into Eq. (7), $Z_{(in)} = 270$ kilohms. This is in reasonable agreement with Table 8.1.

Differential Amplifier Performance. The following table shows experimental results from the differential amplifier using 2N2188's. Five pairs of typical transistors were placed in the amplifier, and data were taken on each pair.

Table 8.1. Typical Characteristics Measured at 25°C

Transistor pair	Input impedance at 1 kc, kilohms	Voltage gain $(e_o/e_{(in)})$ at 1 kc	D-c drift referred to input 25–60°C, $\mu v/C°$	Output impedance at 1 kc, collector to collector, kilohms
1	200	67	38	5.4
2	250	67	29.8	5.4
3	180	66	43.3	5.4
4	200	66	20.4	5.4
5	148	65	10.8	5.4

Operating conditions:

Maximum operating temperature: 60°C.

Output voltage swing before clipping: 16 volts peak to peak at 25°C.

$$A_{V(collector\text{-}collector)} = \cfrac{R_L}{\cfrac{h_{fe}+1}{h_{fe}}(h_{ib}+R_E) + \cfrac{R_g}{h_{fe}}} \cong \frac{R_L}{h_{ib}+R_E}$$

where R_g = effective generator impedance for the differential stage (Q_2, Q_3). Assumptions:

1. All transistors have equal parameters.
2. Output impedance of all transistors is much greater than that of their load resistors.

BIBLIOGRAPHY

Biard, J. R., and W. T. Matzen: Drift Considerations in Low-level Direct-coupled Transistor Circuits, 1959 *IRE Conv. Record,* part III.

Chaplin, G. B. B., and A. R. Owens: Some Transistor Input Stages for High-gain DC Amplifiers, *Proc. Inst. Elec. Engrs.,* vol. 105, part B, pp. 249–257, July, 1958.

Gärtner, W. W.: Temperature Dependence of Junction Transistor Parameters, *Proc. IRE,* vol. 45, no. 5, part 1, pp. 662–680, May, 1957.

Hilsenrath, F.: Thermocouple Differential Amplifier, *Proc. Natl. Telemetering Conf.,* pp. 227–235, June 2–4, 1958.

Korn, G. A., and T. M. Korn: "Electronic Analog Computers," 2d ed., p. 192, McGraw-Hill Book Company, Inc., New York, 1956.

Lin, H. C., and A. A. Barco: Temperature Effects in Circuits Using Junction Transistors, "Transistors I," RCA Laboratories, pp. 369–402, Princeton, N.J., 1956.

Matzen, W. T., and J. R. Biard: Differential Amplifier Features DC Stability, *Electronics,* vol. 32, no. 3, pp. 60–62, Jan. 16, 1959.

Slaughter, D. W.: The Emitter-coupled Differential Amplifier, *Trans. IRE,* vol. CT–3, pp. 51–53, March, 1956.

Stanton, J. W.: A Transistorized D.C. Amplifier, *Trans. IRE,* vol. CT–3, pp. 65–66, March, 1956.

Valley, G. E., Jr., and H. Wallman: "Vacuum Tube Amplifiers," p. 444, McGraw-Hill Book Company, Inc., New York, 1948.

Warren, J. P.: A New Approach to the Design of Low Drift D.C. Amplifiers, *Tech. Dig., Solid-State Circuits Conf.,* pp. 36–37, February, 1959.

9

Voltage Regulators

A voltage regulator provides a constant voltage to specified loads from a limited range of input voltages. Since most applications require the series-type regulator, only the series type will be discussed, although a shunt regulator may be used where the load is relatively constant.

General design procedure may be divided into five elements as shown in the block diagram of Fig. 9.1. Note that regulation is performed by comparing a sample of the output voltage with a reference; any error present is amplified and used to control a series element. The sampling element of the block diagram is usually a simple voltage divider across the regulated output, as shown in Fig. 9.2 with its Thévenin equivalent circuit. For this sampling element, the voltage to the comparison element is

$$A_T V_O = \frac{V_O(R_2 + R_{p2})}{R_1 + R_2 + R_p} \tag{1}$$

where A_T = voltage division of the resistive divider = $\dfrac{R_2 + R_{p2}}{R_1 + R_2 + R_p}$ (2)

and V_O = regulated output voltage

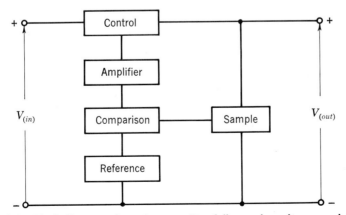

Fig. 9.1.   Block diagram of a series or emitter-follower d-c voltage regulator.

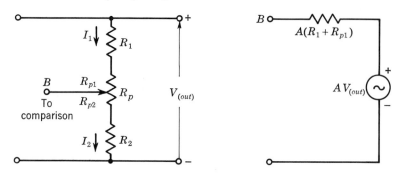

Fig. 9.2.　Sampling element and its Thévenin equivalent circuit.

Equation (1) is valid when resistors R_1, R_2, and R_p are at the same temperature and have the same temperature coefficient, i.e., are of the same type material.

Silicon breakdown diodes are generally used as voltage references in transistor regulators because their breakdown voltage is relatively constant over a wide range of reverse current. The effects of temperature, reverse current, and diode resistance on breakdown voltage are characteristics that must be considered in the selection of a reference diode.

Silicon diodes with low breakdown voltages (on the order of 5 volts or lower) usually have a negative temperature coefficient. As the breakdown voltage increases, the temperature coefficient becomes increasingly positive. Figure 9.3 shows how the temperature coefficient depends upon the nominal breakdown voltage and the diode reverse current of typical breakdown diodes.

The d-c resistance of breakdown diodes is also a function of reverse current and breakdown voltage as shown in Fig. 9.4. The d-c diode resistance of a breakdown diode can be calculated, using

$$R_{d\text{-}c} = R_{a\text{-}c} + \frac{\Delta V_Z}{\Delta T} V_Z \theta \tag{3}$$

where $R_{a\text{-}c}$ = dynamic diode resistance, θ = thermal resistance of the diode, and V_Z and $\Delta V_Z / \Delta T$ are as shown in Fig. 9.3.

Because of the characteristics shown in Figs. 9.3 and 9.4, a series combination of low-voltage diodes is usually preferred over one high-voltage diode if a high reference voltage is needed. A series string of low-voltage breakdown diodes can be made to have a lower net temperature coefficient and total diode resistance than a single diode used to provide the same reference voltage. The combined temperature coefficient can also be changed with very little change in reference voltage by using forward-biased diodes (either general-purpose or breakdown diodes) in series with breakdown diodes.

The combined temperature coefficient of a series string of diodes can be determined from the following equation:

$$\frac{\Delta V_T}{\Delta T} = \frac{\Delta V_{Z1}}{\Delta T} + \frac{\Delta V_{Zn}}{\Delta T} + \frac{\Delta V_{F1}}{\Delta T} + \frac{\Delta V_{Fn}}{\Delta T} \tag{4}$$

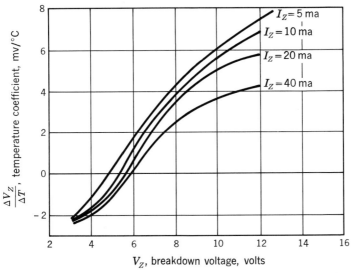

Fig. 9.3. Temperature coefficient vs. breakdown voltage: 1N746 series.

where $\Delta V_T/\Delta T$ = combined voltage change per C°
$\Delta V_Z/\Delta T$ = voltage change per C° for each breakdown diode
$\Delta V_F/\Delta T$ = voltage change per C° for the forward diodes

The temperature coefficient of each diode carries its own sign in Eq. (4). The combined temperature coefficient computed from Eq. (4) is valid at only one current value; therefore a constant diode current must be provided to obtain a stable reference element. A constant diode current is also required to keep the breakdown voltage and the diode resistance constant.

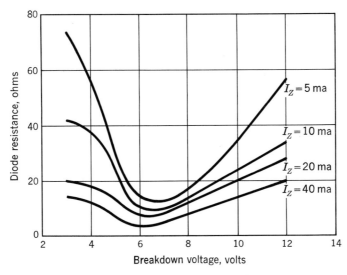

Fig. 9.4. D-c diode resistance vs. breakdown voltage: 1N746 series.

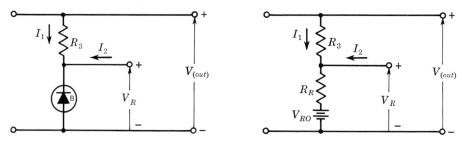

Fig. 9.5.   A reference element and its equivalent circuit.

The importance of maintaining a nearly constant temperature coefficient is apparent.   The reference element and equivalent circuit in Fig. 9.5 are used to show why it is also desirable to keep the resistance of the breakdown diode as low as possible.

Assume ΔI_1 is small so that $\Delta R_R \cong 0$.

Assume $I_1 \gg I_2$.

$$I_1 R_3 + V_R = V_{(out)} \tag{5}$$

$$\Delta I_1 R_3 + \Delta V_R = \Delta V_{(out)} \tag{6}$$

$$\Delta V_R \cong \Delta I_1 R_R \tag{7}$$

$$\frac{\Delta V_R R_3}{R_R} + \Delta V_R \cong \Delta V_{(out)} \tag{8}$$

$$\frac{\Delta V_R}{\Delta V_{(out)}} \cong \frac{R_R}{R_3 + R_R} \tag{9}$$

Equation (9) shows that the change in reference voltage for a change in output voltage can be made very small by selecting a breakdown diode with low resistance and by holding the reverse current nearly constant.   Ideally, the reference voltage in a regulator should not change for any normal output voltage change.

The temperature characteristics needed in the reference and comparison elements are usually determined simultaneously, because each element affects the temperature requirements of the other.

9.1.   COMPARISON ELEMENT

The comparison element takes a sample of the output voltage, compares it with the reference voltage, and produces a signal that is proportional to the difference. A single common-emitter stage or an emitter-coupled differential amplifier may be used for the comparison element.   The choice depends on the degree of regulation and temperature stability required.   The common-emitter stage (Fig. 9.6) is discussed first.

The potentiometers in Fig. 9.6 are used to adjust the output sample to match the reference voltage at specified output voltages.   The current from the potentiometer wiper into the comparison element must be kept much smaller than that through the divider so that the sample voltage remains an accurate portion of the output. I_3 in Fig. 9.6a or I_4 in Fig. 9.6b must be considerably larger than the emitter current of Q_1 or Q_2 so that the diode reverse current can be kept nearly constant.

The sample voltage is applied to the base of Q_1, and the reference voltage is applied to the emitter in Fig. 9.6a. If the output voltage tends to increase, the base-emitter voltage of Q_1 will increase and cause more collector current to flow. A drop in output voltage causes the collector current of Q_1 to decrease. The change in Q_1 collector current and the change in the input current to the control element are out of phase. This means that if the output voltage begins to rise, the amplified difference voltage will decrease the current into the control element and the output voltage will be corrected.

The reference element may be used as shown in Fig. 9.6b for high output voltages. This enables transistors in the comparison element to operate at low voltage levels, regardless of the regulator output voltage.

The collector currents of Fig. 9.6a and 9.6b are of opposite phase because of the different reference-element positions. If Fig. 9.6b is used, a d-c amplifier is required between the comparison element and the series control element to provide the correct phase relationship.

Temperature compensation for the common-emitter comparison element: Since the reference voltage plus the base-emitter voltage of the comparison transistor is equal to the output sample, the following equation applies for Fig. 9.6a:

$$V_{(out)} = (V_R + V_{BE})\frac{R_1 + R_2 + R_p}{R_2 + R_{p2}} \tag{10}$$

where $V_{(out)}$ = regulated output voltage
$\quad\quad V_R$ = reference voltage
$\quad\quad V_{BE}$ = base-emitter voltage of comparison element

If R_1, R_2, and R_p are of the same material,

$$\Delta V_{(out)} = \frac{R_1 + R_2 + R_p}{R_2 + R_{p2}}(\Delta V_R + \Delta V_{BE}) \tag{11}$$

and any change in output voltage is the result of ΔV_R and ΔV_{BE}. Since $\Delta V_{BE}/\Delta T$

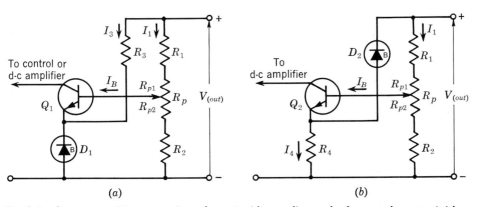

(a)   (b)

Fig. 9.6. Common-emitter comparison element with sampling and reference elements: (a) low output voltage; (b) high output voltage.

is usually negative, the temperature problem can be solved by using a breakdown diode which has a positive temperature coefficient that exactly cancels $\Delta V_{BE}/\Delta T$ of Q_1 in Fig. 9.6a.

The same approach shows that Eq. (12) applies for Fig. 9.6b:

$$\Delta V_{(out)} = \frac{R_1 + R_2 + R_p}{R_1 + R_{p1}}(\Delta V_R - \Delta V_{BE}) \tag{12}$$

If the sampling resistors are of the same material, the breakdown diode must be chosen with a negative temperature coefficient equal to $\Delta V_{BE}/\Delta T$ of Q_2 in Fig. 9.6b.

Temperature compensation can be provided with little difficulty for temperatures below about 100°C, using a single silicon common-emitter stage for the comparison element. The effects from I_{CBO} are usually not critical below this temperature in silicon transistors; therefore, the problems of compensation are due primarily to changes in the base-emitter voltage, V_{BE}, with temperature.

An emitter-coupled differential amplifier is ideal as a comparison element if the regulator is to perform over a wide temperature range or at very high temperatures (Fig. 9.7).

The symmetrical arrangement of the differential amplifier tends to make it self-compensating for temperature effects. Self-compensation can be improved by selecting well-matched transistors and mounting them on a common heat sink. The degree of matching needed is determined by the temperature compensation required. The position of the reference diode, the associated phase shift, and a slight gain variation are the only differences between the high- and low-output stages in Fig. 9.7. The output of the differential amplifier is usually taken from only one side unless cascaded amplifiers are used. The side chosen for the output is determined by the number of phase shifts between the comparison element and the control element.

The currents through the reference element and through the divider must again be much larger than the base currents of the differential amplifier.

If the differential amplifier is perfectly temperature-compensated, the following equations apply:

For Fig. 9.7a,

$$\Delta V_{(out)} = \frac{R_1 + R_2 + R_p}{R_2 + R_{p2}}\Delta V_R \tag{13}$$

and for Fig. 9.7b,

$$\Delta V_{(out)} = \frac{R_1 + R_2 + R_p}{R_1 + R_{p1}}\Delta V_R \tag{14}$$

Equations (13) and (14) show that an output voltage change with temperature variation is due to a change in the reference voltage if the divider resistors are of the same material. In both cases the breakdown diode should be chosen with a temperature coefficient near zero. Equations (13) and (14) were obtained assuming that the base-emitter voltages of Q_1 and Q_2 are equal and also that the base-emitter voltage changes with temperature of Q_1 and Q_2 are equal.

It should be noted that the performance of the voltage regulator with changing

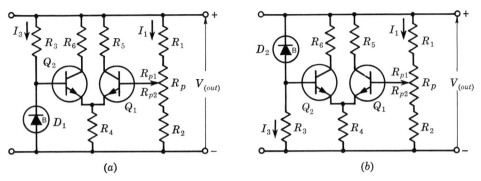

Fig. 9.7. Differential amplifier comparison elements with sampling and reference elements: (a) low output voltage; (b) high output voltage.

temperature is primarily determined in the design of the sampling, reference, and comparison elements. The operation of the other elements is not critically dependent on temperature.

9.2. D-C AMPLIFIER ELEMENT

The d-c amplifier must raise the difference signal from the comparison element to a level sufficient to drive the control element. Because the amplifier is within a strong feedback loop, very critical d-c amplifier design is not necessary. The only requirement in most cases is that a gain be provided that is large enough to supply the required current to the control element and small enough to retain circuit stability.

In many cases, a single transistor or stage functions as both the comparison element and d-c amplifier. Additional amplifier stages may be required for higher loop gain to further improve the regulation and decrease the output resistance of the regulator. The usual d-c amplifier element is similar to the common-emitter comparison element in Fig. 9.7. A breakdown diode is used in the emitter circuit to improve the voltage gain of the amplifier. Temperature compensation is not critical in this portion of the regulator, but the breakdown diode should be chosen with a temperature coefficient that will tend to cancel $\Delta V_{BE}/\Delta T$ of the amplifier transistor.

9.3. CONTROL ELEMENT

The control element interprets the signal from the d-c amplifier and makes the adjustment necessary to maintain a constant output voltage. The basic control elements used in the three regulator types are shown in Fig. 9.8.

The control elements of series and emitter-follower regulators are basically the same except for the base drive, which comes from the d-c amplifier in a series regulator and from the reference element in an emitter-follower regulator. Series and emitter-follower control elements must be capable of carrying the full load current of the regulator, but during normal operation the collector-emitter voltage can be much less than the output voltage.

The shunt control element must be capable of withstanding the entire output voltage; however, it does not have to carry the full load current unless required to regulate from no load to full load. Since the series·dropping resistor used with the shunt regulator has high dissipation, total efficiency of the regulator is degraded.

The preceding observations indicate that a series regulator is preferable for high voltage and medium current outputs with variable loads. The shunt regulator can be used for medium to low voltages and high output currents with relatively constant loads. Application of the emitter-follower regulator is usually limited to low output voltages. It has poor ripple suppression and poor regulation with respect to input variation, compared to the other regulator types.

Some of the quantities that must be considered when selecting a control element are the maximum voltage, current, and power ratings of the transistor. The limitations for a single transistor series or emitter-follower control element can be determined from the following:

$$V_{CE(max)} \geqq V_{(in\ max)} - V_{(out\ min)} \tag{15}$$

$$I_{C(max)} \geqq I_{(out\ max)} \tag{16}$$

$$P_{C(max)} \geqq (V_{(in\ max)} - V_{(out\ min)})I_{(out\ max)} \tag{17}$$

where $V_{(in\ max)}$ = maximum unregulated input voltage
$I_{(out\ max)}$ = maximum load current
$V_{(out\ min)}$ = minimum output voltage
$V_{CE(max)}$ = maximum allowable collector-emitter voltage
$I_{C(max)}$ = maximum allowable collector current
$P_{C(max)}$ = maximum allowable collector dissipation

The shunt control element must satisfy the following requirements: The series dropping resistor, R_S, should be chosen such that the current through the control element can be held to a minimum.

$$R_S \leqq \frac{V_{(in\ min)} - V_{(out\ max)}}{I_{(out\ max)}} \tag{18}$$

$$V_{CE(max)} \geqq V_{(out\ max)} \tag{19}$$

$$I_{C(max)} \geqq \frac{(V_{(in\ max)} - V_{(out\ min)})I_{(out\ max)}}{V_{(in\ min)} - V_{(out\ max)}} - I_{(out\ min)} \tag{20}$$

$$P_{C(max)} \geqq I_{C(max)}V_{(out\ max)} \tag{21}$$

The control element and regulator type can be chosen based upon the preceding limitations if the performance requirements of the regulator are known. The maximum power-dissipation ratings must be observed at all operating temperatures. Power derating at elevated temperatures is given on the transistor data sheet.

The control-element drive current and the collector current of the d-c amplifier are supplied from a common shunt current source.

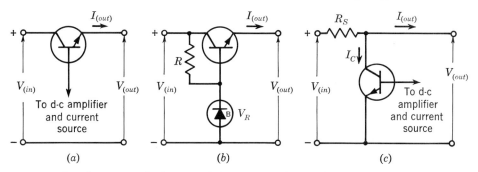

Fig. 9.8. Regulator control elements: (a) series regulator; (b) emitter-follower regulator; (c) shunt regulator.

The series and shunt regulators should be designed so that the collector current of the d-c amplifier is equal to or greater than the maximum current needed for the base drive of the control element. This design consideration is needed to ensure that the control element will have enough base drive current available to maintain the required output current.

Because the current supplied to the base of the control element is usually small, a compound connection is often used to provide the current gain necessary to maintain a required load current. A compound connection, sometimes called a beta multiplier, is shown in Fig. 9.9.

Assuming $h_{FE} \gg 1$,

$$I_{(out)} \cong (h_{FE1}h_{FE2}h_{FE3} \cdots h_{FEn})I_{Bn} \tag{22}$$

Each transistor in the compound connection must withstand a voltage equal to the maximum unregulated input voltage minus the sum of the output voltage and the base-emitter voltage of each preceding transistor. The collector current requirements of each transistor are decreased by the corresponding $h_{FE(n-1)}$, going from Q_1 to Q_n. The power requirements for each transistor can be determined from this information, and the best-suited transistors can be chosen for the compound connection.

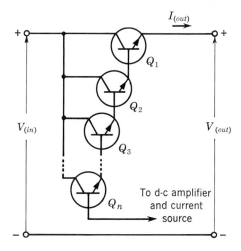

Fig. 9.9. Compound connection used as series control element.

9.4. PREREGULATOR

The preregulator should be included as a functional element if the regulator is to perform to its full capability. The preregulator provides a constant current to the collector of the d-c amplifier and the base of the control element. If point A in Fig. 9.10 is returned through a resistor directly to the positive terminal of the unregulated supply, ripple current caused by the unregulated voltage variations will be injected into the base of Q_2. The ripple will be amplified by the series control element and appear in the output. A preregulated d-c supply obtained from R_1, R_2, and D_1 helps eliminate the ripple current. The breakdown diode tends to keep a constant voltage across R_2 and a constant current to Q_2 and Q_3. The breakdown voltage of D_1 can be any value less than $V_{(in)} - V_{(out)}$ that will supply sufficient current to Q_2 and Q_3. If possible, the breakdown voltage of D_1 should be approximately equal to four times the normal change in base-emitter voltage of the control element. The values of this voltage may be calculated as follows:

$$V_{Z1} = V_{(in\ min)} - V_{(out\ max)} - I_1 R_1 \tag{23}$$

where
$$I_1 = I_{Z1} + I_2 \tag{24}$$

$$I_2 = I_{B2} + I_{C3} \tag{25}$$

I_{B2} and I_{C3} will have been previously determined by the selection of the control element, the comparison element, and the d-c amplifier. Therefore, I_2 is a known value.

$$R_2 = \frac{V_{Z1} - V_{BE1} - V_{BE2}}{I_{B2} + I_{C3}} \tag{26}$$

Knowing the nominal voltage of the breakdown diode, the current through R_2, the input and output voltages, and the maximum allowable current through the diode, the resistance of R_1 can be determined.

$$V_{1(max)} = V_{(in\ max)} - V_{(out\ min)} - V_{Z1} \tag{27}$$

$$I_{1(max)} = I_{Z1(max)} + I_2 \tag{28}$$

so that
$$R_1 \geqq \frac{V_{(in\ max)} - V_{(out\ min)} - V_{Z1}}{I_{Z1(max)} + I_2} \tag{29}$$

The maximum reverse diode current can be determined from the power-dissipation ratings of the breakdown diode.

In addition to improving input regulation, the preregulator reduces the output resistance of the regulator. If the current supply to Q_2 and Q_3 were shunted through only a resistor, a load current increase would tend to cause the output voltage to drop. The drop is caused by an increase in base-emitter voltage of the control element and by a higher voltage drop through the internal resistance of the unregulated supply. When this occurs, the comparison element is forced to compensate for both changes, and the resistance of the unregulated supply as well as the emitter resistance of the control element will contribute to the output resistance of the regulator. Depending upon the source resistance, the output resistance can be reduced by as much as one order of magnitude if the preregulator is used. If the voltage across R_2 is constant with small load changes, the output resistance is independent of the internal resistance of the unregulated supply.

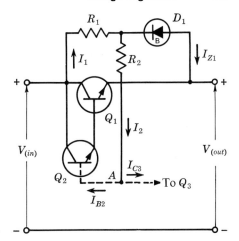

Fig. 9.10. The preregulator.

Improved performance for a preregulator can be obtained by using the circuit of Fig. 9.11 in place of the two resistors (R_1 and R_2) and the breakdown diode D_1 of Fig. 9.10. In the circuit of Fig. 9.11, the collector current of Q_4 is independent of changes in V_{BE} of Q_2 caused by temperature or load variation. In Fig. 9.10, the current I_2 is a function of the combined V_{BE} of Q_2 and Q_1, due to either temperature or regulator load, or both.

From Fig. 9.11,

$$I_{C4} = I_{E4} - I_{B4} = I_{B2} + I_{C3} \tag{30}$$

$$R_4 I_{E4} = V_{Z3} - V_{EB4} \tag{31}$$

or

$$R_4 = \frac{V_{Z3} - V_{EB4}}{I_{E4}} \tag{32}$$

D_3 is chosen to have a temperature coefficient sufficient to cancel $\Delta V_{EB}/\Delta T$ of Q_4. A low breakdown voltage for D_3 will fulfill two requirements: It will allow this type of preregulator to operate with low unregulated input voltages, and will also provide the necessary negative temperature coefficient to cancel $\Delta V_{EB}/\Delta T$ of Q_4. If the $\Delta V_{EB}/\Delta T$ of Q_4 is greater than the available negative temperature coefficient of D_3, a small silicon diode may be added in series with D_3 to provide additional compensation.

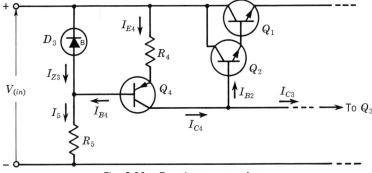

Fig. 9.11. Transistor preregulator.

I_{B2} and I_{C3} have been previously determined; now a transistor is selected which will handle the sum of I_{B2} and I_{C3}. A low-voltage breakdown diode is selected for D_3 with I_{Z3} determined from its power-dissipation rating. R_5 can now be found from

$$R_5 = \frac{V_{(in\ min)} - V_{Z3} - I_{Z3}R_R}{I_{Z3} + I_{B4}} \tag{33}$$

9.5. FILLING IN THE BLOCKS

The elements just described can now be connected to show a complete regulator. Figure 9.12 shows a regulator using a single common-emitter stage as comparison element and d-c amplifier element, and the resistor-breakdown diode-type preregulator.

Figure 9.13 shows a typical regulator using a differential amplifier comparison element, a single-stage d-c amplifier, and the single transistor preregulator of Fig. 9.11. Note that this type of circuit uses both of the best methods of temperature compensation: i.e., the differential amplifier and the temperature-compensated transistor current source.

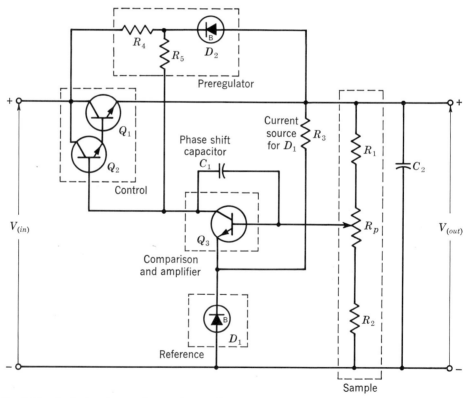

Fig. 9.12. Typical series regulator using single common-emitter stage comparison: d-c amplifier element and resistor-breakdown diode preregulator.

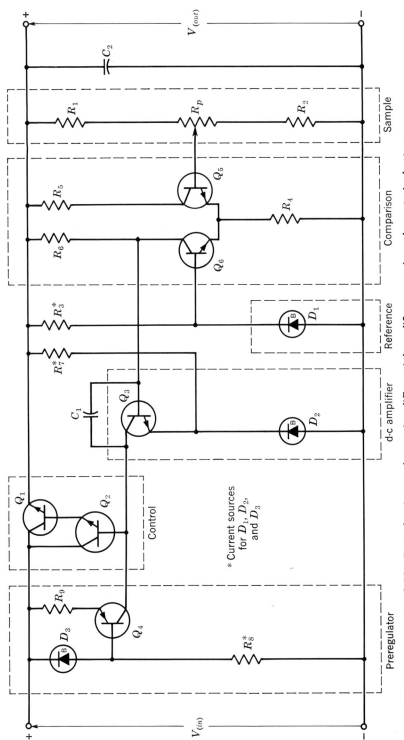

Fig. 9.13. Typical series regulator using differential amplifier comparison element, single-stage d-c amplifier, and single transistor constant-current source.

157

9.6. TYPICAL VOLTAGE-REGULATOR DESIGN

In this section a voltage regulator will be designed from a typical set of regulator requirements. The regulator requirements must be specified before any attempt is made to design the circuit. The problem is then reduced to determining a circuit configuration adaptable to the application and solving for the component values.

The voltage-regulator specifications are as follows:

$$V_{(in)} = 37.5 \text{ to } 70 \text{ volts}$$
$$V_O = 30.0 \text{ volts}$$
$$I_O \leqq 0.40 \text{ amp}$$
$$T = -50 \text{ to } +125°C$$

and
$$R_O \leqq 0.5 \text{ ohm}$$

A regulator which satisfactorily meets these specifications is shown later in this chapter. Performance parameters for this circuit are described after these parameters are first discussed in general.

The following steps are numbered to provide a logical design procedure:

1. The transistors needed in the control element are determined first:

$$V_{CE1(min)} = V_{(in\ min)} - V_o = 37.5 - 30 = 7.5 \text{ volts}$$
$$V_{CE1(max)} = V_{(in\ max)} - V_o = 40.0 \text{ volts}$$
$$I_{E1(max)} = I_o = 0.40 \text{ amp}$$
$$P_{C1(max)} = (V_{CE1(max)})(I_{E1}) = (40 \text{ volts})(0.40 \text{ amp}) = 16 \text{ watts}$$

The data sheet for the TI 2N1049 shows that with a proper heat sink, 16 watts can be dissipated satisfactorily. At 500 ma and $-55°C$, the 2N1049 has a minimum specified d-c gain of 20. Therefore,

$$I_{B1} \geqq \frac{I_{E1}}{h_{FE1(min)} + 1} = \frac{0.40}{20 + 1} \cong 20 \text{ ma}$$

2. Q_2 is used in the compound connection with Q_1. It is selected as follows:

$$V_{CE2(max)} = V_{CE1} - V_{BE1} \cong V_{CE1} = 40 \text{ volts}$$
$$I_{E2} \cong I_{B1} = 20 \text{ ma}$$
$$P_{C2(max)} \leqq (V_{CE2(max)})(I_{E2}) = (40 \text{ volts})(0.02 \text{ amp}) = 0.8 \text{ watt}$$

The data sheet shows that a 2N497 or 2N656 will meet these requirements for Q_2. The 2N656 is selected because of its high current gain. Since $h_{FE1} \geqq 20$ and $h_{FE2} \geqq 25$, then

$$I_{B2} \leqq \frac{I_{E1}}{(h_{FE1(min)} + 1)(h_{FE2(min)} + 1)} = \frac{0.40}{(20 + 1)(25 + 1)} \cong 0.80 \text{ ma}$$

$$I_{C3} \geqq I_{B2} \text{ and } I_{C4} \cong 2 \text{ ma} \qquad \text{(two or more times } I_{B2}\text{)}$$

3. In order to obtain the maximum range of temperature over which this regulator will operate, a silicon PNP 2N1131 is selected for Q_4. It has an $h_{FE(min)}$ of 15 and a V_{EB} of 1.3 volts. Therefore, if $I_{C4} = 2 \cdot \text{ma}$, $I_{E4} = I_{C4} + I_{B4} = 2 \text{ ma} + \frac{2}{15} \text{ ma} = 2.133 \text{ ma}$. If we choose a V_{Z2} of 3.3 volts (1N746), from

Fig. 9.4 we find that it has a resistance of about 50 ohms. Then from Eq. (32),

4.
$$R_4 = \frac{V_{Z2} - V_{EB4}}{I_{E4}} = \frac{3.3 - 1.3}{(2.133)10^{-3}} = 0.935 \text{ kilohm}$$

Use $R_4 = 1.0$ kilohm.
5. From Eq. (33),

$$R_5 = \frac{V_{(in\ min)} - V_{Z2}}{I_{Z2} + I_{B4}} = \frac{37.5 - 3.3}{(7 + 0.135)10^{-3}} = 4.8 \text{ kilohms}$$

Use $R_5 = 5.1$ kilohms.
6. The reference element, sampling element, and comparison element must be specified after the control element and preregulator are designed. The breakdown voltage of D_1 is not critical so long as it remains constant for normal regulator operation. D_1 must be chosen with a low resistance and a slightly positive temperature coefficient for this application. A 1N753 is chosen, having a zener voltage of 6.2 volts. Current through the diode must be sufficient to maintain breakdown; therefore, if I_{Z1} is chosen to be 4 ma, which is large compared to I_{E3}, then

7.
$$R_3 = \frac{V_o - V_{Z1}}{I_{Z1}} = \frac{30 - 6.2}{(4)10^{-3}} \cong 6 \text{ kilohms}$$

Use $R_3 = 6.2$ kilohms.
   Note from the data sheet that using smaller current through the breakdown diode produces a higher positive temperature coefficient. In this case, a 6.2-volt zener carrying 5 ma has a temperature coefficient of 0.03% per C°, or about $+1.86 \times 10^{-3}$ volt/C°. This is close to being the negative of the temperature coefficient of V_{BE}, i.e., about -2.5×10^{-3} volt/C°. We can therefore expect the 1N753 at a current of about 3.5 ma to be even closer to canceling the change of V_{BE} of Q_3 with temperature.
8. Collector current of Q_3 will be about 3 ma, so a 2N338 is chosen for Q_3.
9. A 500-ohm wire-wound potentiometer is used for R_p, and I_{R1} is chosen to be 5 ma.

10.
$$R_1 \gtrapprox \frac{V_o - V_{BE} - V_Z}{I_{R1}} = \frac{30 - 0.8 - 6.2}{5(10^{-3})} = 4.6 \text{ kilohms}$$

Use $R_1 = 4.7$ kilohms.

11.
$$R_2 + R_p = \frac{V_{BE} + V_Z}{I_{R1}} = \frac{7.0}{5(10^{-3})} = 1.4 \text{ kilohms}$$

$$R_2 = 1.4 - 0.5 = 0.9 \text{ kilohm}$$

Use $R_2 = 1.0$ kilohm.

   The 0.01-μf capacitor from collector to base of Q_3 has been added to prevent high-frequency instability. Also, R_6 has been added to provide a path for leakage currents and to allow operation down to low load currents.

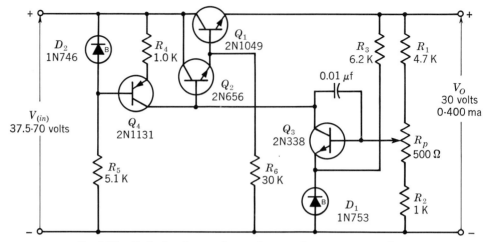

Fig. 9.14. Typical series regulator using transistor-type preregulator.

Figure 9.14 is a schematic of the completed design. Curves of V_o vs. V_{in}, V_o vs. I_o, and V_o vs. temperature are shown in Figs. 9.15, 9.16, and 9.17, respectively. Data from these curves will be used later to determine performance parameters for this circuit.

The regulation factor, F, for various output currents is shown in the curves of Fig. 9.15. Output resistance, R_o, for various input voltages is shown in the curves of Fig. 9.16. The temperature coefficient, K_T, is shown by the curves of Fig. 9.17.

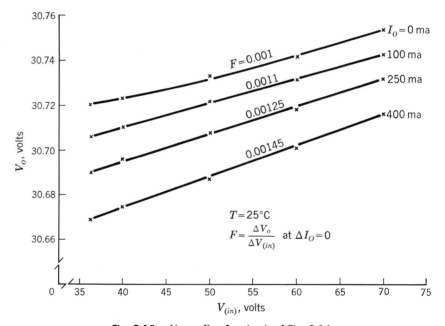

Fig. 9.15. V_o vs. $E_{(in)}$ for circuit of Fig. 9.14.

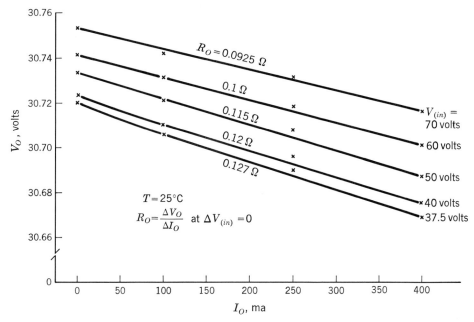

Fig. 9.16. V_o vs. I_o for circuit of Fig. 9.14.

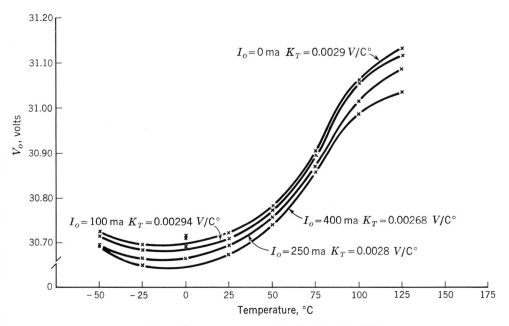

Fig. 9.17. V_o vs. temperature for circuit in Fig. 9.14.

The values for K_T were found by $K_T = \Delta V / \Delta T$, where ΔT was -25 to $+100°C$, or $\Delta T = 125$. Since K_T is the slope of the curves plotted, the worst K_T will be the maximum slope of the curve; since this maximum slope constitutes only a very limited portion of the curve, however, it does not yield a valid K_T. The maximum change in output voltage will then be, from Eq. (44),

$$\Delta V_O = F\Delta V_{(in)} + R_O \Delta I_O + K_T \Delta T$$

This completes the design of the typical series regulator. Note that there are a number of combinations of elements that may be used to obtain the complete circuit. These elements are chosen on the basis of the regulation required over a given temperature range.

9.7. PERFORMANCE PARAMETERS

Regulator performance can be expressed in terms of R_o, F, and K_T in the regulation equation

$$\Delta V_{(out)} = F\Delta V_{(in)} + R_O \Delta I_{(out)} + K_T \Delta T$$

where $\qquad$ Output resistance $= R_O = -\left.\dfrac{\Delta V_{(out)}}{\Delta I_{(out)}}\right|_{\Delta E_{(in)}=0}$ $\hfill (34)$

$$\text{Regulation factor} = F = \left.\frac{\Delta V_{(out)}}{\Delta V_{(in)}}\right|_{\Delta I_{(out)}=0} \tag{35}$$

$$\text{Temperature coefficient} = K_T = \left.\frac{\Delta V_{(out)}}{\Delta T}\right|_{\substack{\Delta I_{(out)}=0 \\ \Delta E_{(in)}=0}} \tag{36}$$

This section discusses methods used to predict the performance of regulators. A black-box approach shows the significance of each performance parameter (Fig. 9.18).

The current and voltage relationships can be expressed in terms of g parameters if the regulator is assumed to be linear.

$$\Delta I_{(in)} = g_{11} \Delta V_{(in)} + g_{12} \Delta I_{(out)} \tag{37}$$

$$\Delta V_{(out)} = g_{21} \Delta V_{(in)} + g_{22} \Delta I_{(out)} \tag{38}$$

where $\qquad g_{11} = \left.\dfrac{\Delta I_{(in)}}{\Delta V_{(in)}}\right|_{\Delta I_{(out)}=0}$ $\hfill (39)$

$$g_{12} = \left.\frac{\Delta I_{(in)}}{\Delta I_{(out)}}\right|_{\Delta E_{(in)}=0} \tag{40}$$

$$g_{22} = \left.\frac{\Delta V_{(out)}}{\Delta I_{(out)}}\right|_{\Delta E_{(in)}=0} \tag{41}$$

$$g_{21} = \left.\frac{\Delta V_{(out)}}{\Delta V_{(in)}}\right|_{\Delta I_{(out)}=0} \tag{42}$$

Emphasis is placed on Eq. (38) because $V_{(out)}$ is the regulated output voltage. The parameters g_{21} and g_{22} should be made as small as possible to minimize variations in $V_{(out)}$. Equation (41) shows that g_{22} has the dimensions of resistance;

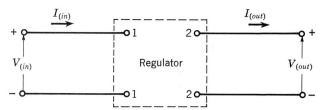

Fig. 9.18. The regulator as a black box.

specifically, it is the output resistance of Fig. 9.18 and is designated as R_o throughout this chapter.

The forward transfer parameter, g_{21}, is a dimensionless quantity that is used to define the regulation factor, F. The per cent regulation with respect to input variation is given by $F \times 100\%$. If the regulator input voltage has $A\%$ ripple, the output voltage has $AF\%$ ripple.

The performance of the regulator with changing operating temperatures requires the definition of another parameter, K_T. Although the effects from changing temperature are nonlinear, the value of K_T obtained from Eq. (43) is usually adequate.

$$K_T = \frac{\Delta V_{(out)}}{\Delta T} \bigg|_{\substack{\Delta I_{(out)}=0 \\ \Delta V_{(in)}=0}} \tag{43}$$

Regulator performance can be expressed in terms of R_O, F, and K_T in the regulation equation:

$$\Delta V_{(out)} = F \Delta V_{(in)} + R_O \Delta I_{(out)} + K_T \Delta T \tag{44}$$

The degree of regulation can be improved by reducing any or all of the three parameters in Eq. (44).

9.8. PERFORMANCE ANALYSIS BY INSPECTION

If the regulator circuit is simple, the approximate performance parameters can often be determined by inspection (Fig. 9.19).

To permit this simplified analysis, many assumptions are usually made. The validity of the assumptions can be determined by checking the regulator require-

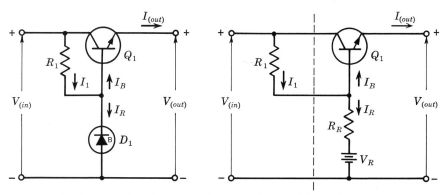

Fig. 9.19. An emitter-follower voltage regulator and its equivalent circuit.

ments and the information on the transistor data sheet. The operating temperature is considered to be nearly constant for this example. The breakdown voltage
and diode resistance, R_R, are assumed to be constant, and any change in reference
voltage is assumed to be caused by a change in reference current. The load variation is considered to be small enough so that h_{FE} will not change appreciably, and
h_{FE} is assumed to be much greater than 1.

$$\Delta V_{(out)} = \Delta I_R R_R - \Delta V_{BE}$$

$$\Delta I_{(out)} = h_{FE}\,\Delta I_B$$

$$R_O = -\frac{\Delta I_R R_R - \Delta V_{BE}}{h_{FE}\,\Delta I_B}$$

$$I_1 = \frac{V_{(in)} - V_R - I_R R_R}{R_1}$$

Assuming $V_{(in)}$, V_R, R_1, and R_R to be constant,

$$\Delta I_1 = \frac{-\Delta I_R R_R}{R_1}$$

$$\Delta I_B = \Delta I_1 - \Delta I_R = -\Delta I_R \frac{R_R + R_1}{R_1}$$

$$R_O = \frac{R_1 R_R}{h_{FE}(R_R + R_1)} - \frac{\Delta V_{BE} R_1}{\Delta I_R h_{FE}(R_R + R_1)}$$

$$\Delta I_{(out)} = -\frac{\Delta I_R h_{FE}(R_R + R_1)}{R_1}$$

so that

$$R_O = \frac{R_1 R_R}{h_{FE}(R_R + R_1)} + \frac{\Delta V_{BE}}{\Delta I_{(out)}}$$

If the load is nearly constant, $\Delta V_{BE}/\Delta I_{(out)} \cong 0$, and

$$R_O \cong \frac{R_1 R_R}{h_{FE}(R_R + R_1)}$$

The regulator can be analyzed as a voltage divider to determine F by inspection.

$$R_B = \frac{R_O R_L}{R_O + R_L}$$

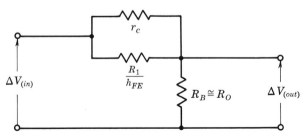

Fig. 9.20.   A voltage divider used to determine F.

R_B is the parallel combination of the output resistance and load resistance. If the load resistance is much larger than R_O (which is usually the case), $R_B \cong R_O$. The circuit can be divided along a line separating the input from the output by a high-impedance path (dashed line, Fig. 9.19).

Using Fig. 9.20 and assuming $h_{FE} \gg 1$,

$$R_A = \frac{R_1 r_c}{R_1 + h_{FE} r_c}$$

$$F = \frac{R_B}{R_B + R_A} \cong \frac{R_O}{R_A + R_O}$$

$$F = \frac{R_R(R_1 + h_{FE} r_c)}{h_{FE} r_c(R_R + R_1) + R_R(R_1 + h_{FE} r_c)}$$

Assume $h_{FE} r_c \gg R_1 \gg R_R$, so that

$$F \cong \frac{R_R}{R_1 + R_R}$$

The preceding steps have been used to determine the approximate parameters by inspection. K_T must be determined experimentally if changing temperature is an important factor.

9.9. PERFORMANCE TEST CIRCUITS

Verification of performance parameters is usually necessary after the regulator has been designed.

Figure 9.21 is a test circuit used to measure R_O, F, and K_T.

The methods used to determine R_O, F, and K_T are not complicated. The main concern is the choice of a voltmeter for measuring $\Delta V_{(out)}$. The meter must be accurate and capable of displaying a voltage to the required sensitivity.

Figure 9.22 is a test circuit used to determine ripple reduction.

The a-c voltage providing the input ripple can be obtained by using a filament transformer, which can be connected to a variable-voltage transformer to obtain a variable input ripple. The peak a-c input and output voltages can be measured with a calibrated scope, or the ratio of the two can be obtained by applying the output ripple to the horizontal deflection and the input ripple through an attenuator to the vertical deflection circuit of the scope. The attenuator can then be adjusted until the scope indicates equal ripple to each deflection. The attenuator will then indicate the reduction in ripple caused by the regulator.

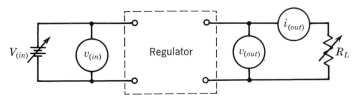

Fig. 9.21. R_O, K_T, and F test circuit.

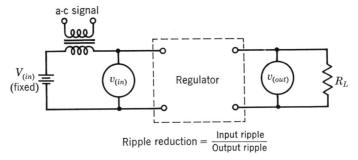

$$\text{Ripple reduction} = \frac{\text{Input ripple}}{\text{Output ripple}}$$

Fig. 9.22.   Ripple reduction test circuit.

Figure 9.23 is a test circuit used to measure the output impedance, Z_O, of the regulator, where

$$|Z_0| = \frac{|v_{(out)}|}{|i_{(out)}|}$$

The output impedance can be obtained by superimposing a small a-c voltage across the regulator output. The ratio of voltage to current measured with the oscilloscope will determine the output impedance. The a-c voltage applied must be small compared with the output voltage. If the a-c voltage is too large, the transistor in the comparison circuit can be driven into saturation or cutoff. Performance changes caused by changing temperatures can be measured by placing the regulator in an oven and taking measurements at the desired temperature.

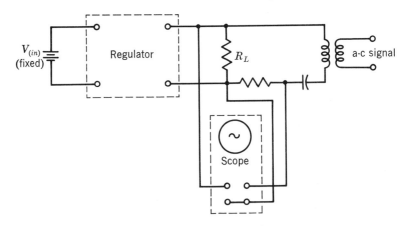

Fig. 9.23. Z_O test circuit.

BIBLIOGRAPHY

Baldinger, E., and W. Czaja: Designing Highly Stable Transistor Power Supplies, *Electronics*, vol. 32, pp. 70–73, September 25, 1959.

Baum, J. R.: Thermal Considerations in the Use of Power Transistors, *Electronic Design*, pp. 56–59, June, 1959.

Brenner, E.: Regulated Transistor Power Supplies, *Electronic Design,* vol. 7, pp. 178–179, March 18, 1959.

Carter, J.: Transistor Regulated Power Supply, *Electronic Equip. Eng.,* vol. 7, pp. 55–56, July, 1959.

Chase, F. H.: Power Regulation by Semiconductor, *Elec. Eng.,* vol. 75, pp. 818–822, September, 1959.

Collins, D. J., and J. E. Smith: Regulated Power Supplies, *Electronic Eng.,* vol. 31, pp. 222–226, April, 1959.

Ervin, H. D.: Transistor Power Supply Has Overload Protection, *Electronics,* vol. 31, pp. 74–75, June 20, 1958.

Franklin, C. A., P. M. Thompson, and W. M. Caton: Precision High-voltage Transistor-overload Power Regulators with Overload Protection, *Proc. Inst. Elec. Engrs.,* vol. 106, pp. 714–725, May, 1959.

Giuffrida, J., and W. O. Hamlin: Transistorized 25-volt Regulated Power Supply, *Electronic Design,* vol. 5, pp. 28–29, January 15, 1957.

Hamm, T.: Equations for Designing Transistor Power Supplies, *Electronics,* vol. 32, pp. 74–75, June 20, 1958.

Hunter, L. P.: "Handbook of Semiconductor Electronics," pp. 13.26–13.28, McGraw-Hill Book Company, Inc., New York, 1956.

Hurley, R. B.: Designing Transistor Circuits: DC Regulators, *Electronic Equip.,* vol. 5, pp. 20–23, April, 1957.

Hurley, R. B.: "Junction Transistor Electronics," pp. 208–229, John Wiley & Sons, Inc., New York, 1958.

Keller, J. W.: Regulated Transistor Power Supply Design, *Electronics,* vol. 29, pp. 168–171, November, 1956.

Lillienstein, M.: Transistorized Regulated Power Supply, *Electronics,* vol. 29, pp. 169–171, December, 1956.

Lowry, H. R.: Transistorized Regulated Power Supplies, *Electronic Design,* parts 1 and 2, vol. 4, pp. 38–41, February 15, 1956; pp. 32–35, March 1, 1956.

Luft, W.: Taking the Heat off Semiconductor Devices, *Electronics,* pp. 53–56, June, 1959.

Mamon, M.: High-voltage Transistor-regulated DC Power Supply, *Elec. Design News,* vol. 2, pp. 46–47, October, 1957.

Middlebrook, R. D.: Design of Transistor Regulated Power Supplies, *Proc. IRE,* vol. 45, pp. 1502–1509, November, 1957.

Mitchell, W. B.: Design Silicon Diodes into Reference and Regulator Circuits, *Electronic Equip.,* vol. 4, pp. 18–21, September, 1956.

Sherr, S., and P. M. Levy: Design Considerations for Semiconductor-regulated Power Supplies, *Electronic Design,* vol. 4, pp. 22–25, July 15, 1956.

Sherr, S., P. M. Levy, and T. Kwap: Semiconductor Diodes Are Important in Design of Transistorized Regulated Power Supplies, *Elec. Design News,* pp. 50–51, October, 1956.

Sherr, S., P. M. Levy, and T. Kwap: Design Procedure for Semiconductor-regulated Power Supplies, *Electronic Design,* pp. 22–25, April 15, 1957.

Spencer, R. H., and T. S. Gray: Transistorized Voltage Regulator, *AIEE Trans.,* part 1, pp. 15–17, March, 1956.

Unvala, B. A.: DC Power Supply Circuits Using Silicon Rectifiers, TI Application Report, revised July, 1959.

Silicon Transistor Voltage Regulator Overload Protection, TI Application Note, June, 1960.

DC Regulated Power Supply Design, TI Application Report, August, 1960.

10

Chopper Amplifiers

10.1. DESIGN OBJECTIVES

Amplifiers capable of responding to direct current or voltage present serious problems to the designer. At first glance it would seem that response to direct current could be obtained simply by eliminating elements which restrict low-frequency response, i.e., capacitors and inductors. If several stages could be coupled together using only resistors, there would then be no low-frequency response limitation, and the resulting amplifier would respond to direct current as well as (or better than) it did to alternating current.

Such circuits are easy to build, and they usually perform quite well with d-c signal inputs—so well, in fact, that they are almost useless. Such an amplifier can make no distinction between signals originating outside and signals originating internally. A change in I_{CBO} with temperature, for example, is just as readily amplified as is an incoming signal. And any attempt to use bias stabilization or negative feedback reduces the gain of the amplifier in the same proportion as it reduces the temperature drift.

An amplifier which responds only to a-c signals need not be subject to this cumulative drift error. Consequently, many d-c amplifiers change the incoming signal into an a-c signal to be amplified and then rectified to form a d-c output. (Alternatively, the incoming signal may be caused to modulate the amplitude of an a-c signal which is then amplified and demodulated to form an output. This approach is used in magnetic and in dielectric amplifiers.)

Typical circuits used to change an incoming signal from direct to alternating current are shown in Fig. 10.1a and b. S_1 and S_2 are switches so arranged that when one is ON the other is OFF, and they are closed alternately at some convenient frequency, say 60 times a second. In Fig. 10.1a the incoming d-c signal is connected between the center tap and first one side and then the other of the transformer primary. The output of the transformer will then be a 60-cps signal proportional in amplitude to the input signal. The phase of the output, that is, whether the closing of S_1 produces a positive or a negative pulse at a given terminal of the secondary, depends on the input polarity. In Fig. 10.1b, capacitor C charges through R when S_1 is closed and discharges when S_2 is closed. In either circuit, the upper-frequency response of the overall amplifier is usually limited to no more

168

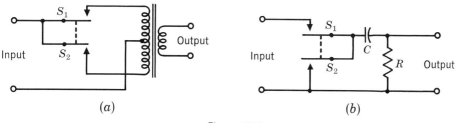

Input S_1 S_2 Output

(a)

Input S_1 C R Output S_2

(b)

Figure 10.1

than one-fourth of the switching frequency. By interchanging the input and output, these circuits may be used as synchronous rectifiers to change the a-c output signal from the amplifier back into d-c. Switches used in these applications are often called choppers.

No semiconductor device acts as a perfect switch; that is, during the ON period the resistance between terminals is not zero, and during the OFF period it is not infinite. These resistances vary with temperature and with current flow through the device. In addition, the back bias which turns the device OFF creates temperature-dependent leakage currents, while the base current turning ON a transistor or the light turning ON a photodiode or phototransistor produces more stray *offset* voltages at the device terminals.

Offset voltage is the potential appearing across the semiconductor switch terminals when the switch is turned ON and no current is allowed to flow through the switch. For example, the offset voltage of a transistor chopper is the collector-emitter saturation voltage when $I_c = 0$. *Offset current* is the current that flows when the semiconductor is reverse-biased. Leakage current through a reverse-biased diode is an example of this.

An idea of the minimum noise power the switch can be designed to inject into the circuit is indicated by the product of the ON offset voltage and the OFF leakage current. The optimum impedance to be seen by the switch for this minimum noise power is approximately equal to the offset voltage divided by the leakage current.

10.2. RING MODULATORS

The circuit concept of Fig. 10.1a can be modified to use diode switches, as in the so-called *ring modulator* shown in Fig. 10.2. When a square-wave switching voltage is applied to the primary of T_1, diodes D_1 and D_2 conduct during one-half the cycle, while D_3 and D_4 are back-biased. Then, as the switching voltage reverses, D_3 and D_4 conduct while D_1 and D_2 are turned OFF. Each set of diodes acts as a voltage divider across the secondary of T_1. If the diodes are balanced, and if the two halves of the secondary of T_1 are balanced, the voltages at points A, B, and C will be equal when there is no signal input, and no current will flow through the primary of T_2. As soon as a d-c signal is applied to the input, this switching action will cause the direct current to flow alternately through the two halves of the primary of T_2. The result will be an a-c signal at the output proportional to the d-c input and of a frequency equal to the switching frequency. If the incoming d-c signal contains an a-c component, the output will also contain frequencies equal to the switching frequency plus and minus the incoming frequencies. This is true for all chopper

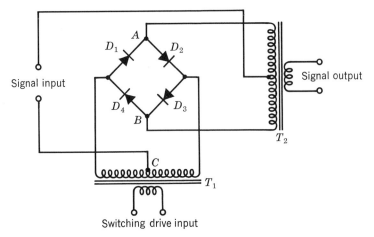

Fig. 10.2. Ring modulator.

circuits. The a-c amplifier associated with a chopper must therefore be able to pass a band of frequencies centered about the switching frequency. (The width of this passband will be one of the limits imposed upon the high-frequency response of the overall amplifier.)

Switching at high frequencies, even radio frequencies, is possible with this type circuit. Linearity is good over the entire operating range, and switching frequency is limited only by wiring capacitance, transformer characteristics, and diode response time. Maximum signal current and voltage are set by the usual diode limitations.

Figure 10.3 is an equivalent circuit of the resistances which determine a diode's behavior. R_{SL} is surface leakage resistance (ohmic), R_B is bulk resistance (ohmic), and R_D is diode resistance (variable).

$$R_D = \frac{V_D}{I_s(\epsilon^{qV_D/kT\lambda} - 1)} \tag{1}$$

where V_D = applied voltage R_D (+ for forward conduction)

I_s = diode saturation current (+ in sign)

$q/k = 1.161 \times 10^4$ (coulombs)(°K)/joule

T = temperature, °K

λ = a factor which is approximately 1 for germanium at room temperature and may vary from 1 to 2 for silicon

The familiar diode equation has been modified by a factor, λ, which is a function of transistor temperature, current density, and semiconductor material. (A good discussion of the variation of λ and its cause is given by Moll and Pritchard.[1,2]) Since R_{SL} and R_B are constant, diodes may be matched for these quantities by placing external resistors in shunt and in series with each diode. I_s is temperature-dependent, and for the reverse-biased case may be approximated by

$$I_s = Ne^{BT} \tag{2}$$

where N and B are constants peculiar to each diode.[3] Actually, extreme methods for matching and compensating are not always necessary if ambient temperature and signal level can be restricted. Using selected Texas Instruments type-601C diodes and driving from high-impedance sources, Keonjian and Schmidt have detected signal currents as low as 10^{-10} amp at room temperature.[4]

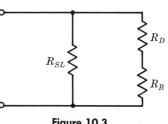

Figure 10.3

In their circuit, a low-level constant-current switching drive serves to balance the diode forward impedances.

Transistor Choppers—Equivalent Circuits. In order to use transistors, the simple circuits of Fig. 10.1a and b must be modified. If a single transistor replaces each switch, the collector and emitter will become the switch terminals. Switching will be performed by a signal applied between the base and either the emitter or the collector acting as an emitter.

Figure 10.4 is the equivalent circuit for the ON condition of an NPN transistor. The circuit is correct for PNP transistors when the polarity of $V_{CE(on)}$ is reversed. Positive current convention is assumed.

$$V_{CE(on)} = I_B r'_E + \frac{kT\lambda}{q} \ln \frac{1}{\alpha_i} \tag{3}$$

$$R_{(on)} = \frac{kT\lambda(1 - \alpha_i\alpha_n)}{q\alpha_n I_B} + r'_E + r'_C \tag{4}$$

where I_B = base switching current
  r'_E = ohmic emitter bulk resistance
  r'_C = ohmic collector bulk resistance
  α_n = common-base emitter-to-collector current transfer ratio, or normal alpha
  α_i = common-base collector-to-emitter current transfer ratio, or inverted alpha
  $q/k = 1.161 \times 10^4$ (coulombs)(°K)/joule
  T = temperature, °K
  $\lambda = h_{fe}/h_{FE}$

An equally simple equivalent for the OFF condition is not always possible. The expression for the OFF collector current is

$$I_{C(off)} = \frac{I_{CBO}}{1 - \alpha_i\alpha_n}[1 - e^{q\theta c/kT\lambda} - \alpha_i(1 - e^{q\theta e/kT\lambda})] - \frac{\theta_c}{R_{CB}} \tag{5}$$

where $I_{CBO} \cong$ collector-base diode saturation current (+ in sign)
  θ_c = voltage across the collector diode taken as + in the forward-biased direction
  θ_e = voltage across the emitter diode taken as + in the forward-biased direction
  R_{CB} = collector-to-base ohmic leakage resistance

Fig. 10.4. ON condition equivalent circuit.   Emitter o———$\bigwedge\!\!\bigwedge$———————|||————o Collector
  $R_{(on)}$ $V_{CE(on)}$

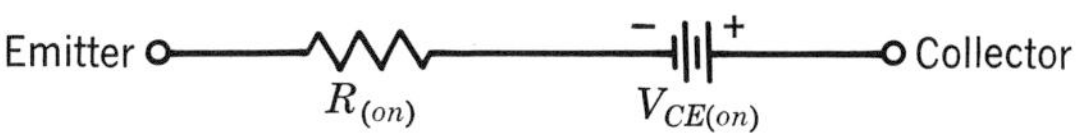

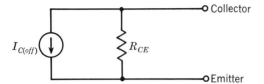

Fig. 10.5. OFF condition equivalent circuit.

If both the collector and the emitter diodes are back-biased greater than about 0.2 volt at room temperature, Eq. (5) may be simplified to

$$I_{C(off)} \cong \frac{I_{CBO}(1 - \alpha_i)}{1 - \alpha_i\alpha_n} - \frac{\theta_c}{R_{CB}} \tag{6}$$

Figure 10.5 is an OFF equivalent circuit for an NPN transistor, based on Eq. (5) or (6). R_{CE} is the collector-to-emitter ohmic leakage resistance. The circuit is correct for PNP transistors when the direction of the current source $I_{C(off)}$ is reversed.

Inverted Operations. The quantities $V_{CE(on)}$ and $I_{C(off)}$ appearing at the switch terminals form a source of noise signal. Notice, however, that the absolute magnitudes of $V_{CE(on)}$ and of $I_{C(off)}$ may be reduced by increasing α_i. If α_n and α_i are measured while the two transistor diode junctions function in the circuit as marked by the manufacturer, that is, if the diode terminal marked "collector" is actually used in the circuit as the collector diode terminal, etc., then α_n will generally be larger than α_i. But if the diode marked collector is actually used for the emitter, and vice versa, then the new α_i will be larger than the new α_n. This *inverted* operation substantially reduces the magnitudes of $V_{CE(on)}$ and of $I_{C(off)}$. The disad-

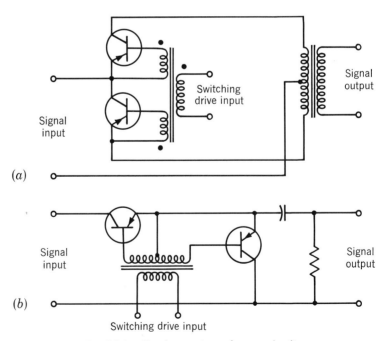

Fig. 10.6. Simple transistor-chopper circuits.

vantages of this technique lie in the increase of r'_E and possible increase in I_{CBO}. (In normal operation these quantities were r'_c and I_{EBO}, respectively, but inverted operation exchanges the normal collector for the normal emitter. Note also that the former BV_{EBO} becomes BV_{CBO} in inverted operation. Grown- and diffused-junction transistors may not respond well to this technique because of a large increase in the inverted r'_E .)

10.3. TRANSISTOR CHOPPERS—PRACTICAL CIRCUITS

Many chopper circuits use two transistors in such a way that the offset voltages and/or leakage currents appearing at the switch terminals either oppose each other or add to produce a constant d-c signal into the amplifier. Figures 10.6a and b are simple transistorized examples of Fig. 10.1a and b, respectively. The success of this approach depends on the degree to which the quantities $I_{C(off)}$ and $V_{CE(on)}$ can be matched over the operating temperature range. A mismatch of $V_{CE(on)}$ may be compensated by placing selected resistors in each emitter lead. $R_{(on)}$ and I_B are stabilized by resistors in the base leads which maintain constant and equal base-drive currents. Good temperature compensation may be had by making one of the base resistors temperature-sensitive.

The effect of the OFF currents may be minimized by selected resistors shunting the emitter-collector terminals. Germanium diodes shunting the emitter-base diode can reduce the reverse bias $V_{BE(off)}$. (Silicon diodes would produce a somewhat higher voltage and therefore a larger $I_{C(off)}$.) However, perfect temperature compensation requires that the transistors be matched for I_{CBO}. Although the ON and OFF resistances of the switch are degraded by these additions, this loss is often outweighed by the decrease in noise level.

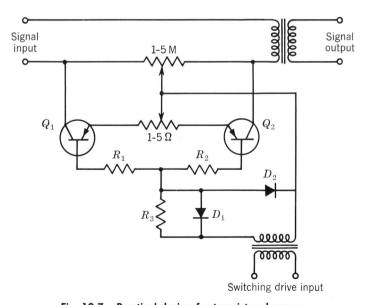

Fig. 10.7.   Practical design for transistor chopper.

Figure 10.7 shows a circuit which employs all these techniques.[5] Transistors Q_1 and Q_2 are turned ON and OFF in unison. A small tapped resistor in the emitter leads permits balancing in the ON condition, while a large tapped resistor across both collectors permits a balance in the OFF portion of the cycle. Base currents are held constant by the base resistors R_1 and R_2. Diodes D_1 and D_2 operate with resistor R_3 to reduce the base OFF voltage and thus help lower the OFF noise current.

Switching Transients. During the actual instant of switching, the transistors are not matched and may produce a noise spike. The obvious remedy would be to minimize the duration of the mismatch by switching very quickly with a square-wave base drive. Two considerations limit this technique. First, wideband transformers having very low leakage inductances and very low interwinding capacitances are expensive. Second, if the rise time of the square wave is short, a large noise pulse may be coupled into the circuit by stray capacitances, including the transistor capacitance. Careful attention to these points is extremely important.

10.4. PHOTODIODES AND PHOTOTRANSISTORS

Photodiodes or phototransistors may be substituted for S_1 and S_2 in Fig. 10.1a and b without modifications. Since these call for a modulated light beam to perform the switching operation, their use is limited. During the OFF period, these devices act as simple diodes, and the same matching considerations will apply. If enough light is available during the ON period, the devices act as an ohmic resistance in series with a voltage source and a maximum current limiter. The amount of light affects the photovoltage developed and the level of signal current at which limiting takes place.

10.5. MODULATED CARRIER SYSTEM

A complete chopper d-c amplifier may be regarded as a modulated carrier system. The chopper frequency would correspond to the carrier frequency, while the slowly varying d-c level would represent the modulating signal. Figure 10.8 shows a simple block diagram of a carrier system.

The oscillator ideally produces a square wave with fast rise and fall times. This allows fast switching of the modulator and demodulator (choppers). In the case of Fig. 10.8, the oscillator drives both the modulator and demodulator so as to

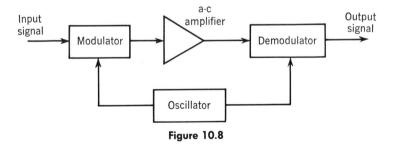

Figure 10.8

keep the same phase relationship between the two; i.e., both are switched at the same time. Thus, the demodulator is synchronized with the modulator and is known as a synchronous demodulator. Phase information as well as amplitude information may be transferred through the system of Fig. 10.8.

If the demodulator consists of only a rectifier and an integrator as is the case in many common radio receivers, only amplitude information may be transmitted through the system.

An advantage of the a-c amplifier is that any d-c drift occurring in any of its single stages is not passed along as signal, as is the case with d-c amplifiers. The amplifier should have enough gain to be useful for its intended application. The mid-band gain of the amplifier should be centered about the chopping or carrier frequency and should have an adequate bandwidth to take care of all sidebands that are produced in any modulating system.

BIBLIOGRAPHY

1. Moll, J. L.: The Evaluation of the Theory for the Voltage-Current Characteristic of P-N Junctions, *Proc. IRE,* vol. 46, pp. 1076–1082, June, 1958.
2. Pritchard, R. L.: Advances in the Understanding of the P-N Junction Triodes, *Proc. IRE,* vol. 46, pp. 1130–1141, June, 1958.
3. Biard, J. R., and W. T. Matzen: Drift Considerations in Low-level Direct-coupled Transistor Circuits, 1959 *IRE Conv. Record,* part III, pp. 27–33.
4. Keonjian, E. J., and J. D. Schmidt: Ring-modulator Reads Low-level DC, *Electronic Ind. Tele-Tech,* vol. 17, pp. 86–89, April, 1958.
5. Hurley, R. B.: "Junction Transistor Electronics," John Wiley & Sons, Inc., New York, pp. 376–382, 1958.

General References

Bright, R. L., and A. P. Kruper: Transistor Choppers for Stable D-C Amplifiers, *Electronics,* vol. 28, pp. 135–137, April, 1955.
Chaplin, G. B. B., and A. R. Owens: Some Transistor Input Stages for High-gain DC Amplifiers, *Proc. Inst. Elec. Engrs.,* vol. 105, part B, pp. 249–257, July, 1957.
Chaplin, G. B. B., and A. R. Owens: A Transistor High-gain Chopper-type D-C Amplifier, *Proc. Inst. Elec. Engrs.,* vol. 105, part B, pp. 258–266, November, 1957.
Ebers, J. J., and J. L. Moll: Large-signal Behavior of Junction Transistors, *Proc. IRE,* vol. 42, pp. 1761–1772, December, 1954.
Ettinger, G. M.: Transistor Modulator for Flight Trainers, *Electronics,* vol. 28, pp. 126–127, September, 1955.
Grubbs, W. J.: Hall Effect Devices, *Bell System Tech. J.,* vol. 38, pp. 853–876, May, 1959.
Hurley, R. B.: Transistorized Low-level Chopper Circuits, *Electronic Inds. Tele-Tech,* vol. 15, p. 42, December, 1956.
Kruper, A. P.: Switching Transistors Used as a Substitute for Mechanical Low-level Choppers, *Communs. and Electronics,* no. 17, pp. 141–144, March, 1955.
Roy, R.: Transistorized High Frequency Chopper Design, *Electronic Design,* vol. 6, pp. 52–55, August, 1958.
Williams, A. J., Jr., J. U. Egnon, and N. E. Polster: Some Advances in Transistor Modulators for Precise Measurement, *Proc. Natl. Electronics Conf.,* vol. 13, pp. 40–54, 1957.

11

AGC of Audio Circuits

Automatic Gain Control (AGC) of an audio amplifier consists of controlling the amplifier's transfer characteristics with a d-c control voltage that is proportional to the input signal. The purpose of this is to compress the dynamic range of signals being handled, and it should be accomplished without adding appreciable distortion to the input signal.

Block Diagram. The block diagram of a typical AGC amplifier is shown in Fig. 11.1. In many cases the low-level amplifier is not used, and the input signal is fed directly into the control stage. A typical power rectifier can consist of a half-wave rectifier and capacitance filter driving a d-c amplifier, as shown in Fig. 11.2. In many cases the base-emitter diode of the transistor is used for rectification, which results in a saving of components at the expense of power gain.

Control Stage. The operation of the control stage can be resolved into two main types:

1. Variation of the forward transfer characteristic of a transistor with the d-c bias current.
2. Variation of the dynamic resistance of a diode or transistor used as a two-terminal feedback or shunting element.

An example of the first type is shown in Fig. 11.3. The transistor is normally biased in the active region and the AGC voltage tends to turn the transistor off, thus decreasing y_{fe}. Although it is simple, the disadvantage of this kind of AGC is that large input signals will result in distorted output, since the bias point approaches cutoff as the signal is increased. The AGC action obtainable in this mode of operation, without introducing serious nonlinear distortion into the signal, is limited to about 20 db/stage.

Examples of the second type are shown in Figs. 11.4 and 11.5. In 11.4a, the input current divides between the diode resistance, R_D, and the input resistance of the amplifier. As the signal is increased, the AGC voltage increases, decreasing R_D (Fig. 11.4b), which limits the overall gain of the stage. For this AGC method to perform satisfactorily, the signal source must have a high resistance, and the input resistance to the amplifier must also be high. In Fig. 11.5a, a transistor is

176

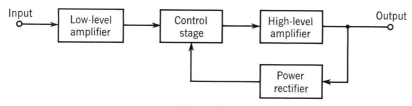

Figure 11.1

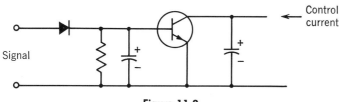

Figure 11.2

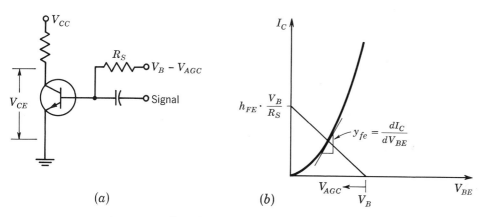

(a)   (b)

Fig. 11.3. Typical y_{FE} curve.

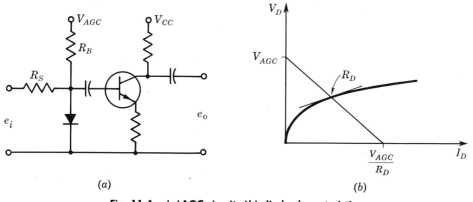

(a)   (b)

Fig. 11.4.   (a)AGC circuit; (b) diode characteristics.

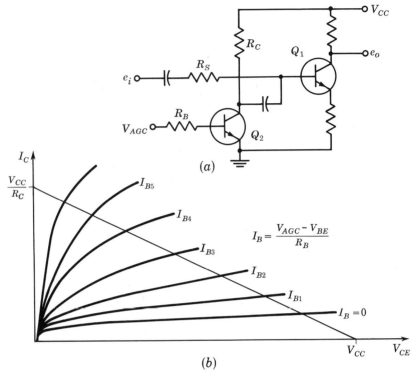

$$I_B = \frac{V_{AGC} - V_{BE}}{R_B}$$

(a)

(b)

Figure 11.5

used as the two-terminal shunting element.   Most of the AGC action is in the region near saturation where the slope of the transistor output characteristic is changing most rapidly.

The foregoing are three simple examples of the application of the two types of control.   The number of ways in which these types can be applied is limited only by the imagination of the designer.

Design Example.   Figure 11.6 is an example of an AGC circuit using a shunting diode (D_1). Q_1 and Q_2 are the active elements in a low-noise low-level amplifier, designed to operate with a source resistance of from 500 to 50 kilohms. Q_3 controls the bias current to D_1; it obtains its base drive from the rectifier D_2 and associated low-pass filter. Q_5 and Q_6 form a high-level amplifier, while Q_4 is an emitter-follower whose function is to present a high resistance to the AGC network.   The specifications of this amplifier when driven from a 500-ohm source are given below:

Temperature-compensated (open-loop) gain	97 db
AGC range	60 db
Maximum output signal	1 volt
Maximum input signal	2 mv
F (noise figure)	$\leq$6 db

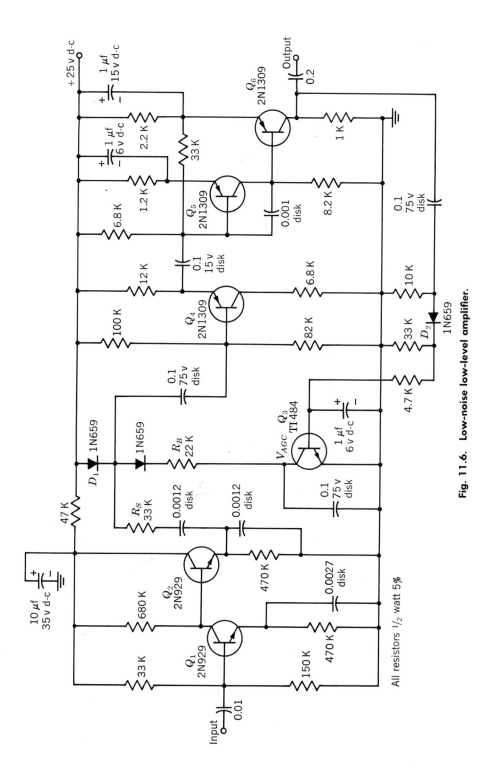

Fig. 11.6. Low-noise low-level amplifier.

179

12

Low-frequency Harmonic Oscillators

The principle of oscillator circuits using vacuum tubes is well known, and a number of the techniques which apply to vacuum-tube circuits are applicable to transistor circuits. This chapter reviews some of the fundamentals of oscillator circuit design and theory, and shows how these are applicable to designs using transistors.

The term *harmonic oscillators* may be applied to those oscillators which are operated in such a way as to produce a reasonably sinusoidal output voltage. In these circuits, a resonator is usually employed to fix the frequency of operation. The resonator acts to make the output sinusoidal, even though the current or voltage applied to the circuits may be highly distorted.

12.1. CRITERIA FOR OSCILLATION

It will be helpful to examine some of the basic concepts of a sine-wave oscillator. Figure 12.1 shows that such an oscillator is composed of an amplifier to provide power gain, a resonator to fix the frequency of oscillation, and a feedback network to provide oscillation. If this arrangement is to operate as a stable oscillator, the gain around the closed loop should be unity. If a gain greater than this exists, the output will increase until the loop gain is reduced to unity, because of the limiting which will occur at high levels.

It can also be shown that the phase shift around the closed loop of Fig. 12.1 should be zero. If the phase shift is not zero, the frequency of oscillation will

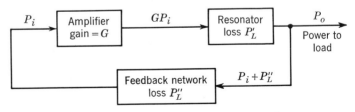

Fig. 12.1. Elements of an oscillator circuit.

change in such a way as to make it zero. These two conditions of unity power gain and zero phase shift around the loop are known as *Barkhausen criteria for oscillations.*

12.2. FEEDBACK PATHS

The *feedback path* class of oscillators embraces those that require an external path to couple the energy from the output to the input. Only a general discussion of these circuits will be given here, to show some of the various configurations which may be used to obtain oscillations.

Figure 12.2 shows several circuits which employ *LC* circuits as resonators to fix the frequency of oscillation. These circuits are shown using PNP transistors; however, NPN transistors are equally suitable if the biasing potentials are reversed.

In Fig. 12.2a, the resonant circuit is in the collector, and the feedback is obtained by transformer coupling from the collector to the base. In Fig. 12.2b, the resonant circuit is placed again in the collector; however, this time the feedback is taken to the emitter. In this case, it is necessary to use a somewhat larger turns ratio than that in Fig. 12.2a, since the input impedance of the emitter is lower than that of the base.

The circuit of Fig. 12.2c is the same as Fig. 12.2a except that the tank circuit is a-c coupled to the collector with a coupling capacitor.

The circuit of Fig. 12.2d is similar to that of Fig. 12.2b except that the coupling from the tank is accomplished by using the tank inductor as an autotransformer. The capacitor is needed only to block the d-c potential which exists between the collector and emitter.

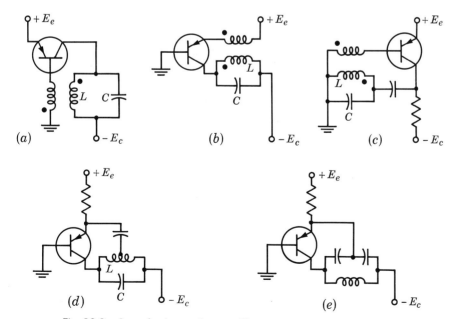

Fig. 12.2. Some basic transistor oscillators using external feedback.

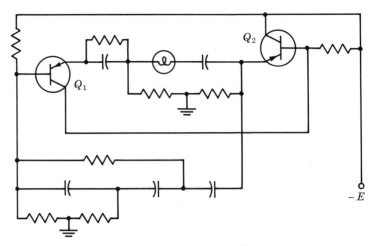

Fig. 12.3. Bridge-type oscillator.

The circuit of Fig. 12.2e is similar to those of 12.2a and 12.2d except that the coupling in this case is obtained through tapped capacitors instead of a tapped inductor. This technique results in a voltage and impedance transformation similar to that resulting from a tapped coil.

The circuits shown here are only a representation of a few of the many circuits which have evolved. Other types of external feedback oscillators, which produce a sinusoidal output but do not employ an LC resonant circuit, are the bridge and phase-shift oscillators.

A bridge oscillator in one of its simplest forms is shown in Fig. 12.3. Q_1 is operated as a grounded-base amplifier with a very high collector load so as to give a large voltage gain. Q_2 is used as a grounded-collector amplifier (emitter-follower) to couple this high-impedance collector to two feedback paths. One feedback path to the emitter is broad-tuned and is regenerative, and the other path is to the base and is made up of a bridged-T network. The feedback through this network is all degenerative; however, the bridged-T has a sharp null at one frequency which reduces the degenerative feedback and causes oscillation to occur at this frequency.

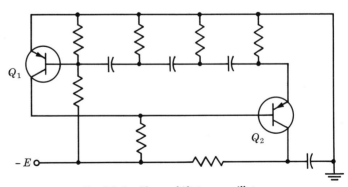

Fig. 12.4. Phase-shift-type oscillator.

The nonlinear element shown in the positive-feedback path provides a limiting action, so that the transistor can operate in a class A condition.

A phase-shift oscillator can be built using a similar circuit. In Fig. 12.4, two transistors are used again, one (Q_1) to obtain high voltage gain and one (Q_2) to obtain an impedance match. In this circuit the feedback is applied to the base of Q_1. A phase shift of 180° is obtained in three RC networks, and the additional 180° required for oscillation is obtained through the grounded-emitter amplifier Q_1.

12.3. DESIGN DATA

In order to illustrate the design of a transistor oscillator, a procedure for the design of a typical circuit is given:

As stated before, the Barkhausen criteria require that the power gain around the loop be unity and the phase shift around the loop be zero. These two factors are easily separated in oscillators having only external feedback loops. A block diagram of a feedback oscillator is given in Fig. 12.5. The amplifier has been converted to an equivalent Thévenin voltage generator with a voltage $e_1 K \underline{/\theta}$ in series with a resistance, r_o, the output impedance of the amplifier which is considered to be part of the feedback network. The input impedance of the amplifier is considered infinite, since any reactive component may be canceled at any one frequency, and the resistive component may be considered as a part of R. The phase angle, θ, is assumed to be a function of all external parameters, such as temperature and voltage. The primary factors affecting the stability of the frequency of operation now become $\phi(f)$, the resonator phase-shift characteristics as a function of frequency and $\theta(s)$, the variation of phase shift of the amplifier due to external effects. For stable frequency operation, it is desirable to make $d\theta/ds$ as small as possible and $d\phi/df$ as large as possible.

The factors influencing $\phi(f)$ are the geometry and element values of the frequency-controlling network. The choice of the network geometry is limited only by practical values of K and r_o. For most transistors, r_o is too large unless a transformer is used, in which case the ratio K^2/r_o remains constant for any transformer. This is true because the reflected impedance of a transformer varies as the square of the voltage ratio. Thus, the amplifier and transformer may be characterized in terms of θ and $K^2/r_o = A$.

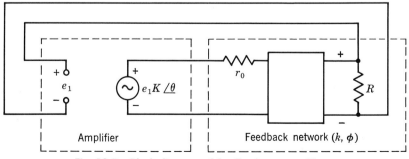

Fig. 12.5. Block diagram of feedback-type oscillator.

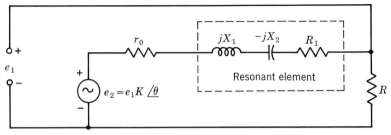

Fig. 12.6.   Simplified schematic of feedback oscillator.

To illustrate this method for designing a practical oscillator, the network shown in Fig. 12.6 is analyzed as follows: Let

$$jX = jX_1 - jX_2$$

Then

$$e_1 = e_2 \frac{R}{R + R_1 + jX + r_o} \tag{1}$$

or

$$\frac{e_2}{e_1} = K\underline{/\theta} = K\underline{/\tan^{-1} \frac{X}{R + r_o + R_1}} \tag{2}$$

Here, series resonance, $d\phi/df$, increases as $(R + r_o)$ decreases. The minimum value of $(R + r_o)$ that will permit oscillations is found as follows: For $X = 0$,

$$e_1 = \frac{Re_2}{r_o + R_1 + R} = \frac{Re_1 K}{r_o + R_1 + R}$$

But

$$K^2/r_o = A$$

or

$$K = r_o^{1/2}A^{1/2}$$

Therefore,

$$Rr_o^{1/2}a^{1/2} = r_o + R_1 + R$$

or

$$R = \frac{r_o + R_1}{r_o^{1/2}A^{1/2} - 1} \tag{3}$$

from which

$$R + r_o = \frac{r_o + R_1}{r_o^{1/2}A^{1/2} - 1} + r_o$$

$R + r_o$ is minimum when $\dfrac{d(R + r_o)}{dr_o} = 0$, or when

$$2r_o^{3/2}A^{1/2} - 3r_o - R_1 = 0 \tag{4}$$

By substituting R_1 as determined from the resonant element chosen for the oscillator and A as determined for the amplifier, r_o can be determined from Eq. (4). When r_o is known, then the correct turns ratio of the transformer can be determined.

If r_o and R could both be made zero and still maintain oscillations, the change in frequency produced by a small change in amplifier phase shift, $\Delta\theta$, would be

$$\Delta f = \frac{\Delta\theta f_o}{2Q} \qquad \text{for } \Delta\theta \text{ small} \tag{5}$$

where
$$Q = \frac{X_1}{R_1}$$

and
$$f_o = \frac{1}{\sqrt{LC}} \quad \text{for the resonant element}$$

For values of $(r_o + R)$ other than zero, Eq. (5) must be modified by making

$$Q = \frac{X_1}{R_1 + R + r_o}$$

13

Frequency Response and Stability
of Feedback Amplifiers

Feedback techniques are commonly used in transistor amplifiers to reduce the effects of transistor parameter variations on gain and distortion, and to improve the characteristics of the amplifier.

This chapter describes the importance of frequency response of a feedback amplifier with respect to stability against oscillation, how to obtain the frequency response of the amplifier from the transfer function, and how to shape the response in order to ensure a stable amplifier.

General Stability Criterion. Consider the block diagram of a feedback amplifier (Fig. 13.1), where

A = voltage gain of the amplifier without feedback
ϕ_a = phase shift of amplifier
β = fraction of output voltage fed back to the input
ϕ = phase shift of feedback network

At the frequency of operation, the amplifier is assumed to have an inherent 180° phase shift, and generally the feedback network will have zero phase shift; hence the gain can be computed as follows:

$$\text{Input voltage to the amplifier} = v = v_{(in)} - \beta v_o$$

$$\text{Output voltage} = v_o = A(v) = A(v_{(in)} - \beta v_o)$$

$$\text{Gain} = G = \frac{v_o}{v_{(in)}} = \frac{A}{1 + A\beta} \qquad (1)$$

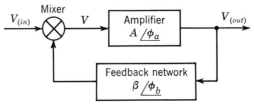

Figure 13.1

Unfortunately, the amplitude and phase relationships of the amplifier and feedback network are functions of frequency, owing to the use of coupling and decoupling capacitors, transformers, and to the frequency dependence of transistor parameters, etc.   Also, at some frequency it is possible for the loop phase shift (i.e., the phase shift of the amplifier plus the feedback network) to be 360°, and if a signal of this frequency is applied to the amplifier, the voltage fed back will be in phase with the input voltage and will therefore add to it.   The resulting gain will be $G = A/(1 - A\beta)$ and is effectively increased.   This is called *positive feedback*.

If the loop gain (i.e., gain of the amplifier times the feedback fraction) is greater than one at this frequency, and no signal is applied, any noise or transients in the power supply appearing at the input with the same component of frequency will be amplified, and the voltage fed back will be greater than the original signal.   This feedback voltage is amplified and fed back, etc., the output voltage getting progressively larger until some component in the circuit saturates, whence the output voltage will be stabilized.   Thus we are getting an output voltage for no input signal, and the amplifier is therefore oscillating.

For stability against oscillation, two conditions must be satisfied:

1. When the loop gain ($A\beta$ product) is greater than one, the total loop phase shift must be less than 360°.
2. When the loop phase shift is 360°, the loop gain must be less than one.

The amount by which the phase shift is less than 360° at the unity-gain frequency is called the *phase margin,* and the amount of gain less than one at the 360° frequency is called the *gain margin.*   The magnitudes of these quantities give an indication as to how stable an amplifier is and will depend on the application of the amplifier.   For example, a linear amplifier requiring good stability would require a gain and phase margin of at least 10 db and 50°, respectively, but a pulse amplifier of limited bandwidth, in order to have a good transient response, would require less than this.

Relationship between the Transfer Function and the Frequency Response. Consider the network in Fig. 13.2.   The transfer function of the circuit is as shown.

$$\frac{v_o}{v_{(in)}} = \frac{R}{R + 1/j\omega C} = \frac{1}{1 + 1/j\omega CR} \tag{2}$$

The response of this circuit is shown in Fig. 13.3.   It can be seen that the asymptote of the frequency-response curve (the slope of which is 6 db/octave or 20 db/decade) can be used as an approximation to the actual frequency response, with negligible error.

The phase response can also be calculated from the transfer function, as is shown in Fig. 13.4.   It can be seen that the phase response can also be approximated to a straight line, of slope equal to 45°/decade.

Table 13.1 shows the approximate amplitude and phase response of common transfer functions.

The use of this table may be illustrated by the following section of a transistor circuit (Fig. 13.5). Assuming that the output impedance of the preceding stage and the input resistance of the following stage

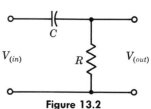

Figure 13.2

Table 13.1

Transfer function	Amplitude response	Phase response
$G = K(1 + j\omega CR)$	db; 6 db/octave; $20 \log_{10} K$; $\omega = \dfrac{1}{CR}$; $\log \omega$	$90°$ Phase lead; $45°$; $\omega = \dfrac{1}{CR}$; $\omega = \dfrac{10}{CR}$
$G = K \dfrac{1}{(1 + j\omega CR)}$	db; $20 \log_{10} K$; $\omega = \dfrac{1}{CR}$; $\log \omega$; 6 db/octave	$\omega = \dfrac{1}{CR}$; 0; $45°$; $45°/\text{decade}$; Phase lag; $90°$
$G = K\left(1 + \dfrac{1}{j\omega CR}\right)$	db; 6 db/octave; $20 \log_{10} K$; $\omega = \dfrac{1}{CR}$; $\log \omega$	$\omega = \dfrac{1}{CR}$; 0; Phase lag; $45°$; $90°$
$G = K \dfrac{1}{1 + \dfrac{1}{j\omega CR}}$	db; $20 \log_{10} K$; $\omega = \dfrac{1}{CR}$; $\log \omega$; 6 db/octave	$90°$; Phase lead; $45°$; 0; $\omega = \dfrac{1}{CR}$

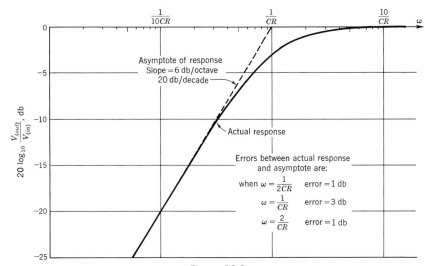

$$\frac{1}{10CR} \qquad \frac{1}{CR} \qquad \frac{10}{CR} \qquad \omega$$

Asymptote of response
Slope = 6 db/octave
20 db/decade

Actual response

Errors between actual response
and asymptote are:

when $\omega = \dfrac{1}{2CR}$ error = 1 db

$\omega = \dfrac{1}{CR}$ error = 3 db

$\omega = \dfrac{2}{CR}$ error = 1 db

$20 \log_{10} \dfrac{V_{(out)}}{V_{(in)}}$, db

Figure 13.3

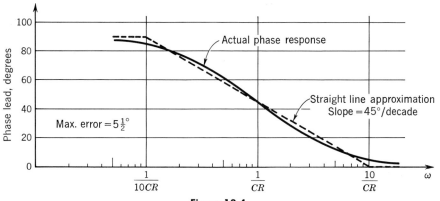

Actual phase response

Straight line approximation
Slope = 45°/decade

Max. error = $5\frac{1}{2}°$

Phase lead, degrees

$$\frac{1}{10CR} \qquad \frac{1}{CR} \qquad \frac{10}{CR} \qquad \omega$$

Figure 13.4

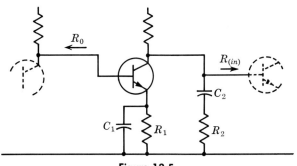

R_0

$R_{(in)}$

C_2

C_1 R_1 R_2

Figure 13.5

are essentially resistive at the frequencies concerned and that these frequencies are well below the h_{fe} cutoff frequency of the transistors, analysis of the circuit yields the following transfer function.

$$G = A_v \frac{1 + 1/j\omega C_1 R_1}{1 + (h_{fe}R_1 + R_o + h_{ie})/j\omega C_1 (R_o + h_{ie})R_1}$$

$$\frac{1 + j\omega C_2 R_2}{1 + j\omega C_2 (R_o R_{(in)} + R_2 R_{(in)} + R_o R_2)/(R_{(in)} + R_o)} \quad (3)$$

where A_v = mid-frequency voltage amplification. The frequency response is as shown in Fig. 13.6.

The phase-angle diagram may be approximated in the same way.

Shaping the Frequency Response to Ensure Stability against Oscillation. It will be noticed in the phase response of the RC network of Fig. 13.2 that at some frequency the phase angle reached 90°, and if there were two such networks in a circuit, the phase angle would reach 180°, the fall in amplitude response then being 12 db/octave. This together with the 180° phase shift in the amplifier could result in oscillation, if the loop gain were greater than one at this frequency. Consequently, it is important that when the loop gain is greater than one, the response should be controlled so that it does not rise or fall at a rate equal to or greater than 12 db/octave; and, in general, 9 or 10 db/octave is the maximum allowable for good stability.

At the low-frequency end, the fall in response is generally due to coupling and decoupling capacitors, together with any transformers in the circuit. One com-

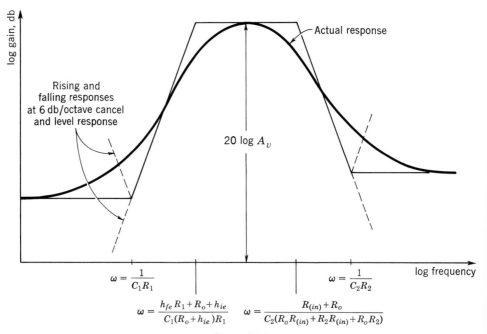

Figure 13.6

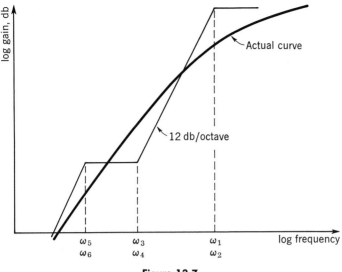

log gain, db

log frequency

Actual curve

12 db/octave

ω_5 ω_3 ω_1
ω_6 ω_4 ω_2

Figure 13.7

monly used method of stabilizing is the dominant-lead technique. Using this method for low-frequency shaping, one time constant is chosen to have its break frequency just below the lowest used frequency in the amplifier, the response thereafter falling at 6 db/octave until the unity gain frequency has been passed. After this point has been reached, the other time constants may cause the response to fall at any rate, while still maintaining a stable amplification. In high-loop-gain amplifiers, this technique is often difficult to apply, since it requires a very wide frequency response, resulting in large decoupling capacitors, etc., and transformers with high primary inductance. In these cases the time constants are chosen so that the response falls at a maximum of 9 db/octave as illustrated in Fig. 13.7.

Plotting the actual response curve, it can be seen that the response cannot possibly be greater than 12 db/octave, and by careful choice of ω_1, ω_2, etc., the slope can be controlled to 9 or 10 db/octave (Fig. 13.7).

At the high-frequency end of the frequency response, the chief causes of the fall in response are high-frequency response of the transistors and transformers and stray capacitances. Similar techniques to those used at the low-frequency end may be used, but, in general, these require the use of additional shaping networks, as illustrated in Fig. 13.8 (see next page).

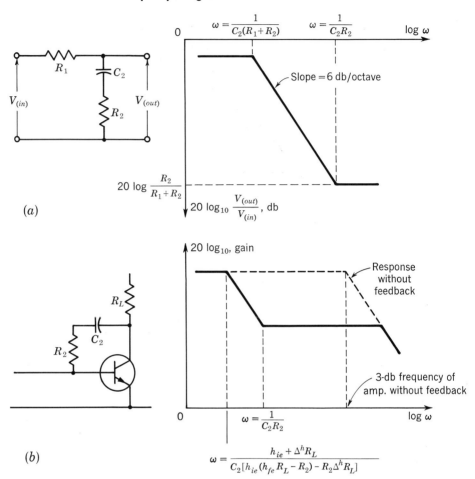

(a)

(b)

Figure 13.8

14

Operational Amplifiers

By the use of feedback elements, certain amplifiers may be made to produce an output which is proportional to the algebraic sum, the time derivative, the integral with respect to time, or simply a multiple of the input signal voltage or other mathematical operations. Such designs are widely used as building blocks for analog computers. Because of their mathematical versatility they are called *operational amplifiers*.

Operational amplifiers must meet these requirements:

1. The gain (without feedback) must be very large.
2. The passband must be wide, often extending from d-c (zero frequency) to tens of kilocycles.
3. The phase-gain characteristics must allow for a strong negative-feedback loop around the amplifier.
4. D-c drift must be minimized.
5. The amplifier must have either a very low output impedance and very high input impedance, or vice versa. Low output impedance is the more popular, but low input impedance has definite advantages for transistor amplifiers.

When operational amplifiers are used in analog computation, the system may be represented as in Fig. 14.1.

The amplifier (represented by the triangle) has a gain of A (open loop without external feedback). $e_{(in)}$ and e_o represent the input and output signals, respectively.

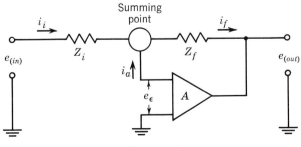

Figure 14.1

e_ϵ represents an error signal that is applied directly between the amplifier and ground.

The output signal is the product of the error signal and the gain of the amplifier. If the gain of the amplifier is sufficiently large ($A = 10^4$ to 10^6), e_ϵ will be small compared to $e_{(in)}$, and the summing point is assumed to be at zero or ground potential. The e_o connected through Z_f tends to force the summing point to maintain a small potential close to ground.

An example will serve to illustrate the above point. Suppose the amplifier has a gain of -10^6, an output swing of -20 volts, and an input signal of 1 volt. The gain of the system $e_o/e_{(in)} = -20\,\text{volts}/1\,\text{volt} = -20$. The error signal $= -e_o/-A = 20/10^6 = 20\ \mu\text{v}$. Thus, e_ϵ is 50,000 times smaller than $e_{(in)}$. $i_i = (e_{(in)} - e_\epsilon)/Z_i \cong e_{(in)}/Z_i$, and $i_f = (e_\epsilon - e_o)/Z_f \cong -e_o/Z_f$. If no current is assumed to flow into the amplifier ($i_a = 0$),

$$i_i = i_f \qquad \frac{e_{(in)}}{Z_i} = -\frac{e_o}{Z_f} \qquad A = -\frac{Z_f}{Z_i} \tag{1}$$

Since the summing point is at ground, the input impedance of the system equals Z_i. In our example, for a gain of -20 we could assume values of 100 kilohms for Z_i and 2 megohms for Z_f. Thus, the gain $A = (2 \times 10^6)/10^5 = -20$, and the input impedance $Z_i = 100$ kilohms.

Note that, in Eq. (1), Z_f and Z_i may be complex impedances and are not limited to pure resistance as in the example. Two examples will be given to show how integration and differentiation are possible with this type of amplifier. If Z_f is represented by a capacitor C, and Z_i by a resistor R, then from Eq. (1) (using the Laplace operator $S = \sigma + j\omega$),

$$A = -\frac{1/CS}{R} = -\frac{1}{RCS}$$

Noting that $1/S$ corresponds to integration and $A = e_o/e_{(in)}$,

$$e_o = -\frac{1}{RC} \int_0^t e_{(in)}\, dt$$

Thus we see that the output voltage is a constant ($1/RC$) times the integral of the input voltage. Differentiation is performed in a similar manner. Assume that the two impedances have been interchanged from the previous example; again, using Eq. (1),

$$A = -\frac{R}{1/CS} = -RCS \tag{2}$$

Noting that S corresponds to differentiation and $A = e_o/e_{(in)}$,

$$e_o = -RC\frac{de_{(in)}}{dt} \tag{3}$$

Thus we see that the output voltage is a constant multiplied by the time derivative of the input voltage.

The amplifier shown in Fig. 14.2 is a chopper-stabilized amplifier that can be used as an operational amplifier. This amplifier is shown in block-diagram form in Fig. 14.3.

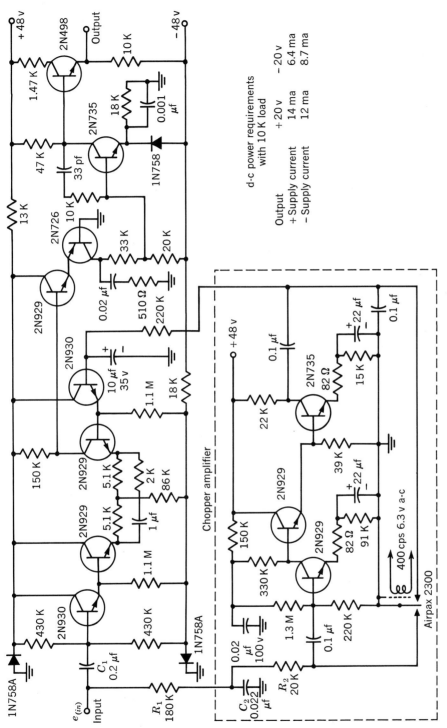

Fig. 14.2.   Chopper-stabilized d-c operational amplifier.

d-c power requirements with 10 K load		
Output	+ 20 v	− 20 v
+ Supply current	14 ma	6.4 ma
− Supply current	12 ma	8.7 ma

195

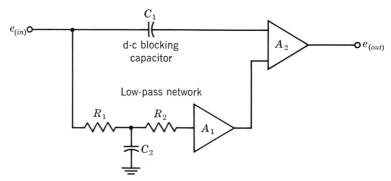

Figure 14.3

The input signal $e_{(in)}$ is composed of a d-c level with a-c information superimposed on it. The circuit shown in Fig. 14.3 consists of amplifier 1 which amplifies the low-level d-c portion of $e_{(in)}$, and of amplifier 2 which amplifies both the a-c portion of $e_{(in)}$ and the output from amplifier 1. Both 1 and 2 are d-c amplifiers.

Amplifier 1 is a mechanical chopper amplifier having excellent drift characteristics and a high gain, but a limited bandwidth. R_1, R_2, and C_2 form a low-pass filter that blocks the a-c signal to this amplifier. The output from amplifier 1 is large enough so that any drift in amplifier 2 will be small in comparison to the signal. Gain of the d-c signal is A_1A_2.

C_1 prevents any direct current from reaching amplifier 2, allowing only alternating current to pass. Thus, the a-c gain of the circuit is A_2. Amplifier 2 is a d-c amplifier whose drift characteristics are not quite so good as those of amplifier 1, but it has a larger bandwidth.

The circuit shown in Fig. 14.2 has both excellent d-c stability and a wide bandwidth. The d-c gain of this circuit is greater than 120 db, while the gain at 10 kc is 45 db. A curve of the typical frequency response of the amplifier is given in Fig. 14.4.

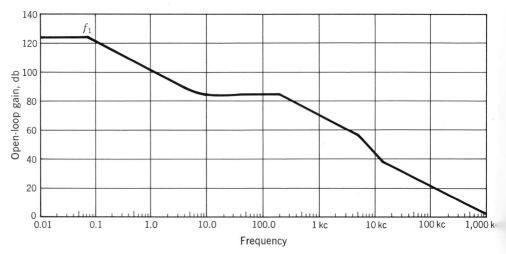

Figure 14.4

15

Low-level Audio Stage Analysis

One of the most-used circuits in transistor applications is the cascaded common-emitter audio amplifier. This circuit performs a variety of functions, is fairly easy to design, and gives good performance.

The function of a low-level amplifier is to raise a signal level from the millivolt range to a workable level of several volts. For example, the input signal may be derived from the output of a piezoelectric crystal, while the output may be required to drive a power amplifier.

In the examples of the two- and three-stage amplifiers that follow, the transistors are used in the common-emitter (CE) configuration. In a cascade of similar stages, the CE connection is the only configuration that gives both voltage and current gain. The common-base (CB) and common-collector (CC) configurations offer only voltage gain and current gain, respectively. However, these configurations are often useful for matching impedances where the CE stage would not function properly.

Stages are capacitance-coupled for a-c operation and d-c stability. Class A biasing is most often used, because it allows the output to follow the input, whether the input excursion is plus or minus.

Bias currents and voltages are selected such that they are large compared with the a-c signal. In small-signal operation, the transistor parameters are measured at given bias levels and are assumed to remain constant as the signal causes the operating point to make small excursions on either side of the bias point. With correct biasing, class A operation allows for linear operation of the a-c signal; distortion is usually kept to a fairly low value.

A typical single-stage amplifier circuit is shown in Fig. 15.1. In the following analysis, all power supplies and capacitors are considered to be short circuits to a-c signals. Figure 15.2 shows the a-c portion of Fig. 15.1. Resistors R_1 and R_2 form a parallel combination of R_A, while R_C and R_L may be replaced by R_B. R_L may be the input impedance of the next stage or an external load, but must nevertheless be taken into account. R_g and R_A form a voltage-divider circuit that attenuates the signal before it reaches the transistor. Thus, it can be seen that the bias resistors and the generator affect the gain of the circuit.

The following analysis of a two-stage a-c coupled amplifier demonstrates how

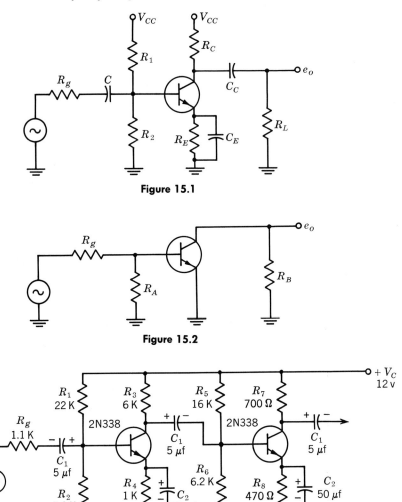

Figure 15.1

Figure 15.2

Fig. 15.3.   Two-stage cascaded CE audio amplifier.

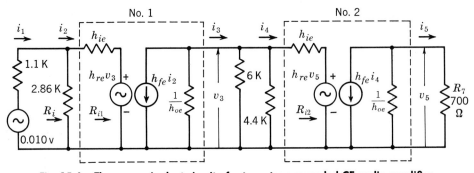

Fig. 15.4.   The a-c equivalent circuit of a two-stage cascaded CE audio amplifier.

the total amplifier gain may be calculated by the use of equivalent circuits.   The d-c biasing of each stage is also illustrated.

15.1. EQUIVALENT CIRCUITS

The first step in performing an analysis of the capacity-coupled CE amplifier of Fig. 15.3 is to reduce the circuit to its equivalent circuit.   This consists of removing the battery and replacing it with its internal impedance, if any, and eliminating those resistors which are bypassed by capacitors.   Also, the base bias resistors are replaced by their Thévenin equivalent circuit, and the coupling capacitors are shorted if their reactance is sufficiently small.   The a-c equivalent circuit of Fig. 15.3 is given in Fig. 15.4.

The Thévenin equivalent (parallel combination) of R_1 and R_2 in Fig. 15.3 equals 2.86 kilohms, and of R_5 and R_6 equals 4.4 kilohms.   These values and the load-resistor values for R_3 and R_7 are inserted in Fig. 15.4.

15.2. DETERMINATION OF h PARAMETERS

The h parameter values for the 2N338 transistor are obtained from the manufacturer's data sheet and converted to the common-emitter values, corrected for the operating conditions.   The conversion formulas are obtained from the equivalent circuit section.

The operating point for the second stage is set by the bias and load resistors at $V_{CE} = 5$ volts, $I_E = 6$ ma.   The operating point for the first stage is set at $V_{CE} = 5$ volts and $I_E = 1$ ma.

15.3. OPERATING POINT AND PARAMETER CORRECTIONS

To determine the d-c operating points, the first and second-stage circuits are drawn separately to illustrate the various direct currents and voltage drops across the resistors (Fig. 15.5).   The operating points and load lines for the two stages have been plotted in Fig. 15.6 on the static-output characteristic curves for the

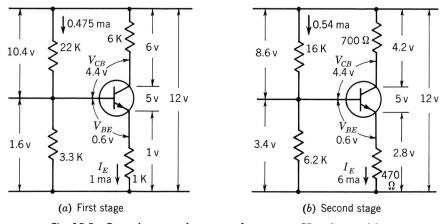

(a) First stage   (b) Second stage

Fig. 15.5.   D-c voltages and currents of two-stage CE audio amplifier.

2N338 transistor. Knowing the I_E and V_{CB} values for the two stages, the hybrid parameter correction factors (shown in Table 15.1) are obtained from the transistor data sheet. (Data sheets on the 2N338 transistor do not show these correction factors, and so it is necessary to use those given for the 2N335, which has similar characteristics.)

First-stage CE Hybrid Parameters

$$h_{ie} = \frac{h_{ib}}{1 + h_{fb}} = \frac{50}{0.01} = 5,000 \text{ ohms}$$

$$h_{re} = \frac{h_{ib}h_{ob}}{1 + h_{fb}} - h_{rb} = \frac{50 \times 0.2 \times 10^{-6}}{0.01} - 300 \times 10^{-6} = 700 \times 10^{-6}$$

$$h_{fe} = \frac{-h_{fb}}{1 + h_{fb}} = \frac{-(-0.99)}{1 - 0.99} = \frac{0.99}{0.01} = 99$$

$$h_{oe} = \frac{h_{ob}}{1 + h_{fb}} = \frac{0.2 \times 10^{-6}}{0.01} = 20 \times 10^{-6} = 20 \text{ } \mu\text{mhos}$$

Second-stage CE Hybrid Parameters

$$h_{ie} = \frac{h_{ib}}{1 + h_{fb}} = \frac{11}{0.0086} = 1,280 \text{ ohms}$$

$$h_{re} = \frac{h_{ib}h_{ob}}{1 + h_{fb}} - h_{rb} = \frac{11 \times 0.72 \times 10^{-6}}{0.0086} - 600 \times 10^{-6} = 320 \times 10^{-6}$$

$$h_{fe} = \frac{-h_{fb}}{1 + h_{fb}} = \frac{0.9914}{0.0086} = 115$$

$$h_{oe} = \frac{h_{ob}}{1 + h_{fb}} = \frac{0.72 \times 10^{-6}}{0.0086} = 84 \times 10^{-6} = 84 \text{ } \mu\text{mhos}$$

15.4. GAIN AND OUTPUT POWER

From the above information, it is possible to calculate the power gain, power output, and transducer gain for the CE circuit shown in Fig. 15.3. The power gain for a CE amplifier is equal to the product of the current gain and the voltage gain.

In the analysis, it is necessary to start with the second or output stage and work toward the first stage, because the input resistance of the second stage depends on its load resistance. The load resistance of the first stage is dependent on the input resistance of the second stage.

Second Stage. Referring to Fig. 15.4, the power gain of the second stage is equal to

$$G_2 = A_{i2}A_{v2} = \frac{I_5}{I_4}\frac{v_5}{v_3} \quad \text{and} \quad \frac{v_5}{v_3} = \frac{I_5 R_7}{I_4 R_{i2}}$$

Therefore,

$$G_2 = \left(\frac{I_5}{I_4}\right)^2 \frac{R_7}{R_{i2}} = (A_{i2})^2 \frac{R_7}{R_{i2}}$$

Table 15.1. *h*-parameter Values and Correction Factors for 2N338 Transistor

Parameter	Parameter value from data sheet	Correction factor for second stage, $I_{E2} = 6$ ma $V_{CB} = 4.4$ volts	Correction factor for first stage, $I_{E1} = 1$ ma $V_{CB} = 4.4$ volts	Corrected parameters	
				Second stage	First stage
h_{ib}	50 ohms	0.22	1	11 ohms	50
h_{rb}	300×10^{-6}	2.0	1	600×10^{-6}	300×10^{-6}
h_{fb}	-0.99	1.0015	1	-0.9914	-0.99
$1 + h_{fb}$	0.01	0.86	1	0.0086	0.01
h_{ob}	0.2×10^{-6} mho	3.6	1	0.72×10^{-6}	0.2×10^{-6}

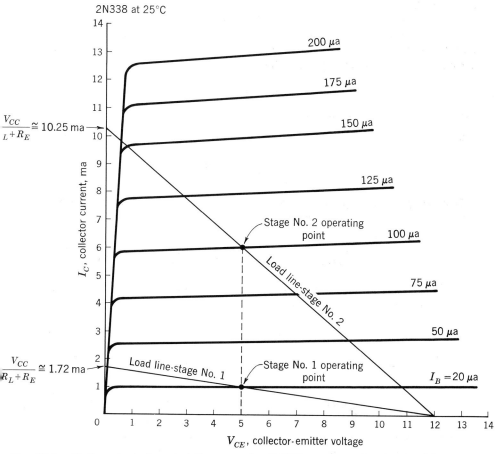

Fig. 15.6. Static output characteristic curves for 2N338 transistor showing load lines and operating points of two-stage CE audio amplifier.

$$*A_{i2} = \frac{I_5}{I_4} = \frac{h_{fe}}{h_{oe}R_7 + 1} = \frac{115}{84 \times 10^{-6} \times 700 + 1}$$

$$= 108 = \text{second-stage current gain}$$

$$*R_{i2} = \frac{h_{ie} + (h_{oe}h_{ie} - h_{fe}h_{re})R_7}{1 + h_{oe}R_7}$$

$$R_{i2} = \frac{1{,}280 + (84 \times 10^{-6} \times 1{,}280 - 115 \times 320 \times 10^{-6})700}{1 + 84 \times 10^{-6} \times 700}$$

Therefore,

$$G_2 = (108)^2 \times \frac{700}{1{,}220} = 6{,}700 = \text{power gain of second stage}$$

Interstage. Not all the first-stage output current, I_3, flows into the second-stage input, I_4 (Fig. 15.4); therefore, the ratio of I_4 to I_3 or the current attenuation produced by the interstage network must be known. The interstage network is given in Fig. 15.7a.

The 6- and 4.4-kilohm resistors in parallel give a combined value of approximately 2.5 kilohms, as shown in Fig. 15.7b. Also, 2.5 kilohms and 1,220 ohms in parallel provide an equivalent resistance, $R_{eq} \cong 820$ ohms. Since the voltages across both resistors are the same, then

$$1.22I_4 = 2.5(I_3 - I_4) = 2.5I_3 - 2.5I_4$$

and

$$3.72I_4 = 2.5I_3$$

Therefore, the interstage current gain, which here represents an attenuation, is

$$\frac{I_4}{I_3} = \frac{2.50}{3.72} = 0.670$$

First Stage. The equivalent resistance, R_{eq}, from above, forms the a-c load resistance of the first stage. The current gain is

$$A_{i1} = \frac{I_3}{I_2} = \frac{h_{fe}}{h_{oe}R_{eq} + 1} = \frac{99}{(20 \times 10^{-6} \times 820) + 1} = \frac{99}{1.016} = 98$$

* From standard h-parameter equations, input impedance $= z_i = h_{ie} - h_{fe}h_{re}R_L/(1 + h_{oe}R_L)$; current gain $= A_i = h_{fe}/(1 + h_{oe}R_L)$.

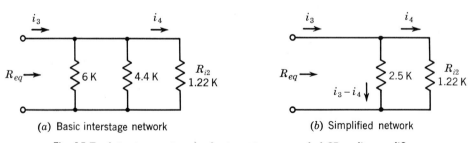

(a) Basic interstage network   (b) Simplified network

Fig. 15.7. Interstage network of a two-stage cascaded CE audio amplifier.

The input resistance is

$$R_{i1} = \frac{h_{ie} + (h_{oe}h_{ie} - h_{fe}h_{re})R_{eq}}{1 + h_{oe}R_{eq}}$$

$$R_{i1} = \frac{5,000 + (20 \times 10^{-6} \times 5,000 - 99 \times 700 \times 10^{-6})\, 820}{1 + (20 \times 10^{-6} \times 820)} = 4.94 \text{ kilohms}$$

Pre–First Stage. It is also necessary to find the current amplification (attenuation) and input resistance to the resistor preceding the first stage. This is the 2.86-kilohm Thévenin (parallel) resistance of R_1 and R_2 forming the base bias voltage-divider network for the first stage (see Figs. 15.3 and 15.4). The pre–first-stage circuit, excluding the source voltage generator, is shown in Fig. 15.8.

The pre–first current gain is

$$(A_i) \text{ prestage} = \frac{I_2}{I_1} = \frac{2.86}{2.86 + 4.94} = \frac{2.86}{7.80} = 0.366$$

The input resistance is

$$R_i = \frac{2.86 \times 4.94}{2.86 + 4.94} = 1.8 \text{ kilohms}$$

Total Power Gain of the Two-stage Amplifier. The total current gain of the two-stage amplifier (Fig. 15.3) can be found by multiplying all the individual gains. The total current gain is

$$(A_i) \text{ total} = \frac{I_5}{I_1} = (0.366)(98)(0.670)(108) = 2,560$$

The total power gain is

$$A_p = (A_i \text{ total})^2 \frac{R_7}{R_i}$$

$$A_p = (2,560)^2 \frac{700}{1,800} = 2,560,000$$

$$A_p = 2.56 \times 10^6 = 64 \text{ db}$$

Therefore, the two-stage amplifier (Fig. 15.3) has a total power gain of 64 db.

Power Output. Continuing the analysis, the power output must be calculated. By using the source values shown in Fig. 15.3, that is, a generator (source) imped-

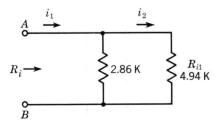

Fig. 15.8. Pre–first-stage circuit.

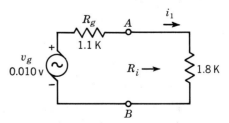

Fig. 15.9. Transducer input circuit.

ance, R_g, of 1,100 ohms, and a generator (source) voltage of 0.010 volt (10 mv), the transducer input circuit will resemble the circuit shown in Fig. 15.9.   From this circuit, it can be seen that

$$I_1 = \frac{V_g}{R_g + R_i} = \frac{0.010}{1,100 + 1,800} = \frac{0.010}{2,900} = 3.45 \ \mu a$$

The input power supplied by the generator to the amplifier is

$$P_{(in)} = (I_1)^2 R_i = \frac{V_g^2 R_i}{(R_g + R_i)^2}$$

$$P_{(in)} = (3.45)^2 \times 10^{-12} \times 1,800 = 11.9 \times 1,800 \times 10^{-12}$$

$$P_{(in)} = 0.0214 \ \mu w = \text{input power}$$

The input power multiplied by the power gain gives the amplifier output power, that is,

$$P_{(out)} = P_{(in)} A_p = 0.0214 \times 10^{-6} \times 2.56 \times 10^6 = 0.055 \text{ watt}$$

Therefore, $P_{(out)} = 55 \text{ mw}$

Transducer Gain.   The transducer gain is defined as the ratio of actual power supplied to the load, to the power generated by the signal source.   When compared with the total power gain of the amplifier, it is a measure of how efficiently the signal source is being used.

If the input resistance of the amplifier exactly matched the signal source resistance, maximum power transfer from the signal source to the amplifier would be obtained, and R_i would equal R_g.   The power available at the transducer would then be

$$P_{gen} \text{ available} = \frac{E_g^2}{4R_g} = \frac{(0.01)^2}{4 \times 1,100} = \frac{10^{-4}}{4.4 \times 10^3} = 0.0226 \text{ mw}$$

The transducer gain would then be

$$\text{Transducer gain} = \frac{P_{(out)}}{P_{gen} \text{ available}} = \frac{55 \times 10^{-3}}{0.0226 \times 10^{-6}} = 2.43 \times 10^6 = 63.8 \text{ db}$$

The transducer gain is nearly equal to the power gain; therefore, the generator is being used efficiently because the generator impedance nearly matches the amplifier input impedance.

Voltage Gain.   All the necessary information is known for the voltage gain:

$$A_v = \frac{e_o(\text{across } R_7)}{e_{(in)}(\text{across } R_i)} = A_i \frac{R_7}{R_i} = \frac{2,560 \times 700}{1,800} = 998$$

15.5. A COMPLETED DESIGN

A complete amplifier design using the 2N1565 is given in Fig. 15.10.   Its performance is given in Table 15.2.

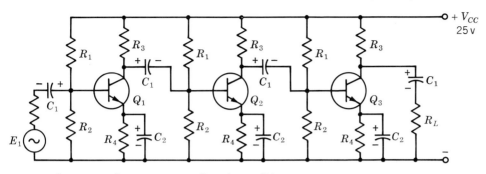

Component values:

R_L = 560 ohms
R_1 = 16 kilohms
R_2 = 6.2 kilohms
R_3 = 1.6 kilohms
R_4 = 1.0 kilohm
Q_1, Q_2, Q_3 = 2N1565

Operating conditions:

Temperature range: -55 to $+125°C$.
Output voltage swing of stage: 2 volts peak to peak.

Notes: C_1 and C_2 depend upon frequency response desired. Amplifiers were tested with C_1 = 10 μf and C_2 = 100 μf.

Figure 15.10

Table 15.2. Performance Characteristics at 1 kc

Temperature, °C	Typical current gain, db
-55	83
$+25$	88
$+125$	91

16

Class A Driver and Output Stages

The most common type of driver for a class B output stage is the transformer-coupled class A amplifier. The design of such a driver stage is discussed in this chapter.

Because of the many variables involved in the design of a class A amplifier, it is difficult to arrive at a completely general design procedure. Consequently, the design procedure presented here emphasizes circuit analysis rather than circuit synthesis. The primary purpose of the design procedure and design example presented is to emphasize the variety of factors to be considered in achieving a reliable circuit design.

16.1. THE IDEAL AMPLIFIER

An understanding of the basic class A configuration is of fundamental importance, but since many textbooks cover the subject, only a cursory explanation will be presented. Figure 16.1a illustrates the basic circuit as it is encountered in most textbooks.

The a-c and d-c load lines for the basic or ideal configuration are shown in Fig.

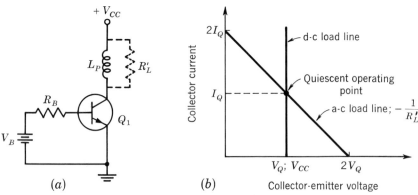

Fig. 16.1. Basic configuration.

16.1*b*. R'_L represents the load impedance reflected to the primary and, consequently, determines the a-c load line. The intersection of the a-c and d-c load lines is the quiescent operating point (I_Q, V_Q). Under quiescent conditions, I_Q is the collector current flowing through the transistor, and V_Q is the voltage appearing across its collector and emitter terminals. Thus, the power dissipated in the transistor under quiescent conditions is $V_Q I_Q$:

$$P_{J(max)} = V_Q I_Q \cong V_{CC} I_Q \tag{1}$$

When an a-c signal is applied, the a-c load line becomes the locus of the transistor's operating point. In order to achieve maximum symmetrical swing of current and voltage (neglecting transistor saturation resistance for the moment), the quiescent point must be located midway between the a-c load-line intersections of the horizontal and vertical axes, as shown in Fig. 16.1*b*. Since the transistor is assumed to be ideal, i.e., $R_{(sat)} = 0$ and $I_{CO} = 0$, then the maximum power, P'_0, which can be put into the transformer as a sine-wave signal is the rms voltage $V_Q/\sqrt{2}$ times the rms current $I_Q/\sqrt{2}$:

$$P'_0 = \frac{V_Q I_Q}{2} \cong \frac{V_{CC} I_Q}{2} \tag{2}$$

Since the average power supplied to the class A stage is constant at any signal level, it becomes apparent that the maximum collector efficiency is 50% and occurs only at maximum signal output.

16.2. THE PRACTICABLE AMPLIFIER

The circuit shown in Fig. 16.2*a* represents a practical circuit. The obvious differences between this circuit and the ideal one are the additional resistors and the capacitor. In a detailed analysis of the circuit, however, many more complicated differences appear. Examination of the load lines shown in Fig. 16.2*b* reveals several important considerations which should be taken into account in the design of a practical circuit.

Circuit Resistance Considerations. Resistors R_Y, R_{E1}, and R_{E2} determine the d-c load line, while R'_L, R_Y, and R_{E1} determine the a-c load line. The emitter resistors are necessary to ensure bias-point stability as well as thermal stability. All the emitter resistance could be bypassed, i.e., $R_{E1} = 0$, and it frequently is, but since this is to be a general case, R_{E1} will be included in the analysis. R_{E1} provides a-c negative feedback which increases the input and output impedances. It may also extend the lower cutoff frequency of the bypass capacitor C_1. R'_L represents the reflected load resistance, and R_Y represents the d-c winding resistance of the transformer primary plus the internal impedance of the power supply. Since R_Y serves no useful function, it should be minimized for improved performance.

Another undesirable resistance affecting circuit operation unfavorably is plotted in Fig. 16.2*b* as R_x. This is the *resistance* of the transistor at an arbitrary point approaching saturation. As a general rule, R_x can be assumed to be two or three times the saturation resistance specified on the data sheet, since saturation resistance is usually measured with the transistor hard in saturation. The point worth

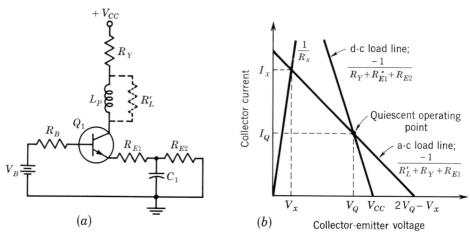

Fig. 16.2.   Practical configuration.

consideration is that, because of the rapid change of the transistor characteristics when close to saturation, the area to the left of $1/R_x$ in Fig. 16.2b is unsuitable for linear operation.

Bias-point Considerations.   For maximum symmetrical swing of current and voltage, the quiescent point must be located on the a-c load line at $I_x/2$, where I_x is the current determined by the intersection of the a-c load line with $1/R_x$, as shown in Fig. 16.2b.   With such a bias point for a sine-wave signal, the maximum possible a-c power out of the transistor is the rms voltage $(V_Q - V_x)/\sqrt{2}$ times the rms current $I_Q/\sqrt{2}$:

$$P_O = \frac{(V_Q - V_x)I_Q}{2} = \frac{V_Q'I_Q}{2} \tag{3}$$

where

$$V_Q' = V_Q - V_x \tag{4}$$

and

$$V_Q = V_{CC} - I_Q(R_Y + R_{E1} + R_{E2}) \tag{5}$$

If the bias point should shift, the available peak current or voltage would decrease, and less a-c power could be obtained from the transistor.   Figure 16.3 illustrates the shift in the a-c load line which occurs when I_Q increases to $\overline{I}_Q$ or decreases to $\underline{I}_Q$.   A well-designed circuit would keep the bias point relatively stable and would make allowances for shifts which may occur when using standard-tolerance components.   Allowance must be made for the increased power dissipation in the transistor which will occur if I_Q increases to $\overline{I}_Q$.   Also, the desired a-c power output of the transistor must be obtainable in spite of a bias-point shift to either $\overline{I}_Q$ or $\underline{I}_Q$. Calculations concerning bias-point shifting have been presented in Chap. 7.

Power Dissipation and Thermal Considerations.   The instantaneous power dissipated in any transistor under any circumstances is given by

$$p_J = v_{CE}i_C + v_{BE}i_B \tag{6}$$

If the transistor is not driven into saturation, the contribution of $v_{BE}i_B$ to the

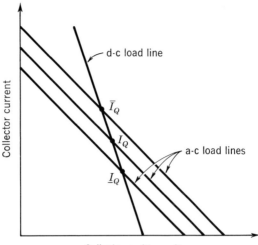

Fig. 16.3. Bias-point shifting.

peak instantaneous power $p_{J(peak)}$, and to the maximum average dissipation $P_{J(max)}$, is quite small and can usually be neglected.

The maximum average dissipation of a class A stage occurs at quiescent conditions:

$$P_{J(max)} = I_Q V_Q = I_Q [V_{CC} - I_Q(R_Y + R_{E1} + R_{E2})] \tag{7}$$

The peak instantaneous power can be found by expressing power dissipation as a function of a signal current, and differentiating to determine the value of i_c which causes $p_{J(peak)}$.

Thus:

$$p_{J(peak)} = \frac{[V_{CC} + I_Q(R_L' - R_{E2})]^2}{4(R_L' + R_Y + R_{E1})} \tag{8}$$

and at that instant

$$i_c \cong \frac{V_{CC} + I_Q(R_L' - R_{E2})}{2(R_L' + R_Y + R_{E1})} \tag{9}$$

if $\quad R_{E2}C_1 \gg \dfrac{1}{f_o} \quad$ and $\quad \dfrac{L_p}{R_L'} \gg \dfrac{1}{f_o} \quad f_o = $ signal frequency

The significance of $P_{J(max)}$ and $p_{J(peak)}$ have been explained in the chapter on general biasing, Chap. 7. The peak power dissipation described by Eq. (8) will only occur with unsymmetrical bias. Unfortunately, unsymmetrical biasing can occur because of a-c load variations, which are common when the load is another transistor stage. For symmetrical biasing as shown in the basic configuration of Fig. 16.1, both the peak instantaneous power and maximum average power occur at the quiescent point.

As explained previously in Chap. 7, a conservative thermal design results from using

$$\Delta T_{J\text{-}A(max)} = \theta_{J\text{-}C} p_{J(peak)} + \theta_{C\text{-}A} P_{J(max)} \tag{10}$$

Another important consideration which is explained in Chap. 7 concerns thermal stability. A simplified version of Eq. (58) of Chap. 7 which must be satisfied for thermal stability is

$$\frac{1}{\theta_T} > V_{CC}\left[\left(1 + \frac{R_B}{R_E}\right)\left(0.0693 I_{CBO} - I_Q\frac{dh_{FB}^*}{dt_J}\right) + \frac{0.0025}{R_E}\right] \tag{11}$$

where I_Q is the quiescent collector current.

This equation is subject to the restrictions and conditions originally imposed. Recall that the equation is for *silicon* transistors (0.0693 becomes approximately 0.0495 for germanium transistors), and that the resistances R_B and R_E refer to the equivalent circuit shown in Fig. 7.4 of Chap. 7.

Output Power Considerations. Another important consideration in the design of a class A driver stage is the a-c power requirement. For a load power of P_L, the power required at the primary of the transformer is

$$P_L' = \frac{P_L}{\eta} \tag{12}$$

where η = transformer efficiency.

The a-c power output of the transistor has been expressed in terms of the quiescent current and voltage in Eq. (3). The portion of this power which will be delivered to the reflected load impedance, R_L', is

$$P_o' = \frac{V_Q' I_Q \delta}{2} \tag{13}$$

or

$$P_o' = \frac{I_Q^2 R_L'}{2} \tag{14}$$

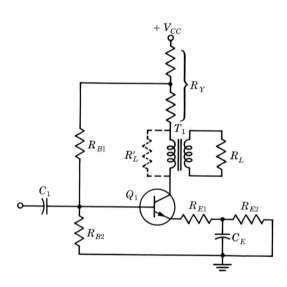

Fig. 16.4. Design circuit.

where
$$\delta = \frac{R'_L}{R'_L + R_Y + R_{E1}} \qquad (15)$$

Actually, $P'_o = P'_L$, but because of bias-point variations it is best during the design of a stage to make P'_o larger by an amount P_B to ensure that its minimum value (which occurs during bias-point shifts) will still equal P'_L . Thus:

$$P'_o - P'_L = P_B \qquad (16)$$

Transistor and Transformer Considerations. The primary transistor considerations are the current, voltage, and thermal ratings. The transistor should have a useful h_{FE} at $2I_Q$ and a voltage rating of

$$BV_{CEO} > 2V_Q \qquad (17)$$

16.3. DESIGN PROCEDURE

The design procedure presented is based on the following factors being known:

Supply voltage V_{CC}; its tolerance and internal resistance.
Frequency range.
Ambient temperature.
Load power, P_L.
Load resistance, R_L.
Configuration as shown in Fig. 16.4.

The following step-by-step procedure is intended to be a logical approach to the design of a class A driver stage when reliability is of primary importance.

1. Determine the a-c power requirement of the transistor.
    a. Estimate transformer efficiency, η.
    b. Calculate power delivered to the transformer: $P'_L = P_L/\eta$.
    c. Estimate P_B, the extra power necessary because of expected bias-point shifting.
    d. Determine the a-c power output of the transistor: $P'_o = P'_L + P_B$.
2. Determine the average power-dissipation requirements of the transistor.
    a. Estimate δ: $\delta = R'_L/(R'_L + R_{E1} + R_Y)$.
    b. Calculate the maximum average power dissipation: $P_{J(max)} = V_Q I_Q \cong 2P'_o/\delta$.
3. Select a transistor or series of transistors from the available data sheet information to meet power, temperature, and frequency requirements.
4. Select a quiescent current from examination of the transistor data sheet information; the collector current versus h_{FE} curve should indicate what current range is appropriate.
5. Determine the quiescent voltage.
    a. V'_Q can be determined from Eq. (13): $P'_o = V'_Q I_Q \delta/2$.
    b. Estimate a value of V_x from the data sheet information.
    c. Calculate the value of quiescent voltage: $V_Q = V'_Q + V_x$.

d. Choose a different value of quiescent current if the quiescent voltage appears unreasonable.

e. Determine the required minimum voltage rating of the transistor from Eq. (17): $BV_{CEO} > 2V_Q$.

6. Determine the required value of reflected load impedance.

a. Determine reflected load impedance from Eq. (14): $P'_0 = I_Q^2 R'_L/2$.

b. Determine the transformer turns ratio.

7. Choose values for the remaining a-c impedances.

a. Estimate a value for R_Y. It comprises the power supply and transformer primary resistances.

b. Decide upon a value for R_{E1}. At this time, the effect of a particular value of R_{E1} can be evaluated by comparing it with R'_L.

c. Calculate δ, since R_L, R_{E1}, and R_Y are now known. If it is noticeably different from the estimated value, $P_{J(max)}$ may require recalculation.

8. Calculate the value of bypassed emitter resistance R_{E2}. The value of R_{E2} can be determined from Eq. (5): $V_Q = V_{CC} - I_Q(R_{E1} + R_{E2} + R_Y)$.

9. Determine the maximum junction temperature.

a. For any given heat sink, the designer must ascertain that the junction temperature $T_{J(peak)}$ obtained will be less than the manufacturer's specified maximum.

b. If the transistor is assumed to have a thermal time constant of zero, the peak instantaneous power $p_{J(peak)}$ becomes an important consideration. $p_{J(peak)}$ can be evaluated from Eq. (8).

c. A maximum value of case-to-ambient thermal resistance can be determined from Eq. (10).

10. Determine the maximum value of base resistance from thermal stability considerations.

a. A simplified version of the thermal stability equation is given by Eq. (11). Chapter 7 on biasing gives considerable detail on the derivation of this equation.

b. Although solving for the base resistance from the thermal stability equation gives an upper limit, a value of resistance approaching this limit may be quite impractical in view of bias-point stability considerations previously covered in the text. For a minimum limit, it is desirable that the base resistance be large with respect to the input impedance of the transistor.

c. The exact values of R_{B1} and R_{B2} can be determined from base resistance and bias voltage considerations.

11. Determine the bias-point stability. This procedure is covered in Chap. 7.

12. Determine the effects of possible bias-point shifts.

a. Determine whether the estimated *extra* power, P_B, is sufficient.

b. Determine whether the transistor is capable of dissipating the additional power which could result from a possible quiescent point shift.

13. Determine the values of the coupling and bypass capacitors, and select a transformer.

14. Breadboard and test the circuit.

16.4. DESIGN EXAMPLE

Known:

Supply voltage = 40 volts; impedance = 1 ohm.
Frequency = 400 cps (single frequency).
Ambient temperature = −25 to +100°C.
Load power, P_L = 400 mw.
Load resistance, R_L = 15 ohms.
Configuration as shown in Fig. 16.4.

1. Determine the a-c requirements of the transistor. The transformer efficiency η is assumed to be 75%. Therefore,

$$P'_L = \frac{P_L}{\eta} = \frac{400}{0.75} = 534 \text{ mw}$$

Adding a safety factor of 300 mw gives

$$P'_0 = 534 + 300 = 834 \text{ mw}$$

2. Determine the average power-dissipation requirements of the transistor. δ is estimated to be 0.75. Thus, the average power dissipation is

$$P_{J(max)} \cong \frac{2P'_0}{\delta} = \frac{2(834 \times 10^{-3})}{0.75} = 2.22 \text{ watts}$$

3. Select a transistor or series of transistors to meet the power, temperature, and frequency requirements. The 2N1718 series is selected based on these considerations. The selection is narrowed even further by deciding upon the 2N1720, to obtain the highest possible gain.
4. Select a quiescent current from examination of the transistor data sheet information. h_{FE} is a maximum at 200 ma, and remains high at $2I_Q$ or 400 ma. Therefore, a quiescent current of 200 ma is chosen.
5. Determine the quiescent voltage. The required peak a-c voltage swing, V'_Q, can be determined from Eq. (13).

$$V'_Q = \frac{2P'_0}{\delta I_Q} = \frac{(2)(0.834)}{(0.75)(0.2)} = 11.1 \text{ volts}$$

This seems quite small with respect to the 40-volt supply, so that a smaller quiescent current might be appropriate. A quiescent current of 100 ma will be tried.

$$V'_Q = \frac{2P'_0}{\delta I_Q} = \frac{(2)(0.834)}{(0.1)(0.75)} = 22.2 \text{ volts}$$

V_x is estimated to have a worst-case value of 4 volts at $2I_Q$ or 200 ma. Thus, the quiescent voltage is

$$V_Q = V'_Q + V_x = 26.2 \text{ volts}$$

The transistor will require a $BV_{CEO} > 2V_Q$ or 52.4 volts. It appears that the 2N1720, which has a 60-volt BV_{CEO}, can be used if the bias point does not shift excessively.

6. Determine the required value of reflected load impedance. The reflected load impedance can be determined from Eq. (14).

$$R_L' = \frac{2P_o'}{I_Q^2} = \frac{2(0.834)}{(0.1)^2} = 166.8 \text{ ohms}$$

The turns ratio of the transformer is, therefore,

$$a = \sqrt{\frac{R_L'}{R_L}} = \sqrt{\frac{166.8}{15}} = 3.33$$

7. Choose values for the remaining a-c impedances. The total value of R_Y is assumed to be 20 ohms. R_{E1} is chosen as 5 ohms. This will help to increase the input impedance and lower the emitter bypass capacitance cutoff frequency, yet will not appreciably affect the gain, since $R_L' > 35R_{E1}$. δ is calculated:

$$\delta = \frac{R_L'}{R_L' + R_Y + R_{E1}} = \frac{166.8}{166.8 + 20 + 5} = 0.87$$

The estimated value 0.75 appears to be close enough to the calculated value 0.87 so that $P_{J(max)}$ need not be recalculated.

8. Calculate the value of unbypassed emitter resistance R_{E2}. R_{E2} can be determined from Eq. (5).

$$R_{E2} = \frac{V_{CC} - V_Q - I_Q(R_{E1} + R_Y)}{I_Q} = \frac{40 - 26.2 - (0.1)(5 + 20)}{0.1}$$
$$= 113 \cong 110 \text{ ohms}$$

9. Determine the maximum junction temperature and required value of heat sink thermal resistance. Since thermal-time-constant information is not available on the data sheet of the transistor, and since the operating frequency is fairly low, a conservative design will be achieved by assuming the thermal time constant to be zero. The $p_{J(peak)}$ for a class A stage can be determined from Eq. (8).

$$p_{J(peak)} = \frac{[V_{CC} + I_Q(R_L' - R_{E2})]^2}{4(R_L' + R_Y + R_{E1})} = \frac{[40 + (0.1)(166.8 - 110)]^2}{4(166.8 + 20 + 5)}$$
$$= 2.72 \text{ watts}$$

The maximum value of case-to-ambient thermal resistance can be determined from Eq. (10).

$$\Delta T_{J-A} = \theta_{J-C} p_{J(peak)} + \theta_{CA} P_{J(max)}$$

Since the ambient is 100°C, ΔT_{J-A} could be 75 C°, but 70 C° will be used to introduce a safety factor.

$$70 \text{ C}° = (7.5)(2.72) + \theta_{CA} 2.22 \qquad \theta_{CA} \leq 22.3 \cong 22 \text{ C}°/\text{watt}$$

Thus, the heat sink, mica washer, and interface-contact thermal resistance must all be less than 22 C°/watt.

10. Determine the maximum value of base resistance from thermal stability considerations. The simplified stability expression is used. Since the power-supply resistance of the circuit is small, the resistances of Eq. (11) will be applicable to the circuit shown in Fig. 16.4. Equation (11) is:

$$\frac{1}{\theta_T} > V_{CC} \left[\left(1 + \frac{R_B}{R_E} \right) \left(0.0693 I_{CBO} - I_Q \frac{dh^*_{FB}}{dt_J} \right) + \frac{0.0025}{R_E} \right]$$

$$\theta_T = 7.5 + 22 = 29.5 \text{ C°/watt}$$

$$V_{CC} = 40 \text{ volts}$$

$$R_E = 110 + 5 = 115 \text{ ohms}$$

$$I_{CBO} = 500 \ \mu\text{a} \qquad \text{(from data sheet)}$$

$$0.0693 I_{CBO} = 34.6 \times 10^{-6} \text{ amp}$$

In most instances, it will be necessary to calculate I_{CBO} from the following equation:

$$I_{CBO} \cong I'_{CBO} + 2^n I''_{CBO} \qquad (18)$$

where I'_{CBO} = the voltage-dependent portion of I_{CBO}
I''_{CBO} = the temperature-dependent portion of I_{CBO}
n = the number of 10 C° increments (for silicon transistors, or 14 C° increments for germanium transistors) between the junction temperature at which I''_{CBO} is known and the junction temperature for which I_{CBO} is being determined. This rule of thumb is applicable for high temperatures over relatively small temperature ranges.

$$I_Q = 100 \text{ ma}$$

$$\frac{dh^*_{FB}}{dt_J} \cong \frac{\Delta h_{FB}}{\Delta t_J} \cong \frac{h_{FE1}/(1 + h_{FE1}) - h_{FE2}/(1 + h_{FE2})}{t_{J2} - t_{J1}}$$

Table 16.1 lists information obtained from the 2N1720 data sheet concerning the variation of h_{FE} with temperature. The temperature range of

Table 16.1. h_{FE} **Characteristics of 2N1720 at 100 ma**

T_J, °C	Guaranteed minimum h_{FE}	Typical h_{FE}	Estimated minimum h_{FE}
150	. . .	125	$\frac{38}{82} \cdot 125 = 57.9 \cong 58$
75	. . .	97	$\frac{38}{82} \cdot 97 = 44.9 \cong 45$
25	38	82	$\frac{38}{82} \cdot 82 = 38$

+75 to 150°C was chosen for the evaluation of dh_{FB}^*/dt_J since h_{FE} information at these temperatures is available on the data sheet and because the choice results in a conservative design. Ideally, the variation of h_{FB}^* with temperature would be evaluated at the maximum anticipated junction temperature, which in this instance is 170°C. However, since h_{FB}^* decreases at lower temperatures, a safety factor is achieved by calculating $\Delta h_{FB}/\Delta t_J$ over a temperature range below the maximum anticipated junction temperature.

$$\frac{dh_{FB}^*}{dt_J} \cong \frac{h_{FE1}/(1 + h_{FE1}) - h_{FE2}/(1 + h_{FE2})}{t_{J2} - t_{J1}} = \frac{45/46 - 58/59}{150 - 75}$$
$$= -63.9 \times 10^{-6}/C°$$

$$-I_Q \frac{dh_{FB}^*}{dt_J} \lessgtr -(0.1)(-63.9 \times 10^{-6}) = 6.39 \times 10^{-6} \text{ amp/C°}$$

$$R_B < \frac{R_E/\theta_T V_{CC} - 0.0025 - R_E(0.0693 I_{CBO} - I_Q \, dh_{FB}^*/dt_J)}{0.0693 I_{CBO} - I_Q \, dh_{FB}^*/dt_J} \quad \text{ohms}$$

$$R_B < \frac{115/(29.5)(40) - 0.0025 - 115(34.6 \times 10^{-6} + 6.39 \times 10^{-6})}{34.6 \times 10^{-6} + 6.39 \times 10^{-6}} \quad \text{ohms}$$

$$R_B < 2.2 \text{ kilohms}$$

Although this is the maximum limit for thermal stability, it will not necessarily ensure the desired bias-point stability. A rule of thumb sometimes useful in obtaining a stable bias point is to limit the ratio of the base resistance to the emitter resistance to 5 or less. A base resistance of approximately five times the emitter resistance, or 575 ohms, will be tried. A value of $R_{B1} = 2$ kilohm and $R_{B2} = 1$ kilohm closely satisfies this requirement as well as the necessary bias requirement, i.e., an emitter voltage of $I_{EQ}(R_{E1} + R_{E2})$ or 11.5 volts. This parallel combination of R_{B1} and R_{B2} is actually 667 ohms instead of 575 ohms.

11. Determine the bias-point stability. From Chap. 7 the expression for minimum quiescent current can be expressed as

$$\underline{I_Q} \gtrless \frac{\underline{h_{FE}}(\underline{V_B} - \overline{V_{BE}})}{\overline{R_B} + \overline{R_E}(1 + \underline{h_{FE}})}$$

and maximum quiescent current can be expressed as

$$\overline{I_Q} \lessgtr \frac{\overline{V_B} - \underline{V_{BE}} + \overline{I_{CBO}}(\overline{R_B} + \underline{R_E})}{\underline{R_E}}$$

Because the power-supply resistance is small with respect to other circuit resistances, it is not necessary to convert the circuit of Fig. 16.4 to an equivalent circuit to obtain the correct resistance values for these equations. In this analysis, 1% resistor tolerances are used, and no allowance is made for the change of this tolerance with temperature, aging, etc.

The following characteristics are estimated data sheet information at worst-case temperatures.

$$\underline{h}_{FE} \cong 25 \qquad \overline{h}_{FE} \cong \infty$$

$$\underline{V}_{BE} \cong 0.4 \text{ volt} \qquad \overline{V}_{BE} \cong 1.2 \text{ volts}$$

$$\overline{I}_{CBO} = 500 \ \mu\text{a}$$

The possible resistor and bias voltage limits are:

$$\overline{R}_E = 115 + 1.15 = 116.15 \text{ ohms} \qquad \underline{R}_E = 115 - 1.15 = 113.85 \text{ ohms}$$

$$\overline{R}_{B1} = 2 \text{ K} + 20 = 2.02 \text{ kilohms} \qquad \underline{R}_{B1} = 2 \text{ K} - 20 = 1.98 \text{ kilohms}$$

$$\overline{R}_{B2} = 1 \text{ K} + 10 = 1.01 \text{ kilohms} \qquad \underline{R}_{B2} = 1 \text{ K} - 10 = 0.99 \text{ kilohm}$$

$$\overline{R}_B = \frac{\overline{R}_{B1}\overline{R}_{B2}}{\overline{R}_{B1} + \overline{R}_{B2}} = 680 \text{ ohms}$$

$$\overline{V}_{CC} = 40.5 \text{ volts} \qquad \underline{V}_{CC} = 39.5 \text{ volts}$$

$$\overline{V}_B = \overline{V}_{CC} \frac{\overline{R}_{B2}}{\underline{R}_{B1} + \overline{R}_{B2}} = \frac{(40.5)(1.01 \text{ kilohms})}{1.98 \text{ kilohms} + 1.01 \text{ kilohms}} = 13.7 \text{ volts}$$

$$\underline{V}_B = \frac{\underline{V}_{CC}\underline{R}_{B2}}{\overline{R}_{B1} + \underline{R}_{B2}} = \frac{(39.5)(0.99 \text{ kilohm})}{2.02 \text{ kilohms} + 0.99 \text{ kilohm}} = 13.0 \text{ volts}$$

Solving for I_Q,

$$I_Q \geq \frac{(25)(13.0 - 1.2)}{680 + 116.15(1 + 25)} = 79.5 \text{ ma}$$

$$\overline{I}_Q \leq \frac{13.7 - 0.4(0.5 \times 10^{-3})(680 + 113.85)}{113.85} = 114 \text{ ma}$$

12. Determine the effects of possible bias-point shifts. Since I_Q is capable of varying 20.5 ma, the peak alternating current can also be decreased by this amount. Under such conditions, the a-c power supplied to the transformer would be

$$P_L' = \frac{(0.1 - 0.0205)^2 R_L'}{2} = \frac{(0.0795)^2(166.8)}{2} = 526 \text{ mw}$$

This is within several per cent of the required value of 534 mw. In view of the conservative estimates made in determining these results, it is reasonable to assume that the required output power can be achieved despite possible shifts in the bias point.

13. Determine the values of the coupling and emitter bypass capacitors and select a transformer. The value of the coupling capacitor C_1 can be determined if the signal source impedance is known. When the source resistance, R_S, equals 1 kilohm, the coupling capacitor will affect the gain less than 3 db if

$$C_1 > \frac{1}{\omega(R_S + R_{(in)})}$$

$$R_{(in)} \cong \frac{R_B R_E (1 + h_{FE})}{R_B + R_E(1 + h_{FE})} \cong 110 \text{ ohms}$$

$$\omega = 2\pi f = 2\pi(400) = 800\pi \text{ radians/sec}$$

$$C_1 > \frac{1}{800\pi(1.110 \text{ kilohms})} = 0.359 \ \mu f$$

A value greater than ten times this, or 5 μf, will be used.

The emitter bypass capacitor C_E can also be determined from gain considerations. The emitter capacitor and resistors will lower the gain less than 3 db if

$$C_E > \frac{1}{\omega \left[R_{E2} \| \left(R_{E1} + \frac{R_B \| R_S}{1 + h_{FE}} \right) \right]}$$

$$C_E > \frac{R_B R_S + (R_{E2} + R_{E1})(R_B + R_S)(1 + h_{FE})}{\omega R_{E2}[R_B R_S + R_{E1}(R_B + R_S)(1 + h_{FE})]}$$

A conservative simplification gives

$$C_E > \frac{1}{\omega R_{E1}} = 79.5 \ \mu f$$

Transformer efficiency and output power considerations require that the open-circuit primary inductive reactance be much greater than the reflected load impedance. The open-circuit primary inductance must exist with a direct current of I_Q flowing through the primary. Good low-frequency response, however, dictates a more stringent requirement. The inductive reactance must be less than the parallel combination of reflected load impedance and the output impedance of the transistor. Because the size of the transformer is also an important consideration, the low-frequency gain is often sacrificed, and only the requirement that the inductive reactance be much larger than the reflected load impedance is satisfied. In this particular example a square stack of 56EI laminations with 442 turns of no. 30 wire was chosen as the transformer. A secondary was not actually wound on the core, but slightly more than half the window area is available for this purpose.

14. Breadboard and test the circuit. The completely designed circuit is shown in Fig. 16.5 with performance data obtained for high- and low-limit h_{FE} transistors over the specified temperature range.

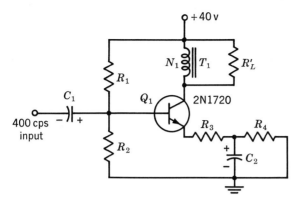

Component list	*Transformer data*	*Circuit characteristics*

R'_L = 166.7 ohms, ½ watt

R_1 = 2 kilohms, 1 watt

R_2 = 1 kilohm, ½ watt

R_3 = 5 ohms, ½ watt

R_4 = 110 ohms, 2 watts

C_1 = 5 µf, 50 volts

C_2 = 100 µf, 50 volts

Q_1 = 2N1720

N_1 = 442 turns no. 30 AWG

Core—Allegheny 56EI SL-14

1 × 1 interleaved

½ window area available for
   secondary

D-c resistance of primary =
   9 ohms

*at 400-mw power output
and 400 cps*

Power gain $\geq$ 24 db

Voltage amplification $\geq$ 22 db

Input resistance $\cong$ 260 ohms

Ambient temperature range =
   -25 to $+100°$C

Total harmonic distortion
   $< 5\%$

Notes:

1. All resistance values in ohms—1% tolerance.
2. Resistance wattage ratings and capacitance voltage ratings at 100°C.
3. Q_1 on heat sink allowing thermal resistance from case to ambient $< 22°$C/watt.
4. Signal source impedance of 1 kilohm used during performance measurements.

Fig. 16.5.   400-mw class A amplifier.

17

Low-frequency Transformer-coupled Class B Output Stages

A class B stage may be defined as one biased close to cutoff, so that any upward signal fluctuations turn the active device ON, while for downward fluctuations it remains OFF. If the incoming signal were a sinusoid, for example, the active device (in our case, the transistor) would be turned ON during 180° of the signal. A second active device is necessary to handle the remaining 180° of the signal cycle. The most popular means of driving the two amplifying devices and combining their individual outputs is the center-tapped transformer. A typical circuit is shown in Figure 17.5.

Class B stages are often used for the output stages of transistor power amplifiers for the following reasons:

1. Even harmonic distortion can be reduced to a minimum.
2. Theoretical maximum efficiency is 78% for a class B vs. 50% for a class A stage.
3. Quiescent power drain is very small, whereas a class A stage draws a constant power from the supply at all times.
4. Power dissipation is shared between two transistors.
5. Because no net direct current flows through the output transformer, the net d-c magnetizing flux is zero and transformer weight is low.

17.1. DISTORTION

We will now discuss a few of the causes of distortion in a class B stage. Some will be quite common; some are rather obscure.

A waveform which is symmetrical in amplitude about an axis drawn through its average value and symmetrical in time about the $\omega t = \pi/2$ axis contains no even harmonics. A push-pull type of circuit uses this fact to reduce the even-harmonic distortion in the output signal. We have said that in a strict class B push-pull amplifier, the positive portion of an input signal is amplified by one transistor and the negative portion by another. If the transistors have identical characteristics, when the two amplified portions of the signal are recombined, the output will be symmetrical, and no even harmonics will be present.   This type of operation is illustrated in Fig. 17.1.

Bias.   Figure 17.1 reveals a potential source of trouble.   If both transistors are allowed to turn OFF at zero instantaneous signal, then the composite transfer characteristic obtained by combining the V_{BE} vs. I_C curves for both transistors can be far from linear.   The large change in di_C/dv_{BE} as the instantaneous signal voltage crosses the zero axis will cause *crossover* distortion.   Similar effects result from the combined I_B vs. I_C curves.

There is an instant while the input signal reverses polarity that both transistors of Fig. 17.1 are OFF.   The collector current through the output transformer is changing very rapidly at this moment, and the collector impedance is very high. The interaction of these effects with the transformer leakage inductance will produce a notch in the output waveform each time it crosses the zero axis.   This effect is commonly known as a switching transient and is another design problem attendant upon truly class B operation.   Some decrease in switching transients may be realized by the use of bifilar windings in the output transformer to achieve better symmetry and tighter coupling.   Unless this is done carefully, however, it may result in high-frequency response deterioration.

Switching transients can be reduced and the composite transfer characteristic made almost linear by biasing the transistors to conduct a few milliamperes with no applied signal.   A composite for this type of operation is shown in Fig. 17.2.

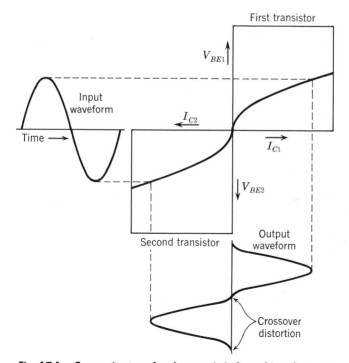

Fig. 17.1.   Composite transfer characteristic for unbiased stage.

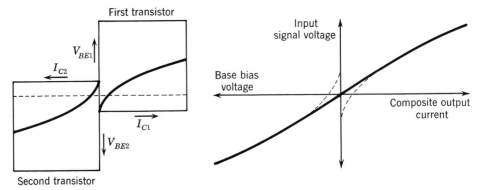

Fig. 17.2. **Composite transfer characteristic for biased stage.**

The amount of bias required is fairly critical: too little will fail to eliminate cross-over distortion, while too much will cause distortion at high power levels.   The correct bias voltage for a particular transistor type must be found by experiment.

Thus, practicable *class B* amplifiers usually do not operate, strictly speaking, class B.   Each transistor is usually biased into slight conduction rather than at the edge of cutoff.

Source Impedance.   For certain transistors the V_{BE} vs. $I_C(y_{FE})$ characteristic has a curvature of opposite sign to that of the I_B vs. $I_C(h_{FE})$ characteristic.   At low signal source impedance (constant-voltage drive), the stage operates on the y_{FE} characteristic; at high source impedances, on the h_{FE}.   For some optimum a-c source impedance, r_g, defined by Fig. 17.3, the effects of these two curvatures will almost cancel, and the distortion of the stage will minimize.   In terms of transistor small-signal parameters,

$$r_g = \frac{(h_{fe}/y_{fe})^2 dy_{fe}/dI_c}{- dh_{fe}/dI_c} - R_E = \frac{h_{fe}\,dh_{ie}/dI_c}{dh_{fe}/dI_c} - h_{ie} - R_E$$

but this is of little practical help.   For large-signal operation, r_g must be determined by experiment, especially if diodes are used in the base bias circuit.

Another source impedance consideration is given under Transformers.

High-current h_{FE} Fall-off.   Another form of distortion occurs for large signals if the current gain of the transistors falls off at high current levels.   This appears as a gentle clipping or compression of the instantaneous signal peaks.   The effect is shown in Fig. 17.4.

If the clipping is sharp and sudden, the transistor is probably driven into saturation and the peak current is being limited as in Eq. (9).

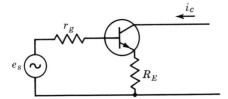

Figure 17.3

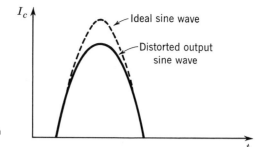

Fig. 17.4. Distortion from h_{FE} **fall-off.**

Transformers. No attempt is made to match the output transformer primary impedance to the transistor output impedance; the transformer turns ratio is set by other considerations. In fact, the disparity is usually so great that the transformer *sees* the transistors as a constant-current source. Low-frequency response is determined only by the transformer inductances and the load resistance. Distortion from magnetizing current is calculated accordingly.

Since the input impedance of the transistors varies with the current gain and the instantaneous collector current, the load on the driver transformer secondary is constantly fluctuating. To guarantee a particular low-frequency response, the primary inductance must be determined by the driver source impedance alone with the secondary open-circuited.

Description of I_{CBO} **and** I_{EBO}. At high reverse-bias voltages and high junction temperatures, the I_{CBO} and I_{EBO} of many power transistors becomes strongly voltage-dependent. If the class B circuit forces the OFF transistor into this voltage range, considerable leakage current will flow on signal peaks. Besides adding to the transistor dissipation, these currents may cause substantial distortion.

17.2. PRIMARY DESIGN CONSIDERATIONS

Usually, a particular power output is the first design requirement. An understanding of output power limitations can be developed from the typical circuit in Fig. 17.5. The maximum average undistorted sine-wave power into Z, P_o', is given by

$$P_o' \cong \tfrac{1}{2}(V_{CC} - V_{CE(sat)} - I_{C(peak)}R_E)I_{C(peak)} \tag{1}$$

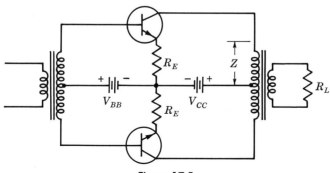

Figure 17.5

Not all this power will be delivered to the load; some will be lost in the output transformer. The efficiency of this transformer may range from 95% for a design without space or weight restrictions to 50% for a subminiature design. The requirement for P_o' must be increased accordingly.

The quantities comprising Eq. (1) are subject to many restrictions and complex interactions. We will now discuss these in some detail.

Description of V_{CC}. A transistor stage achieves power gain through two mechanisms: the current amplification of the transistor, and the difference in impedance between the load on the transistor and the input presented by the transistor. The current gain is fixed by the transistor alone, but the impedance gain is circuit-dependent. To take maximum advantage of impedance gain, a class B stage should operate with the largest possible load voltage swing, which, in turn, implies the largest possible supply voltage.

Except for abnormal voltage spikes, such as might be caused by removing the amplifier load during an applied signal, the maximum supply voltage for a class B stage is limited by one of two requirements:

$$|V_{CC}| < \frac{|BV_{CBX}|}{2} \quad \text{where the emitter diode is reverse-biased} \tag{2}$$

or $$|V_{CC}| < |BV_{CER}| \quad \begin{array}{l}\text{where } R \text{ is the base-to-emitter circuit im-}\\ \text{pedance seen by the transistor}\end{array} \tag{3}$$

Of course, operating at high supply voltages makes the stage more sensitive to transient voltage spikes and may also influence the reliability of some transistor types. Voltage spikes generated in the output transformer may be reduced by bifilar-winding the transformer primary, and completely eliminated by protective *breakdown* diodes (not shown in Fig. 17.5) between each collector and circuit ground.

Heat Dissipation and $(R_E + Z)$. The ease with which heat energy can be dissipated from the junction into the ambient limits the number of independent variables in Eq. (1). The nature of thermal resistance is discussed in Sec. 4.4. The transistor data sheet will give sufficient information to calculate junction-to-case thermal resistance, θ_{J-C}, and for transistors designed to operate without a heat sink, junction-to-ambient thermal resistance, θ_{J-A}, also. The thermal resistance from the transistor case through a particular heat sink into the ambient, θ_{C-A}, must be determined by the transistor user, not the manufacturer. The design and analysis of heat sinks is a complex study; references are given at the end of Chap. 4.

From Eq. (21) of Sec. 7.2,

$$\Delta T_{J-A} = p_{J(peak)}\,\theta_1 + P_{J(max\ avg)}\,\theta_2 \tag{4}$$

where θ_1 = portion of total θ_{J-A} which may be considered unbypassed by any thermal capacitance at the lowest signal frequency (see Sec. 4.4)

θ_2 = portion of total θ_{J-A} for which the pulsations of p_J have been smoothed out by thermal capacitances

For class B power amplifiers carrying signals of very low audio frequencies, θ_1 may be assumed to be θ_{J-C}, and θ_2 may be taken to be θ_{C-A}. If $\theta_{J-C} > 2C°/watt$, or if only upper audio frequencies and higher are considered, then this value for θ_1 may be too large.

In terms of power dissipation, the worst signal waveshape which a class B stage might be required to amplify is a square wave of an output peak amplitude about one-half the available peak instantaneous output voltage. For that waveform, if I_{CBO} and I_{EBO} do not cause significant dissipation in the OFF transistor,

$$p_{J(peak)} \cong 2P_{J(max\ avg)} \tag{5}$$

Therefore, from Eqs. (4) and (5) an upper limit for junction temperature can be assured if

$$p_{J(peak)} \lesssim \frac{2\Delta T_{J\text{-}A}}{2\theta_1 + \theta_2} \tag{6}$$

It can be seen by inspection of Fig. 17.5 that

$$p_{J(peak)} \cong \frac{V_{CC}^2}{4(R_E + Z)} \tag{7}$$

R_E and Z must be chosen so that this peak junction power is held within the restrictions of Eq. (6).

$$R_E + Z \geq \frac{V_{CC}^2(2\theta_1 + \theta_2)}{8\Delta T_{J\text{-}A}} \tag{8}$$

In practice, the peak signal current on which the designer can rely is limited by the maximum saturation voltage of the transistor over the whole operating temperature range.

$$I_{C(peak)} \cong \frac{V_{CC} - V_{CE(sat)}}{R_E + Z} \tag{9}$$

If the stage must be designed for the maximum possible output power, $(R_E + Z)$ must obviously be minimized. Using the minimum value from Eq. (8),

$$I_{C(peak)} \lesssim \frac{8\Delta T_{J\text{-}A}(1 - V_{CE(sat)}/V_{CC})}{V_{CC}(2\theta_1 + \theta_2)} \tag{10}$$

Here, then, is an upper limit, imposed by heat-dissipation considerations, upon the peak collector current for which the stage may be designed.

Substituting Eq. (10) into Eq. (1),

$$P_o' = 4\frac{\Delta T_{J\text{-}A}}{2\theta_1 + \theta_2}\left(1 - \frac{V_{CE(sat)}}{V_{CC}}\right)^2\left(1 - \frac{8R_E}{V_{CC}^2}\frac{\Delta T_{J\text{-}A}}{2\theta_1 + \theta_2}\right) \tag{11}$$

If Eq. (11) does not yield a sufficient P_o', one solution is to parallel output transistors. Note that even if the transistor and circuit were *perfect* (i.e., $R_E = 0$ and $V_{CE(sat)} = 0$), P_o' could not exceed $4\Delta T_{J\text{-}A}/(2\theta_1 + \theta_2)$.

Description of R_E. The resistor R_E reduces the current gain, the available output power and, sometimes, the high-frequency response of a class B stage. Why, then, have any R_E at all? Because R_E serves two very important functions: it helps stabilize the transistor against thermal runaway, and it helps establish the quiescent operating point necessary to prevent crossover distortion. (It may also stabilize gain and reduce distortion by providing negative feedback for the signal, but this is a dubious incidental benefit. There are other ways to accomplish this end without sacrificing output power.) The value of R_E is dependent upon the nature of the base bias network, and the quiescent-operating-point stability is closely related to the thermal stability. For clarity in our discussion we shall treat each of these considerations separately, but an actual design must satisfy all simultaneously.

Figure 17.6 shows a very general representation of the elements of class B bias. R_{B2} is the d-c resistance of the driver transformer secondary seen by each transistor. V_{BB} and R_{B1} are the Thévenin equivalent of the bias voltage source.

To ensure quiescent (no signal) thermal stability, a simplification of Eq. (59), Sec. 7.3, will probably suffice. Only the result is given here; Sec. 7.3 should be consulted for a complete explanation.

$$R_E > \frac{\theta_{J\text{-}A} V_{CC}[(R_{B1} + R_{B2} + r'_B)(0.0693 I_{CBO} - I_{CQ}\, dh^*_{FB}/dt_J) + 0.0025]}{1 - \theta_{J\text{-}A} V_{CC}(0.0693 I_{CBO} - I_{CQ}\, dh^*_{FB}/dt_J)} \quad (12)$$

This assumes silicon transistors [Sec. 7.3, Eq. (48)] having no common heat sink. If the two transistors were tightly coupled thermally, then it would be necessary to double the values of I_{CBO} and I_{CQ} in Eq. (12).

Thus, the smaller $(R_{B1} + R_{B2})$, the smaller R_E.

It is advisable to use a separate emitter resistor for each transistor. This serves to

1. Equalize $I_{C(peak)}$ and $I_{C(quiescent)}$ through each transistor.
2. Reduce the peak inverse base-emitter voltage at the OFF transistor.
3. Simplify the thermal stability analysis so that Eq. (12) is valid.

Another restriction upon R_E is set by the breakdown voltage of the emitter diodes. For a minimum of safety,

$$|BV_{EBX}| > |I_{C(peak)}| \left(R_E + \frac{2R_{B1} + R_{B2} + R_E}{h_{FE}}\right) + |V_{BE(on\ peak)}| - 2\,|V'_{BB(min)}| \quad (13)$$

Equation (13) can be put in the form

$$R_E < \frac{N h_{FE}}{I_{c(peak)}(1 + h_{FE})} - \frac{R_{B1} + R_{B2}}{1 + h_{FE}} - \frac{R_{B1}}{1 + h_{FE}} \quad (14)$$

where
$$N = BV_{EBX} + 2V'_{BB(min)} - V_{BE(on\ peak)} \quad (15)$$

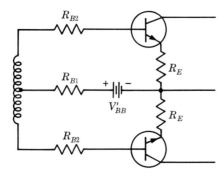

Figure 17.6

Also, a solution of Eq. (12) in terms of R_E and $(R_{B1} + R_{B2} + r_B')$ will take the form

$$R_E \gtrless A + B(R_{B1} + R_{B2} + r_B') \tag{16}$$

Substituting Eq. (16) into Eq. (14),

$$R_E < \frac{N h_{FE}/I_{c(peak)} + A/B + r_B' - R_{B1}}{1 + h_{FE} + 1/B} \tag{17}$$

If

$$\frac{A}{B} + r_B' > R_{B1} + \frac{N}{I_{c(peak)}}\left(1 + \frac{1}{B}\right) \tag{18}$$

then the worst restriction on R_E occurs for high h_{FE}. Letting $h_{FE} \to \infty$,

$$R_E < \frac{N}{I_{c(peak)}} \tag{19}$$

This result is also obtained if Eq. (18) is an equality. If the inequality sign in Eq. (18) must be reversed, then the minimum h_{FE} is used in Eq. (17). In these equations V_{BB}', h_{FE}, and R_{B1} must be evaluated for the exact circuit conditions existing where $I_{c(peak)}$ occurs.

Thought must be given to the conditions for measurement of BV_{EBX}. The amount of base current (i.e., $I_{EBX} + I_{CBX}$) which flows in the OFF transistor during signal voltage peaks must be kept small, not only to prevent excessive power dissipation, but also because this current may act as a distortion component in the signal. Since some emitter diodes tend to relatively high leakage and gradual breakdown *knees,* it is a good practice to check the diode reverse characteristic at the expected maximum temperature. Reasonable rules of thumb might be that at $T_{J(max)}$,

$$2V_{CC}I_{CBX}\big|_{(V_{CB}\cong 2V_{CC})} < 0.1 p_{J(peak)} \tag{20}$$

and

$$|I_{CBX}|_{(V_{CB}\cong 2V_{CC})} + |I_{EBX}|_{(V_{EB}\cong BV_{EBX})} < 0.1|I_{B(peak\ on)}| \tag{21}$$

Equation (20) places a limit upon I_{CBX}, and Eq. (21) sets a limit for I_{EBX} at $V_{EB} \cong BV_{EBX}$. If the manufacturer does not guarantee I_{EBX} and I_{CBX}, I_{EBO} and I_{CBO} may be used.

17.3. BASE BIAS CIRCUITS

Equation (11) of Sec. 7.1 enumerates the factors affecting the quiescent operating point of any isolated transistor stage. Particularly important in class B design is the variation of V_{BE} with temperature. Unless compensated, V_{BE} may change the circuit operation from class C at low temperatures to class A at high. An obvious solution is to vary V_{BB}' accordingly so that $(V_{BB}' - V_{BE})$ remains constant over the temperature range. The effects of I_{CBO} and h_{FE} variation can be reduced by minimizing $(R_{B1} + R_{B2})$.

The goals of our bias design are clear: R_{B1} should be as small as possible, V_{BB}' should vary with temperature at the same rate as dV_{BE}/dt_J (approximately -0.002 volt/C°), and V_{BB}' should be no larger than is needed to eliminate crossover dis-

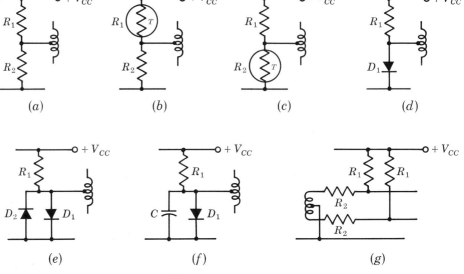

Fig. 17.7. Bias circuits.

tortion. Many circuits are used to these ends, with varying degrees of success. Figure 17.7 gives examples.

Example a is a simple voltage divider. It does not provide temperature compensation for V_{BB} and cannot be used for a wide junction temperature range. The design equations are

$$R_1 = \frac{R_{B1}V_{CC}}{V'_{BB}} \tag{22}$$

and

$$R_2 = \frac{R_{B1}}{1 - V'_{BB}/V_{CC}} \tag{23}$$

Examples b and c are similar in design, except that each uses a temperature-sensitive resistor to compensate V'_{BB}. In example b, R_1 must have a temperature coefficient

$$\text{TC} = +\frac{0.0025(R_1 + R_2)^2}{V_{CC}R_1R_2} \times 100\% \text{ per C}° \tag{24}$$

In example c, R_2 must have

$$\text{TC} = -\frac{0.0025(R_1 + R_2)^2}{V_{CC}R_2(R_1 + R_2 - 1)} \times 100\% \text{ per C}° \tag{25}$$

The linear positive temperature coefficient for R_1 is easily and accurately obtained with *sensistor** resistors, alone or combined with fixed resistors. The negative temperature coefficient for R_2 is usually approximated by a thermistor in parallel with a fixed resistor.

The success of example d depends on the fact that the diode D_1 can exhibit the

---

* Trademark of Texas Instruments Incorporated.

same temperature coefficient for its forward voltage drop as do the emitter diodes of the transistors. R_1 is adjusted to pass a current just slightly greater than the peak signal current into the transistor bases, so that D_1 remains forward-biased at all times. R_{B1} and V'_{BB} are fixed by the forward characteristics of D_1 and the current through it.

Let us examine the behavior of a forward-biased diode in some detail. The voltage across a diode is related to the current through it by the expression

$$V_D = I_D r'_D + \frac{kT\lambda}{q} \ln \left(1 - \frac{I_D}{I_S}\right) \tag{26}$$

where V_D = voltage across the diode (positive in sign for a forward-biased diode)
I_D = current through the diode (positive in the forward-biased direction)
k/q = 8.616×10^{-5} volt/K°
r'_D = bulk (ohmic) resistance of the diode
λ = a correction factor (usually one to two)
T = absolute temperature, °K
I_S = *saturation* current of diode (negative in sign)

This characteristic is illustrated in Fig. 17.8. Operation of the diode at some current I_1 produces a voltage V_1. If a line is drawn through point (V_1, I_1) tangent to the diode characteristic curve, it will intersect the voltage axis at some point (V'_D, O). The slope of the line will be

$$r_D \equiv \frac{dV_D}{dI_D} = r'_D + \frac{kT\lambda}{q(I_D - I_S)} \tag{27}$$

$$V'_D = \frac{kT\lambda}{q} \left[\ln \left(1 - \frac{I_D}{I_S}\right) - \frac{I_D}{I_D - I_S}\right] \tag{28}$$

If $I_D \gg - I_S$, then

$$r_D \cong r'_D + \frac{kT\lambda}{qI_D} \tag{29}$$

and

$$V'_D = \frac{kT\lambda}{q} \left[\ln \left(\frac{I_D}{-I_S}\right) - 1\right] \tag{30}$$

Thus, at any instantaneous forward-biased operating current I_D, the diode may be represented by an equivalent Thévenin circuit as shown in Fig. 17.9. At

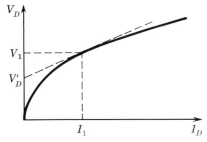

Fig. 17.8.   Diode forward characteristic.

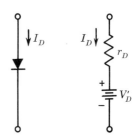

Fig. 17.9.   Diode equivalent circuit.

$T_J = +150°C$ and $\lambda = 1$, $kT\lambda/q = 0.03646$ volt.   If this substitution is made into Eq. (27), it is easy to see that r_D' may dominate r_D at diode currents larger than 36 ma.   It is not always easy to determine r_D'.   However, a line through points (I_1,V_1) and $(0,0)$ will always have a greater slope than a line through (I_1,V_1) and $(V_D',0)$.   Therefore, the d-c resistance of the diode, V_1/I_1, will always be greater than its instantaneous a-c resistance, r_D.

$$ r_D < \frac{V_D}{I_D} \tag{31} $$

This is a helpful limitation to remember in the initial stages of a design.
   Relating example d to Fig. 17.6,

$$ R_{B1} = \frac{r_D R_1}{r_D + R_1} \tag{32} $$

and
$$ V_{BB}' = V_D' + \frac{(V_{CC} - V_D')r_D}{r_D + R_1} \tag{33} $$

Three disadvantages result from the high diode current required in example d:

1. Considerable power may be thrown away in R_1.
2. The magnitude of V_{BB}' cannot be adjusted readily.
3. In Eq. (26) the temperature coefficient of $(kT\lambda/q) \ln (1 - I_D/I_S)$ is negative because I_S increases almost exponentially with temperature.   But the coefficient of r_D' is positive, so that the coefficient of V_D goes from negative to positive as $I_D r_D'$ increases.   Thus the whole purpose of example d may be nullified.

Examples e and f attempt to reduce the diode current required.   In example e, R_1 and D_1 must pass only sufficient bias current to give the desired R_{B1} and V_{BB}' as defined by Eqs. (29), (30), (32), and (33).   When the instantaneous base signal current exceeds this amount, D_1 becomes back-biased but D_2 takes over to provide a low-impedance return path for the base drive. D_2 must be large enough to carry the peak base current.   Some distortion is introduced into the driver-signal-voltage-vs.-collector-current transfer function of the stage, but the driver-signal-*current*-vs.-collector-current transfer function is unchanged, and if the driver signal generator impedance is reasonably high, the increase in total distortion will be low.

   In example f, the capacitor bypasses the a-c component of the signal current flow through D_1 so that R_1 need carry only one-half the peak base current.   This circuit is most convenient at high frequencies where C can be small.   The shift in d-c voltage across C with signal level may cause annoying transient changes in stage gain if C is too large or if the driver signal generator impedance is too low.

   Example g is similar to example a except that the driver transformer secondary resistance (R_{B2} of Fig. 17.6) has become a part of R_2.   For the same $V_{BB}' R_{B1}$ and R_{B2}, example g will always require more drive power.   However, if in example a, $R_2 < R_{B2} (1 + R_2/R_1)$, then example g will require less bias current.

17.4. OUTPUT TRANSFORMER DESIGN

The output transformer does not attempt to match the load impedance to the transistor output impedance. Instead, it must present a load, Z, to the ON transistor such that

$$Z \gcong \frac{V_{CC}^2(2\theta_1 + \theta_2)}{8\Delta T_{J\text{-}A}} - R_E \tag{34}$$

the smallest Z giving the greatest output power. Since the OFF transistor is inactive, that half of the center-tapped primary does not enter into the picture. Therefore, the ratio of total primary turns, N_1, to secondary turns, N_2, is

$$\frac{N_1}{N_2} = 2 \sqrt{\frac{Z}{R_L}} \tag{35}$$

The inductance of the transformer is computed from R_L only, the output impedances of the transistors being high enough to act as a virtual open circuit for the primary. If the load varies, it may not be practical to design for an inductance to suit the largest value of R_L. Then the inductances are set for the value of R_L corresponding to maximum output power, and overall feedback is added to reduce the distortion resulting from nonlinear magnetizing currents. Alternatively, the transistor output impedance might be lowered with collector-to-base feedback.

Bifilar winding reduces distortion. The peak-to-peak voltage across N_1 used for computing maximum flux density is approximately $4V_{CC}$.

17.5. DRIVER TRANSFORMER DESIGN

The design problems of the driver transformer are similar to those of the output, with one exception. The transistor input impedance loading the secondary varies widely both with instantaneous operating point and from unit to unit, so that the secondary load cannot be used to set the inductance for low-frequency response unless maximum h_{ie} and h_{fe} are guaranteed. Instead, these inductances are usually determined by the driver source impedance. If the driver source is a class A transistor stage, it may be necessary to establish a maximum for this by shunting the transformer primary with a resistor or reducing the transistor output impedance with feedback. These niceties are often overlooked through carelessness or for economic reasons, but their effect upon phase-gain stability margins in an amplifier with overall feedback is considerable.

The peak current, I_{TS}, which must be supplied by one-half the driver secondary is

$$I_{TS(peak)} = I_{B1(on\ peak)} + I_{B2(off\ peak)} = \frac{I_{C(peak)}}{h_{FE(min)}} + I_{CBX(max)} + I_{EBX(max)} \tag{36}$$

The peak voltage to be supplied at the ON base is

$$V_{B1(peak)} = V_{BE1(on\ peak)} + R_{E(max)}I_{C(peak)}\left(1 + \frac{1}{h_{FE(min)}}\right) \tag{37}$$

The worst cases for these requirements generally appear simultaneously with minimum h_{FE} transistors at the lowest junction temperature. How much voltage must be supplied by the secondary to meet $V_{B1(peak)}$ at $I_{B1(on\ peak)}$ depends upon which circuit of Fig. 17.7 is chosen.

17.6. A TYPICAL CLASS B DESIGN

A typical problem might be to design a class B stage to provide some sinusoidal audio output power, P_o. Usually other factors in the design may dictate the range of ambient temperature, T_A, and the worst thermal impedance from transistor to case to ambient, $\theta_{C\text{-}A}$. Sometimes the supply voltage, V_{CC}, may be fixed, sometimes not. Let us assume that

$$f = 400 \text{ cps}$$
$$P_o = 5 \text{ watts}$$
$$\theta_{C\text{-}A} \leqq 15 \text{ C}°/\text{watt for each transistor}$$
$$T_A = -55 \text{ to } +125°\text{C}$$
$$V_{CC} = \text{as required}$$

We may further assume that the output transformer efficiency is at least 85%, so that the true output power expected of the transistors, P_o', is 5.9 watts.

At this point, there is nothing to do but peruse data sheets for a likely candidate. But the search may be narrowed somewhat by the following reasoning.

A maximum ambient temperature over about 80°C will restrict the device material to silicon. For good reliability, present silicon transistors are seldom operated at junction temperatures higher than +175 to +200°C.

For *perfect* transistors, Eq. (11) reduces to

$$P_o' \leqq \frac{4\Delta T_{J\text{-}A}}{2\theta_1 + \theta_2} \tag{38}$$

Substituting the known information into Eq. (38),

$$5.9 \text{ watts} \leqq \frac{4(175°\text{C} - 125°\text{C})}{2\theta_1 + 15 \text{ C}°/\text{watt}} \qquad \therefore \theta_{J\text{-}C} \leqq 9.45 \text{ C}°/\text{watt}$$

This should be quite conservative, since at these values of $\theta_{J\text{-}C}$, $\theta_1 < \theta_{J\text{-}C}$.

If the maximum collector voltage may be used to aid stage gain, then from Eqs. (1) through (3),

$$|I_{c(peak)}| > \frac{23.6}{|BV_{CBX}|} \qquad \text{and} \qquad |I_{c(peak)}| > \frac{11.8}{|BV_{CER}|}$$

We now know we must have a silicon transistor with $\theta_{J\text{-}C} < 9.45 \text{ C}°/\text{watt}$, and we know what collector currents to expect based upon the breakdown voltage of the transistor. With these limits as guides, the search may begin.

Among the contending types, the 2N1719 seems an excellent possibility. A maximum I_{CES} is specified for $V_{CE} = 150$ volts, which indicates that $BV_{CEX} > 150$ volts. This would allow a safe V_{CC} of 70 volts. Support for this choice comes from an I_{CEO} specified at 90 volts, indicating that $BV_{CEO} > 90$ volts. At $V_{CC} = 70$

volts, $I_{c(peak)}$ will be about 0.17 amp—well within the transistor capability. Also, $f_T \geqq 16$ mc, so that the problems of closing a feedback loop around this stage are minimized. A $\theta_{J\text{-}C} \leqq 7.5$ C°/watt betters the estimated requirement.

A minimum limit for Z in terms of R_E can be found from Eq. (8).

$$R_E + Z \geqq \frac{(70 \text{ volts})^2[2(7.5 \text{ C°/watt}) + 15 \text{ C°/watt}]}{8(175°\text{C} - 125°\text{C})}$$

$$Z \geqq 367.5 - R_E$$

If R_E has a $\pm 5\%$ tolerance, this becomes

$$Z \geqq 367.5 - (0.95)R_E$$

The boundary values for this inequality are graphed as the lower line of Fig. 17.10.

The voltage drops around the collector circuit at $I_{c(peak)}$ are:

$$V_{CC} = ZI_{c(peak)} + V_{CE(sat)} + \frac{1 + h_{FE}}{h_{FE}} R_E I_{c(peak)}$$

A minimum value for h_{FE} at $-55°$C at $I_c = 0.2$ amp is guaranteed by the data sheet:

$$h_{FE(min)} \geqq 10$$

Extrapolated from the guaranteed $V_{CE(sat)}$ at $I_c = 0.2$ amp, $I_B = 20$ ma, and $T_A = 25°$C, the typical $V_{CE(sat)}$ vs. T_A data sheet curves indicate that

$$V_{CE(sat)}\Big|_{\substack{T_A=175°\text{C} \\ I_c=0.2 \text{ amp} \\ I_B=20 \text{ ma}}} \leqq 3.3 \text{ volts}$$

A minimum value for $I_{c(peak)}$ can be found in terms of Z from

$$P_o' = \tfrac{1}{2}Z(I_{c(peak)})^2 \qquad I_{c(peak)} \geqq \sqrt{\frac{11.8 \text{ watts}}{Z}}$$

Allowing a $\pm 5\%$ tolerance for R_E and substituting into the equation for collector voltage drops,

$$70.0 \text{ volts} \geqq \sqrt{Z(11.8 \text{ watts})} + 3.3 \text{ volts} + \frac{1 + 10}{10}(1.05)R_E\sqrt{\frac{11.8 \text{ watts}}{Z}}$$

This inequality can be solved for a maximum value of Z in terms of R_E. The solution is graphed as the top line of Fig. 17.10. Thus, Fig. 17.10 indicates a permissible area of solution for Z in terms of R_E when R_E has a $\pm 5\%$ tolerance.

In order to decide what type of bias circuit to use, we must have a feel for the dependence of $(R_{B1} + R_{B2})$ on R_E. Equation (12) will provide this.

The data sheet gives $I_{CES} = 500$ μa at $+170°$C. If I_{CS} doubles for each 10 C° rise, then at $+175°$C, $I_{CBO} = 7.1 \times 10^{-4}$ amp.

Equation (69) of Sec. 7.3 suggests a method of evaluating dh_{FB}^*/dt_J. As a rule of thumb, the quiescent collector current will not be greater than 0.2 nor less than about 0.1 of the peak current expected. From Eq. (10), as an approximation,

$$I_{c(peak)} \leqq \frac{8(175°C - 125°C)(1 - 3.3 \text{ volts}/70 \text{ volts})}{(70 \text{ volts})[2(7.5 \text{ C°}/\text{watt}) + 15 \text{ C°}/\text{watt}]}$$

$$I_{c(peak)} \leqq 0.1815 \text{ amp}$$

Considerations of the data sheet typical curves and guaranteed minimums indicate that at $I_{EQ} = -20$ ma,

$$h_{FE} \geqq 17 \qquad \text{at } +75°C$$

and

$$h_{FE} \geqq 55 \qquad \text{at } +150°C$$

Over this range,

$$\frac{\Delta h_{FB}}{\Delta t_J} = \frac{-1/(17 + 1) + 1/(55 + 1)}{+150°C - 75°C} = -0.0005026/C°$$

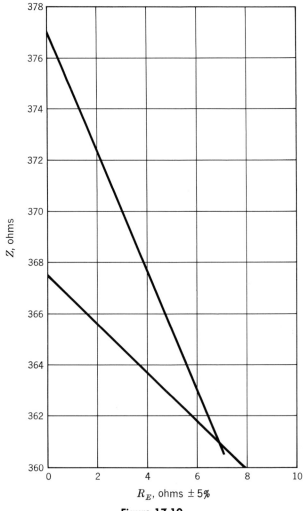

Figure 17.10

This is likely to be larger in absolute magnitude than dh_{FB}^*/dt_J at $+175°C$ or at moderately high currents.

Substituting these worst-case conditions into Eq. (12),

$$R_E \geqq \frac{\left(7.5\frac{C°}{\text{watt}} + 15\frac{C°}{\text{watt}}\right)(70 \text{ volts})\left\{(R_{B1} + R_{B2} + r_B')\left[\frac{0.0693}{C°}(7.1 \times 10^{-4} \text{ amp})\right.\right.}{1 - \left(7.5\frac{C°}{\text{watt}} + 15\frac{C°}{\text{watt}}\right)(70 \text{ volts})\left[\frac{0.0693}{C°}(7.1 \times 10^{-4} \text{ amp})\right.}$$

$$\left.\left. + (0.2)(-0.1815 \text{ amp})\frac{-0.0005026}{C°}\right] + \frac{0.0025 \text{ volt}}{C°}\right\}$$
$$\left. + (0.2)(-0.1815 \text{ amp})\frac{-0.0005026}{C°}\right]$$

$$R_E \geqq 4.405 \text{ ohms} + 0.1189(R_{B1} + R_{B2} + r_B')$$

The peak base current required at $I_{c(peak)}$ and $h_{FE(min)}$ is 0.01815 amp. This modest requirement makes the bias circuit d of Fig. 17.7 feasible. The complete circuit is shown in Fig. 17.11.

The current through R_1 must be slightly greater than $I_{B(peak)}$; 20 to 25 ma should be satisfactory. The diode voltage drop at $-55°C$ at 25 ma will surely be no greater than about 0.7 volt.

$$\therefore \quad R_1 \cong \frac{70.0 \text{ volts} - 0.7 \text{ volt}}{0.02 \text{ amp}} = 3,465 \text{ ohms}$$

The TI 1N538 would be a good choice for the diode. The dynamic resistance of this type can be extrapolated from the data sheet to about 6 ohms at 20 ma at $+175°C$, and it should decrease at higher current and at lower temperatures.

$$\therefore \quad R_{B1} \leqq 6 \text{ ohms}$$

The solution of Eq. (12) indicates that we had better choose the largest possible value for R_E in order to permit a reasonable R_{B2} and an inexpensive driver transformer. The largest 5% MIL standard resistance value which falls within the

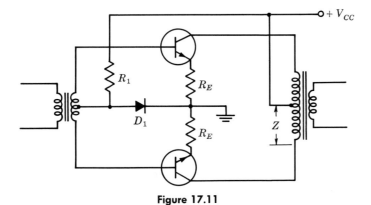

Figure 17.11

restrictions of Fig. 17.10 is 6.81 ohms. If the resistor has a low temperature coefficient, this will be satisfactory. Substituting into the solution of Eq. (12),

$$(0.95)(6.81 \text{ ohms}) \geq 4.405 \text{ ohms} + (0.1189)(6 \text{ ohms} + R_{B2} + r_B')$$

$$R_{B2} + r_B' \leq 11.37 \text{ ohms}$$

For an exact solution of R_{B2}, r_B' may be evaluated with the technique suggested at the end of Sec. 7.3. But for a transistor with this current capability, r_B' should not be very large, and if R_{B2} is held less than about 7 ohms when the driver transformer is at $+125°C$, all should be well.

To verify that this value for $R_{E(max)}$ will not cause excessive voltage across the OFF emitter diode, we must examine Eq. (18). From the solution of Eq. (12),

$$A = 4.405 \text{ ohms} \qquad B = 0.1189$$

From the data sheet,

$$BV_{EBX} \geq BV_{EBO} = 6 \text{ volts}$$

Extrapolating from the guaranteed V_{BE} at $I_c = 0.2$ amp at 25°C on the typical V_{BE} vs. T_A curves in the data sheet,

$$V_{BE(on\ peak)} = 1.7 \text{ volts}$$

For any of the bias circuits in Fig. 17.7, the worst that can happen is

$$V_{BB}' = 0$$

$$\therefore \qquad N = 6 + (2)(0) - 1.7 = 4.3 \text{ volts}$$

Substituting into Eq. (18),

$$\frac{4.405 \text{ ohms}}{0.1189} + r_B' > R_{B1} + \frac{4.3 \text{ volts}}{0.1815 \text{ amp}} \left(1 + \frac{1}{0.1189}\right)$$

$$37.07 \text{ ohms} + r_B' > R_{B1} + 223.0 \text{ ohms}$$

Since Eq. (12) will obviously be false (r_B' will not be so high), Eq. (17) will be required. A minimum h_{FE} of 10 is guaranteed at $I_c = 0.2$ amp at $-55°C$. Therefore,

$$R_E < \frac{(4.3 \text{ volts})(10)/0.1815 \text{ amp} + 4.405 \text{ ohms}/0.1189 + r_B' - R_{B1}}{1 + 10 + 1/0.1189}$$

$$R_E < 14.11 \text{ ohms} + \frac{r_B' - R_{B1}}{19.41}$$

The chosen value of R_E will obviously be safe.

To summarize,

$$V_{CC} = 70 \text{ volts}$$
$$R_E = 6.81 \text{ ohms} \pm 5\%$$
$$R_1 = 3.16 \text{ kilohms} \pm 5\%$$
$$Z = 361.1 \text{ ohms}$$
$$R_{B2} < 7 \text{ ohms} \qquad \text{at } 125°C$$

The final step is to calculate the peak current and voltage which the driver transformer must supply.

$$I_{B(peak)} = \frac{I_{c(peak)}}{h_{FE(min)}} = \frac{1}{10}\sqrt{\frac{11.8 \text{ watts}}{361.1 \text{ ohms}}} = 18.1 \text{ ma}$$

At $-55°C$ the driver transformer must supply a peak voltage of

$$V_{T(peak)} = |I_{E(peak)}|R_E + |V_{BE(peak)}| - |V_{diode}|$$

The minimum diode voltage at this time will surely not be less than 0.5 volt. Substituting,

$$V_{T(peak)} = (0.1989 \text{ amp})(1.05)(6.81 \text{ ohms}) + 1.7 \text{ volts} - 0.5 \text{ volt}$$
$$V_{T(peak)} = 2.62 \text{ volts}$$

The peak driver power which could ever be required is

$$P_{D(peak)} = (2.62 \text{ volts})(0.0181 \text{ amp}) = 0.0474 \text{ watt}$$

18

Servo Amplifiers

This chapter presents seven recommended class B servo amplifier circuits using silicon power and medium-power transistors. These amplifiers are designed to include entire parameter spreads and provide average power outputs of 1.5 to 35 watts. Their common characteristics are:

Frequency: 400 cps.
Ambient temperature: -55 to $+125°C$.
Total harmonic distortion: 5% maximum at rated output.

Output Stages. The output stages follow conventional class B design except for special techniques used to ensure thermal stability. Good thermal stability generally requires that the ratio R_B/R_E be kept low, where R_B and R_E are defined as in Fig. 18.1 for an ideal transistor. This ratio is usually less than four, and R_E is as large as the desired efficiency will permit.

For this reason, if a balance control is needed, it should be used in the emitter circuit. Some resistance must be included on both sides of the balance control (as shown in the 7.5-watt circuit, Fig. 18.4) so that R_E is never too small for good thermal stability. Disadvantages of using a balance control are that it decreases the stage efficiency and increases the required drive voltage. This can cause the negative signal swing to exceed BV_{EBO}, making blocking diodes necessary.

Any bias network used in the base to decrease crossover distortion will increase R_B. Silicon diodes are used in these circuits because they minimize this increase. The diodes also help to temperature-compensate the quiescent bias point of the output transistors, thus preventing the transistors from moving into an unstable

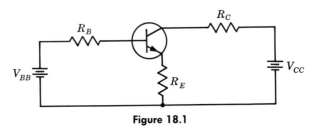

Figure 18.1

condition as the base-emitter threshold voltage decreases with increasing temperature. This compensation is not complete, however, since the transistor and diode junction temperatures do not conform precisely.

Since the d-c resistance of the driver transformer's secondary usually constitutes the greatest part of R_B, it is a major consideration in the transformer specifications. The 35-watt amplifier uses emitter-followers; with a negative supply, they provide an extremely low R_B for the output transistors. The $+12$-volt supply can be eliminated by connecting the collectors of Q_2 and Q_3 to Q_4 and Q_5, respectively. This will reduce the output voltage, because $V_{CE(sat)}$ of Q_4 and Q_5 is effectively increased. TI 2N1721's must then be used rather than 2N1720's because a higher BV_{CEO} will be required.

The Driver Stage. The first three circuits use straightforward class A drivers. The 10- and 35-watt circuits are modified to decrease the phase shift caused by low primary inductance of the driver transformer. The practicable inductance may be limited by the turns ratio, the d-c resistance of either winding, physical size, and/or direct current present in the primary.

The 10-watt amplifier uses collector-to-base shunt feedback to lower the output impedance of the transistor. Since this feedback also lowers the input impedance and the gain, another stage is added. This is probably the best method for correcting phase shift caused by low transformer inductance, since little driver power is lost and since the driver would usually be preceded by a preamplifier in any case.

The 35-watt amplifier uses a constant collector load on the driver to minimize the phase shift. Although this causes considerable power loss, the decrease in gain is small. An alternative method involves shunt-feeding the transformer through a capacitor; the advantage is the absence of direct current in the primary. This technique is not used here because of the more serious power loss involved.

18.1. 1.5-WATT CLASS B DESIGN

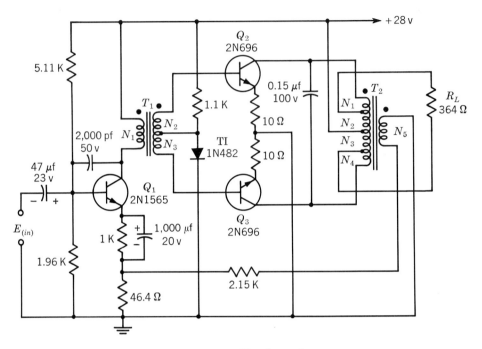

Circuit characteristics

Actual power gain: 38 db min.
Voltage amplification: 40.5 ± 1.5 db.
Input resistance: 1.2 kilohms min.

Transformer data

T_1—N_1 = 2050 turns No. 35 AWG. N_2 = N_3 = 466 turns No. 29 AWG, bifilar wound. Core: Magnetic Metals 75 El, SL-14, or equivalent, butt-jointed.

T_2—N_1 = N_4 = 90 turns No. 29 AWG. N_2 = N_3 = 433 turns No. 29 AWG, bifilar wound. N_5 = 303 turns No. 38 AWG. Core: Magnetic Metals Carpenter 49, 0.006-in. 375 El or equivalent, 8 × 8 interleaved.

Notes:

1. Q_2 and Q_3 on heat sinks with thermal resistance from case to ambient $\leqq$15 C°/watt each. Two 3- by 3- by ⅛-in. copper plates with appropriate holders meet this requirement.
2. Q_2 and Q_3: h_{FE}'s matched 10%.
3. All resistance values are ±5% tolerance.

Fig. 18.2. 1.5-watt 2N696 servo amplifier (400 cycles).

18.2. 4.0-WATT CLASS B DESIGN

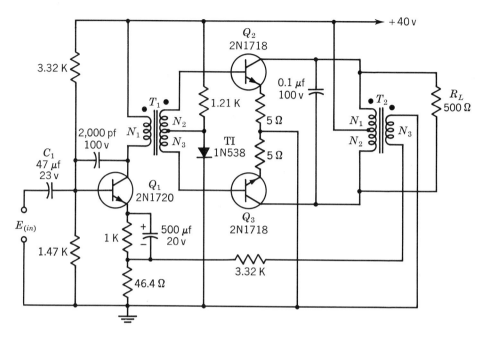

Circuit characteristics

Actual power gain: 42 db min.

Voltage amplification: 42.5 ± 2.5 db.

Input resistance: 820 ohms min.

Transformer data

T_1—N_1 = 1630 turns No. 35 AWG; N_2 = N_3 = 510 turns No. 29 AWG, bifilar wound. Core: Magnetic Metals 75 El, SL-14, or equivalent, 5 × 5 interleaved.

T_2—N_1 = N_2 = 460 turns No. 27 AWG, bifilar wound. N_3 = 304 turns No. 35 AWG. Core: Magnetic Metals 75 El, SL-14, or equivalent, butt-jointed.

Notes:

1. Q_2 and Q_3 on heat sinks with thermal resistance from case to ambient ≦20 C°/watt each. Two 3- by 3- by ⅛-in. copper plates will meet this requirement.

2. Q_2 and Q_3: h_{FE}'s matched 10%.

3. All resistance values are ±5% tolerance.

Fig. 18.3. 4.0-watt 2N1718 servo amplifier (400 cycles).

18.3. 7.5-WATT CLASS B DESIGN

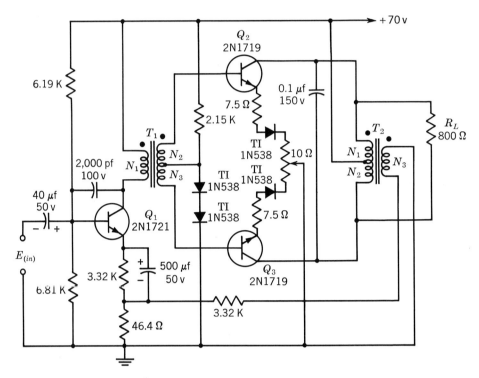

Circuit characteristics
    Actual power gain: 45 db min.
    Voltage amplification: 44 ± 2 db.
    Input resistance: 1.9 kilohms min.

Transformer data
    T_1—N_1 = 1630 turns No. 35 AWG. N_2 = N_3 = 510 turns No. 29 AWG, bifilar wound. Core: Magnetic Metals 75 El, SL-14, or equivalent, 5 × 5 interleaved.
    T_2—N_1 = N_2 = 460 turns No. 27 AWG, bifilar wound. N_3 = 304 turns No. 35 AWG. Core: Magnetic Metals 75 El, SL-14, or equivalent, butt-jointed.

Notes:
    1. Q_2 and Q_3 on heat sinks with thermal resistance from case to ambient $\leq$12 C°/watt each. Two 3- by 3- by 18-in. copper plates will meet this requirement.
    2. All resistance values are ±5% tolerance.

Fig. 18.4. 7.5-watt 2N1719 servo amplifier (400 cycles).

18.4. 10-WATT CLASS B DESIGN

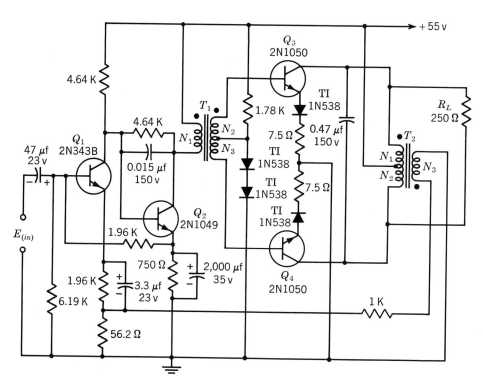

Circuit characteristics

Actual power gain: 39 db min.

Voltage amplification: 32.5 ± 1 db.

Input resistance: 1.3 kilohms min.

Transformer data

T_1—N_1 = 755 turns No. 32 AWG. N_2 = N_3 = 510 turns No. 29 AWG, bifilar wound. Core: Magnetic Metals 75 El, SL-14, or equivalent, 5 × 5 interleaved.

T_2—N_1 = N_2 = 450 turns No. 26 AWG, bifilar wound. N_3 = 300 turns No. 36 AWG. Core: Magnetic Metals 75 El, SL-14, or equivalent, 1 × 1 interleaved.

Notes:

1. Q_3 and Q_4 on heat sinks with thermal resistance from case to ambient ≤5 C°/watt each. Two 4- by 4- by $\frac{1}{16}$-in. aluminum plates suffice.
2. Q_2 on heat sink with thermal resistance from case to ambient ≤15 C°/watt. A 2- by 2- by $\frac{1}{16}$-in. aluminum heat sink suffices.
3. Q_2 and Q_3: h_{FE}'s matched 10%.
4. All resistance values are ±5% tolerance.

Fig. 18.5. 10-watt 2N1050 servo amplifier (400 cycles).

18.5. 35-WATT CLASS B DESIGN

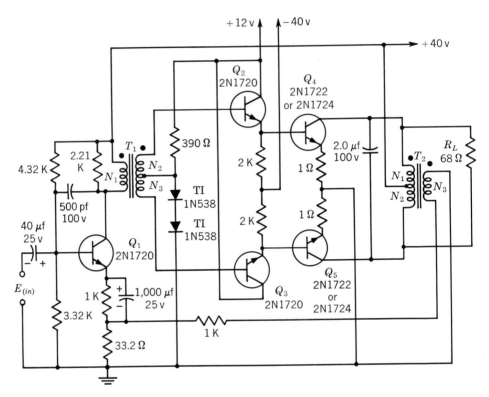

Circuit characteristics

    Actual power gain: 45 db min.

    Voltage amplification: 36.5 ± 1.5 db.

    Input resistance: 700 ohms min.

Transformer data

    T_1—$N_1 = 755$ turns No. 30 AWG. $N_2 = N_3 = 330$ turns No. 28 AWG, bifilar wound. Core: Magnetic Metals 75 El, SL-14, or equivalent, 1×1 interleaved.

    T_2—$N_1 = N_2 = 100$ turns No. 20 AWG, bifilar wound. $N_3 = 67$ turns No. 28 AWG. Core: Magnetic Metals 100 El, SL-14, or equivalent, butt-jointed.

Notes:

    1. Q_1 on heat sink with thermal resistance from case to ambient $\leqq 40$ C°/watt. A 1.5- by 2- by $\frac{1}{16}$-in. copper plate suffices.

    2. Q_2 and Q_3 on the same heat sink with thermal resistance from case to ambient $\leqq 40$ C°/watt each. A 3- by 3- by $\frac{1}{16}$-in. copper plate will meet this requirement.

    3. Q_4 and Q_5 on heat sinks with thermal resistance from case to ambient $\leqq 1.5$ C°/watt each. Refer to TI data sheet on these transistors, bulletin DL-S 61431, March, 1961.

    4. Q_4 and Q_5: h_{FE}'s matched 10%.

    5. All resistance values are $\pm 5\%$ tolerance.

Fig. 18.6. 35-watt 2N1722 servo amplifier (400 cycles).

18.6. 2-WATT DESIGN WITH HIGH EFFICIENCY

It can be shown that a transistorized servo amplifier using unfiltered rectified alternating current for the collector supply voltage has higher collector efficiency than a conventional class B push-pull amplifier.* This section describes such an amplifier, designed to deliver 2 watts into the control winding of a servo motor. No output coupling transformer is employed, and no center tap is required on the control winding of the motor. Negative feedback is employed to provide temperature stability and interchangeability of components.

This amplifier represents a substantial improvement in transistorized servo amplifiers. The use of this technique reduces size, weight, and power-supply requirements. The higher efficiency results in greater transistor reliability, smaller heat-sink requirements, and/or higher allowable ambient temperatures. An additional advantage is the lack of distortion caused by overdriving the amplifier. The type of clipping that occurs in conventional push-pull amplifiers when overdriven will not occur in this amplifier. Its output remains sinusoidal even if the driver output is many times that required to produce full output.

Output Stage. Since the output stage is somewhat unconventional, its operation should be explained. (See the simplified circuit in Fig. 18.7.) Assume that an input signal, $V_{(in)}$, is present which is in phase with the supply voltage, V_S. During the first half-cycle, transistor Q_4 is turned ON and Q_5 is OFF. A half-cycle of current, I_1, will flow from terminal A of transformer T_1 through D_1, Q_4,

---

* Bruce M. Benton, Servo Amplifiers Use Power Transistors, *Electronics,* pp. 153–155, September, 1956.

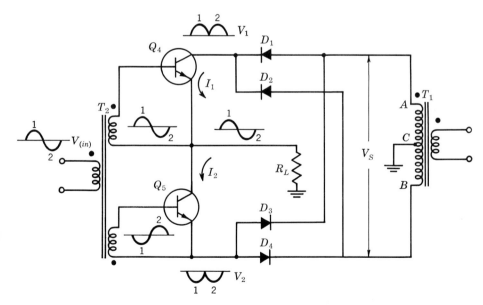

Figure 18.7

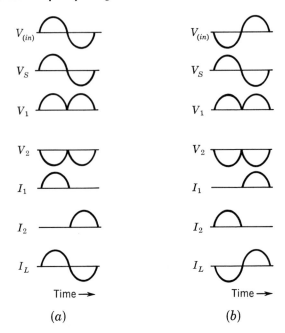

Figure 18.8

and R_L back into the transformer center tap C. During the next half-cycle, transistor Q_4 is turned OFF and Q_5 is turned ON. A half-cycle of current I_2 will flow out of the transformer center tap C, through R_L, Q_5, and D_3, then back into transformer terminal A.

For the condition just described, Fig. 18.8a shows the voltage and current waveforms vs. time when $V_{(in)}$ is in phase with V_S. Figure 18.8b shows the voltage and current waveforms vs. time when $V_{(in)}$ is 180° out of phase with respect to V_S. Note that in both cases the load current is in phase with $V_{(in)}$, which should be either in phase or 180° out of phase with V_S.

Complete Servo Amplifier. The complete servo amplifier including preamplifier and driver stages is shown in Fig. 18.9.

This circuit provides the required 2-watt power output for ambient temperatures between −55 and +125°C. Silicon transistors, solid-tantalum electrolytic capacitors, and carbon film resistors were used to ensure reliable operation over this temperature range. The output-stage operation is essentially the same as that described above for Fig. 18.7. R_{17}, R_{18}, C_{13}, and D_5 comprise a filter and divider network to provide a d-c base bias for transistor Q_4. R_{19}, R_{20}, C_{14}, and D_6 provide a similar bias for Q_5. This bias is necessary to minimize *crossover* distortion. The temperature coefficient of D_5 and D_6 matches that of Q_4 and Q_5 so that the correct bias is provided over the entire temperature range. R_{16} and R_{21} serve the usual emitter-resistor functions of temperature stabilization and distortion reduction. T_2 is the driver transformer, and it couples signal power from the driver Q_3 to the base-emitter circuits of Q_4 and Q_5.

The preamplifier and driver stages are direct-coupled and have considerable d-c feedback to ensure stability of bias conditions. Positive and negative voltages are

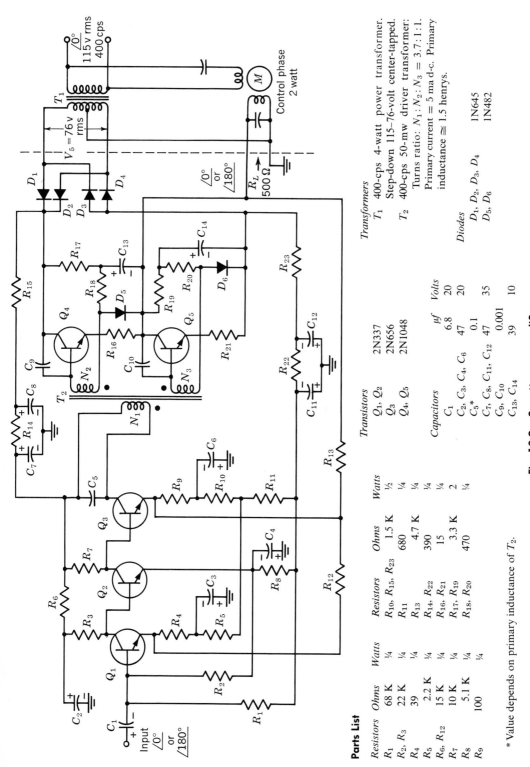

Parts List

Resistors	Ohms	Watts		Resistors	Ohms	Watts
R_1	68 K	¼		R_{10}, R_{15}, R_{23}	1.5 K	½
R_2, R_3	22 K	¼		R_{11}	680	¼
R_4	39	¼		R_{13}	4.7 K	¼
R_5	2.2 K	¼		R_{14}, R_{22}	390	¼
R_6, R_{12}	15 K	¼		R_{16}, R_{21}	15	¼
R_7	10 K	¼		R_{17}, R_{19}	3.3 K	2
R_8	5.1 K	¼		R_{18}, R_{20}	470	¼
R_9	100	¼				

Transistors	
Q_1, Q_2	2N337
Q_3	2N656
Q_4, Q_5	2N1048

Capacitors	μf	Volts
C_1	6.8	20
C_2, C_3, C_4, C_6	47	20
C_5*	0.1	
C_7, C_8, C_{11}, C_{12}	47	35
C_9, C_{10}	0.001	
C_{13}, C_{14}	39	10

Transformers

T_1 400-cps 4-watt power transformer. Step-down 115–76-volt center-tapped.

T_2 400-cps 50-mw driver transformer: Turns ratio: $N_1 : N_2 : N_3 = 3.7 : 1 : 1$. Primary current = 5 ma d-c. Primary inductance $\cong$ 1.5 henrys.

Diodes

D_1, D_2, D_3, D_4	1N645
D_5, D_6	1N482

*Value depends on primary inductance of T_2.

Fig. 18.9. 2-watt servo amplifier.

247

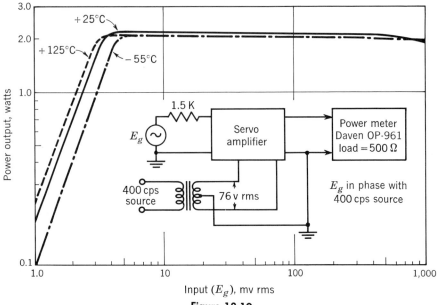

Figure 18.10

obtained from the full-wave rectifier circuits consisting of D_1, D_2, and D_3, D_4, respectively. These voltages are filtered and reduced to $+20$ volts and -20 volts d-c by C_7, C_8, R_{14}, R_{15}, and C_{11}, C_{12}, R_{22}, R_{23}, respectively.

Negative feedback is applied to the emitter of Q_3 from the amplifier output through R_{13} and to the emitter of Q_1 from the emitter of Q_3 through R_{12}. Voltage gain of the amplifier with the feedback loop closed is approximately 10,000. Input impedance is 10,000 ohms, and output impedance is on the order of 150 ohms. Power output vs. input voltage characteristics at ambient temperatures of -55, $+25$, and $+125°C$ are shown in Fig. 18.10. At an output level of 2 watts, the change in gain due to temperature variations is less than 3 db. The maximum power output decreases slightly with increasing temperature, owing to the positive temperature coefficient of the saturation resistance of the output transistors. As mentioned above, the type of clipping that occurs in conventional class B push-pull amplifiers when overdriven does not occur in this amplifier. The output remains essentially sinusoidal even if the input signal is many times that required to produce full output. The output distortion is only 7% when the input voltage is 30 db greater than that required to produce full power output.

At rated power output, the efficiency of the complete amplifier is greater than 50%. Under the most adverse signal conditions, the total dissipation of the amplifier is approximately 2 watts.

18.7. 6-WATT DESIGN WITH HIGH EFFICIENCY

Figure 18.11 shows a 6-watt circuit employing the same general circuit concept. Overall efficiency is 55%.

Design Information. The following design information is presented for those who wish to design similar amplifiers for a specified power output.

It can be shown that the maximum power output of this circuit is given by the formula

$$P_{O(max)} = \left(\frac{0.5V_S}{R_L + R_{CS} + R_E}\right)^2 R_L \tag{1}$$

where R_L = load resistance (control winding of servo motor)
V_S = rms value of full secondary voltage from T_1
R_{CS} = collector-emitter saturation resistance of Q_4 and Q_5
R_E = emitter circuit resistance for Q_4 and Q_5

In Eq. (1) the voltage drop across the rectifiers is neglected. The peak value of the supply voltage, $\sqrt{2}V_S$, should not exceed the maximum collector-emitter voltage rating of the transistors. The peak collector current of each transistor is given by Eq. (2).

$$I_{C(max)} = \frac{0.707V_S}{R_L + R_{CS} + R_E} \tag{2}$$

The value of R_{CS} used in Eqs. (1) and (2) should be the maximum value which may be encountered in a production spread of the transistor type used and over the temperature range for which the amplifier is designed to operate.

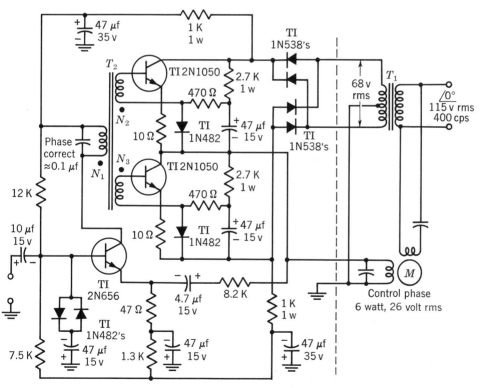

Transformers: T_1 400 cps 12-watt power transformer step-down 115 volt to 68 volt c.t.
T_2 400 cps 65-mw driver transformer. Turns ratio $N_1 : N_2 : N_3 = 2 : 1 : 1$
Primary current = 10 ma d-c.   Primary inductance = 1.5 hy.

Fig. 18.11. 6-watt servo amplifier.

The peak base current which must be supplied by the driver transformer is given by Eq. (3).

$$I_{B(max)} = \frac{I_{C(max)}}{h_{FE}} \tag{3}$$

The driver transformer must provide the peak base voltage necessary to produce the peak collector current given by Eq. (2). The collector current vs. base voltage characteristic is usually given on the transistor data sheet. The peak driver-transformer output voltage required is given by Eq. (4),

$$V_{D(max)} = V_{BE(max)} + (1 + h_{FE})I_{B(max)}R_E - V_B \tag{4}$$

where V_B is the zero-signal bias voltage developed across diode D_5. Since the signal current through D_5 is in the opposite direction to the bias current supplied through D_5, the bias must be at least equal to the $I_{B(max)}$ given by Eq. (3). The same is true for D_6.

Part **3**

High-frequency Designs

19

Wideband or Video Amplifiers

This chapter discusses basic design theory for wideband transistorized amplifiers, considers effects of negative feedback, offers a step-by-step design procedure, and presents several design examples.

19.1. NEGATIVE FEEDBACK

By using negative feedback, the operating characteristics of an amplifier can be considerably modified. In general, negative feedback stabilizes amplifier operation and increases the bandwidth at the expense of reduced A_i and A_v. This results in a smaller change in closed-loop gain for a given change in open-loop gain brought about by changes in transistor parameters at different frequencies. Feedback in general can be classified as series feedback and shunt feedback.

With Negative Series Feedback. If negative feedback is accomplished through a series resistance, R_F, as shown in the simplified circuit of Fig. 19.1, the characteristics of the amplifier are modified as follows:

1. Input impedance, Z_i, and output impedance, Z_o, are increased.
2. Voltage amplification, $A_v = v_2/v_1$, is reduced, but it also becomes less dependent on individual transistor parameters.
3. Current amplification, $A_i = i_2/i_1$, is slightly reduced, but not nearly to the extent of the A_v reduction.

These characteristics are particularly useful in high-input-impedance amplifiers.

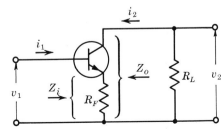

Fig. 19.1. Simplified series feedback circuit.

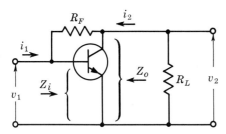

Fig. 19.2. Simplified shunt feedback circuit.

With Negative Shunt Feedback. If a shunt feedback resistance, R_F, is used as shown in the simplified circuit of Fig. 19.2, the characteristics of the amplifier are modified as follows:

1. Z_i and Z_o are reduced.
2. A_i is reduced, but it also becomes less dependent on individual transistor parameters.
3. A_v is slightly reduced, but not nearly so much as A_i.

The characteristics of shunt feedback amplifiers immediately suggest possible application in low-input- and low-output-impedance amplifiers.

The design analysis in this section gives a step-by-step approach to design for negative shunt feedback only, but series feedback can be analyzed in the same manner. A circuit using a combination of series and shunt feedback is shown in an example at the end of this chapter.

If low impedances are desired at the input and output of the amplifier, as is usually the case when 50-ohm coaxial cable is used, shunt feedback networks are employed in each stage. Since the input and output impedances are usually the same, the amplifier will have identical voltage and current amplification.

$$A_i = -A_v \frac{Z_i}{Z_L} \tag{1}$$

where A_i = current amplification
A_v = voltage amplification
Z_i = input impedance
Z_L = output load impedance

Therefore, under the condition of equal input and output impedances, the feedback stabilizes both A_i and A_v.

Neglecting the d-c bias networks, a simplified circuit of a common-emitter shunt feedback amplifier is shown in Fig. 19.3.

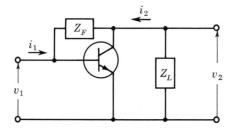

Fig. 19.3. Shunt feedback equivalent circuit.

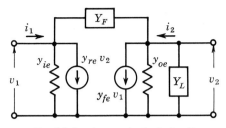

Fig. 19.4.   A-c equivalent circuit.

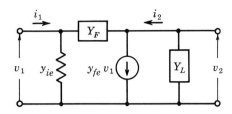

Fig. 19.5.   Simplified a-c equivalent circuit.

For the purpose of circuit analysis, this amplifier may be represented by the a-c equivalent circuit of Fig. 19.4.

This circuit employs small-signal parameters, y_{ie} and y_{oe}, and two constant-current generators, $y_{re}v_2$ and $y_{fe}v_1$.   The current generator in the input circuit, $y_{re}v_2$, represents the component of input current, i_1, produced by output voltage, v_2.   The y_{re} therefore represents an internal feedback, or reverse transfer function.   The current generator in the input circuit of this amplifier may generally be neglected because the external feedback is much larger than the internal feedback.   The output admittance, y_{oe}, when multiplied by the output voltage, v_2, represents the contribution of v_2 to the output current, i_2.   The load admittance, Y_L, is usually much larger than y_{oe} so that the current through y_{oe} may be neglected.   Therefore, the equivalent circuit of Fig. 19.4 may be considerably simplified, as shown in Fig. 19.5.

The important transistor parameters for the analysis of a low-impedance shunt feedback amplifier are therefore y_{ie} and y_{fe}.

19.2.   FREQUENCY CHARACTERISTICS OF $y_{ie}, h_{fe},$ AND y_{fe}

The input circuit of a transistor, with the output short-circuited, may be represented as in Fig. 19.6:[1]

$$g_1 \cong \frac{1}{h_{feo}r_e} \qquad c_1 = \frac{1}{2\pi f_T r_e}$$

where f_T = frequency at which $|h_{fe}| = 1$, and h_{feo} = low-frequency value of h_{fe}. When the resistance r_b' is small and the frequency is less than f_T, r_b' may be neglected and y_{ie} may be approximated by

$$y_{ie} = y_{ieo}\left(1 + j\frac{f}{f_{yie}}\right) \tag{2}$$

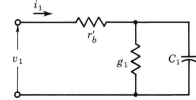

Fig. 19.6.   Input equivalent circuit.

where y_{ieo} = low-frequency value of y_{ie}
f = operating frequency
f_{yie} = frequency at which $|y_{ie}| = \sqrt{2}\,y_{ieo}$

When the log magnitude of y_{ie} is plotted as a function of the log frequency, a curve of the type shown in Fig. 19.7 is obtained. Note that the curve representing y_{ie} is asymptotic both to the low-frequency value of y_{ie} or y_{ieo}, and to a line crossing y_{ieo} at the corner frequency, f_{yie}, and at an angle of $+45°$ with the horizontal. The $45°$ angle on a log-log plot represents a slope of 6 db/octave. Therefore, the values of y_{ieo} and f_{yie} of Eq. (2) may be determined from a log magnitude vs. log frequency plot of y_{ie} measurements. This procedure provides both the magnitude and phase angle of y_{ie}, as defined by Eq. (2) from simple magnitude measurements.

For frequencies below f_T, h_{fe} may be approximated by

$$h_{fe} = \frac{h_{feo}}{1 + jf/f_{hfe}} \tag{3}$$

where h_{feo} = low-frequency value of h_{fe}, and f_{hfe} = frequency at which h_{fe} = $(1/\sqrt{2})h_{feo}$. When the log magnitude of h_{fe} is plotted as a function of the log frequency, a curve of the type shown in Fig. 19.8 is obtained. Note that the curve representing $|h_{fe}|$ is asymptotic both to h_{feo} and to a line that crosses the value of h_{feo} at the corner frequency, f_{hfe}, and at an angle of $-45°$ with the horizontal. The values of h_{feo} and f_{hfe} of Eq. (3) may be determined from a log magnitude vs. log frequency plot of h_{fe} measurements. Thus, both the magnitude and phase angle of h_{fe} may be defined. The measurements required to evaluate y_{ie} and h_{fe} are given in Chap. 5.

After equations for y_{ie} and h_{fe} have been obtained, a general expression for y_{fe} may be derived from Eq. (4).

$$y_{fe} = y_{ie}h_{fe} = y_{feo}\frac{1 + jf/f_{yie}}{1 + jf/f_{hfe}} \tag{4}$$

where y_{feo} = low-frequency value of y_{fe}, and is equal to $y_{ieo}h_{feo}$. Once the transistor parameters have been evaluated at the desired d-c operating points, amplifier performance may be predicted by using the equivalent circuit of Fig. 19.5 and conventional circuit analysis.

One approach to the design of a wideband amplifier using only these measured

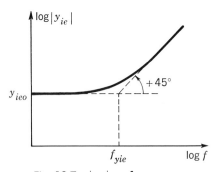

Fig. 19.7. $|y_{ie}|$ **vs. frequency.**

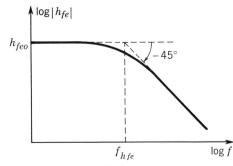

Fig. 19.8. $|h_{fe}|$ **vs. frequency.**

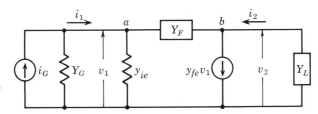

Fig. 19.9. Redrawn a-c equivalent circuit.

parameters follows. This approach is used in the first example at the end of this chapter.

19.3. DESIGN EQUATIONS

The simplified a-c equivalent circuit (Fig. 19.5) may be redrawn as in Fig. 19.9. Equations (5) and (6) are obtained by summing currents at nodes a and b.

$$(y_{ie} + Y_F)v_1 - Y_Fv_2 = i_1 \tag{5}$$

$$(y_{fe} - Y_F)v_1 + (Y_L + Y_F)v_2 = 0 \tag{6}$$

where the voltage amplification, A_v, is defined as the ratio of the output to input voltage, v_2/v_1. This ratio may be obtained from Eq. (6).

$$A_v = - \frac{y_{fe} - Y_F}{Y_L + Y_F} \tag{7}$$

In general, y_{fe}, Y_L, and Y_F will be complex or vector quantities and must be combined in accordance with the rules of a-c circuit analysis. The negative sign indicates the phase reversal obtained in the output voltage with respect to the input voltage for a common-emitter amplifier.

If the input admittance, Y_i, is defined as the ratio of input current to input voltage, i_1/v_1, this quantity may be obtained from Eqs. (5) and (6) as follows:

$$Y_i = y_{ie} + Y_F\left(1 + \frac{y_{fe} - Y_F}{Y_L + Y_F}\right) \tag{8}$$

A_v may be substituted in Eq. (8) to produce

$$Y_i = y_{ie} + Y_F(1 - A_v) \tag{9}$$

Remembering that A_v is a negative quantity, Eq. (9) shows that the driving source (i_G, Y_G) effectively sees an admittance equal to the transistor input admittance in parallel with the feedback admittance, Y_F, multiplied by one minus the voltage amplification. If the feedback impedance is a pure resistance, the effective input circuit of the amplifier is shown in Fig. 19.10.

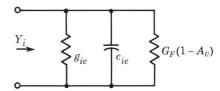

Fig. 19.10. Effective input circuit: resistive feedback.

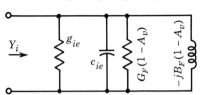

Fig. 19.11. Effective input circuit: inductive feedback.

A shunt feedback resistor increases the amplifier input admittance, or in other words, it reduces the amplifier input impedance. Circuit values may be chosen so that Y_i is determined mainly by the feedback term, $Y_F(1 - A_v)$, while y_{ie} has only a negligible effect. As the voltage amplification drops at higher frequencies, the magnitude of the feedback term becomes smaller. The effective Y_i will therefore tend to drop as A_v falls off, or the input impedance will tend to rise as A_v decreases.

The effect of an inductive feedback admittance on Y_i of the amplifier may be seen from the equivalent circuit of Fig. 19.11. Since the inductive component, $-jB_F(1 - A_v)$, tends to cancel the capacitive component of y_{ie}, circuit components can be selected to produce a resonant effect on Y_i. In other words, the input impedance will peak at the frequency where ωc_{ie} is exactly canceled by $B_F(1 - A_v)$.

Shaping Y_i, or the input impedance, of a multistage amplifier is important because the input impedance of one stage is the output load impedance of the driving stage and therefore affects the voltage amplification of the driving stage.

If a particular Y_i is desired, Eq. (8) may be rearranged to yield the proper value of Y_F, as follows:

$$Y_F = \frac{Y_L(Y_i - y_{ie})}{y_{ie}(1 + h_{fe}) + Y_L - Y_i} \tag{10}$$

The current amplification, A_i, of the amplifier, when defined as the ratio of output to input current, i_2/i_1, is given by

$$A_i = -A_v Y_L Z_i \tag{11}$$

Since A_v is negative, A_i becomes positive, indicating no fundamental phase shift in the output current with respect to the input current for a common-emitter amplifier. If a particular A_i is desired, the required feedback admittance may be calculated by combining Eqs. (9) and (11), as follows:

$$Y_F = \frac{y_{ie}(h_{fe} - A_i)}{1 + A_i[1 + Z_L y_{ie}(1 + h_{fe})]} \tag{12}$$

The effective output impedance of the amplifier may be determined by reducing the generator current, i_G, to zero and removing the load admittance, Y_L, for the

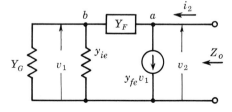

Fig. 19.12. Effective output circuit.

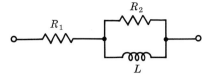

Fig. 19.13. Feedback network.

circuit shown in Fig. 19.9. This results in the circuit of Fig. 19.12. Equations (13) and (14) are obtained by summing currents at nodes a and b.

$$(y_{fe} - Y_F)v_1 + Y_F v_2 = i_2 \tag{13}$$

$$(y_{ie} + Y_G + Y_F)v_1 - Y_F v_2 = 0 \tag{14}$$

The effective output impedance, Z_o, of the amplifier may be defined as the ratio of output voltage to output current, v_2/i_2, with the input generator (voltage or current) reduced to zero and the output load impedance removed, as shown in Fig. 19.12. Using Eqs. (13) and (14), Z_o may be expressed as

$$Z_o = \frac{Z_F(y_{ie} + Y_G) + 1}{y_{fe} + y_{ie} + Y_G} \tag{15}$$

By rearranging Eq. (15), the shunt feedback impedance, Z_F, may be calculated for a particular value of Z_o; that is:

$$Z_F = Z_o + \frac{Z_o y_{fe} - 1}{y_{ie} + Y_G} \tag{16}$$

The circuit shown in Fig. 19.13 is the type of circuit usually used in the feedback loop of an amplifier of this type. The admittance of this circuit is

$$Y_F = G_1 \frac{1 + j\omega L G_2}{1 + j\omega L (G_1 + G_2)} \tag{17}$$

Equation (17) also may be written in the following form:

$$Y_F = G_1 \frac{1 + jf/f_b}{1 + jf/f_a} \tag{18}$$

where
$$f_a = \frac{1}{2\pi L(G_1 + G_2)} \qquad f_b = \frac{1}{2\pi L G_2}$$

Plotting Y_F as a function of frequency yields a curve of the type shown in Fig. 19.14.

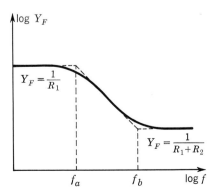

Fig. 19.14. Y_F vs. frequency.

Thus the feedback network, shown in Fig. 19.13, will produce constant feedback at frequencies well below the corner frequency, f_a, and well above the corner frequency, f_b, but will produce a changing feedback characteristic between the two corner frequencies. The desired low-frequency operation of the amplifier will determine the resistance of R_1. The desired high-frequency operation will determine the choice of f_a and f_b in the feedback circuit. The values of R_2 and L may be calculated from these corner frequencies by use of Eqs. (19) and (20).

$$R_2 = R_1\left(\frac{f_b}{f_a} - 1\right) \tag{19}$$

$$L = \frac{R_1}{2\pi}\left(\frac{1}{f_a} - \frac{1}{f_b}\right) \tag{20}$$

Equations (5) through (20) may be used to predict the operation of a shunt feedback amplifier and as a basis for selecting the circuit values for both low- and high-frequency operation.

19.4. SINGLE-STAGE vs. MULTISTAGE OPERATION

The voltage amplification of a single-stage amplifier may be calculated from Eqs. (4) and (7). For a pure resistance load (i.e., $Y_L = G_L$) and no feedback, the normalized voltage amplification becomes

$$\frac{A_v}{A_{vo}} = \frac{1 + jf/f_{yie}}{1 + jf/f_{hfe}} \tag{21}$$

where

$$A_{vo} = -\frac{y_{feo}}{G_L}$$

A typical plot of Eq. (21) is shown by curve a of Fig. 19.15. If resistive shunt feedback is used, the normalized voltage amplification is

$$\frac{A_v}{A_{vo}} = \frac{1 + jf/f_3}{1 + jf/f_{hfe}} \tag{22}$$

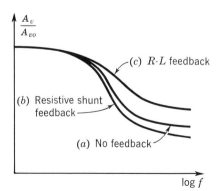

Fig. 19.15. Normalized voltage amplification.

where
$$A_{vo} = -\frac{y_{feo} - G_F}{G_L + G_F}$$

$$f_3 = f_{yie}\frac{y_{feo} - G_F}{y_{feo} - G_F f_{yie}/f_{hfe}}$$

Resistive shunt feedback reduces voltage amplification. Since f_3 is a higher frequency than f_{yie}, the relative high-frequency A_v with feedback is poorer than the relative high-frequency A_v without feedback. This condition is represented by curve b in Fig. 19.15. The high-frequency A_v can be improved by using RL shunt feedback, as shown by curve c in Fig. 19.15.

Amplifiers are not fed from constant-voltage sources with negligible internal impedances. Therefore, the frequency response of an amplifier is also dependent upon its input impedance, Z_i. Typical curves of input impedance vs. frequency, with and without feedback, are shown in Fig. 19.16.

Curve a shows the drop in Z_i as frequency is increased, for a single stage without feedback. If this amplifier is driven from a voltage source with a constant internal impedance, the output voltage will drop faster, with increasing frequency, than the voltage amplification curve of Fig. 19.15 would indicate, because of the drooping Z_i characteristic.

The effect of resistive shunt feedback on Z_i is shown in curve b of Fig. 19.16. Though at high frequencies the voltage amplification is not helped by the addition of resistive shunt feedback, as seen from Fig. 19.15, the amplifier operation is considerably improved because of the flat input-impedance characteristic, shown in Fig. 19.16. The output-voltage characteristic, when driven from a voltage source with a constant internal impedance, will follow the shape of the voltage amplification curve of Fig. 19.15, over the flat section of the input-impedance curve. At high frequencies, the output voltage will drop faster than curve b of Fig. 19.15 indicates because of reducing input impedances.

Introduction of RL shunt feedback improves the voltage amplification characteristic slightly and provides a rising input-impedance characteristic, as shown in curve c of Fig. 19.16. If the RL feedback network is properly chosen, the effect of the rising input-impedance characteristic will offset the drooping voltage amplification characteristic and provide almost a constant output voltage over a wide

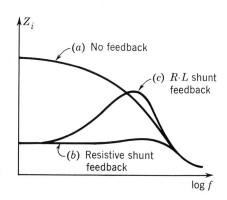

Fig. 19.16. Input impedance vs. frequency.

frequency range (again this assumes that the amplifier is fed from a voltage source with a constant internal impedance).

An amplifier fed from a coaxial cable should have a flat input-impedance characteristic, with frequency, equal to the characteristic impedance of the cable, for maximum input power to the amplifier and minimum reflection at the input terminals. Recalling the previous discussion, a single shunt feedback stage cannot meet this condition and still obtain a good high-frequency output-voltage characteristic. Therefore, a video amplifier of this type should contain two or more stages. *The first stage should have resistive feedback to provide a flat input-impedance characteristic.* The other stages should have *RL* feedback to produce rising input-impedance characteristics for good overall high-frequency response. The major problem in designing the amplifier is to select the feedback networks.

19.5. SELECTING THE DIRECT CURRENT AND VOLTAGE

The optimum d-c operating point for each transistor stage is determined by the expected performance of the circuit, the optimum transistor parameters, and the ratings of the transistors. From a circuit standpoint, the d-c collector voltage must be at least as large as the expected peak a-c voltage swing across the load impedance, to prevent clipping the negative half-cycles of the output voltage. A d-c collector voltage of twice this value is desirable, particularly for amplifiers feeding high-impedance loads. For similar reasons, the d-c collector current must be at least as large, preferably twice as large, as the expected peak alternating current delivered to the load impedance. A low-impedance amplifier will require relatively large current swings. For example, a peak sinusoidal current of 28.28 ma will be required to produce 1 volt rms across a 50-ohm load. Therefore, the maximum output voltage of a low-impedance amplifier will usually be limited by the collector current and power-dissipation ratings of the transistor. Consequently, a large d-c collector current, at least in the last stage, is desirable.

The h_{fe} is not very dependent on d-c collector current and voltage. Very small or very large collector currents and voltages result in reduced values of h_{fe}. For example, a 3N35 has a peak value for h_{fe} at about 1.5 ma and 20 volts. However, a very little change in h_{fe} is obtained with a 2:1 or 3:1 change in d-c collector voltage or current. The d-c operating point that will produce the most favorable h_{fe} characteristic can usually be determined from the transistor data sheet. If this information is not available, it can be determined from curves plotted from experimental measurements. In general, d-c collector currents larger than those recommended by the data sheets will produce smaller low-frequency h_{fe} values and poorer high-frequency h_{fe} characteristics.

The value of y_{ie} is quite dependent on collector current. The approximate relationship between y_{ie} and emitter current is given in Eqs. (23) and (24).[2]

$$g_{ie} \cong \frac{I_E}{26h_{feo}} \tag{23}$$

$$c_{ie} = \frac{I_E}{52\pi f_T} \tag{24}$$

where I_E = d-c emitter current, ma, and

$$y_{ie} = g_{ie} + j\omega c_{ie}$$

These equations show that y_{ie} varies directly with collector current. Since the voltage gain of the amplifier varies almost directly with y_{fe}, which is the product of y_{ie} and h_{fe}, it would immediately appear that a large collector current is desirable in the amplifier. It is true that when the collector current is increased in a particular amplifier while the d-c collector voltage is held unchanged, the overall voltage amplification does increase. At the same time, however, the input impedance of the amplifier is reduced by approximately the same amount. If the feedback network in the first stage is readjusted to provide the original input impedance, essentially no change will be observed in the overall voltage amplification for increased collector currents. Thus, no advantage in overall voltage gain can be obtained by raising the d-c collector currents above the optimum h_{fe} value, because the overall voltage gain must equal the overall current gain in an amplifier having the same input and load impedances. On the other hand, the d-c collector current in the first stage should be relatively low so that the input admittance will be large compared with y_{ie}. In other words, the input impedance will be fixed by the feedback circuit rather than by y_{ie}.

To summarize, the collector current in the last stage should be high in order to provide a high output voltage, but the collector current in the first stage should be low in order to stabilize the input impedance.

19.6. DESIGN PROCEDURE

In example 1 (Sec. 19.7) the steps detailed below were performed in the order shown.

Design of D-C Circuit. The combination of biasing resistors that determines the transistor and circuit direct voltages and currents is the d-c circuit. This circuit is designed as follows:

1. Select bias circuits.
2. Select transistor direct voltages and currents.
3. Select d-c supply voltage and its distribution across the transistors and bias resistors.
4. Calculate bias resistors from the circuit of step 1 and the voltages and currents of steps 2 and 3.

Determination of Applicable Parameters. As shown in the design section (Sec. 19.3), the only transistor parameters of importance in the analysis of a low-impedance shunt feedback amplifier are the admittance parameters, y_{ie} and y_{fe}, or the hybrid parameters, h_{ie} and h_{fe}. It is slightly more convenient to evaluate h_{fe} and y_{ie}. Then y_{fe} is obtained from the product of y_{ie} and h_{fe}. They may be evaluated by either of two methods. The first method is graphical determination:

1. Measure a-c input voltage, input current, and output voltage, for a 50-ohm collector load resistance at desired d-c operating point of each transistor, and over desired range of operating frequency.

2. Calculate $|h_{fe}|$ and $|y_{ie}|$ values from the measurements of step 1 at each frequency.
3. Plot $|h_{fe}|$ and $|y_{ie}|$ on log-log graph paper as functions of frequency.
4. Determine magnitudes of low-frequency values of h_{fe} and y_{ie} and their corner frequencies from curves obtained in step 3.

The second method is determination of h_{fe} and y_{ie} from a set of high-frequency measurements:

1. Measure magnitudes of h_{fe} and y_{ie} at any convenient low frequency. (These are the values of h_{feo} and y_{ieo}.)
2. Measure magnitudes of h_{fe} and y_{ie} at any convenient high frequency, f_3, well above their corner frequencies.
3. Calculate corner frequencies from these measurements and the equations:

$$f_{yie} = \frac{f_3}{\sqrt{(y_{ie3}/y_{ieo})^2 - 1}} \tag{25}$$

where f_{yie} = corner frequency of y_{ie}, and y_{ie3} = value of y_{ie} at frequency f_3.

$$f_{hfe} = \frac{f_3}{\sqrt{(h_{feo}/h_{fe3})^2 - 1}} \tag{26}$$

where f_{hfe} = corner frequency of h_{fe}, and h_{fe3} = value of h_{fe} at frequency f_3.

Design of Low-frequency A-C Circuit.   The low-frequency current amplification, voltage amplification, and input impedance of each stage are determined by the transistor parameters, the low-frequency feedback resistor between collector and base, and the effective collector load impedance. The major factor in designing the low-frequency circuit is selecting feedback resistors that will provide the desired overall A_i and A_v, the desired division of A_i between stages, and the desired input impedance. In general, a compromise must be made between A_i and A_v, and frequency coverage. For a given amplifier, an increase in operating frequency entails a reduction of A_i and A_v. The maximum useful frequency may be estimated from h_{fe} and A_{io}. A_v will be down 3 db at the frequency where h_{fe} equals A_{io}.

The low-frequency a-c circuit may be designed in the following steps:

1. Select A_i, with feedback, for each stage. Allow 4 or 5 db for loss in bias networks and for input-impedance correction in the first stage, so that the total indicated A_i will be slightly higher than the desired overall A_i for the amplifier.
2. From Eq. (12), calculate feedback resistor, R_1, for the last stage to provide the desired low-frequency A_i. Note that Z_L is the effective load impedance, and includes the parallel combination of the a-c load and the d-c collector bias resistor.
3. Calculate A_v and input admittance, Y_i, of the last stage from Eqs. (7) and (9). Note that Y_i, as calculated from Eq. (9), must be corrected because the bias circuit shunts the transistor input circuit.

4. Calculate feedback resistor, R_1, for the second stage, using the procedure explained in step 2. Remember that the a-c load impedance of the second stage is the input impedance of the last stage after correcting for the effects of the d-c collector bias resistor.
5. Calculate A_v and Y_i for the second stage, using the procedure described in step 3.
6. From Eq. (10), calculate feedback resistor, R_1, for the first stage to provide the desired value of input impedance, Z_i.
7. Calculate A_v of the first stage, using the method described in step 3.
8. Calculate capacitances of the coupling capacitors, from calculated input impedances and the lowest desired operating frequency.
9. Connect the low-frequency circuit, and compare measured A_v and Z_i with calculated values.
10. Any correction in input impedance may be made by adjusting the first-stage feedback resistance. Overall voltage amplification may be corrected by adjusting d-c supply voltage or the currents of individual stages.

Design of High-frequency A-C Circuit. A typical voltage amplification vs. frequency plot for an amplifier with resistive feedback only is shown by the solid line of Fig. 19.17. One effect of shunt feedback is to reduce Z_i for that stage. If the feedback network for one stage is designed to decrease feedback as frequency is increased, Z_i of that stage will have a rising impedance vs. frequency characteristic. Therefore the preceding or driving stage will have a rising voltage amplification vs. frequency characteristic. A feedback circuit that has this property was shown in Fig. 19.13. By using RL feedback networks in the last two stages and selecting proper corner frequencies for these networks, the three-stage voltage amplification vs. frequency characteristic can be changed from the solid line to the dotted line, as shown in Fig. 19.17. Since the value of R_1 is determined by the low-frequency circuit after the corner frequencies for the feedback network are selected, the values of R_2 and L in Fig. 19.13 may be calculated from Eqs. (19) and (20).

The following procedure may be used to design the high-frequency circuit:

1. Measure and plot the A_v vs. frequency characteristic of amplifier with re-sistive feedback only, using db and log frequency scales. It will be noted

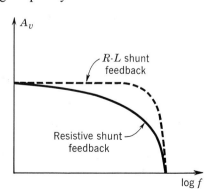

Fig. 19.17. A_V vs. frequency: resistive feedback.

that A_v starts dropping at or near the h_{fe} corner frequency of the last transistor.

2. In the last stage, add a high-frequency feedback network having values of f_a equal to the h_{fe} corner frequency of the last transistor and f_b equal to or greater than the highest expected operating frequency as determined by intersection of the low-frequency A_i with the h_{fe} vs. frequency curve of the last transistor. R_2 and L may be calculated from Eqs. (19) and (20).

3. Measure and plot the A_v vs. frequency characteristic of the amplifier after completing step 2. Considerable improvement will be observed at the high-frequency end of the curve.

4. Select values of f_a and f_b for second-stage feedback network from the curve obtained in step 3. A value of f_a should be selected at or near the frequency at which A_v begins to drop. A value of f_b may be selected at a frequency above f_a.

5. Measure and plot the A_v vs. frequency characteristic of the amplifier after step 4 has been completed. If the selected value of f_b was too large, a pronounced peak will be obtained at the high-frequency end of the characteristic. If f_b was too small, the high-frequency operating range of the amplifier will be too small. Two or three trials should be sufficient to determine optimum values for the corner frequencies of the second-stage feedback network.

6. Measure and plot the Z_i vs. frequency characteristic.

19.7. CIRCUIT EXAMPLES

The following three circuits show the results obtained by using feedback to extend the frequency response of a transistor for use in wideband applications.

Circuit Example 1.   The three-stage silicon wideband amplifier shown in Fig. 19.18 applies the design procedure described in Sec. 19.6. It employs feedback around each of its three stages.

Design objectives for this amplifier were:

1. Voltage and current amplification of 20 db.
2. Flat frequency response to as high a frequency as possible.
3. Input impedance of 50 ohms when feeding a 50-ohm load.
4. Output impedance of 50 ohms when driven from a 50-ohm voltage source.

It will be noticed that a zener diode has been added to each stage of the amplifier. This is done to stabilize V_{CE}. Since y_{ie} is very dependent on I_C, the amplifier should be operated from a well-regulated d-c voltage or from a constant current d-c source to stabilize A_v.

Frequency response of the circuit is shown in Fig. 19.19.

Circuit Example 2.   The three-stage 50-mc wideband-amplifier circuit shown in Fig. 19.20 is a very good example of the maximum bandwidth which can be achieved with a given transistor using standard stability criteria for wideband amplifiers in the design. Because of the difficulties involved with instability at high frequencies, it is difficult to apply feedback over more than two stages at a

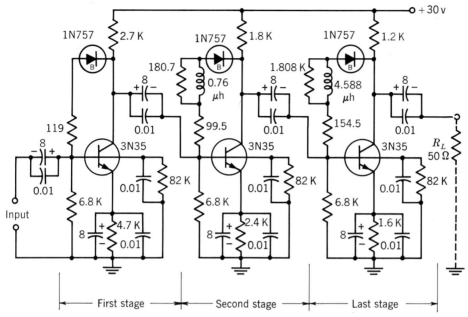

Fig. 19.18.   Video amplifier.

time.   It will be noted here that the feedback is over three stages in this example, but the design includes stability considerations to provide for this.

The delay characteristics of a transistor can be approximated by the equation

$$\alpha = \alpha_o \frac{e^{-jmf/f\alpha}}{1 + jf/f_\alpha}$$

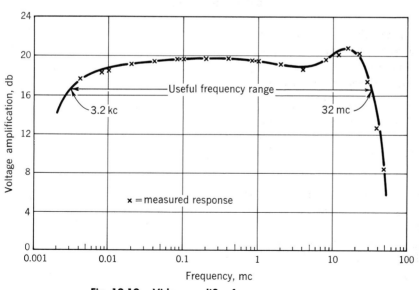

Fig. 19.19.   Video amplifier frequency response.

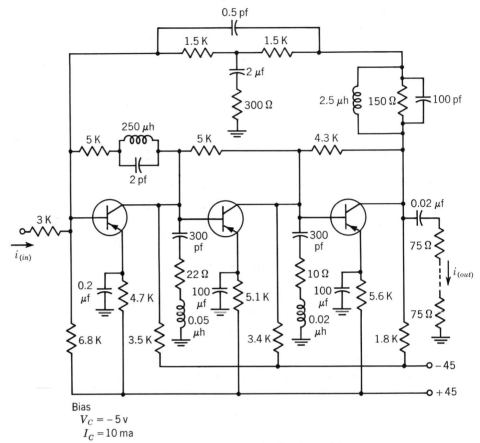

Bias
$V_C = -5$ v
$I_C = 10$ ma

Fig. 19.20. Diffused-base feedback amplifier.

which shows the excess phase that the transistor has in addition to the phase shift exhibited by the simple minimum phase network which approximates its amplitude response.

The design objectives for this amplifier were:

1. An external current gain of 34 db, flat to within 0.01 db up to 5 mc, and flat to 0.1 db up to 10 mc.
2. A negative feedback of 34 db to be maintained from 50 kc to 5 mc.
3. A match between a 3,000-ohm source to a 75-ohm load to within 5% over a frequency range of 50 kc to 5 mc.

The transistor used should be similar to the 2N2415, a diffused-base germanium mesa. It should have a low-frequency common-base current gain, a_o near 0.97, f_t near 600 mc, low collector capacity C_c less than 1 pf, low collector body resistance r_c' less than 20 ohms, and emitter body (point) resistance r_e less than 5 ohms.

The d-c biasing uses both series and shunt feedback to each stage. This provides an extremely stable d-c circuit, enabling the circuit bandwidth to be extended to d-c if necessary.

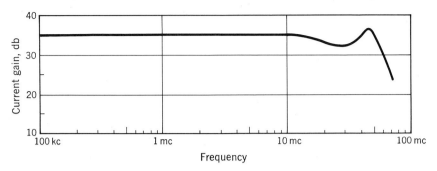

Fig. 19.21.   Current gain, db vs. frequency.

The β network is a bridged T network which appears resistive at mid-band. The shunt arm of the T contains a series capacitor which provides a rising asymptote for the $A\beta$ gain characteristic at low frequencies, and the capacitor which bridges the T provides a high-frequency rising asymptote. A compensating network is placed in series with the bridged T in order to keep the β loss flat to 10 mc.

The $A\beta$ characteristic, without interstage shaping, is flat at 34 db up to 25 mc, where, because of the transistor's current-gain cutoff, it falls at a rate of 18 db/octave to 50 mc, where the rising asymptote of the β network reduces this to 12 db/octave. Since the rising asymptote occurs outside the usable band, the inband characteristics are not appreciably affected.

To approximate an ideal Bode cutoff, the gain between 5 and 100 mc is shaped with the series interstage networks. The Bode fillet is added at 7 mc by the first-stage feedback so that $A\beta$ is down 3 db at 7 mc.

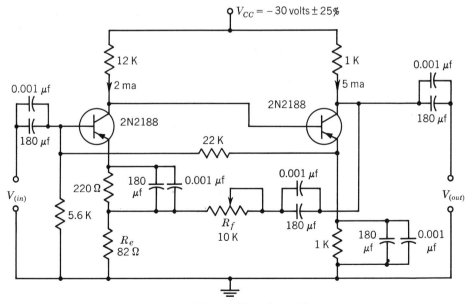

Fig. 19.22.   Wideband amplifier.

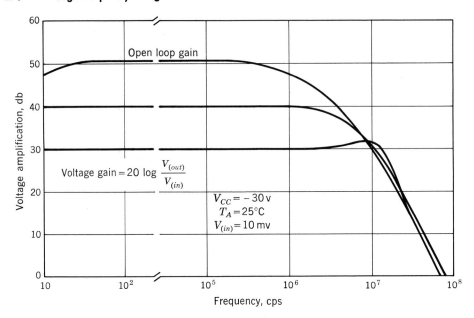

Fig. 19.23.   Typical frequency response of wideband amplifier in Fig. 19.22.

The emitter bypass capacitors control the low-frequency response with the first-stage bypass providing a roll-off frequency of approximately 50 kc.   The other two stages extend to under 0.5 kc to provide stability.

The frequency response of the circuit is shown in Fig. 19.21.

Circuit Example 3.   A two-stage amplifier is shown in Fig. 19.22.   D-c feedback provides stable d-c operation with parameter variations encountered in the normal production spread, as well as those caused by changing temperature. Supply-voltage variations of ±25% have a negligible effect on the performance of the amplifier.

The a-c feedback is a combination of the two types discussed earlier: shunt and series.   A portion of the output is fed back in series with the input.   This extends the bandwidth and stabilizes the amplification.   It also reduces the output impedance and increases the input impedance.

Typical open-loop amplification is 48 to 50 db. R_f controls the closed-loop amplification, A_{C1}. A_{C1} can be approximated by

$$A_{C1} = \frac{A_1 A_2}{1 - A_1 A_2 \, R_e / R_f},$$

where $A_1 A_2$ = open-loop amplification, which is the product of the amplification of stages 1 and 2

R_e = unbypassed emitter resistance of the first stage

R_f = value of the feedback resistor

The open-loop bandwidth is 1 mc, and the bandwidth at 30-db closed-loop amplification is 17 mc. Figure 19.23 shows the typical frequency response of this amplifier.

BIBLIOGRAPHY

1. Pritchard, R. L.: Electric Network Representation of Transistors, *IRE Trans.*, vol. CT-3, p. 14, March, 1956.
2. Hunter, L. P.: "Handbook of Semiconductor Electronics," p. 4.12, McGraw-Hill Book Company, Inc., New York, 1956.

20

Low-level RF Stage Stability

20.1. UNILATERALIZATION

A serious problem in RF and IF amplifiers is the internal feedback of the device. Because of internal feedback, a general range of frequencies exists for which a transistor can be made to oscillate by properly choosing passive terminations. In addition, internal feedback causes the transistor input impedance to be a function of load impedance. This makes multistage IF amplifier alignment difficult.

In general, two design methods are available to overcome internal feedback effects. One technique is to neutralize the effect of the reverse feedback ratio or unilateralize the transistors in the amplifier. The second technique involves mismatching the transistors. (Mismatching is considered in the next section.)

Neutralization is the process of balancing out an undesirable effect. *Unilateralization* may be defined as a method for converting a bilateral four-terminal network to a unilateral network. Comparing the definitions, it is clear that unilateralization is a special type of neutralization. However, the reverse is not necessarily true. For example, hum-neutralized circuits are not unilateralized.

Unilateralization vs. Mismatching. Unilateralization offers three advantages: First, if the transistor is exactly unilateralized, the stability of the amplifier stage is completely independent of passive networks connected at the input and output of the stage. Second, the input and output circuits are completely isolated from each other. The input and output impedances of the transistor are independent of the load and generator impedances, respectively. Third, by conjugate-matching the generator and load impedance to the transistor, power gains may be obtained very nearly equal to MAG.

Unilateralization has three serious disadvantages. First, for the design method to be useful, the unilateralization network must very nearly eliminate the internal feedback of the transistor. In practice, the passive network may have to be tailored for each transistor individually. Second, unilateralization circuits often employ a transformer for phase inversion; these transformers limit the unilateralized bandwidth. Furthermore, if a transformer is avoided, the passive network can only roughly unilateralize the transistor over a broad band. For this reason, unilateralization techniques are usually limited to narrow-band, high-gain applications. A third disadvantage is that the amplifier may become unstable if the transistor parameters vary.

The mismatching design technique, on the other hand, has three important advantages: First, stability may be ensured for all transistors of a particular type. Second, the input impedance of a stage can be made essentially independent of the load impedance, permitting practical multistage amplifier alignment. Third, the design technique is particularly useful in broad-band applications.

Unilateralized Gain.[1] The derivation of the high-frequency unilateralized gain, G_U, starts with two basic relations using the transistor's four-terminal admittance parameters.

$$\begin{vmatrix} i_1 \\ i_2 \end{vmatrix} = \begin{vmatrix} y_{11} & y_{12} \\ y_{21} & y_{22} \end{vmatrix} \begin{vmatrix} v_1 \\ v_2 \end{vmatrix} \tag{1}$$

For admittance unilateralization, a second two-port network is added in parallel to the transistor,

$$y = \begin{vmatrix} y_n & -y_n \\ -y_n & y_n \end{vmatrix} \tag{2}$$

such that

$$|y_n| = y_{12} \tag{3}$$

The combined matrix of transistor plus unilateralizing network is

$$\begin{vmatrix} i_1 \\ i_2 \end{vmatrix} = \begin{vmatrix} (y_{11} + y_{12}) & 0 \\ (y_{21} - y_{12}) & (y_{22} + y_{12}) \end{vmatrix} \begin{vmatrix} v_1 \\ v_2 \end{vmatrix} \tag{4}$$

For conjugate-matched input and output,

$$P_{(in)} = \frac{|i_1|^2}{4\mathrm{Re}\,(y_{11} + y_{12})} \tag{5}$$

where the Re represents the real part of the complex expression.

$$P_{(out)} = \frac{|(y_{21} - y_{12})V_1|^2}{4\mathrm{Re}\,(y_{22} + y_{12})} \tag{6}$$

$$G_U = \frac{4|(y_{21} - y_{12})V_1|^2\,\mathrm{Re}\,(y_{11} + y_{12})}{4\mathrm{Re}\,(y_{22} + y_{12})|i_1|^2} \tag{7}$$

Since

$$\left|\frac{V_1}{i_1}\right|^2 = \left[\frac{1}{2\mathrm{Re}\,(y_{11} + y_{12})}\right]^2 \tag{8}$$

$$G_U = \frac{|y_{21} - y_{12}|^2}{4\mathrm{Re}\,(y_{11} + y_{12})\,\mathrm{Re}\,(y_{22} + y_{12})} \tag{9}$$

Equation (9) is the G_U of the composite network. Ordinarily, this equation is used in a simplified form.

Defining

$$h'_{21} = \frac{y_{21} - y_{12}}{y_{11} + y_{12}} \tag{10}$$

$$h'_{11} = \frac{1}{y_{11} + y_{12}} \tag{11}$$

and

$$\operatorname{Re} y'_{22} = \operatorname{Re}(y_{22} + y_{12}) \tag{12}$$

then

$$G_U = \frac{|h'_{21}|^2}{4\operatorname{Re} y_{22} \operatorname{Re} h_{11}} \tag{13}$$

If

$$y_{12} \ll y_{11} \tag{14}$$

then

$$G_U = \frac{|h_{21} + h_{12}|^2}{4\operatorname{Re} h_{11} \operatorname{Re} y'_{22}} \tag{15}$$

where h_{21} and h_{12} are the unneutralized network parameters.
    If two other approximations can be made,

$$h_{21} \gg h_{12} \tag{16}$$

and

$$\operatorname{Re} y_{12} \ll \operatorname{Re} y_{22} \tag{17}$$

the power gain then reduces to

$$G_U \cong \frac{|h_{21}|^2}{4\operatorname{Re} h_{11} \operatorname{Re} y_{22}} \tag{18}$$

This expression is also referred to as maximum available gain, MAG.
    Methods of Unilateralization.[2]   Three methods* for unilateralizing common-emitter circuits are shown in Fig. 20.1.   In the bridge circuit, the combination L and C_F provide the necessary phase shift in the output signal (approximately 180°). L and C_F should resonate at a factor of 5 or more below the center frequency of the amplifier passband.
    If E_1 is the voltage across the parallel resonant circuit, E_2 is the voltage across C_F, and I is the signal current through L and C_F, the following equations obtain:

$$I = \frac{E_1}{j\omega_o L} \qquad \text{for } X_{CF} \ll X_L \tag{19}$$

$$E_2 = IX_{CF} = \frac{E_1}{j\omega_o L}\frac{1}{j\omega_o C_F} \tag{20}$$

since

$$\omega_o L = \frac{1}{\omega_o C_1} \tag{21}$$

and

$$\frac{E_2}{E_1} = -\frac{C_1}{C_F} \tag{22}$$

---

* See Ref. 2 for other practical circuits.

The bridge is completed by feeding back E_2 to the input across a capacitance:

$$C_N = \frac{C_F}{C_1} C_C \tag{23}$$

This provides a feedback current equal to, but 180° out of phase with, the internal current feed-through C_c.

The capacity tap circuit is similarly designed. The transformer provides the 180° phase reversal, and C_N should be chosen so that

$$C_N = \frac{N_1}{N_2} C_C \tag{24}$$

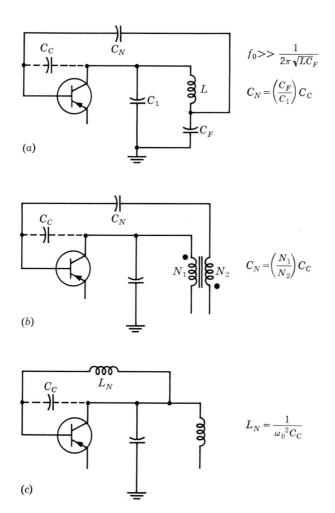

$$f_0 >> \frac{1}{2\pi\sqrt{LC_F}}$$

$$C_N = \left(\frac{C_F}{C_1}\right) C_C$$

$$C_N = \left(\frac{N_1}{N_2}\right) C_C$$

$$L_N = \frac{1}{\omega_0^2 C_C}$$

(a)

(b)

(c)

Fig. 20.1. Methods of unilateralization: (a) capacitance bridge circuit; (b) capacitance tap circuit; (c) inductive feedback circuit.

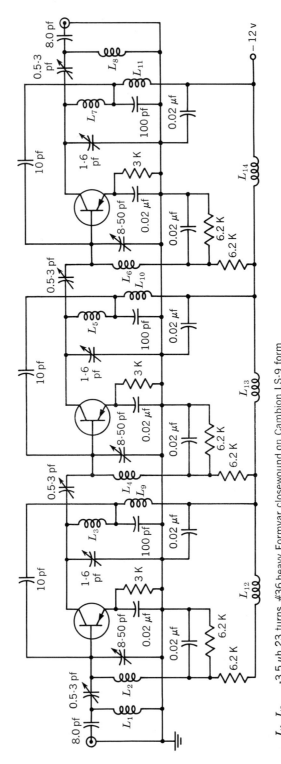

L_1, L_8 - 3.5 μh 23 turns #36 heavy Formvar closewound on Cambion LS-9 form
L_2, L_4, L_6 - 0.53 μh 9 turns #36 heavy Formvar space $^1\!/_{62}''$ apart on Cambion LS-9 form
L_3, L_5, L_7 - 5.3 μh 29 turns #36 heavy Formvar closewound on Cambion LS-9 form
L_9-L_{14} - 15 μh rfc

Fig. 20.2.   30-mc IF amplifier: 3-mc BW, 65- to 75-db gain, all transistors 2N1405.

The inductive feedback circuit should satisfy the approximate condition

$$L_N = \frac{1}{\omega_0{}^2 C_c} \qquad (25)$$

The circuit shown in Fig. 20.2 employs the unilateralization shown in Fig. 20.1a.

Design Example. To design the unilateralization circuit, a scheme for interstage coupling must be chosen. The capacitive coupling network shown in Fig. 20.3 was used.

In this design:

Q_1 = loaded uncoupled Q of the primary
Q_2 = loaded uncoupled Q of the secondary
k = coefficient of coupling

The following assumptions are made:

1. $Q_1 = Q_2$
2. $k > k_c$; k is larger than the value for critical coupling or flat response. This condition yields a double-peaked response. The ratio of output voltage at either peak to that at the valley (center frequency) is given by

$$\frac{E_{(valley)}}{E_{(peak)}} = \frac{2\,k/k_c}{1 + (k/k_c)^2} \qquad (26)$$

where

$$k_c = \frac{1}{Q_L} \qquad (27)$$

Therefore,

$$\frac{E_{(valley)}}{E_{(peak)}} = \frac{2kQ_L}{1 + (kQ_L)^2} \qquad (28)$$

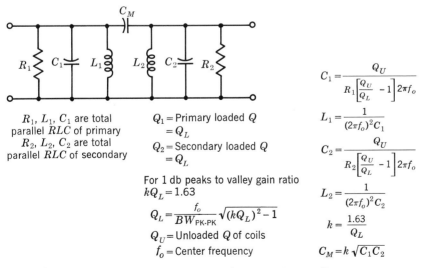

R_1, L_1, C_1 are total parallel RLC of primary
R_2, L_2, C_2 are total parallel RLC of secondary

Q_1 = Primary loaded Q
$\quad = Q_L$
Q_2 = Secondary loaded Q
$\quad = Q_L$

For 1 db peaks to valley gain ratio
$kQ_L = 1.63$

$$Q_L = \frac{f_o}{BW_{\text{PK-PK}}} \sqrt{(kQ_L)^2 - 1}$$

Q_U = Unloaded Q of coils
f_o = Center frequency

$$C_1 = \frac{Q_U}{R_1 \left[\dfrac{Q_U}{Q_L} - 1\right] 2\pi f_o}$$

$$L_1 = \frac{1}{(2\pi f_o)^2 C_1}$$

$$C_2 = \frac{Q_U}{R_2 \left[\dfrac{Q_U}{Q_L} - 1\right] 2\pi f_o}$$

$$L_2 = \frac{1}{(2\pi f_o)^2 C_2}$$

$$k = \frac{1.63}{Q_L}$$

$$C_M = k \sqrt{C_1 C_2}$$

Fig. 20.3.   Design equations for capacitive coupling.

If 1 db is specified as the allowable ripple, it follows that

$$kQ_L = 1.63 \tag{29}$$

The other important relationship is

$$Q_L = \frac{f_o}{BW_{(pk\text{-}pk)}}\sqrt{(kQ_L)^2 - 1} \tag{30}$$

The design of Fig. 20.2 is now given:

$$BW_{(pk\text{-}pk)} = 3 \text{ mc} \qquad Q_U = 50 \qquad f_o = 30 \text{ mc} \qquad Q_L = Q_1 = Q_2$$

For the 2N1405,

$$r_{oep} = 18 \text{ kilohms} \qquad \text{and} \qquad c_{oep} = 2 \text{ pf}$$

From Eq. (29), $kQ_L = 1.63$, $(kQ_L)^2 = 2.65$, and from Eq. (30),

$$Q_L = \frac{30 \times 10^6}{3 \times 10^6}\sqrt{2.65 - 1} = 12.9$$

$$C_{tot} = \frac{Q_U}{r_{oep}(Q_U/Q_L - 1)\omega_o} = \frac{50}{18,000(50/12.9 - 1)6.28 \times 30 \times 16^6} = 5.2 \text{ pf}$$

Allowing for transistor capacitance variations and circuit strays, let

$$C_1 = 1 \text{ to } 6 \text{ pf variable capacitor} \qquad L_1 = 5.3 \text{ }\mu\text{h}$$

For the secondary:

$$r_{iep} = 1.8 \text{ kilohms} \qquad c_{iep} = 13 \text{ pf}$$

$$C_{tot} \frac{50}{1,800(50/12.9 - 1)6.28 \times 30 \times 10^6} = 52 \text{ pf}$$

Again allowing for circuit conditions and transistor variations, set

$$C_2 = 8 \text{ to } 50 \text{ pf variable capacitor} \qquad L_2 = 0.53 \text{ }\mu\text{h}$$

Since $$kQ_L = 1.63 \qquad \text{and} \qquad Q_L = 12.9 \qquad k = 0.126$$

$$C_M = k\sqrt{C_{tot\,pri}C_{tot\,sec}} = 0.126\sqrt{52 \times 5.2} = 2 \text{ pf}$$

To allow for alignment adjustment, use a variable capacitor.

$$C_M = 0.5 \text{ to } 3 \text{ pf}$$

The unilateralization network may now be designed. For

$$C_1 = 5 \text{ pf} \qquad C_F = 100 \text{ pf} \qquad C_c = 0.5 \text{ pf} \qquad C_N = {}^{100}\!/_5(0.5) = 10 \text{ pf}$$

20.2. MISMATCHING

General Theory. A second method of achieving stability is by the mismatch technique. If the device is mismatched at its input and output terminals, useful stable gains can be obtained up to very high frequencies and over broad bandwidths.

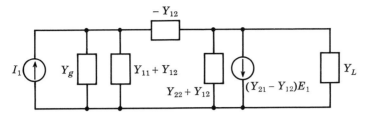

Fig. 20.4.   Single-stage two-port driven and terminated.

Two-port theory using admittance parameters provides a convenient approach to the problem.   Figure 20.4 shows the single-stage equivalent circuit.   The general transducer power gain is

$$G_T = \frac{4|Y_{21}|^2 G_g G_L}{[(Y_{11} + Y_g)(Y_{22} + Y_L) - Y_{12}Y_{21}]^2} \tag{31}$$

Equation (31) is not a stable gain in many cases.   Note that for a conjugate match of Y_{11} and Y_{22}, if the $Y_{12}Y_{21}$ product is real, the denominator may approach zero. However, these very high gains can be realized only at the expense of stability. Oscillation is interpreted as the case where G_T equals infinity.

The power gain of a unilateralized network is given by Eq. (18) as

$$G_U \cong \frac{|h_{21}|^2}{4\mathrm{Re}\, h_{11}\, \mathrm{Re}\, y_{22}}$$

The typical unilateralized power gain is plotted in Figs. 20.5 to 20.8 for the TI type 2N1141 series germanium mesa transistor, at two bias points for the frequency range of 60 to 400 mc.

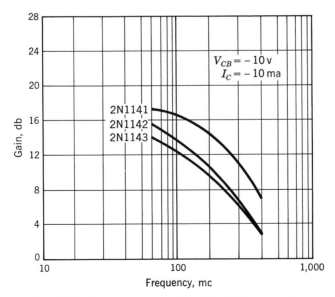

Fig. 20.5.   Common-base unilateralized RF power gain.

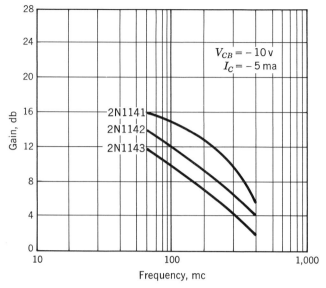

Fig. 20.6.   Common-base unilateralized RF power gain.

The optimum conditions of mismatch, i.e., highest gain for a given degree of stability, have been determined by several authors.[3, 4]   These are:

$$\frac{G_{11}}{G_g} = \frac{G_{22}}{G_L} \qquad G_g = mG_{11} \qquad G_L = mG_{22} \tag{32}$$

That is, the parallel input and output conductances measured with the other port short-circuited must be mismatched by the same factor, *m*.

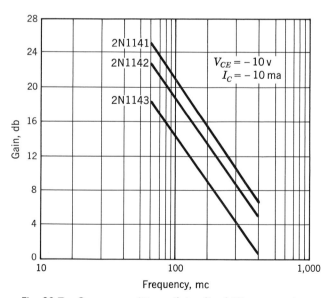

Fig. 20.7.   Common-emitter unilateralized RF power gain.

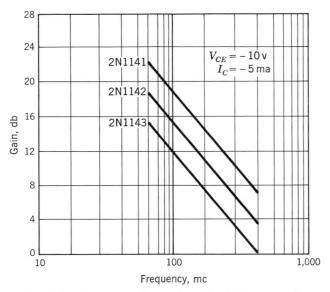

Fig. 20.8. Common-emitter unilateralized RF power gain.

The RF gain stability factor, ρ, is defined by the equation[4]

$$\rho = \frac{2(G_{11} + G_g)(G_{22} + G_L)}{|y_{21}y_{12}|(1 + \cos \angle y_{21}y_{12})} \tag{33}$$

If $\rho > 1$, the stage will be stable; however, well-designed stages will provide a stability margin of $\rho = 5$ or more. The advantage of an amplifier having a high stability factor is its gain stability with variations in temperature and bias, and with interchange of transistors. It can be shown that ρ at a given frequency will be a function of m alone and will have the following form:

$$\rho = \rho'(1 + m)^2 \tag{34}$$

The coefficient ρ' is plotted against frequency for the 2N1141 series in Figs. 20.9 through 20.12. Based on these figures, it appears desirable from the standpoint of stability to design amplifiers in the common-base configuration at frequencies above 100 mc. The tendency of the common-emitter configuration to be unstable at higher frequencies is believed to be due to the feedback introduced through the header-to-collector connection.

The transducer power gain of a stage which is stabilized by mismatch will now be calculated. This will be done by computing a loss factor, which, multiplied by G_U, will yield the mismatched transducer gain, G_{TM}; L is the product L_1L_2, which is defined as

$$L_1 = \frac{P_{OM}}{P_{IM}G_U} \tag{35}$$

and

$$L_2 = \frac{P_{IM}}{P_A} \tag{36}$$

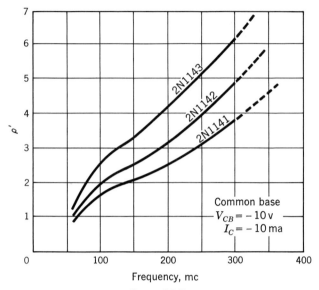

Figure 20.9

where P_{OM} = output power for a mismatched condition

P_{IM} = input power for a mismatched condition

P_A = available power from the generator

In logarithmic form,

$$G_{TM}(\text{db}) = 10 \log G_U + 10 \log L \tag{37}$$

L will be shown to be a function of m only, as in the case of ρ (see Fig. 20.13).

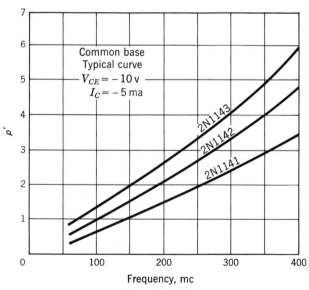

Figure 20.10

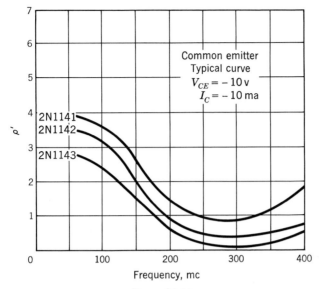

Figure 20.11

To calculate G_{TM}, take the difference of the unilateralized transducer gain read from Figs. 20.5 to 20.8 and the loss factor read from Fig. 20.13. The stability factor may then be evaluated, using Eq. (34) and the data from Figs. 20.9 to 20.12.

L will now be calculated. If the input and output susceptances are canceled by tuning, the output power is given by

$$P_{OM} = \frac{|Y_{21}|^2 I_1^2 G_L}{|(G_{11} + G_g)(G_{22} + G_L) - Y_{12} Y_{21}|^2} \tag{38}$$

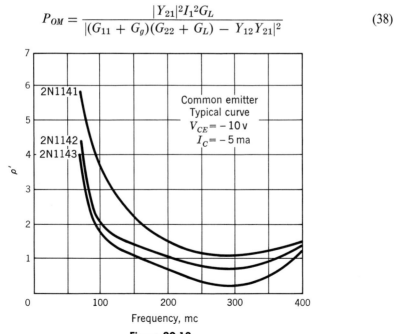

Figure 20.12

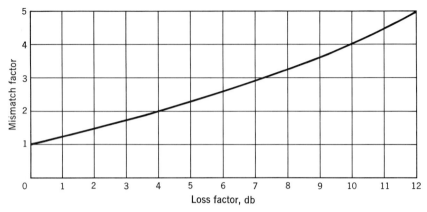

Fig. 20.13.   Loss factor vs. mismatch factor.

Furthermore, if the stage is mismatched at input and output by the factor m,

$$P_{OM} = \frac{|Y_{21}|^2 I_1^2 G_L}{|(m + 1)^2 G_{11} G_{22} - Y_{12} Y_{21}|^2} \tag{39}$$

In most cases $G_{11} G_{22}(m + 1)^2 \gg y_{12} y_{21}$, and

$$P_{OM} = \frac{|Y_{21}|^2 I_1^2 G_L}{|(m + 1)^2 G_{11} G_{22}|^2} \tag{40}$$

The input power available for amplification by the transistor when mismatched can be seen from Fig. 20.14 to be

$$P_{IM} = \frac{I_1^2}{(m + 1)^2 G_g} = \frac{I_1^2}{(m + 1)^2 G_{11}} \tag{41}$$

The power gain under mismatch is then

$$G_{TM} = \frac{|Y_{21}|^2 G_{11} G_L (m + 1)^2}{|(m + 1)^2 G_{11} G_{22}|^2} \tag{42}$$

and, because $G_L = m G_{22}$,

$$G_{TM} = \frac{m}{(m + 1)^2} \frac{|Y_{21}|^2}{G_{11} G_{22}} \tag{43}$$

If this expression is normalized with respect to G_U, the ratio is the first loss factor:

$$L_1 = \frac{4m}{(m + 1)^2} \tag{44}$$

The second loss factor is simply the ratio of Eq. (41) to the power available from the generator, $P_A = I_1^2/4 G_g$:

$$L_2 = \frac{4}{(m + 1)^2} \tag{45}$$

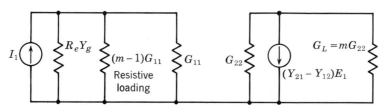

(1) Net input and output susceptances have been tuned out
(2) I_1 and its internal impedance have been transformed so that $R_e Y_g = R_e Y_{11} = G_{11}$
(3) Mismatch has made Y_{11} negligible

Fig. 20.14. Equivalent circuit for calculating mismatched gain.

The composite loss factor, $L = L_1 L_2$, is given by

$$L = \frac{16m}{(m + 1)^4} \tag{46}$$

In logarithmic form,

$$L \text{ (db)} = 10 \log \frac{16m}{(m + 1)^4} \tag{47}$$

and the mismatched transducer gain is, therefore,

$$G_T \text{ (db)} = 10 \log G_U + 10 \log \frac{16m}{(m + 1)^4} \tag{48}$$

Measurement of Characteristics. The design data presented in Figs. 20.15 to 20.20 were taken on a General Radio 1607A transfer function and immittance

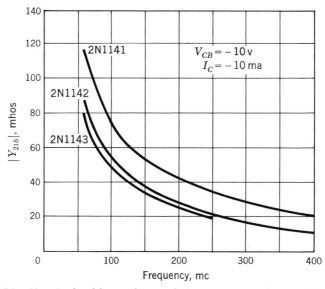

Fig. 20.15. Magnitude of forward transadmittance common base vs. frequency.

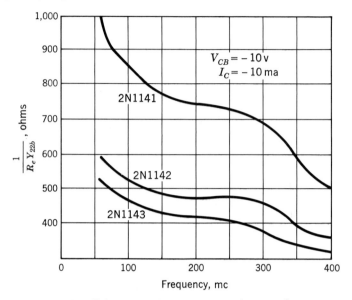

Fig. 20.16.   Parallel output resistance common base vs. frequency.

bridge.   These are the typical characteristics of several tested samples.   The accuracy of the measurements is ±10%.

The 1607A bridge is a coaxial instrument which is capable of measuring two-port admittance and hybrid parameters in the frequency range of 25 to 1,500 mc.   The range of the measurements in this report was restricted to 60 to 400 mc because this range covers most of the applications of the 2N1141 series.

The test-equipment block diagram is given in Fig. 20.21.   The signal source is a

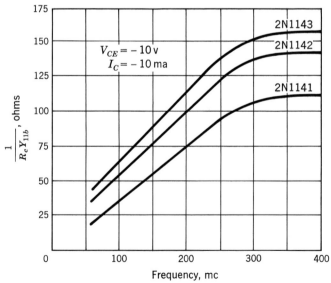

Fig. 20.17.   Parallel input resistance common base vs. frequency.

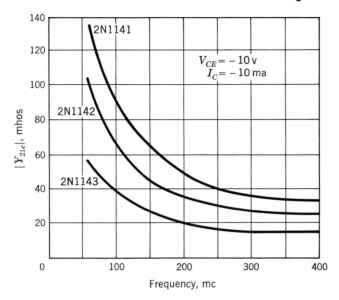

Fig. 20.18. **Magnitude of forward transadmittance common emitter vs. frequency.**

Hewlett-Packard 608C VHF generator which is set to 50 to 100 mv, depending on the measurement being taken. The null detector employed is a Nems-Clarke 1502A receiver with a Nems-Clarke REU 300B frequency-range extension unit. Nulls of about 1 μv were obtained.

No input susceptance data are given in the graphs because they are immaterial in the power-gain calculations. Table 20.1 gives data representative of these characteristics over the 60- to 400-mc frequency range.

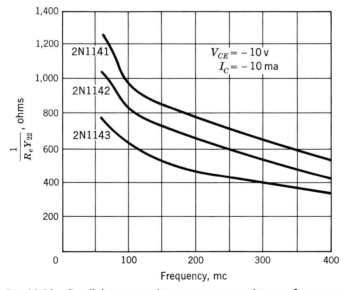

Fig. 20.19. **Parallel output resistance common emitter vs. frequency.**

Table 20.1

Characteristic	Parameter	
	Common-base	Common-emitter
Parallel input inductance	0.02–0.05 μh	6–20 pf
Parallel output capacitance	2–5 pf	5–15 pf

100-mc Design Example. The example chosen to illustrate the mismatch design is a three-stage common-base 100-mc amplifier (Fig. 20.24). The input and output circuits to be matched are shown in Fig. 20.22. Because the common-base input is inductive with a Q equal to approximately 2, the self-inductance ratio transformer shown in Fig. 20.23 is used. The value of L needed is obtained from the $R_{(in)}$, R_i relationship. Substituting the values $R_{(out)} = 850$ ohms for $R_{(in)}$, $R_{(in)} = 37$ ohms for R_i, and $L_{(in)} = 0.02$ μh for L_i yields $L = 0.08$ μh. The total parallel inductance of the interstage is

$$L_T = 0.02 + 0.08 \text{ μh} = 0.1 \text{ μh}$$

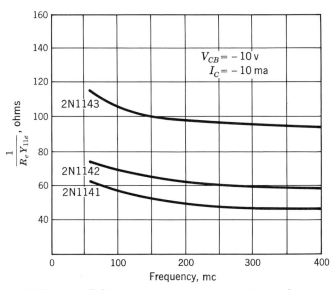

Fig. 20.20.   Parallel input resistance common emitter vs. frequency.

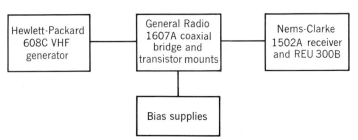

Fig. 20.21.   Test-equipment block diagram.

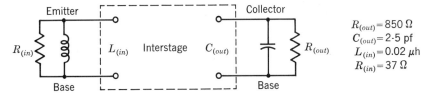

Fig. 20.22.   Input-output circuit to be matched for design of 100-mc RF amplifier.

The parallel capacitance is 25 pf for resonance at 100 mc.   A 4- to 30-pf trimmer capacitor is used in the circuit to facilitate tuning.   For $m = 2$, an 850-ohm resistor must be added in parallel with the 100-mc tank circuit.   This determines the loaded Q of the interstage,

$$Q_L = \frac{R_{tot\ parallel}}{X_{L\ tot\ parallel}} \qquad \text{or} \qquad Q_L = 4.7$$

Since the single-stage bandwidth is related to the loaded Q by the expression

$$BW = \frac{f_o}{Q_L}$$

where f_o is the mid-band frequency, the single-stage bandwidth will be

$$BW = \frac{100\ \text{mc}}{4.7} = 21\ \text{mc}$$

For three cascaded stages of this same interstage Q, the bandwidth will be

$$BW = 21\ \text{mc} \times 0.43 = 9.0\ \text{mc}$$

The output-matching network was chosen to be an autotransformer to match $R_{(out)} = 850$ ohms to the 50-ohm output load.   The same total parallel inductance and capacitance are used to set $Q_L = 4.7$.   The tap position for the 50-ohm load is experimentally determined.

The input network is required to match the 50-ohm impedance of the source to 19 ohms, which is approximately one-half the parallel input resistance of the input stage.   The necessary inductance is calculated as before:

$$\frac{L + 0.02\ \mu\text{h}}{0.02\ \mu\text{h}} = \frac{50}{19} \qquad L = 0.01\ \mu\text{h}$$

With this required L, the necessary input capacitance is approximately 80 pf.

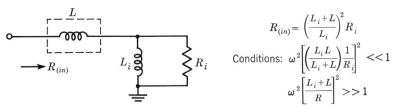

$$R_{(in)} = \left(\frac{L_i + L}{L_i}\right)^2 R_i$$

Conditions: $\omega^2 \left[\left(\frac{L_i L}{L_i + L}\right)\frac{1}{R_i}\right]^2 \ll 1$

$$\omega^2 \left[\frac{L_i + L}{R}\right]^2 \gg 1$$

Fig. 20.23.   Self-inductance ratio transformer.

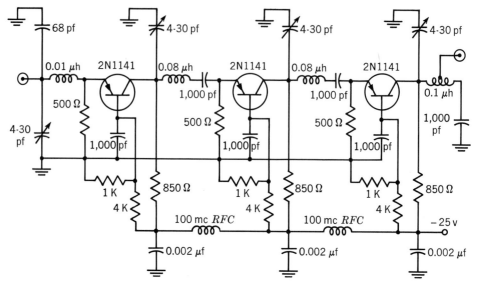

0.08 and 0.1 μh coils are 3 and 4 turns respectively of No. 18 tinned bus wire, ¼″ diameter

0.01 μh coil is 1 turn of NO. 00 enameled wire, ³⁄₈″ diameter.
All loading resistors are TI MIL-LINE 1%.

Fig. 20.24.   100-mc RF amplifier.

Next, the expected gain is calculated. The loss factor for $m = 2$ is read from the graph as 4 db. Subtracting this from G_U for the common-base stage at 100 mc, the result is $16.5 - 4.0$ db. This means that the gain per stage should be approximately 12.5 db, or the overall gain should be 37.5 db.

The stability data can be determined from the appropriate graph as $\rho' = 1.6$. For $m = 2$, this means that $\rho = 14.4$.

Data were taken on the amplifier for three values of m which provide adequate stability. The center frequency gain calculated and measured along with the amplifier response is shown in Fig. 20.25 for the three values of m and ρ. Gain stabilities of ± 1 db for interchange of transistors were noted for the $\rho = 25.6$ condition.

The following are other design examples using the mismatch technique.

60-mc Design Example. Figure 20.26 shows a single stage of an eight-stage 60-mc IF amplifier using TI type 3N35 silicon tetrode transistors. All eight stages are identical except for the input and output stages, whose transformers are designed for the appropriate driving and load resistances, respectively. Transitionally coupled, double-tuned interstages are used. The design of these networks is treated extensively in a report by Lawson and Stone.[5] A 5:1 mismatch provides stability and ease of alignment while allowing a stage gain of about 12.5 db.

The interstage description and calculation of the necessary constants are:

$$\lambda_1 = \frac{1}{\omega_0^2 C_1}\left(1 + \frac{\alpha_1^2}{8} + \frac{3\alpha_2^2}{8}\right) \qquad \lambda_2 = \frac{1}{\omega_0^2 C_2}\left(1 + \frac{\alpha_2^2}{8} + \frac{3\alpha_1^2}{8}\right) \qquad \lambda_3 = \frac{1}{\omega_0^4 C_1 C_2}$$

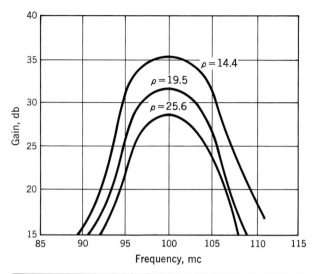

M	ρ	Single stage L(db)	3 stage L_3(db)	G_{TM3} calculated G_{U3}(db) $- L_3$(db)	G_{TM3} measured
2	14.4	4 db	12 db	37.5 db	36 db
2.5	19.5	5.75 db	17.3 db	32.2 db	32 db
3	25.6	7.25 db	21.8 db	27.7 db	28 db

G_U=16.5 db for this example   Gain stability of ± 1 db for interchange in transistors
G_{U3}=49.5 db for 3 stage   was noted for the ρ=25.6 condition

Fig. 20.25. 100-mc RF amplifier data.

$$M = \sqrt{\lambda_1\lambda_2 - \lambda_3} \qquad k = \frac{M}{\sqrt{\lambda_1\lambda_2}} = \sqrt{1 - \frac{\lambda_3}{\lambda_1\lambda_2}}$$

$$\alpha_1 = \frac{1}{\omega_o R_1 C_1} \qquad \text{and} \qquad \alpha_2 = \frac{1}{\omega_o R_2 C_2}$$

where $\omega_o = 2\pi f_o$
   f_o = design center frequency
   λ_1 = primary inductance
   λ_2 = secondary inductance
   M = mutual inductance
   k = coefficient of coupling
   α_1 = primary dissipation factor
   α_2 = secondary dissipation factor
   R_1 = common-emitter parallel output resistance
   C_1 = total parallel primary circuit capacitance
   R_2 = common-emitter parallel input resistance
   C_2 = total parallel secondary circuit capacitance

Each stage is designed with a 32-mc bandwidth. Thus,

$$b = \frac{\Delta f}{f_o} = {}^{32}\!/_{60} = 0.533 \qquad \text{where } b = \text{fractional bandwidth}$$

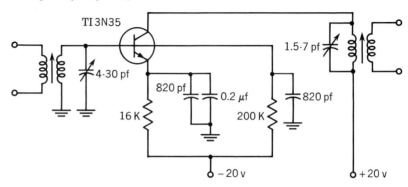

Fig. 20.26.   One stage of the amplifier.

However,

$$b = \frac{1}{\sqrt{2}}(\alpha_1 + \alpha_2)$$

so that the relationship $\alpha_1 + \alpha_2 = \sqrt{2}\,(0.533) = 0.754$ is obtained.   It was decided to design the transformer using a typical value of 5,000 ohms for R_1 and 6 pf for C_1.

$$\alpha_1 = \frac{1}{\omega_o R_1 C_1} = \frac{1}{(2\pi)(60 \times 10^{-6})(5,000)(6 \times 10^{-12})} = 0.0885$$

Thus, $\alpha_2 = 0.754 - 0.0885 = 0.6655$

Values of $R_2 = 133$ ohms and $C_2 = 30$ pf were chosen.

$$\alpha_2 = \frac{1}{\omega_o R_2 C_2}$$

The transformer constants then were calculated as follows:

$$\lambda_1 = \frac{1}{(377)^2(10^{12})(6 \times 10^{-12})}\left[1 + \frac{(0.0885)^2}{8} + \frac{3(0.6655)^2}{8}\right] = 1.365 \times 10^{-6}\ \text{henry}$$

$$\lambda_2 = \frac{1}{(377)^2(10^{12})(30 \times 10^{-12})}\left[1 + \frac{(0.6655)^2}{8} + \frac{3(0.0885)^2}{8}\right] = 0.2475 \times 10^{-6}\ \text{henry}$$

$$\lambda_3 = \frac{1}{(377)^4(10^{24})(6 \times 10^{-12})(30 \times 10^{-12})} = 0.275 \times 10^{-12}\ \text{henry}^2$$

$$k = \sqrt{1 - \frac{0.275 \times 10^{-12}}{1.365 \times 10^{-6} \times 0.2475 \times 10^{-6}}} = 0.43$$

The proper biasing of the stage is important to ensure optimum gain and interchangeability of units.   Measurements made on large quantities of 3N35 units show that this device has optimum gain characteristics at an operating point of $V_{CE} = 20$ volts, $I_E = -1.3$ ma, and $I_{B2} = -0.1$ ma.   To ensure adequate bias circuit performance from unit to unit under conditions of large ambient temperature variations, a two-battery circuit was employed.   The negative supply was made 20 volts, thereby providing a symmetrical arrangement.   Each transistor is biased common base even though the RF circuitry is common emitter.   The large

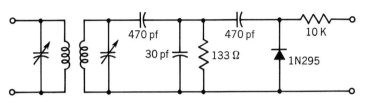

Fig. 20.27. Demodulator probe.

resistors in the emitter and base-2 leads assure that the circuits in these elements will remain constant. These resistors are bypassed for signal frequencies by appropriate capacitors. An additional 0.2-μf capacitor helps ensure that the bias point will remain constant with a pulsed input signal.

The RF circuitry is straightforward. Trimmer capacitances tune both sides of the transformer: a 4- to 30-pf unit at the input to the transistor and a 1.5- to 7-pf unit in the collector circuit.

Figure 20.27 shows the demodulator probe which is used to simplify alignment. It consists of a resistor and a capacitor which simulate the input to the stage following the one to be tuned, plus a diode for demodulating the signal. The demodulated signal may be viewed on a high-gain, low-frequency oscilloscope. The probe has low stray capacitances and a flat frequency response so that the circuit under alignment will not be detuned by the probe. All measurements were made on the low-impedance side of the transformers.

The testing was done using a sweep generator. This method permits the effect of minor adjustments to be evaluated rapidly, and is recommended for any wide-band amplifier work. The effects of regeneration show up on this test as spikes or otherwise unexplainable lobes in the passband. In aligning the entire amplifier, the stages can be tuned by moving the probe one stage at a time.

5.5-mc Design Example. Figure 20.28 shows a three-stage 5.5-mc amplifier using TI type 2N2189 germanium transistors. This amplifier has a 3-db bandwidth and mid-band gain equal to 200 kc and 60 db, respectively.

The interstage networks consist of single-tuned transformers with the collectors tapped down on the primary (Fig. 20.29). This tap-down method of IF transformer design has been described by Webster[6] and Cooke.[7]

The interstage calculations using their notation are

$$Q_L = \frac{f_o}{BW_A} \sqrt{2^{1/n} - 1} \tag{49}$$

where $BW_A = 200$ kc
$f_o = 5.5$ mc
$Q_L = $ single-stage loaded Q
$n = 3$

Substituting these values into Eq. (49) gives

$$Q_L = \left(\frac{5.5 \text{ mc}}{0.200 \text{ mc}}\right)\left(0.51\right)$$

$$Q_L = 14$$

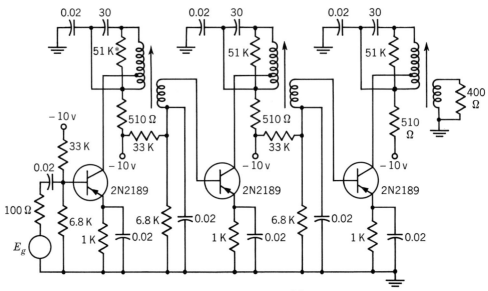

Fig. 20.28.   5.5-mc amplifier.

At this point we must decide on the total loss allowable for interstage.   This loss is divided into a mismatch loss, ML, and a coil loss, n.   ML is defined in this design procedure as the efficiency of match.

$$ML \text{ (db)} = 10 \log \frac{4a}{(1 + a)^2} \tag{50}$$

where $a = R_L'/R_g'$ (called the mismatch factor).

   R_L' = load impedance (transistor's input impedance) referred to unit turns ratio

   R_g' = generator impedance (transistor's output impedance) referred to unit turns ratio

The coil loss is defined as the efficiency of the transformer,

$$\eta \text{ (db)} = 10 \log \left(1 - \frac{Q_L}{Q_U}\right)^2 \tag{51}$$

where Q_U = unloaded Q of the primary.   Using an $a = 0.5$ results in a mismatch loss:

$$ML \text{ (db)} = 10 \log \frac{4(0.5)}{(1 + 0.5)^2} \qquad ML \text{ (db)} = -0.5 \text{ db}$$

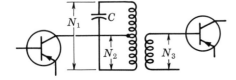

Figure 20.29

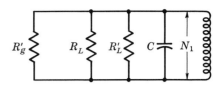

Figure 20.30

For this amplifier, a total loss equal to 10 db/transformer provides stable operation and minimizes interaction between the tuned circuits.
  Therefore,

$$n \text{ (db)} = -10 + 0.5 \text{ db} = -9.5 \text{ db} = 0.112 \qquad \text{(numeric)}$$

Solving for the Q_U from Eq. (51) gives

$$Q_U = \frac{Q_L}{1 - \sqrt{n}} \qquad (52)$$

Substituting values for Q_L and n,

$$Q_U = \frac{14}{1 - \sqrt{0.112}} = 21.0$$

Figure 20.30 shows the transformer with all impedances referred to the total primary. Assuming a value of $C = 30$ pf gives, for the antiresonant unloaded coil impedance,

$$R_C = \frac{Q_U}{\omega_o C} \qquad (53)$$

$$R_C = \frac{21.0}{1.038 \times 10^{-3}} = 20.2 \text{ kilohms}$$

The total shunting impedance across C required to give the correct Q_L is

$$R_T = \frac{Q_L}{\omega_o C} = \frac{14}{1.038 \times 10^{-3}} = 13.5 \text{ kilohms} \qquad (54)$$

R_T is equal to the parallel combination of R_c, R_g', and R_L'; therefore, we must determine the value of resistance, R_x, which parallels R_C to give R_T.

$$R_T = \frac{R_x R_c}{R_x + R_c} \qquad (55)$$

$$R_x = \frac{R_c R_T}{R_c - R_T} \qquad (56)$$

Substituting values for R_C and R_T gives

$$R_x = \frac{(20.2)(13.5)}{4.8} \qquad R_x = 56.9 \text{ kilohms}$$

R_x represents the loading referred to total primary caused by R_g' and R_L'.

We have

$$R_x = \frac{R_g' R_L'}{R_g' + R_L'} \tag{57}$$

$$= \frac{R_g' a R_g'}{R_g' + a R_g'} \tag{58}$$

$$= R_g' \frac{a}{1 + a} \tag{59}$$

or

$$R_g' = R_x \frac{1 + a}{a} \tag{60}$$

Also

$$R_g' = \left(\frac{N_1}{N_2}\right)^2 R_g \tag{61}$$

Therefore

$$\frac{N_1}{N_2} = \sqrt{\frac{R_x(1 + a)/a}{R_g}} \tag{62}$$

Using $R_g = 6$ kilohms and substituting the above values for R_x and a gives

$$\frac{N_1}{N_2} = \sqrt{\frac{(56.9 \text{ kilohms})(3)}{6 \text{ kilohms}}} = \sqrt{28.4} = 5.33$$

The ratio N_1/N_3 is determined from the equations

$$R_L' = a R_g' = a R_g \left(\frac{N_1}{N_2}\right)^2 \tag{63}$$

and

$$R_L' = \left(\frac{N_1}{N_3}\right)^2 R_L \tag{64}$$

Therefore

$$\frac{N_1}{N_3} = \sqrt{\frac{a R_g (N_1/N_2)^2}{R_L}} \tag{65}$$

Using $R_L = 400$ ohms,

$$\frac{N_1}{N_3} = \sqrt{\frac{0.5(6)(28.4)}{0.4}} = \sqrt{213} = 14.6$$

Transformer data

$N_1 = 30$ turns of No. 40 Gripeze* wire.
$N_2 = 6$ turns of No. 40 Gripeze wire.
$N_3 = 2$ turns of No. 40 Gripeze wire.

The windings are bifilar-universal wound using El Rad* IF assemblies with ferrite cup and core.

_____

* Registered trademarks.

BIBLIOGRAPHY

1. Cote, A. J., and J. B. Oakes: "Linear Vacuum Tube and Transistor Circuits," McGraw-Hill Book Company, Inc., New York, 1961.
2. Sands, H. F., and H. K. Schlegelmilch: Design Considerations of Transistor I-F Amplifiers for TV Receivers, *Proc. NEC,* vol. 13, p. 433, 1957.
3. Bahrs, G. S.: Amplifiers Employing Potentially Unstable Elements, doctoral thesis, Stanford University, 1956.
4. Frazier, R. M.: Methods of Designing and Cascading Unneutralized Tuned Transistor Amplifiers, address presented at Solid State Circuits Conference, Philadelphia, 1960.
5. Lawson, J. L., and A. M. Stone: Double Tuned Circuit with Transitional Coupling, *MIT Rad. Lab. Rept.* 784, Cambridge, Mass., October 8, 1945.
6. Webster, R. R.: How to Design I-F Transistor Transformers, *Electronics,* pp. 156*ff*, August, 1955.
7. Cooke, H. F.: Tap-down Method of I-F Transformer Design, unpublished paper.

21

Noise

21.1. TRANSISTOR NOISE FIGURE

Noise figure[1] and gain determine receiver or amplifier sensitivity in the VHF range, and are therefore important quantities in the application of VHF small-signal amplifying devices.

Noise figure is defined by the equation

$$NF = \frac{\text{input signal-to-noise power ratio}}{\text{output signal-to-noise power ratio}} \tag{1}$$

An ideal amplifier would amplify the incoming signal and incoming noise equally and would introduce no additional noise. From Eq. (1) such an amplifier would have a noise figure equal to unity (0 db).

The noise figure of several cascaded amplifier stages is

$$NF = NF_1 + \frac{NF_2 - 1}{G_1} + \frac{NF_3 - 1}{G_1 G_2} + \cdots + \frac{NF_n - 1}{\prod\limits_{1}^{n} G_n} \tag{2}$$

where NF = total noise figure

NF_n = noise figure of the nth stage

G_n = available gain of the nth stage

From Eq. (2), the gain and noise figure of the first stage of a cascaded chain will largely determine the total noise figure.

Transistor noise figure is defined as the noise figure the device can yield under the specified conditions of source resistance, frequency, and bias levels. It is important to note the effect of input circuitry losses (P_{CL}) on noise figure. Any input losses (expressed in decibels) add directly to the noise figure (in decibels) because the input signal is effectively attenuated while the available input noise power remains the same. Any noise test circuit should have input losses negligible compared to device noise figure.

In tuned networks the losses are given by

$$P_{CL} = 20 \log \left(1 - \frac{Q_L}{Q_U}\right) \tag{3}$$

Example.   If $Q_L = 10$ (loaded Q) and $Q_U = 50$ (unloaded Q), then

$$P_{CL} = 20 \log (1 - {}^{10}\!/_{50}) = -2 \text{ db}$$

In some designs a compromise of input selectivity may be necessary to keep the input losses low.

Neilson[2] has shown that transistor noise figure is dependent on several physical device characteristics. His treatment of the subject, based on the noise equivalent circuit of Fig. 21.1, attributes noise in transistors to three noise generators: (1) emitter and (2) collector noise current generators representing fluctuations due to diffusion and recombination in the base region, and (3) a base noise voltage generator representing the effect of thermal noise in r_b'.

On the basis of this equivalent circuit, Neilson's expression for common-base and common-emitter noise figure is

$$NF = 1 + \frac{r_b'}{R_g} + \frac{r_e}{2R_g} + \frac{\{1 + [1/(1 + h_{fbo})](f/f_{hfb})^2\}(R_g + r_b' + r_e)^2}{2h_{feo}r_eR_g} \quad (4)$$

where h_{feo} is the low-frequency common-emitter short-circuit forward current transfer ratio.

The good agreement of Eq. (4) with measurements for two 2N1405 series transistors having somewhat different parameters is shown in Figs. 21.2 and 21.3. For these two transistors, $f_{hfb} = 500$ mc and h_{fbo} may be computed from h_{feo} by the well-known relationship

$$h_{fbo} = \frac{-h_{feo}}{1 + h_{feo}} \quad (5)$$

Neilson's treatment does not account for low-frequency transistor noise. Experimentally it is found that noise figure has a low-frequency corner of about 2 mc (with $R_g = 50$ ohms, $I_C = -2$ ma, $V_{CE} = -6$ volts) for 2N1405 series types. This low-frequency corner can be made to extend below 2 mc for higher source-impedance levels.

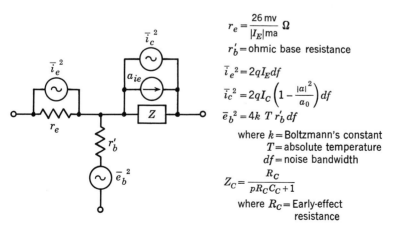

Fig. 21.1.   Noise equivalent circuit of transistor, and definitions.

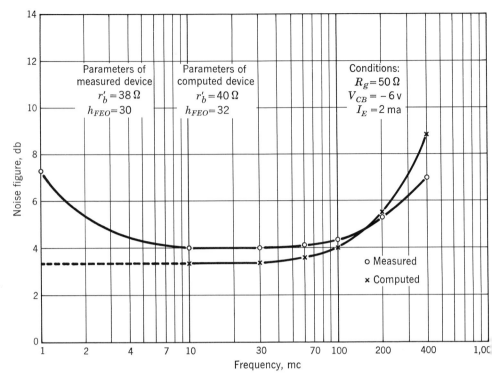

Figure 21.2

Two important conclusions may be drawn from Eq. (4):

1. Low r_b' and high h_{feo} are necessary for low noise-figure mid-frequency (30-mc) range.
2. NF is also a function of the source resistance, R_g, and bias conditions. Normally, however, the noise figure is not seriously degraded by designing the input circuitry for a maximum power-transfer match (i.e., R_g equal to input resistance).

21.2. TRANSISTOR UPPER NOISE-CORNER FREQUENCY

The expression usually quoted[3] for the upper noise-corner frequency, f_A, shown in Fig. 21.4 is

$$f_A = f_{hfb} \sqrt{1 - h_{fbo}} \tag{6}$$

This expression is calculated from the formula given by Neilson [Eq. (4)], considering only the collector noise term (fourth term on the right-hand side).

In many practical cases, the first terms in Eq. (4) may be significant, so the f_A derived will, in general, be too low. Also, the upper noise-corner frequency is determined by f_{hfb} rather than by the transition frequency, f_T, which is defined as the frequency for which the magnitude of the common-emitter forward current transfer ratio, $|h_{fe}|$, can be extrapolated to one (assuming that $|h_{fe}|$ is decreasing at the rate of 6 db/octave).

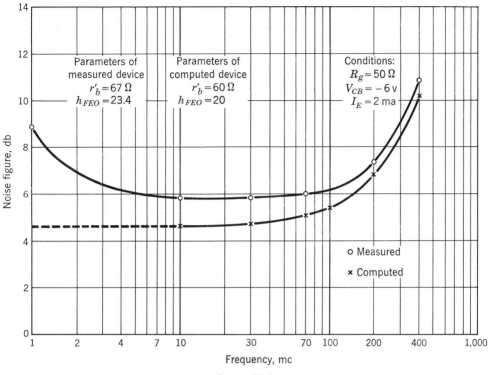

Figure 21.3

A more exact form for f_A is obtained by equating the frequency-dependent term in Eq. (4) to the sum of the four non-frequency-dependent terms and solving for f_A.

$$f_A = f_{hfb} - \sqrt{h_{fbo}r_e \frac{2R_g + 2r'_b + r_e}{(R_g + r_e + r'_b)^2} + (1 + h_{fbo})} \tag{7}$$

or, if $h_{fbo} = -1$,

$$f_A = \frac{f_{hfb}}{R_G + r_e + r'_b}\sqrt{r_e(2R_G + 2r'_b + r_e)} \tag{8}$$

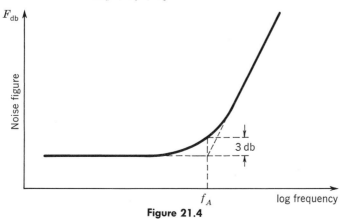

Figure 21.4

Table 21.1

Transistor type	f_T, mc	f_{hfb}, mc	h_{fbo}	r_b', ohms	r_e, ohms	Upper noise-corner frequency f_A, in mc, when $R_g = 50$ ohms			
						Measured	Computed, Eq. (6)	Computed, Eq. (7) with f_{hfb}	Computed, Eq. (7) with f_T
2N544 (drift)	28	40	−0.991	22	16.6	24	3.8	23.5	16.5
OC170 (PADT®)	88	110	−0.992	34	16.6	62	9.8	64.0	49
T1832 (MADT®)	275	470	−0.9615	38	16.6	280	91.7	268	155
2N1405 (Mesa)	460	620	−0.984	46	16.6	320	78.4	330	245

21.3. EXPERIMENTAL RESULTS

Transistor parameters are presented in Table 21.1 for four types of transistor structures, together with calculated values for f_A (for $R_g = 50$ ohms), using the classic equation and the more exact expression [Eq. (7)]. Also shown is the calculated f_A, using the more exact expression but substituting the frequency f_T in place

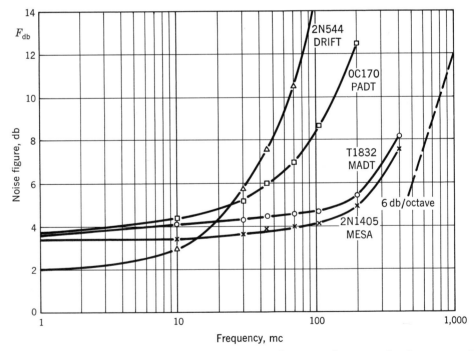

Fig. 21.5. Experimental values for transistor noise figure vs. frequency for four types of germanium high-frequency transistors. $R_g = 50$ ohms, $I_E = 1.5$ ma, $V_{CB} = -9.0$ volts.

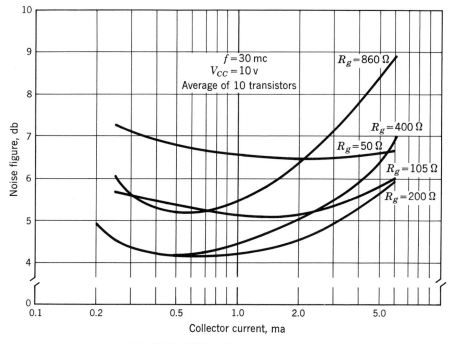

Fig. 21.6. NF **vs.** I_C**, transistor 2N743.**

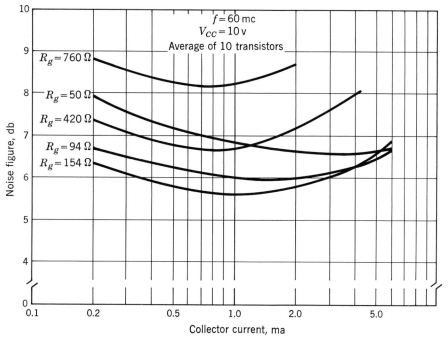

Fig. 21.7. NF **vs.** I_C**, transistor 2N743.**

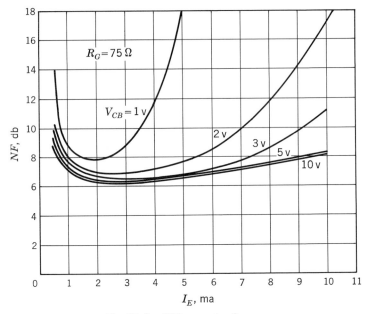

Fig. 21.8. 200-mc noise figure.

of f_{hfb}. The measured values for f_A were obtained from Fig. 21.5 by locating the frequency at which the noise figure had risen 3 db above the low-frequency (1-mc) value. Note the very good agreement between measured values and the noise corner calculated according to Eq. (7), employing f_{hfb} rather than f_T. This is true for a wide variety of transistors with cutoff frequencies ranging from 40 to over 600 mc.

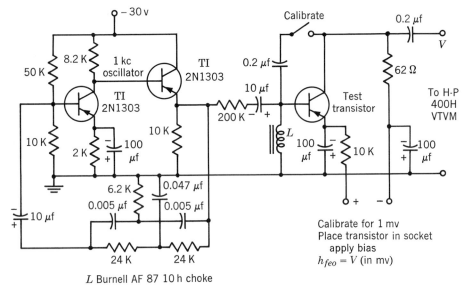

Fig. 21.9. h_{feo} at 1-kc test circuit.

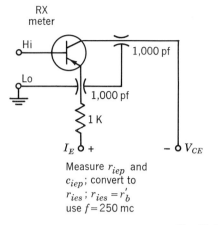

Measure r_{iep} and c_{iep}; convert to r_{ies}; $r_{ies} = r'_b$ use $f = 250$ mc

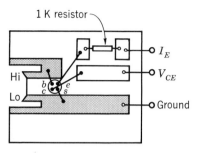

Emitter and collector terminals of transistor socket are fitted into Erie type 2405-102 feed-through capacitors. Shield terminal is wired to ground

Fig. 21.10. r'_b **test circuit.**

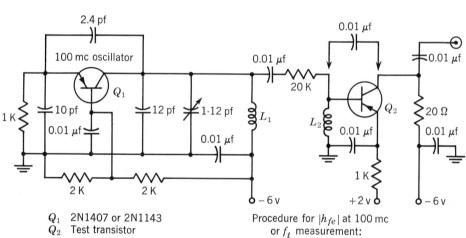

Q_1 2N1407 or 2N1143
Q_2 Test transistor
L_1 5 turns #18 tinned buss $1/4''$ dia $7/16''$ length no core
L_2 3.3 μh rfc

Procedure for $|h_{fe}|$ at 100 mc or f_t measurement:

(1) With calibrating capacitor in position read $E_1 = I_{(in)} \times 20\,\Omega$

(2) Remove capacitor, place transistor in socket, apply bias read $E_2 = I_{(out)} \times 20\,\Omega$

$$|h_{fe}| = \frac{I_{(out)}}{I_{(in)}} = \frac{E_2}{E_1}$$

$$|h_{fe}|\,\text{db} = 20\,\log_{10}\left[\frac{E_2}{E_1}\right]$$

Since $|h_{fe}|$ decreases 6 db/octave at high frequency

$$f_t = \left[\frac{E_2}{E_1}\right] \times 100\,\text{mc}$$

Fig. 21.11. $|h_{fe}|$ **at 100 mc or** f_T **test circuit.**

Experimental values for noise figure as a function of frequency are shown in Fig. 21.5. These values are in good agreement with values calculated from Neilson's equation, using the appropriate transistor parameter data. Emitter current bias for optimum noise figure is about 2 ma for the 2N1405 series.

It is found experimentally that noise figure increases at low emitter currents. This effect is caused by the degradation of h_{feo} and the noise contribution of reverse saturation currents (I_{CBO}) in the low-current range. Illustrations of this effect are shown in Figs. 21.6 to 21.8. Figures 21.6 and 21.7 also illustrate the *NF* dependence on R_g for the 2N743, a silicon epitaxial mesa device. Figure 21.8 contains *NF* information for a VHF germanium mesa transistor. For this device, MAG is greatly reduced in the 5-ma emitter range by decreasing V_{CB} below about 3 volts, thus causing an increase in *NF*.

The parameters having greatest effect on noise figure can be measured by the following methods:

1. h_{feo}—use test set in Fig. 21.9
2. r_b'—use RX meter in conjunction with jig of Fig. 21.10.*
3. f_{hfb}—measure f_T, using test set of Fig. 21.11, and convert to h_{hfb} by extrapolation or $f_{hfb} = 1.4 f_T$.†

BIBLIOGRAPHY

1. Kronlage, J. W.: Characteristics and Applications of 2N1405, 2N1406, and 2N1407 Diffused Base Mesa Transistors, TI Application Report, January, 1961.
2. Neilson: Behavior of Noise Figure in Junction Transistors, *Proc. IRE,* vol. 45, p. 957, July, 1957.
3. Cooke, H. F.: Transistor Upper Noise Corner Frequency, *Proc. IRE,* vol. 49, p. 648, March, 1961.
4. Transistor Internal Parameters for Small Signal Representation, *Proc. IRE,* vol. 49, no. 4, April, 1961.

*This measurement is not valid for 2N743 (Ref. 4).
† This approximation is valid for the 2N1405 series only.

22

RF Harmonic Oscillators

This chapter discusses some of the fundamentals of RF harmonic oscillator design. The characteristic equation for the various oscillator configurations is used to develop expressions for the natural frequency of oscillation and the necessary conditions for buildup of oscillation. Causes of frequency instability and methods of improving stability are discussed. The effects of changing load, changing passive parameters, and changing active parameters are analyzed. A brief treatment of crystal oscillators is presented along with a discussion of the crystal itself. Finally, a design procedure is proposed, and circuit examples are presented.

The general treatment of oscillators in this chapter is on a linear basis. However, the conditions of self-sustained oscillation must necessarily be nonlinear. Because of this linear analysis restriction, certain interesting topics such as limiting output voltage and current amplitude will be treated on a very approximate basis. To analyze these aspects more accurately would require limit-case solutions of the nonlinear differential equation describing the oscillator current or voltage in the phase plane, which are beyond the scope of this treatment.

22.1. OSCILLATOR CONFIGURATIONS

Necessary Conditions for Oscillation. The first necessary condition for self-sustained oscillation in a circuit is that the active device permit power gain at the frequency of oscillation. Furthermore, the device must have sufficient gain to overcome circuit losses and establish exactly unity gain around the feedback loop. The second necessary condition is that the phase shifts introduced by the active device and the feedback network result in exactly zero phase shift around the overall circuit.

These conditions will permit sustained oscillations, but they do not guarantee that oscillations will occur. In other words, it is not enough that unity loop gain can exist. There must be more than unity loop gain at first to cause buildup of oscillations. These, then, are the necessary and sufficient conditions for the buildup and maintenance of self-sustained oscillation in a circuit.

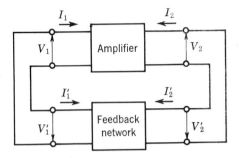

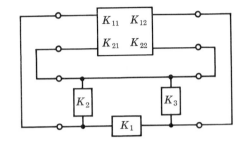

Fig. 22.1.   Feedback oscillator configuration.   Fig. 22.2. π-type feedback oscillator.

Basic Configurations.   Most oscillator circuits can be regarded as having two basic components: the amplifier and the frequency-selective feedback circuit. This arrangement is known as a *feedback oscillator,* and is shown in Fig. 22.1. The frequency-selective circuit can be further reduced to the network arrangement shown in Fig. 22.2. This configuration allows a clear visualization of each of the basic oscillator types. If K_2 and K_1 are capacitors and K_3 is an inductor, the circuit is a Colpitts type. Figure 22.3 shows this configuration. If K_1 and K_2 are inductors and K_3 is a capacitor, the configuration is called a Hartley oscillator and is shown in Fig. 22.4. Figure 22.5 shows the Hartley configuration realized with a two-winding transformer. The choice between a two-winding transformer and a tapped coil depends partly on the frequency of operation, since the expressions for the natural frequency of oscillation are slightly different. Also, the tapped coil requires an extra d-c isolation capacitor, which is not necessary with the two-winding transformer. Because of the possibility of obtaining phase reversal with the two-winding transformer, the transistor can be changed from common base to common emitter.

A modification to the Colpitts circuit results in the Clapp oscillator. In this circuit, the resonant frequency is determined primarily by the series combination of L and C. Figure 22.6 shows the arrangement. Where there is a requirement for high stability, crystals may be used for the frequency-determining element. A configuration using a crystal is shown in Fig. 22.7.

Some of the many possible modifications to the above basic configurations are shown in the circuit performance section. These arrangements of the active device and passive structure have been made so that it will be easy to combine the two-

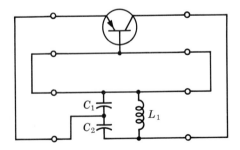

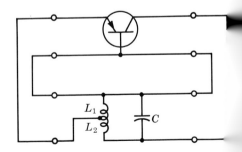

Fig. 22.3.   The Colpitts type circuit.   Fig. 22.4.   The tapped Hartley circuit

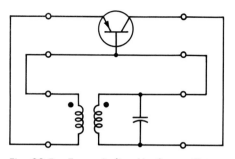

Fig. 22.5.   Two-winding Hartley oscillator.

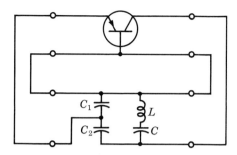

Fig. 22.6.   The Clapp oscillator.

terminal pair parameters of each *black box* into one equation characterizing the composite network.   The set of equations characterizing the active device in *h* parameters is shown in Eqs. (1) and (2).

$$V_1 = h_{ib}I_1 + h_{rb}V_2 \tag{1}$$

$$I_2 = h_{fb}I_1 + h_{ob}V_2 \tag{2}$$

Equations (3) and (4) characterize the passive structure.

$$V_1' = h_{11}I_1' + h_{12}V_2' \tag{3}$$

$$I_2' = h_{21}I_1' + h_{22}V_2' \tag{4}$$

The combination of these black boxes results in a set of equations which completely characterize the composite network.   For the networks of the type shown in Fig. 22.2, the combination must be accomplished as indicated in Eqs. (5) and (6).*

$$V_1'' = (h_{ib} + h_{11})I_1'' + (h_{rb} - h_{12})V_2'' \tag{5}$$

$$I_2'' = (h_{fb} - h_{21})I_1'' + (h_{ob} + h_{22})V_2'' \tag{6}$$

Oscillator connections are special cases, however, since $V_1'' = 0$ and $I_2'' = 0$.   These restrictions create the set of simultaneous homogeneous linear equations shown in Eqs. (7) and (8).

$$0 = (h_{ib} + h_{11})I_1'' + (h_{rb} - h_{12})V_2'' \tag{7}$$

$$0 = (h_{fb} - h_{21})I_1'' + (h_{ob} + h_{22})V_2'' \tag{8}$$

This set is, by definition, the characteristic equation of the combined network; and

---

* See Ref. 3, p. 553, for further discussion.

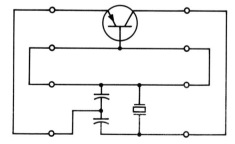

**Fig. 22.7.   Crystal oscil-
lator.**

its solution for the imaginary part will yield the natural frequency of the system. This may be done by inserting actual circuit values into Eq. (9) and solving for the imaginary part equated to zero.

$$(h_{ib} + h_{11})(h_{ob} + h_{22}) - (h_{rb} - h_{12})(h_{fb} - h_{21}) = 0 \qquad (9)$$

Evaluation of the real part of the expression is done in a similar way to yield the unity gain and, hence, starting conditions. Table 22.1 lists the natural frequencies and starting conditions for various configurations.

22.2. TANK CIRCUIT

Considerations for the Tank Circuit. Tuned LC circuits can be made to store energy. Used for this purpose, they have acquired the nickname of "tank" circuits. The frequency-determining LC circuit of an oscillator is such an example. The three essential parameters of the oscillator tank circuit are natural frequency of oscillation, selectivity, and characteristic impedance. The tank performs the following functions:

1. It determines the frequency of oscillation.
2. It is the feedback network.
3. It determines the stability of the oscillator.
4. It is a part of the coupling network to the load.
5. It affects the noise energy output of the oscillator.
6. It is a principal factor determining the circuit efficiency.

For a well-designed oscillator, the reactive components surrounding the tank are negligible in their effect on the resonant frequency set by the L and C of the tank.

It is easily seen in Figs. 22.1 to 22.3 that the tank can be treated as a feedback network connected across the active device. Even in the Clapp connection of Fig. 22.6 this is still true, but now the feedback is primarily determined by divider action of C_1 and C_2, and the frequency is determined by L and C in series.

Frequency stability is primarily determined by the Q_L of the tank. The reason for this is that the frequency deviation required to develop a given phase correction to establish exactly 360° phase shift around the feedback loop is inversely proportional to the loaded Q. Frequency stability is usually the most difficult specification to meet, and meeting it will usually more than satisfy the other requirements of constant Q and constant characteristic impedance. In other words, the environment of the tank tends to change not only f_o, but also Q and Z_o:* By satisfying the requirement for stability of f_o, one usually satisfies the requirements of stability of Q and Z_o also.

The load on a transistor oscillator is usually magnetically or capacitively coupled into the tank circuit. The load determines both the power drawn from the oscillator and the loaded Q of the tank circuit. The ratio of loaded Q to unloaded Q for the tank circuit should be low for good circuit efficiency.

---

* Z_o is the antiresonant tank resistance.

Components of the Tank. *Capacitors.* One of the most desirable types of capacitors for use in RF oscillators is the silvered-mica type. Since the silver plates are applied on the mica by vacuum evaporation, the silvered-mica capacitor is much more stable than ordinary mica capacitors with plates of foil pressed against the mica insulation. Mica has high secular* stability, a low temperature coefficient of capacity, and a low power factor. Typical values are $+20$ ppm/°C temperature coefficient and 0.015% power factor at 1 mc, over a range of -60°C to $+80$°C. Dielectric constants of 6 are typical. Very low parasitic inductance and d-c leakage (the leakage is principally over the surface of the plastic jacket) are features of the silvered-mica capacitor.

Ceramic capacitors offer two interesting advantages. Ceramic has, when mixed with titanium, negative temperature coefficients as high as 750 ppm/°C and about 10 times greater dielectric constant than mica. These advantages lead to the following possibilities: First, owing to the negative temperature coefficient, some compensation can be made for the positive coefficient of most inductance coils. Second, since such high dielectrics are available, it is possible to obtain large capacitance in small noninductive structures. Secular stability is very good, and power factors range from 0.02 to 0.05% at 1 mc to 0.04 to 0.1% at 100 mc. The temperature coefficient with frequency is about constant between 1 and 100 mc.

Inductance. Normally, the capacitors used in *LC* tank circuits of RF oscillators have very low losses compared to the losses in the coil. For this reason, the unloaded Q of a resonator depends almost entirely on the Q of the coil. The exact design of a coil is quite complicated because of the many factors which must be considered. The coil must have the correct inductance and be stable with time and temperature. It must have low parasitic capacitance and a high, reasonably stable unloaded Q.

The form of inductance coil most frequently used in RF circuitry is the single-layer solenoid, although powdered iron cores are sometimes used for better Q or for a variable inductance. The inductance is determined by the number of turns and the geometry of the coil. The self-inductance and the resistivity will vary with the frequency because of proximity and skin effects. Since the resistivity of a conductor varies rapidly with temperature changes, the inductance of a coil may be very sensitive to temperature changes, even though no appreciable change occurs in its dimensions. The problem, therefore, is to design the coil so that its dimensions are independent of time, temperature, and atmospheric conditions. The current distribution through the wire cross section must also be independent of temperature over the range specified.

If severe vibration is not expected, a coil may be self-supported at one end and connected at the other end by flexible braid. This results in reasonably stable coils having low losses. If both ends are rigidly attached, temperature-expansion coefficients may become a problem.

As stated before, the self-inductance of a coil is a function of skin effect. Skin effect is, in turn, a function of conductivity. At high frequencies the penetration

---

* Secular stability is the property of a material to retrace its path when one of its parameters is cycled with respect to temperature.

of current into the conductor is very shallow, while at low frequencies it may cover the entire cross section. The inductance is a function of both frequency and resistivity. Since this resistivity increases rapidly with temperature, the inductance also increases. The temperature coefficient of copper is about 4,000 ppm/°C, and the inductance coefficient due to this effect alone may be as high as 100 ppm/°C. At higher frequencies, where small inductance values are needed, sheet-copper strap is used to form the coil. This provides a large surface area and reduces skin effect for a given inductance.

Because it is expensive as well as difficult to build coils with low positive temperature coefficients of inductance, negative-temperature-coefficient capacitors are often used for compensation. This method is sometimes impractical, however, since the elements must track each other and must be reproducible in large-scale production.

Typically, a poorly built LC resonator may be affected by temperature so that its self-resonant frequency drifts by about 40 ppm/°C. The drift of a GT cut crystal will usually be 1/10,000 as great.

Crystal Discussion. When extreme frequency stability is required of an oscillator, a crystal is usually used as a substitute for the tank circuit or in the feedback loop to stabilize the frequency. The tolerance on most commercial crystals is about 0.002% from −55 to +90°C. An example of a Colpitts-Pierce crystal-oscillator configuration is shown in Fig. 22.7. Here the crystal is operated at a frequency just slightly below its parallel resonant frequency so that it will appear as an inductance.

The equivalent circuit for a crystal is shown in Fig. 22.8.

The L is analogous to the mass of the crystal structure, C is analogous to the crystal elasticity, and R is analogous to mechanical friction, accounting for energy lost as heat in the crystal. C_o is the total effective shunt capacitance contributed by the distributed capacitance of the leads and terminals of the mounting structure, the nonvibrating electrostatic capacitance across the quartz-crystal faces with the quartz serving as the dielectric, and any capacitance added by the crystal holder.

Crystals may also be operated at certain overtones of the fundamental, but even though the overtone Q is approximately the same as the fundamental Q, the activity or piezoelectric effect will be progressively smaller, the higher the overtone. Also, since in the parallel mode the activity is inversely proportional to the square of the terminal capacitance, care should be taken to minimize external capacitance so as to preserve crystal activity.

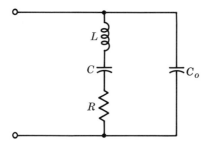

Fig. 22.8. Equivalent circuit of a quartz crystal.

In RF circuits, the dissipation must often be held to a few milliwatts. Temperature coefficients are normally specified in the form of Eq. (10):

$$\text{Drift} = \frac{\Delta f / f_o}{\Delta T} \tag{10}$$

In other words, the specification is in parts per million per degree or in per cent per degree. This coefficient can be positive, negative, or zero over small temperature ranges, depending on the crystal cut. Crystal-oscillator design will not be elaborated here, in view of the wide range of crystal types and possible circuits.

22.3. ACTIVE DEVICE

Requirements. The primary function of the active device is to develop enough output power at the frequency of operation to supply the required load power, the tank losses, and the drive power for itself. It should also generate as little noise voltage as possible. The active device should have a maximum frequency of oscillation well above the design frequency. Because these requirements are rather loose, many transistor types will function properly as oscillators. However, certain types of manufacturing processes result in device parameters which yield better oscillator performance. Paramount among these is the epitaxial mesa technique which allows a relatively lower value of effective collector bulk resistance, permitting higher operating efficiency.

Parameter Variation. At low frequencies the transistor parameters in the characteristic equation do not have large imaginary components, but at RF frequencies these parameters must be inserted in the characteristic equation in complex form. Solution of the real and imaginary parts, therefore, will include the effects of input, output, and transfer immittances. The sensitivity of frequency and starting conditions to changes in any of these immittances with the temperature, age, or bias point can be evaluated. Examination of Table 22.1 and the design example shows the form of these equations and the specific parameters involved.

22.4. FREQUENCY STABILITY

Causes of Frequency Instability. Oscillator frequency stability is a measure of the amount of drift in frequency away from the design center value. There are two causes of drift. First, the active parameters may change. The equations for ω^2 in Table 22.1 indicate the particular active parameters involved. Inserting actual values gives an indication of their influence. Second, the passive parameters may change. Both active and passive parameters generally change for two reasons: temperature and age.

Specification of Frequency Stability. An explicit expression for frequency variation with temperature is given in Eq. (11).

$$\text{Drift} = \frac{\Delta f / f_o}{\Delta T / T_o} \tag{11}$$

Table 22.1

Circuit	Natural frequency (ω^2)	Starting condition
Colpitts	$$= \frac{1}{LC} + \frac{r}{L}\,\frac{1}{C_1 h_{ie}} + \frac{\Delta h_e^*}{C_1 h_{ie}} + \frac{h_{oe}}{C_1 C_2 h_{ie}}$$ $$\cong \frac{1}{LC}\left(1 + \frac{LC h_{oe}}{C_1 C_2 h_{ie}}\right)$$ where $C = \dfrac{C_1 C_2}{C_1 + C_2}$ and $\quad r$ = a-c series resistance of coil L	$$h_{fe} > \frac{r(C_1 + C_2)h_{ie}}{L} + \frac{C_2}{C_1} + \frac{C_1}{C_2}\,\Delta h_e \cong \frac{C_2}{C_1}$$
Colpitts	$$= \frac{1}{LC} + \frac{h_{ob}}{h_{ib}C_1 C_2} \cong \frac{1}{LC}$$	$$h_{fb} > \frac{-C_2}{C_1 + C_2}$$
Hartley (tapped)	$$= \frac{h_{ie}}{C(Lh_{ie}) + (L_1 r_2 + L_2 r_1)h_{ie} + (L_1 L_2 - M^2)h_{oe}}$$ $$\cong \frac{1}{LC + (L_1 L_2 - M^2)\,\dfrac{h_{oe}}{h_{ie}}}$$ where $L = L_1 + L_2 + 2M$ r_1 = a-c series resistance of coil L_1 r_2 = a-c series resistance of coil L_2	$$h_{fe} > \frac{rLC h_{ie} + (M + L_1)^2 + (L_1 r_2 + L_2 r_1)\dfrac{\Delta h_e^*}{h_{ie}}}{(L_1 + M)(L_2 + M)}$$ $$\cong \frac{L_1 + M}{L_2 + M} \cong \frac{1 + KN}{1/N^2 + KN}$$ where $K = \dfrac{M}{\sqrt{L_1 L_2}}$ $N = \sqrt{\dfrac{L_2}{L_1}}$
Hartley (tapped)	$$= \frac{1}{LC + (h_{ob}/h_{ib})(L_2 L_1 - M^2)} \cong \frac{1}{LC}$$ where $L = L_1 + L_2 + 2M$	$$h_{fb} > \frac{L_1 + M}{L_1 + L_2 + 2M} \cong -\frac{N_1}{N_2}$$ where N_1 = number of turns of L_1 N_2 = number of turns of L_2
Clapp	$$\cong \frac{1}{LC} + \frac{1}{L}\,\frac{C_1 + C_2}{C_1 C_2}$$ where C = series capacity with L	$$h_{fb} > -\frac{C_2}{C_1 + C_2} \qquad h_{fe} > \frac{C_2}{C_1}$$

* Δh_e = common-emitter determinant = $h_{ie}h_{oe} - h_{re}h_{fe}$.

This expression gives the sensitivity of center frequency, f_o, to temperature change at a particular center frequency and operating temperature. Another expression that can be used is given in Eq. (12),

$$\text{Drift} = \frac{\Delta f / f_o}{\Delta T} \tag{12}$$

usually expressed as parts per million per centigrade degree.

Techniques for Improving Frequency Stability. As mentioned earlier, minimization of active device influence will improve stability. For the Colpitts connection, this is satisfied by the following inequality:

$$\frac{h_{ob}}{h_{ib}C_1 C_2} \ll \frac{C_1 + C_2}{L C_1 C_2} \tag{13}$$

Similar inequalities for other oscillator connections may be found from Table 22.1. Selection of an active device which satisfies this inequality is therefore the first technique.

The second technique is to *swamp out* part of the particular active parameter which enters the frequency expression by putting appropriately sized resistances in series with h_{ib} and in parallel with h_{ob}. The characteristic equation below shows the effect of this approach.

$$(h_{ib} + R_1 + h_{11p})(h_{ob} + \frac{1}{R_2} + h_{22p}) - (h_{rb} - h_{12p})(h_{fb} - h_{21p}) = 0 \tag{14}$$

Now if $h_{ib} \ll R_1$ and $h_{ob} \ll 1/R_2$, the equation becomes

$$(R_1 + h_{11p})(G_2 + h_{22p}) - (h_{rb} - h_{12p})(h_{fb} - h_{21p}) = 0 \tag{15}$$

The resonant frequency is solved for in the same way, except that now R_1 and G_2 are the terms in the expression instead of h_{ob} and h_{ib}.

The effect of load change on frequency may be shown by inserting Y_L into the characteristic equation. This is shown in Eq. (16).

$$(h_{ib} + h_{11p})(h_{ob} + h_{22p} + Y_L) - (h_{rb} - h_{12p})(h_{fb} - h_{21p}) = 0 \tag{16}$$

If $Y_L \ll (h_{ob} + h_{22p})$, its change will be minimized in the expression for frequency. This condition is generally established by a buffer stage. On the other hand, the solution of Eq. (16) for Y_L will yield the maximum load conductance which will still satisfy the conditions for oscillation. This load is important if the oscillator is intended as a power source rather than as a frequency source.

22.5. OSCILLATOR DESIGN PROCEDURE

Discussion. The design procedure for transistor oscillators is usually treated on a linear basis even though self-sustained oscillation indicates nonlinear operation. Therefore, the preliminary design calculations provide only approximate values for components, and these components must be adjusted experimentally in the final design.

Since a design procedure must be tailored to the individual oscillator specification no exact procedure can be given other than the general steps involved. The following is a listing of these design steps:

Design Steps

1. Select a transistor capable of providing sufficient gain and desired power output at the operating frequency, based on data sheet specifications.
2. Select the oscillator configuration to be used, based on the application. For example, the oscillator will probably be used either as a frequency-determining element or as a source of power at a given frequency.
3. Design the d-c bias network to establish the bias point and provide the necessary stability.
4. Design the tank or frequency-determining network using the formulas for operating frequency and starting conditions given in Sec. 22.1 (Oscillator Configurations) and in Table 22.1. The table gives natural frequency (ω^2) and starting conditions in terms of h parameters.
5. Make necessary adjustments in the feedback and bias networks to optimize efficiency. Be sure not to sacrifice ease of starting when adjusting the bias network for possible class B or C operation.
6. Use a trimming capacitor to make final adjustments, if necessary, to oscillator frequency.

22.6. DESIGN EXAMPLE

Specifications for the low-power oscillator design example are as follows:

$f_o = 90$ mc
$V_o = 2V_{(rms)}$ across a 1,000-ohm load
$V_{CC} = 10$ volts

The design procedure is as follows:

1. Select the 2N743 to provide this specified output power and voltage. It has an f_t which is, at the normal bias point of 5 volts and 5 ma, about three times f_o.
2. The Colpitts connection is selected for this frequency range because it yields values of tank inductance and capacitance which should be fairly insensitive to transistor parameter variation. The circuit configuration is shown in Fig. 22.9.
3. The d-c values for the network are as follows:
Let the drop across R_3 be 2.5 volts.

$$R_3 = \frac{2.5 \text{ volts}}{5 \text{ ma}} = 500 \text{ ohms}$$

Let the current through R_1 and R_2 be 5 ma, so that the value of R_2 will be

$$R_2 = \frac{3.1 \text{ volts}}{5 \text{ ma}} = 620 \text{ ohms}$$

This leaves $V_{R1} = 10 - 3.1 = 6.9$ volts; if I_B is about 0.4 ma,

$$R_1 = \frac{6.9 \text{ volts}}{5.4 \text{ ma}} = 1.3 \text{ kilohms}$$

R_4 will have about 2.5 volts across it; therefore,

$$R_4 = \frac{2.5 \text{ volts}}{4.5 \text{ ma}} = 550 \text{ ohms}$$

4. The a-c circuit design is carried out as follows. Since R_2 is 620 ohms, adequate bypass is about 5 ohms. This gives $C_1 = 300$ pf; to avoid a self-resonant frequency at or around 90 mc, C_1 must have a total lead length less than 0.4 in. C_4 and C_5 are 500-pf feed-through capacitors.

At 5 volts, 5 ma, and about 90 mc, the h_b parameters for the 2N743 are:

$$h_{ib} = 21.3 \angle 45.6° = (15.2 + j15) \text{ ohms} \tag{17}$$

$$h_{rb} = 0.069 \angle 77° = 0.0672 + j0.0154 \tag{18}$$

$$h_{fb} = 0.97 \angle 182.3° = -0.969 - j0.039 \tag{19}$$

$$h_{ob} = 2.76 \times 10^{-3} \angle 15.3° = (2.66 + j0.73) \times 10^{-3} \text{ mho} \tag{20}$$

The expression for ω^2 is

$$\omega^2 = \left(\frac{h_{ib}}{L} + \frac{h_{ob}}{C_1 + C_2} \right) \frac{C_1 + C_2}{C_1 C_2} \frac{1}{h_{ib}}$$

$$= \frac{1}{L} \frac{C_1 + C_2}{C_1 C_2} + \frac{h_{ob}}{h_{ib}(C_1 C_2)}$$

$$= \frac{1}{L \, C_1 C_2/C_1 + C_2} + \frac{1}{h_{ibr}/h_{obr} \, (C_1 C_2)} \tag{21}$$

By experimentally adjusting the capacitance ratio of the tank, we found that the following ratio gave the desired signal across the 1-kilohm load:

$$\frac{C_2}{C_3} = \frac{43}{91} = 0.47 \qquad \frac{C_2 C_3}{C_2 + C_3} = \frac{(43)(91)}{134} = 29 \text{ pf}$$

The inductance is 0.11 μh ($\cong$ 2 turns no. 18 wire on ½ in. diameter). $V_o = 2$ volts across the 1-kilohm load.

In order to determine the effect of the transistor parameters on the frequency of oscillation, we will compare the values obtained from the following expressions.

Frequency determined by considering only the tank:

$$\omega^2 = \frac{1}{L[C_1 C_2/(C_1 + C_2)]}$$

$$\omega_0^2 = \frac{1}{(0.11 \times 10^{-6})(29 \times 10^{-12})}$$

$$f_o = \frac{1}{(6.28)(3.2 \times 10^{-18})^{1/2}} = \frac{1}{(6.28)(1.79)10^{-9}} = 90 \text{ mc}$$

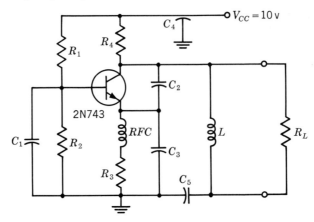

Fig. 22.9. 95-mc oscillator. Circuit uses a silicon epitaxial mesa to deliver about 2 volts (rms) across a 1-kilohm load at 95 mc. Typical circuit efficiency $\cong$ 3%.

Using h_{ibr} and h_{obr} equal to 15.2 ohms and 2.66×10^{-3} mho, respectively,

$$\omega_o{}^2 = \frac{1}{L[C_1C_2/(C_1 + C_2)]} + \frac{1}{(h_{ibr}/h_{obr})(C_1C_2)}$$

$$= \frac{1}{(0.11 \times 10^{-6})(29 \times 10^{-12})} + \frac{1}{(15.2/2.66)\,3.94 \times 10^{-18}}$$

$$= 0.313 \times 10^{18} + 0.044 \times 10^{18}$$

$$\omega_o{}^2 = 0.359 \times 10^{18} \qquad f_o = 95.4 \text{ mc}$$

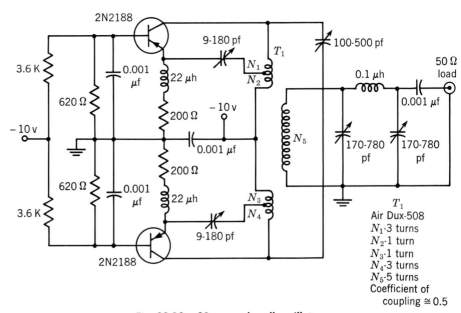

Fig. 22.10. 23-mc push-pull oscillator.

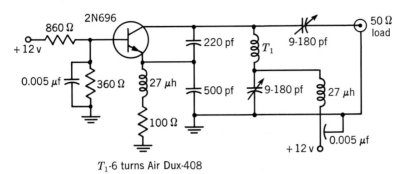

T_1-6 turns Air Dux-408

Fig. 22.11. 24-mc oscillator.

Evaluation of the operating frequency, using the full set of complex values for the *h* parameters, indicates that the frequency is still almost completely determined by the tank components. Experimental measurements of frequency agreed very well with the predicted value. Figure 22.9 shows the circuit and performance.

22.7. ADDITIONAL CIRCUITS AND PERFORMANCE

23-mc Oscillator. The 23-mc push-pull oscillator of Fig. 22.10 was designed to deliver 75 mw to a 50-ohm load. A π-matching network is used to optimize the output to a 50-ohm load with a noncritical design for the output transformer. Transistor type used is the Dalmesa 2N2188.

24-mc Oscillator. Figure 22.11 shows a 24-mc Clapp oscillator designed to deliver 300 mw into a 50-ohm load. Typical collector efficiency is 35%. The transistor type used is the 2N696.

30-mc Oscillator. Figure 22.12 shows a 30-mc oscillator designed to operate over a temperature range of -40 to $+60°C$. Typical power out is 23 mw at

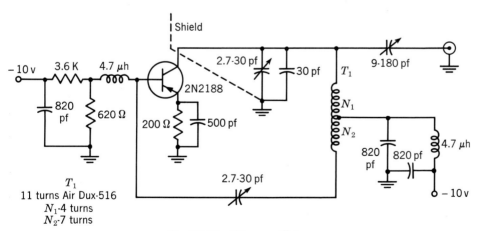

T_1
11 turns Air Dux-516
N_1-4 turns
N_2-7 turns

Fig. 22.12. 30-mc oscillator.

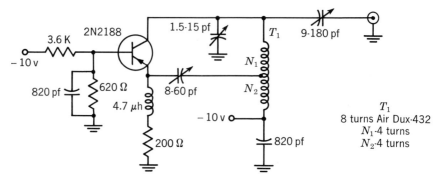

Fig. 22.13. 60-mc oscillator.

$-40°C$ and 20 mw at $+60°C$. Typical collector efficiency is 30%. Transistor type used is the Dalmesa 2N2188.

60-mc Oscillator. The common-base circuit in Fig. 22.13 is a 60-mc oscillator designed to deliver approximately 10 mw to a 50-ohm load at 25°C. Collector efficiency is typically 8 to 10%. Transistor type used is the Dalmesa 2N2188.

BIBLIOGRAPHY

1. Linvill, J. C., and J. F. Gibbons: "Transistors and Active Circuits," McGraw-Hill Book Company, Inc., New York, 1961.
2. Cote, A. J., Jr., and J. B. Oakes: "Linear Vacuum Tube and Transistor Circuits," McGraw-Hill Book Company, Inc., New York, 1961.
3. Gartner, W. W.: "Transistors: Principles, Design, and Applications," D. Van Nostrand Company, Inc., Princeton, N.J., 1960.
4. Reich, H. J.: "Functional Circuits and Oscillators," D. Van Nostrand Company, Inc., Princeton, N.J., 1961.
5. Pullen, K. A.: "Handbook of Transistor Circuit Design," Prentice-Hall, Inc., Englewood Cliffs, N.J., 1961.
6. Edson, W. A.: "Vacuum Tube Oscillators," John Wiley & Sons, Inc., New York, 1953.
7. Guillemin, E. A.: "Communication Networks," 2 vols., John Wiley & Sons, Inc., New York, 1931, 1935.
8. Buchanan, J. P.: Handbook of Piezoelectric Crystals for Radio Equipment Designers, *WADC Tech. Rep.* 56–156, ASTIA Document AD 110448, October, 1956.

23

Frequency Heterodyning and Multiplication

23.1. VHF MIXERS

A transistor frequency mixer is equivalent to a diode converter followed by a transistor amplifier. Frequency conversion is possible at any frequency as long as the emitter-base diode shows diode characteristics. Conversion does not depend on the ability to amplify at the signal frequency. For this reason, a transistor will often be useful as a converter at a higher frequency than it will amplify. The difference frequency (IF frequency), however, must be such that the transistor will function as an amplifier.

Transistors used as mixers must meet the following requirements:

1. Efficient emitter-base diode characteristics.
2. Low emitter input capacitance.
3. Good power gain (MAG) at the IF frequency.

The TI 2N1406 has these properties and is recommended for VHF/UHF mixing applications.

The local-oscillator transistor must supply about 100 to 300 mv at the oscillator frequency for optimum conversion gain. The 2N1406 will more than meet this requirement to about 600 mc.

Mixing action in transistors can be described as follows:

1. The local-oscillator signal modulates the nonlinear impedance of the emitter-base diode of the mixer transistor. The RF signal which is also present across this nonlinear impedance produces sum and difference frequencies, one of which is the converted IF signal. Below about 100 mc, this conversion process is carried out with almost negligible loss, using the 2N1406. At higher frequencies, these losses become significant.
2. The mixer transistor then amplifies the difference frequency (IF) up to an amount approaching MAG, the maximum available gain at the IF frequency.

Conversion gain is defined as

$$CG = \frac{\text{IF power available at mixer output}}{\text{RF power available to mixer input}} \tag{1}$$

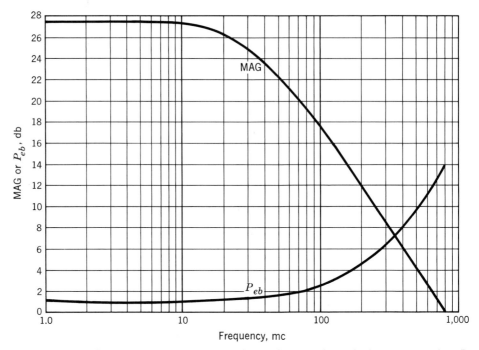

Fig. 23.1. Typical maximum available gain MAG and emitter-base diode conversion loss P_{eb} vs. frequency, 2N1406.

From the two steps of the mixing process outlined above,

$$CG = \text{MAG (db at IF)} - P_{eb} \text{ (db at RF)} \qquad (2)$$

where P_{eb} is the power loss (expressed in decibels) suffered by the input signal in the emitter-base diode conversion process.

Figure 23.1 provides a method of calculating conversion gain for a 2N1406 mixer as a function of the signal and intermediate frequencies.

Example. For a 300-mc signal frequency and a 30-mc intermediate frequency, using Eq. (1) and Fig. 23.1:

$$CG = 24.8 \text{ db} - 6.4 \text{ db} = 18.4 \text{ db}$$

Several possible mixer connections are given in Fig. 23.3.

An IF trap should be used at the signal input terminals. This prevents the loss of generated IF power to the input terminations of the mixer. The Q of the trap should be low enough so that it will not determine the IF passband.

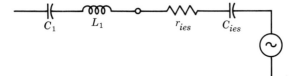

Fig. 23.2. Input equiva-lent circuit.

A design example will now be presented for a mixer having a signal input frequency of 225 mc. The intermediate frequency is 30 mc, and the desired circuit bandwidth is 3 mc. The local oscillator will be designed for 255-mc operation.

Figure 23.2 gives the circuit configuration to be used. The circuit parameters are calculated as follows:

For the 2N1406 at 225 mc with $V_{CE} = -6$ volts, $I_E = 2$ ma:

$$r_{iep} = 50 \text{ ohms} \qquad Q_T = 0.28 \qquad c_{iep} = 4 \text{ pf}$$

$$r_{ies} = \frac{r_{iep}}{1 + Q_T^2} = 46 \text{ ohms} \qquad c_{ies} = c_{iep}\frac{1 + Q_T^2}{Q_T^2} = 54 \text{ pf}$$

Input Circuit. No input transformer is necessary because r_{ies} is sufficiently close to 50 ohms.

Let

$$L_1 = 0.04 \ \mu h \quad \text{and} \quad C' = \frac{1}{4\pi^2 f^2 L_1} = 13 \text{ pf} \quad \text{for series resonance at 225 mc}$$

where $C' = \dfrac{C_1 c_{ies}}{C_1 + c_{ies}}$; therefore $C_1 = 17$ pf.

Output Circuit. For the 2N1406 at 30 mc with $V_{CE} = -6$ volts and $I_E = 2$ ma,

$$r_{oep} = 10 \text{ kilohms} \qquad c_{oep} = 2 \text{ pf}$$

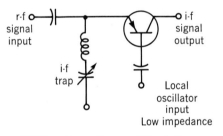

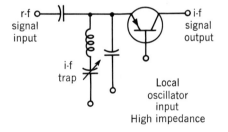

(1) Signal in emitter, oscillator in base

(2) Signal and oscillator in emitter

(a) Common base

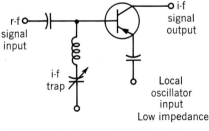

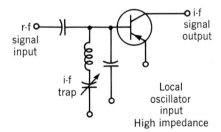

(1) Signal in base, oscillator in emitter

(2) Signal and oscillator in base

(b) Common emitter

Fig. 23.3. Possible mixer configurations.

C_4 will serve to match the 50-ohm load to 10 kilohms, the output resistance of the transistor. Since

$$R_L = \frac{r_{oep}}{1 + Q_M^2}$$

where R_L = load resistance, and $Q_M = Q$ of the matching network,

$$1 + Q_M^2 = \frac{10 \text{ kilohms}}{50} = 200 \quad \text{or} \quad Q = 14$$

and

$$C_4 = \frac{1}{2\pi f R_L Q_M} = \frac{0.159}{30 \times 10^6 \times 50 \times 14} = 7.6 \text{ pf}$$

The equivalent of the matching circuit is a parallel resistance of 10 kilohms and a parallel capacitance of 7.6 pf.

The total parallel resistance from collector to ground is 5 kilohms. To obtain a 3-mc bandwidth, Q_L, the loaded Q of the output circuit must be

$$Q_L = 10$$

Therefore, the parallel inductive reactance is

$$X_{L2} = \frac{5 \text{ kilohms}}{10} = 500 \text{ ohms} \quad \text{or} \quad L_2 = 2.65 \text{ } \mu\text{h}$$

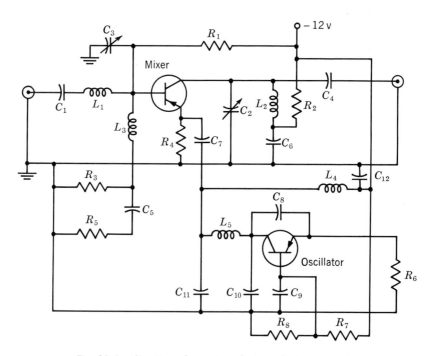

Fig. 23.4.   Circuit configuration of mixer design example.

The required total parallel capacitance must be

$$C_{tot} = \frac{1}{4\pi^2 f^2 L_2} = \frac{1}{4\pi^2 (30 \times 10^6)^2\, 2.65 \times 10^{-6}} = 10 \text{ pf}$$

Let $C_2 = 1$- to 6-pf tuning capacitor.

IF Trap. R_3 is a biasing resistor; C_5 and R_5 combine with L_3 to series-tune at 30 mc. R_5 is included to reduce the Q of the trap. C_3 is used to tune with the parallel reactance of L_3 at the radio frequency.

Let $L_3 = 0.2\ \mu\text{h}$ and $C_3 = 1$- to 11-pf tuning capacitor.

Let $C_5 = 150$ pf and the Q of the trap $Q_S = 3$. Then

$$R_5 = \frac{1}{2\pi f C_5 Q_S} = \frac{1}{6.28 \times 30 \times 10^6 \times 150 \times 10^{-12} \times 3} = 12 \text{ ohms}$$

Bias Circuit. To set the transistor bias at $V_{CE} = -6$ volts and $I_E = 2$ ma, let R_1 and R_3 divide the supply voltage to -2 volts at the base of the mixer. With $R_4 = 1$ kilohm, 2 ma of emitter current will flow. To bias V_{CE} at -6 volts the collector-ground voltage must be -8 volts. This requires a 4-volt drop across R_2. Since 2 ma of collector current bias is used, R_2 should be 2 kilohms.

Oscillator Circuit. The common-base circuit is a convenient high-frequency oscillator configuration. The emitter and collector signals are almost in phase, and so a small capacitor between emitter and collector will provide an adequate feed-back path.

The 255-mc local oscillator must drive the emitter of the mixer at a low impedance level. A π-matching network will suffice to feed this low impedance.

The oscillator load is nonlinear and complex; hence the π network elements must be adjusted experimentally in the final design. A preliminary calculation will now be made to arrive at approximate values.

Assuming that the impedance seen at the emitter of the mixer is approximately 10 ohms, design the π network for an impedance of 500 ohms at the collector of the oscillator. Then

$$X_{L5} = \sqrt{R_{10} R_{11}} = \sqrt{500 \cdot 10} = 70 \text{ ohms}$$

$$L_5 = 0.04\ \mu\text{h} \qquad X_{C11} = X_{L5} = 70 \text{ ohms} \qquad C_{11} = 9 \text{ pf}$$

C_{10} should be about 1 to 6 pf in order to tune the oscillator to the correct frequency.

For the feedback capacitance C_8, a value of 1 pf was found sufficient for all transistors used. A 1,000-pf feed-through-type capacitor was used for base bypass C_9. R_6, R_7, and R_8 bias the oscillator to $V_{CE} = -6$ volts, and $I_E = 2$ ma.

Figure 23.5 gives the final mixer-oscillator circuit. Typical conversion gains of 20 db were realized.

Figure 23.6 gives a common-base mixer designed for 420-mc operation. The mixer input circuit uses a hairpin-shaped inductor which was trimmed to resonance using a Measurements Corporation model 59 grid dip meter. The oscillator-tuned circuit uses a section of copper tubing cut for 480-mc resonance. Oscillators of this type have been made to operate above 900 mc.

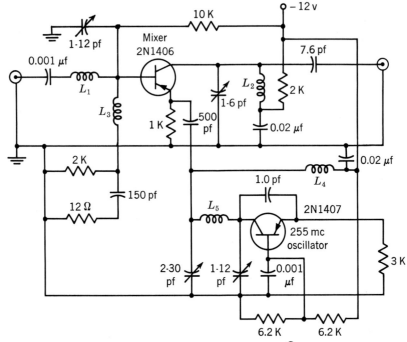

L_1, L_2 4 turns #18 tinned buss on $3/8$" dia Teflon® rod
Length $9/16$"

L_3 25 turns #36 copper enamel on CTC LS 9

L_4 0.68 μh RFC

L_5 1 turn #18 tinned buss on $3/8$" dia Teflon® rod
Length $1/2$"

Fig. 23.5.   225-mc mixer: 30-mc IF, 20-db average conversion gain.

23.2. FREQUENCY DOUBLERS

Frequency multiplication is usually accomplished by feeding a fundamental frequency signal into a nonlinear network; from the harmonics thus produced, one multiple of the fundamental frequency is isolated and amplified. The transistor's emitter-base diode characteristic, as indicated in Fig. 23.7, is often used as the nonlinear network required.

The type of frequency doubling discussed here is the tuned-input, tuned-output type, in which the input is tuned to the fundamental and the output to the second harmonic.

The curve of Fig. 23.7 indicates that the transistor should be biased at low current levels to maximize doubling action.

Typical design steps are:

1. Match the input of the transistor to the source at the fundamental frequency, using conventional matching techniques.
2. Present a load to the output that corresponds to the correct load for the

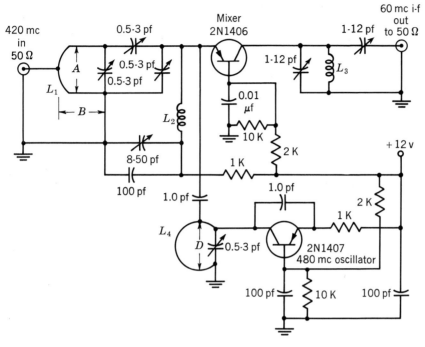

L_1 Rectangular rod bent to U-shape; A $1''$, B $2\ ^1/_8''$
   Rod cross section $^1/_8'' \times ^1/_2''$
L_2 $1\ ^3/_4$ turns #14 buss on Teflon® rod $^3/_8''$ dia $^1/_2''$ length
L_3 $8\ ^1/_2$ turns #36 Formvar wire $^1/_{64}''$ apart on CTC LS 9
L_4 Copper tube $1''$ depth $^1/_8''$ thickness $^3/_4''$ ID

Fig. 23.6. 420-mc mixer: 60-mc IF, 10-db average conversion gain.

predicted power output at the harmonic desired, using the same techniques; π-matching networks are shown in Figs. 23.8 and 23.9. Since a π-matching network is a low-pass filter, a trap is needed in the collector circuit to reject the fundamental. The trap is made up of a parallel and a series circuit as shown in Fig. 23.10. The combination of C_1 and L_1 offers a high impedance in the form of a parallel resonance circuit to the second harmonic. C_1, C_2, and L_1 offer a low impedance in the form of a series circuit to the funda-

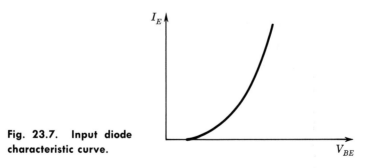

Fig. 23.7. Input diode characteristic curve.

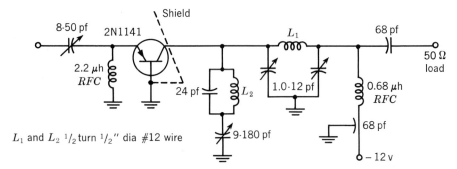

Fig. 23.8.   121.5- to 243-mc doubler.

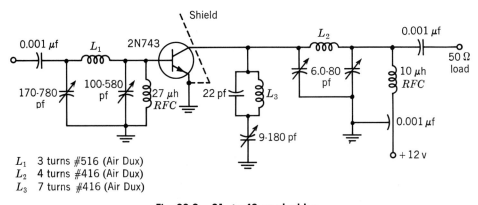

Fig. 23.9.   21- to 42-mc doubler.

mental.   This type of circuit is constructed for the purpose of trapping the fundamental so that it will not appear at the output.   The fundamental rejection for the circuits in Figs. 23.8 and 23.9 was -45 to -55 db.   Fig. 23.8 illustrates the common-base configuration, Fig. 23.9 the common-emitter configuration.   The configuration is chosen on the basis of transistor performance at the frequencies involved.

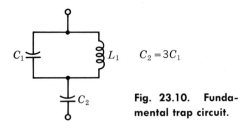

Fig. 23.10.   Fundamental trap circuit.

24

AGC of RF Circuits

In addition to gain and passband requirements, amplifiers must be able to handle input signals having varying dynamic ranges. This requirement is met by controlling transistor gain as a function of input signal strength. Naturally, AGC performance varies with transistor type; the example used to demonstrate gain-control characteristics in this chapter is the TI 2N1405 germanium mesa transistor. Regardless of transistor type, however, the same information must be known.

The following sections illustrate a variety of techniques for controlling a transistor's gain by varying its d-c operating point.

24.1. REVERSE AGC

Reverse AGC is a term generally applied to a transistor amplifier which is gain-controlled by holding the collector voltage relatively constant and changing the current through the device. The expression *forward AGC* indicates a method wherein the collector-base (or collector-emitter) voltage is made to vary in accordance with collector current, the gain being directly dependent upon voltage across, and current through, the transistor. In choosing between the two methods, the desired end result of the AGC amplifier must be kept in mind and a comparison made as to the most practical and efficient method by which that result can be attained. Comparisons can be made in the areas of available power gain, gain variation, noise figure, overload characteristics, and d-c operating point.

Figure 24.1 illustrates 100-mc dynamic transconductance characteristics superimposed upon the d-c transconductance curve. It will be used to demonstrate the transistor's signal-handling capabilities and attenuation characteristics.

Considering the case of the reverse AGC conditions, a collector-emitter potential of -10 volts, a *starting* current of -2 ma, and a *stopping* current of -0.25 ma were assumed for purposes of illustration. At the starting point A of -2 ma, 100-mc small-signal e_{S1} is shown to produce a collector current of i_{C1}. If a smaller d-c voltage is applied between the base and emitter, the operating point will be shifted to the *stop reverse AGC* condition at point B. At this point, considerable reduction in gain has been realized, as illustrated by e_{S2} and i_{C2}. Under these conditions, the maximum signal which can be handled at the base without excessive distortion is

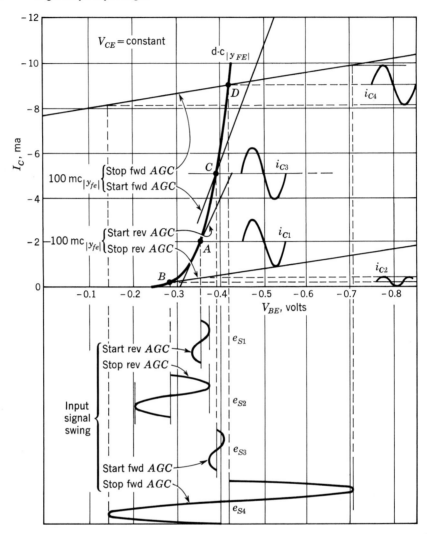

Fig. 24.1. Mesa transconductance characteristics (direct current and 100-mc alternating current).

approximately 60 mv (rms) as shown by e_{S2}. A voltage swing exceeding this amount would drive the instantaneous collector current past the zero axis, and distortion would occur. This demonstrates the gain-control and signal-handling capacity of the germanium mesa transistor in the reverse AGC condition, and shows that amplifiers receiving maximum signal levels of 60 mv (rms) or less can be designed safely by using this type of gain control.

24.2. FORWARD AGC

Consider now the forward AGC characteristics of the mesa transistor. For purposes of illustration, a supply voltage of -12 volts and a total d-c circuit resistance of 1,200 ohms have been assumed. Reasons for, and methods of, selecting the proper value of total circuit resistance will be discussed later, using more appropriate diagrams. The starting conditions using the 1,200-ohm d-c load line will result in a collector-emitter voltage of -6 volts at a collector current of -5 ma. At this point C of Fig. 24.1, a small signal e_{S3} is shown to produce a collector current of i_{C3}. If the d-c collector current is now increased in the transistor to point D by increasing the base-emitter voltage, the *stop forward AGC* conditions will result in a collector-emitter voltage of 1.25 volts at a collector current of -9.0 ma. Again, a considerable reduction in gain has been realized, as shown by e_{S4} and i_{C4}. The signal voltage e_{S4} is now limited by the minimum instantaneous base-emitter voltage swinging past the zero axis. Another limiting factor is also imposed upon the circuit, that of the instantaneous collector voltage swinging below the instantaneous base voltage.

An a-c load line of 500 ohms was assumed in illustrating e_{S4} in Fig. 24.1. At point D, a signal-handling capability of approximately 200 mv (rms) can be realized with negligible distortion. Since the input resistance of the mesa transistor is approximately 45 ohms at this operating point, this signal level is equivalent to 520 mv (rms) across a 300-ohm input. A further increase in signal-handling capability can be realized by lowering the d-c load resistance, by lowering the a-c load resistance, or by introducing degeneration in the emitter circuit (thereby reducing y_{fe}) by means of a small unbypassed resistor. However, if the latter method is used, the maximum available gain will be reduced, and will be accompanied by a deterioration in noise figure.

24.3. MESA CHARACTERISTICS

The 100-mc h_{fe} characteristics as a function of collector voltage and emitter current are shown in Fig. 24.2. The region where $V_{CB} = -10$ volts reveals the desirable reverse AGC characteristics of this transistor, that is, a strong influence of emitter current on h_{fe} in the region below 5 ma. It is particularly interesting to note the relative independence of h_{fe} over a wide range of operating voltage if the current through the device is maintained at or below 3 ma. This is a very desirable characteristic where ability of the device to handle a large collector voltage swing is required, as in a power amplifier, a transmitter final, or a similar application requiring the delivery of large amounts of power into a load.

Further examination of Fig. 24.2 shows a strong dependence of h_{fe} on operating voltage if the current through the device is 5 ma or more. It is this particular characteristic which enables this transistor to be used so effectively as a forward AGC amplifier. The line AB is a plot of h_{fe} using a 12-volt supply voltage and a 1,200-ohm d-c load. Line $A'B'$ is a similar plot, using a d-c load resistance of 845 ohms. Note the increased attenuation of h_{fe} in the lower collector voltage region when the transistor is driven to higher currents. Line AB' shows the variation in h_{fe}, using a supply voltage of 9 volts and a 600-ohm d-c load.

Figure 24.3 is a plot of the same data displayed in Fig. 24.2, except that emitter current becomes the independent variable and collector voltage is held constant. This figure more clearly shows the variation in h_{fe} as a function of current through the transistor, the lower-current region exhibiting relative independence of h_{fe}

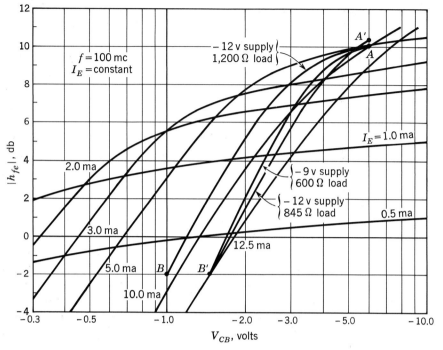

Fig. 24.2. h_{fe} vs. V_{CB} (at $f = 100$ mc).

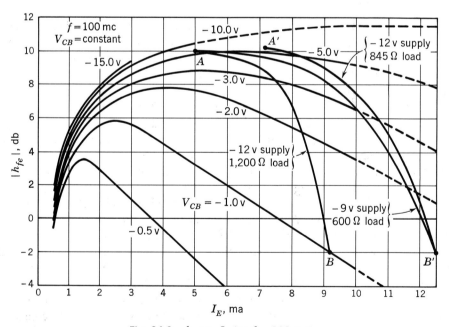

Fig. 24.3. h_{fe} vs. I_E (at $f = 100$ mc).

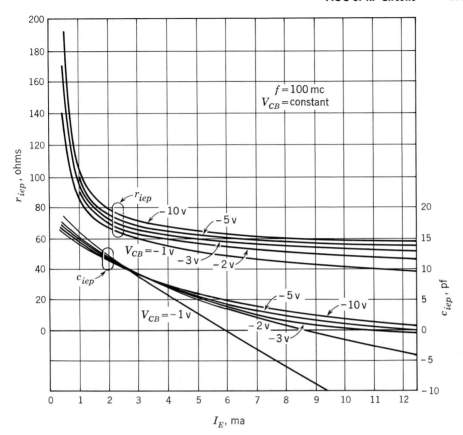

Fig. 24.4. Parallel component of input resistance and capacitance vs. emitter current (at $f = 100$ mc).

from collector voltage. If reverse AGC is desired, the higher-voltage region (10 to 15 volts) is more attractive because of the greater gain and larger change in h_{fe}. The lines shown are the same as those plotted in Fig. 24.2 for forward gain control, and show the amount of current change required for any given change in h_{fe}.

The results of input-impedance measurements, using the neutralized common-emitter configuration, are self-explanatory in Fig. 24.4. It should be noted, however, that the real component of the input impedance, r_{iep}, remains reasonably constant in the forward AGC region. The reactive component becomes inductive at higher currents and low voltages. However, the resistive component predominates in this region and the effect is not of major consequence in circuit design.

Figure 24.5 shows the real and reactive components of output impedance in the neutralized common-emitter configuration. Here, also, the reactive component becomes inductive, but, again, the effect is minimized because of the predominance of the resistive component.

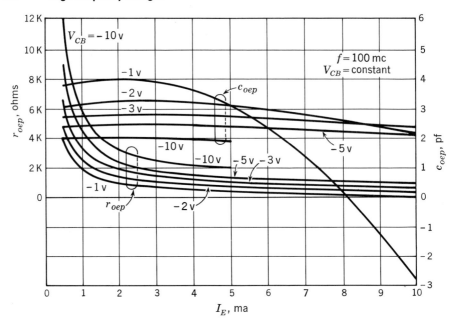

Fig. 24.5. Parallel component of output resistance and capacitance (common emitter) vs. emitter current.

24.4. MAXIMUM AVAILABLE POWER GAINS

Maximum available power gains (neutralized common emitter) at 100 mc are determined by the following formula (see also Fig. 24.6):

$$\text{MAG (db)} = h_{fe}\,\text{(db)} + 10\log\left[(c_{iep})^2 r_{iep} r_{oep} + \frac{r_{oep}}{4r_{iep}}\right] \qquad (1)$$

where c_{iep} is in picofarads and r_{iep}, r_{oep} are in kilohms.

This formula is used in conjunction with the current gains and impedances shown in Figs. 24.3 to 24.5 and, because of the coefficient (0.1) involved, should be used only at 100 mc. The formula shown was derived from the expression

$$\text{MAG (ratio)} = (h_{fe})^2\,\frac{r_{oep}}{4r_{ies}} \qquad (2)$$

Examination of the low-current region at first glance seems to indicate an attractive area for operation of an amplifier, owing to the small current consumption. However, the output-impedance components, r_{oep} and c_{oep} (as seen in Fig. 24.5), yield a rather narrow matched bandwidth. Also, the extreme dependence of impedances on operating conditions eliminates the practicality of attempting to match in this region. Most amplifier designs would necessarily load the transistor very heavily in this region, and as a result the power gain would be due mainly to h_{fe}, which is very small. Figure 24.7 is a similar display of power gain, using emitter current as the independent variable.

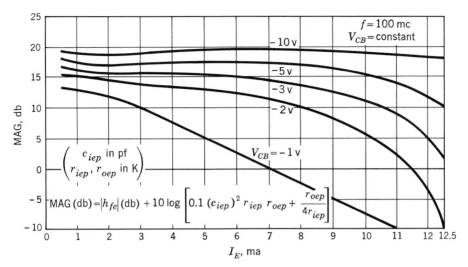

Fig. 24.6. Maximum available power gain vs. I_E.

Figure 24.8 is a combination of Figs. 24.6 and 24.7, and shows constant maximum available gain curves plotted against voltage and current. The d-c load lines correspond to those shown on the h_{fe} curves of Figs. 24.2 and 24.3. Although the actual power gain of any given design will not follow precisely the maximum available gain, this type of display is very useful as a guide in determining what to expect from an amplifier (using the 2N1405) in the way of gain control. Examination of the load lines shows available gain control on the order of 23 db,

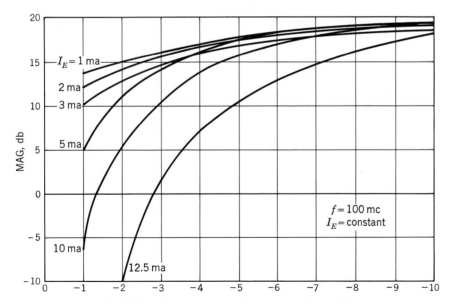

Fig. 24.7. Maximum available power gain vs. V_{CB}.

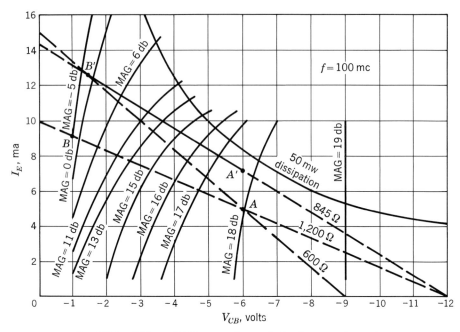

Fig. 24.8.   100-mc MAG curves for variation in operating point.

while changing the collector voltage and emitter current by approximately 5 volts and 5 ma, respectively.

The dynamic transfer characteristics at 45 mc in Fig. 24.9 are used in precisely the same manner as the corresponding 100-mc curves shown in Fig. 24.1.   Again, for purposes of illustration, a 12-volt supply and a 1,200-ohm d-c load have been assumed.   The input-signal limitations are seen to be approximately 63.5 mv (rms) in the stop reverse AGC conditions at point B, and 177 mv in the stop forward AGC conditions at point D.   Here again, the signal-handling capability can be improved by reducing the a-c or d-c load resistance, or by introducing degeneration in the emitter circuit.   The latter method will reduce the maximum available gain, but the accompanying deterioration in noise figure should not be of major concern in an IF amplifier.

Figure 24.10 illustrates the 45-mc h_{fe} characteristics as a function of operating point, and shows clearly the influence of current on h_{fe} in the region below 5 ma at the higher collector voltages.   Here again, the flat h_{fe} characteristics over a wide range of operating voltages should be noted.   This characteristic is very desirable in the output stage of a video IF amplifier where considerable power must be handled in the collector circuit.

The higher-current region shows the strong influence of collector voltage on h_{fe}. Note that somewhat higher currents are required at 45 than at 100 mc to attain similar attenuation characteristics.   The d-c load lines AB, AB', and $A'B'$ are the same as those shown at 100 mc, and need no further explanation.

The line $A''B''$ represents a 12-volt supply with a 720-ohm load, and has been added to this diagram to show the more linear change in h_{fe} at higher operating currents. The start forward AGC point A results in a 6-volt, 8.3-ma operating point with the stop forward AGC point at 1.5 volts, 14.6 ma. In applications where this higher-current drain is undesirable, such as battery-operated portable equipment, the possibility of using a lower supply voltage to reduce power consumption should be considered. Another method of reducing battery current consumption is a d-c circuit arrangement whereby two or more amplifiers are cascaded in series with a 12- to 18-volt supply.

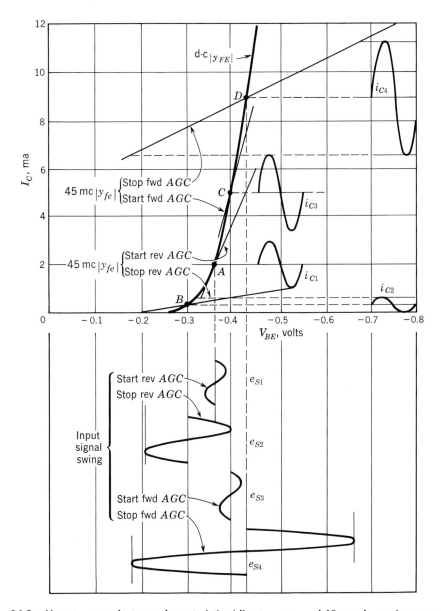

Fig. 24.9. Mesa transconductance characteristics (direct current and 45-mc alternating current).

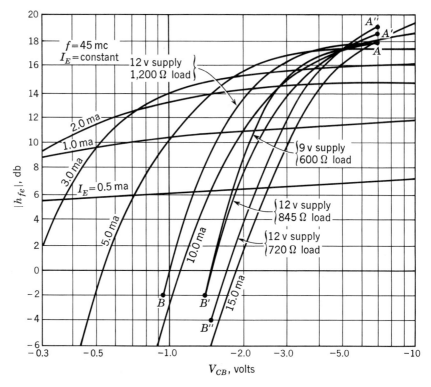

Fig. 24.10. h_{fe} vs. V_{CB} (at $f = 45$ mc).

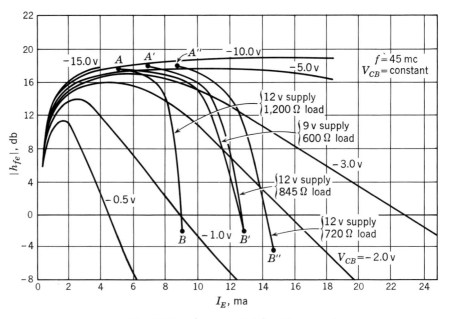

Fig. 24.11. h_{fe} vs. I_E (at $f = 45$ mc).

The excellent power gains available in the neighborhood of 5 volts make either of the aforementioned arrangements practical. Pursuing the same line of thought, consideration should be given to the use of a combination of forward and reverse AGC control, wherein one or more of the stages is forward-controlled and the remainder are reverse-controlled. The regions applicable to both forward and reverse AGC control can be seen in Fig. 24.11 (same data as in Fig. 24.10, with current as the independent variable).

The resistive and reactive components of the neutralized common-emitter input impedance under various operating conditions are shown in Fig. 24.12. Figure 24.13 displays the output-impedance components at various voltage and current levels. The power gains shown in Fig. 24.14 were determined, using the values of h_{fe} and impedances obtained from Figs. 24.11 to 24.13 in conjunction with the formula

$$\text{MAG (db)} = h_{fe}\text{ (db)} + 10\log\left[0.02(c_{iep})^2 r_{iep}r_{oep} + \frac{r_{oep}}{4r_{iep}}\right] \qquad (3)$$

(Here, again, it should be pointed out that the formula is valid only at 45 mc.)

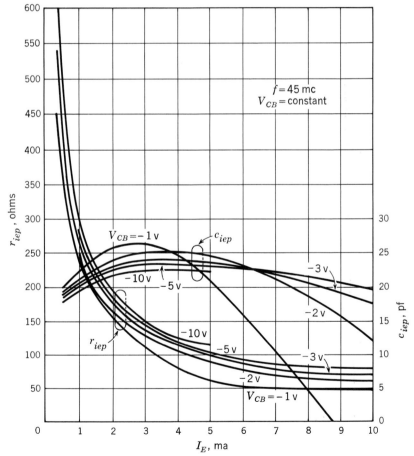

Fig. 24.12. Parallel component of input resistance and capacitance vs. emitter current (at $f =$ 45 mc).

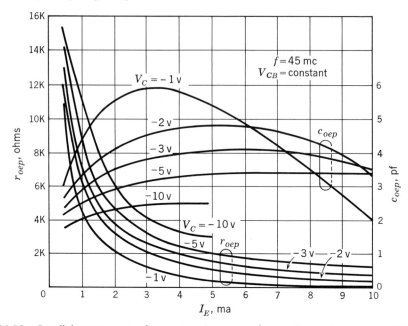

Fig. 24.13. Parallel component of output resistance and capacitance (common emitter) vs. emitter current (at $f = 45$ mc).

The maximum available gain plotted as a function of collector voltage in Fig. 24.15 contains the same information as Fig. 24.14. Combining Figs. 24.13 and 24.14, Fig. 24.16 illustrates constant maximum available gain curves as a function of operating point. The load lines AB, AB', and $A'B'$ are the same as those shown for 100-mc operation. Line $A''B''$ corresponds to the additional load line shown in

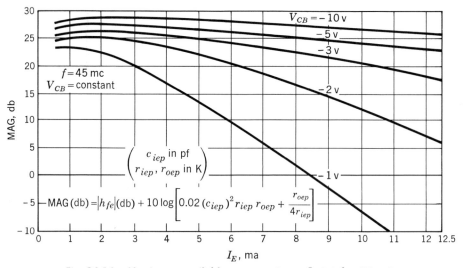

Fig. 24.14. Maximum available power gain vs. I_E (at $f = 45$ mc).

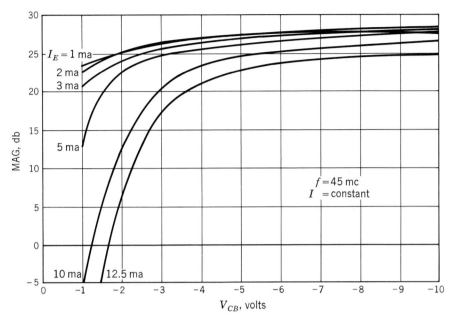

Fig. 24.15. Maximum available power gain vs. V_{CB} **(at** $f = 45$ **mc).**

Fig. 24.10. It can be seen from this graph that available gain control on the order of 30 db can be realized by changing the collector voltage and emitter current by 5 volts and 5 ma, respectively.

24.5. D-C CHARACTERISTICS

Figure 24.17 shows the variation in typical d-c forward current gain (h_{FE}) over a wide range of operating conditions and is used, in the following section, to determine AGC power required. The variation in d-c circuit transconductance as a function of emitter circuit resistance in Fig. 24.18 is referred to in conjunction with the offset emitter-ground voltage scale V_E to calculate the portion of total d-c load resistance which should be inserted in the emitter circuit.

24.6. DESIGN PROCEDURE

The following design procedure is useful as a guide to determining proper values of d-c load resistance, AGC power required, and transformer-turns ratio for forward AGC operation:

1. Using Fig. 24.8 (100 mc) or Fig. 24.16 (45 mc), draw a d-c load line starting at $V_c =$ supply voltage, and sloping through the desired MAG variation. Total circuit d-c resistance $(R_E + R_C)$, as shown in Fig. 24.19, is represented by reciprocal of slope of the line.
2. Assume a maximum V_B available from the AGC supply. Locate the intersection of the coordinates of maximum V_B available and maximum I_E

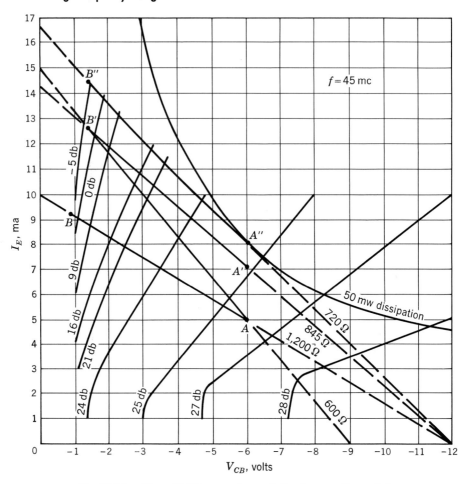

Fig. 24.16.   45-mc MAG curves for variation in operating point.

(from Fig. 24.8 or 24.16) desired in Fig. 24.18.   From this point, construct a line through point A.   This line is the slope of R_E.

3. Determine AGC power required from the formula

$$P_{AGC} \cong \Delta V_B \frac{\Delta I_E}{h_{FE}} \qquad (h_{FE} \text{ can be obtained from Fig. 24.17})$$

4. Find MAG at starting point from Fig. 24.8 or 24.16.
5. Determine required interstage loss (IL).

$$\text{IL (db)} = \text{MAG (db)} - \text{desired power gain (db)}$$

6. Convert IL (db) to IL (ratio) by

$$\text{IL (ratio)} = \log^{-1} \frac{\text{IL (db)}}{10}$$

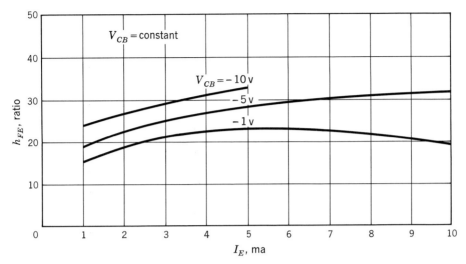

Fig. 24.17. D-c forward current transfer ratio (h_{FE}) vs. I_E.

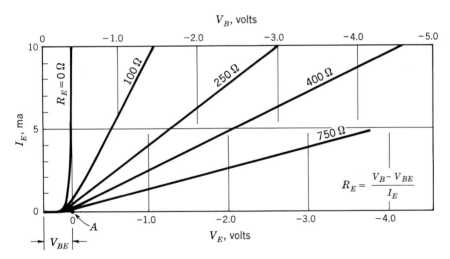

Fig. 24.18. D-c transconductance linearization.

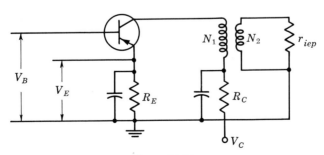

Figure 24.19

7. Determine N_1/N_2 by

$$\frac{N_1}{N_2} = \sqrt{a \frac{r_{oep}}{r_{iep}}}$$

where a (generator mismatch factor) $= r'_{iep}/r_{oep}$, and $r'_{iep} = r_{iep}$ reflected to primary. The value of a is given by

$$a = 2IL - 1 - \sqrt{4IL(IL - 1)} \qquad IL \text{ (ratio)}$$

It can be shown that

$$IL \text{ (ratio)} = Q_U \frac{[(r_{oep} + r'_{iep})/(Q_U - Q_L)]^2}{4r_{oep}r'_{iep}}$$

$$IL \text{ (ratio)} = \left[\frac{1}{4a} \frac{Q_U(1 + a)}{Q_U - Q_L}\right]^2$$

For $Q_U \gg Q_L$,

$$IL \text{ (ratio)} = \frac{(1 + a)^2}{4a}$$

Solving for a,

$$a = 2IL - 1 \pm \sqrt{4IL(IL - 1)}$$

For $a \leqq 1$,

$$a = 2IL - 1 - \sqrt{4IL(IL - 1)}$$

25

VHF Power Amplifiers

25.1. SELECTING THE OPTIMUM CONFIGURATION

The most important of the transistor parameters which limit the maximum RF power output are:

Breakdown voltage.
PG vs. bias–power-gain variation with bias.
$P_{D(max)}$—allowable power dissipated at the collector junction.

These parameters and how they influence the choice of configuration are discussed here.

Breakdown Voltage. If ideal class B operation is assumed, the static operating point would exist as shown in Fig. 25.1. An arbitrary load line has been constructed on a typical set of collector characteristics (either common base or common emitter). The collector voltage for class B operation will have a minimum of $E_{(min)}$ (see Fig. 25.1) and a maximum of $(2V_{CC} - E_{(min)})$. Figures 25.2 and 25.3 illustrate the voltage and current waveforms for idealized class B operation.

Because it is necessary to stay within the normal operating region of the transistor, the breakdown voltage (common base or common emitter) limits the peak voltage, E_P,

$$E_P = V_{CC} - E_{(min)} \leqq \frac{BV_C - E_{(min)}}{2} \tag{1}$$

where BV_C is the collector breakdown voltage.

The power output can be written as

$$P_O = \frac{E_P^2}{2R_L} \tag{2}$$

Thus, for a given R_L and $E_{(min)}$ fixed by other considerations, the breakdown voltage limits the available output power. The maximum output power can be found by combining Eqs. (1) and (2):

$$P_{O(max)} = \frac{(BV_C - E_{(min)})^2}{8R_L} \tag{3}$$

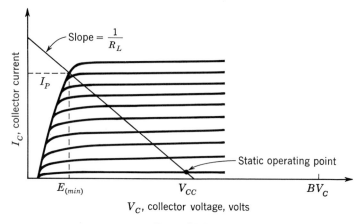

Figure 25.1

Power Dissipation from Thermal-stability Considerations. The maximum allowable junction temperature $T_{j(max)}$ limits the power that can be dissipated in a transistor. However, in circuit configurations which have high thermal-stability factors, thermal runaway may occur before $T_{j(max)}$ is reached. Thermal runaway occurs when the increase in leakage current due to increasing temperature causes power dissipation to increase, causing a further increase in temperature and leakage current. If this series of events becomes self-sustained, thermal runaway occurs.

In the common-base circuit, the thermal-stability factor is unity. The common-emitter circuit may have a thermal-stability factor as great as the common-emitter forward current gain h_{FE}. A large thermal-stability factor may cause thermal runaway to occur before the junction temperature reaches its maximum rated value $T_{j(max)}$. When this condition occurs, the power-dissipation rating of the common-emitter circuit is decreased.

Additional information on thermal parameters appears in Sec. 4.4 and Chap. 7.

Power Gain vs. Bias. At relatively low frequencies (low compared to the cutoff frequency of the device under consideration), current and voltage swings are usually limited by such factors as breakdown voltage, saturation voltage, and maximum power dissipation. As the operating frequency is increased, the variation in power

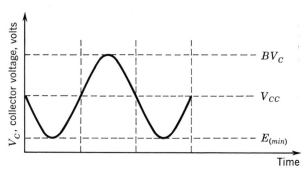

Figure 25.2

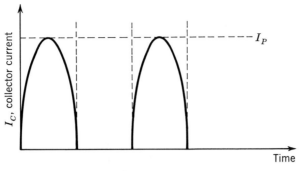

Figure 25.3

gain becomes more important, and in some cases it is the dominant limitation. Figure 25.4 illustrates the variation of power gain for the 2N1142 at 108 mc; this graph shows the changes in power gain for various bias conditions. Small-signal measurements were used to calculate the power gain shown in Fig. 25.4, with the assumption that the transistor is unilateralized and conjugately matched at each

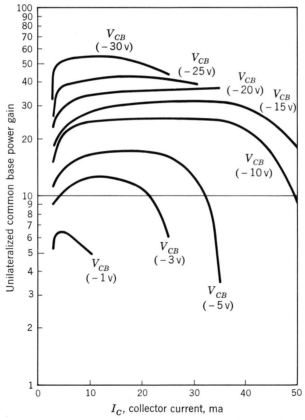

Fig. 25.4. Unilateralized power gain vs. bias of the 2N1142 at 108 mc in common-base configuration.

measurement point. If the short-circuit admittance parameters are used, then power gain is given by

$$PG = \frac{|y_{21}|^2}{4G_{11}G_{22}} \tag{4}$$

The rapid decrease of power gain at low voltages and high currents (shown in Fig. 25.4) severely limits the maximum power output obtainable from the 2N1142.

A more graphic method of displaying this limitation is to construct curves of constant power gain, using the collector voltage and collector current as coordinates. Figure 25.5 shows these constructions for the 2N1142 at 108 mc with resistive load line included. When power output is of prime importance, the instantaneous bias point should be restricted to a point which has a power gain equal to or greater than unity, because operation beyond this point requires a greater increase in input signal than is obtained in the output. This causes a large decrease in efficiency and an increase in harmonic distortion.

If the limit of unity power gain is accepted, then an optimum load line can be established. The determination of the best load line may be accomplished by noting that the locus of the minimum voltage, $E_{(min)}$, and the maximum current, I_P, is the unity-power-gain curve. This curve establishes a relationship between $E_{(min)}$ and I_P:

$$I_p = f(E_{(min)}) \tag{5}$$

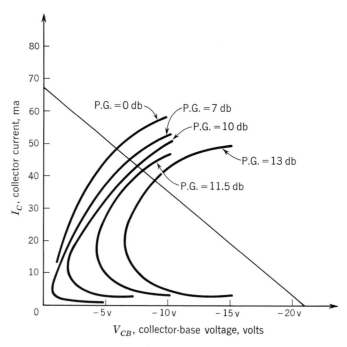

Fig. 25.5. Curves of constant unilateralized power gain of the 2N1142 at 108 mc in common-base configuration.

The peak voltage is

$$E_P \leqq \frac{BV_C - E_{(min)}}{2} \qquad \text{[Same as Eq. (1)]}$$

The output power may be expressed in terms of BV_C and $E_{(min)}$:

$$P_O = \frac{E_P I_P}{2} = \frac{BV_C - E_{(min)}}{4} f(E_{(min)}) \tag{6}$$

By differentiating expression (6) with respect to $E_{(min)}$, the conditions for the maximum output power are obtained:

$$\frac{dP_O}{dE_{(min)}} = \frac{1}{4} [(BV_C - E_{(min)}) f'(E_{(min)}) - f(E_{(min)})] = 0 \tag{7}$$

or

$$E_{(min)} = BV_C - \frac{f(E_{(min)})}{f'(E_{(min)})} \tag{8}$$

This value of $E_{(min)}$ is optimum, provided the power-dissipation rating is not exceeded.

Power Dissipation. The value of $E_{(min)}$ given by Eq. (8) may result in power dissipation in excess of the transistor rating. In this case $E_{(min)}$ is selected by writing power dissipation in terms of $E_{(min)}$. Power dissipation $P_D \leqq P_{D(max)}$, where $P_{D(max)}$ is the maximum allowable dissipation of the transistor for the particular ambient temperature and heat-sink configuration. Power dissipation (see Figs. 25.2 and 25.3) is given by

$$P_D = \frac{1}{2\pi} \int_0^{\pi} (I_P E_P \sin \theta + I_P E_{(min)} \sin \theta - I_P E_P \sin^2\theta)\, d\theta \tag{9}$$

$$P_D = \frac{I_P E_P}{\pi} + \frac{I_P E_{(min)}}{\pi} - \frac{I_P E_P}{4} \leqq P_{D(max)} \tag{10}$$

Substituting Eqs. (1) and (5) into (10),

$$P_D = \frac{f(E_{(min)})}{8\pi} [BV_C(4 - \pi) + E_{(min)}(4 + \pi)] \leqq P_{D(max)} \tag{11}$$

This equation gives the largest value of $E_{(min)}$ which may be used.

Optimum Load Line. The load resistance, R_L, may be written as

$$R_L = \frac{E_P}{I_P} = \frac{BV_C - E_{(min)}}{2f(E_{(min)})} \tag{12}$$

The optimum value of R_L is obtained by substituting the smallest value of $E_{(min)}$ given by Eq. (8) or (11) into Eq. (12).

As stated previously, the above values of $E_{(min)}$, R_L, etc., are calculated to deliver the maximum power output. If more gain is needed, instantaneous bias points must be restricted to constant power-gain curves significantly greater than unity (3- or 4-db gain curves). This decreases the variation in power gain, thus increasing overall gain and decreasing harmonic distortion. The new power-gain curves are used to obtain values of $E_{(min)}$ and R_L in exactly the same manner as previously described.

25.2. MATCHING NETWORKS

Output Matching Networks. VHF transistor power amplifiers are usually required to drive a load of approximately 50 ohms. A matching network must be used to transform the 50-ohm load to the value given by Eq. (12) at the output of the transistor. The matching network shown in Fig. 25.6 is one of the more useful of those commonly used. L, C_1, and C_2 are given by the following equations:

$$C_1 = \frac{Q_L}{\omega_o R_p} \tag{13}$$

$$C_2 = \frac{1}{\omega_o R_o} \sqrt{\frac{R_o}{R_s} - 1} \tag{14}$$

$$L = \frac{L_p R_p{}^2}{R_p{}^2 + (\omega_o L_p)^2} + \frac{1}{\omega_o{}^2 C_s} \tag{15}$$

where Q_L is the desired loaded Q of the circuit and

$$R_p = \frac{R_L R_{(out)}}{R_L + R_{(out)}} \tag{16}$$

$R_{(out)}$ is the output resistance of the transistor at the operating conditions

$$R_s = \frac{R_p (\omega_o L_p)^2}{R_p{}^2 + (\omega_o L_p)^2} \tag{17}$$

$$C_s = \sqrt{\frac{1}{\omega_o{}^2 R_s (R_o - R_s)}} \tag{18}$$

$$L_p = \frac{R_p}{\omega_o Q_L} \tag{19}$$

It may be impractical to transform R_o to R_L for the desired value of Q_L. In this case, a second network can be used to transform R_o to a lower value at the output of the first network. This network is calculated exactly like the first, but with the ends reversed.

Another useful matching network is shown in Fig. 25.7. This network eliminates

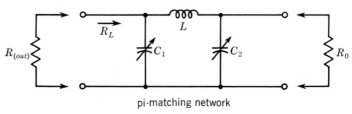

pi-matching network

Figure 25.6

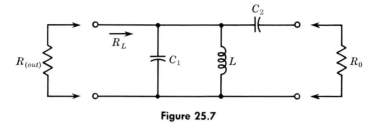

Figure 25.7

a coupling capacitor; loaded Q's of ten or above are easily obtained. The equations for the circuit elements are:

$$C_1 = \frac{Q_L}{\omega_o R_p} - C_2 \left(1 - \frac{R_o}{R_p}\right) \tag{20}$$

$$R_p = \frac{R_L R_{(out)}}{R_L + R_{(out)}} \tag{21}$$

$$R_L = \frac{(E_p)^2}{2P_o} \tag{22}$$

$$L = \frac{R_p}{\omega_o Q_L} \tag{23}$$

$$C_2 = \frac{1}{\omega_o R_o \sqrt{R_p/R_o - 1}} \tag{24}$$

Input Matching Section. Either of the above circuits may be used to match the input. The circuit of Fig. 25.7 is recommended because a low input impedance makes a high loaded Q difficult to obtain.

25.3. DESIGN EXAMPLE

As an illustration of the design technique, a 108-mc power amplifier has been built, using a Texas Instruments 2N1142. The goal is maximum power output with a gain greater than 6 db.

Selecting the Optimum Configuration. Figure 25.8 shows the 0-db power-gain curve for the common-base configuration of a typical 2N1142, and Fig. 25.9 shows $|h_{fe}|$ vs. collector current at 100 mc. Power-gain variation is approximately the same in both configurations. Since the breakdown voltage is -35 volts in the common-base configuration compared to -20 volts in the common-emitter configuration, and since the thermal-stability factor is unity in the common base compared to a possible value equal to the common-emitter forward current gain in the common emitter, common base is selected as the optimum configuration.

Selecting the Optimum Load. The 0-db power-gain curve of Fig. 25.8 is closely approximated by

$$I_P = 55 \text{ ma } [1 - \exp(-\alpha E_{(min)})] \qquad \alpha = 0.33 \text{ volt}^{-1} \tag{25}$$

where α is determined experimentally to make Eq. (25) fit the curve of Fig. 25.8.

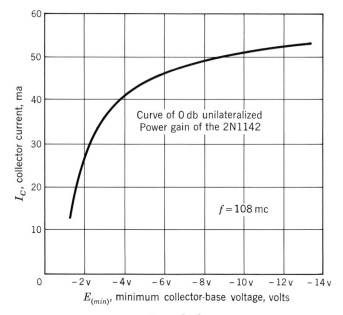

Figure 25.8

From Eq. (6), the output power is

$$P_o = \frac{55 \text{ ma}}{4} (BV_{CBO} - E_{(min)})[1 - \exp(-\alpha E_{(min)})] \tag{26}$$

When power output is maximized with respect to $E_{(min)}$, the above equation becomes

$$\frac{\partial P_o}{\partial E_{(min)}} = 0 = \alpha BV_{CBO} \exp(-\alpha E_{(min)}) - \alpha E_{(min)} \exp(-\alpha E_{(min)}) + \exp(-\alpha E_{(min)})^{-1} \tag{27}$$

and $\exp(-\alpha E_{(min)}) + \alpha BV_{CBO} \exp(-\alpha E_{(min)}) - \alpha E_{(min)} \exp(-\alpha E_{(min)}) = 1$ (28)

Dividing both sides by $\exp(-\alpha E_{(min)})$ and taking the natural logarithm gives

$$E_{(min)} = \frac{\ln(\alpha BV_{CBO} - \alpha E_{(min)} + 1)}{\alpha} \tag{29}$$

Using 35 volts for BV_{CBO} gives

$$E_{(min)} = \frac{\ln(11.55 - 0.33E_{(min)})}{0.33} \tag{30}$$

A graphic solution for $E_{(min)}$ is shown in Fig. 25.10, and yields the value

$$E_{(min)} = -7.0 \text{ volts}$$

The 0-db gain curve shows the value of current that corresponds to an $E_{(min)}$ of -7.0 volts (Fig. 25.8). This current I_P is

$$I_P = 48 \text{ ma}$$

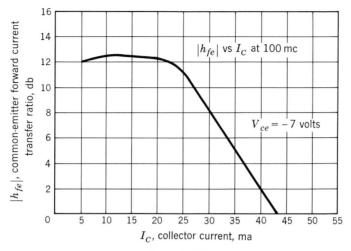

Figure 25.9

The collector voltage supply, V_{CC}, is given by

$$V_{CC} = \frac{BV_C + E_{(min)}}{2} = -21 \text{ volts}$$

From Eq. (1),

$$E_P = \frac{BV_{CBO} - E_{(min)}}{2} = \frac{35 - 7 \text{ volts}}{2} = 14 \text{ volts}$$

and from Eq. (12),

$$\text{Load } R_L = \frac{E_P}{I_P} = \frac{14 \text{ volts}}{48 \text{ ma}} \cong 300 \text{ ohms}$$

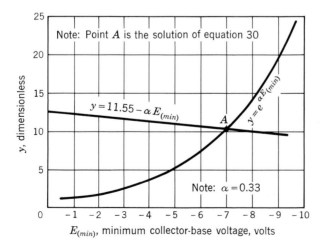

Figure 25.10

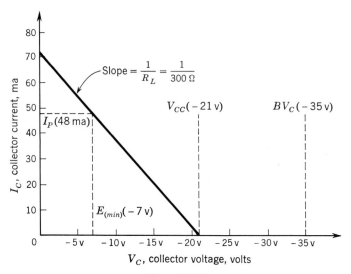

Figure 25.11

Figures 25.11 to 25.13 show the predicted collector current and voltage waveforms of the 2N1142 at 108 mc. Using Eq. (2), the power output is given by

$$P_o = \frac{E_P^2}{2R_L} = \frac{196 \text{ volts}^2}{600 \text{ ohms}} = 327 \text{ mw}$$

Power dissipated in the transistor is

$$P_D = \frac{E_P I_P}{\pi} + \frac{I_P E_{(min)}}{\pi} - \frac{I_P E_P}{4} = 153 \text{ mw} \leqq P_{D(max)}$$

Power-dissipation rating of the 2N1142 in free air at 25°C ambient is 300 mw. The derating of maximum power dissipation as ambient temperature increase is 4 mw/°C; therefore the 2N1142 is capable of dissipating 153 mw up to 62°C ambient. The collector efficiency is given by

$$\text{Collector efficiency} = \frac{\text{power output}}{\text{d-c power input}} = \frac{P_o}{P_o + P_D} = 68\%$$

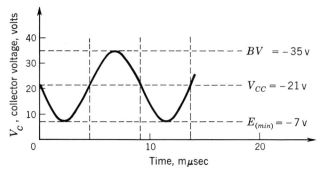

Figure 25.12

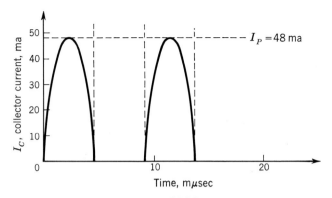

Figure 25.13

To calculate the input drive, the overall power gain, P_G, must be determined, since RF power input is given by

$$P_{(in)} = \frac{P_o}{P_G}$$

A good approximation of overall power gain in the common base is given by

$$PG = (R_L)\mathrm{Re}\,y_{ib}$$

where R_L = load resistance = 300 ohms, and $\mathrm{Re}\,y_{ib}$ = real part of the input admittance. The plots of $1/\mathrm{Re}\,y_{ib}$ given in Figs. 25.14 and 25.15 show that the average value is approximately 40 ohms. Thus,

$$\text{Power gain PG} = \frac{300}{40} = 7.5$$

and $$\text{RF power input } P_{(in)} = \frac{P_o}{P_G} = \frac{325 \text{ mw}}{7.5} = 43 \text{ mw}$$

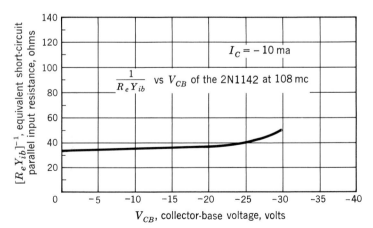

Figure 25.14

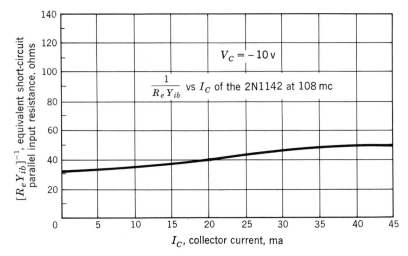

Figure 25.15

The power gain may be obtained by averaging the values associated with the constant power-gain curves. This method is probably more accurate but requires plotting a large number of curves.

Matching Networks. *Output Matching.* The circuit of Fig. 25.7 is selected as the output matching network. From Eq. (24),

$$C_2 = \frac{1}{\omega_o R_o \sqrt{R_p/R_o - 1}}$$

where $\omega = 2\pi f = 2\pi \times 1.08 \times 10^8$ cps
$R_o = 50$ ohms
$R_p = R_L = 300$ ohms

Thus, $C_2 = 13.2$ pf

From Eq. (23),

$$L = \frac{R_p}{\omega_o Q_L} = \frac{300}{(2\pi)(1.08 \times 10^8)(10)} = 0.44 \ \mu h$$

and from Eq. (20),

$$C_1 = \frac{Q_L}{\omega_o R_p} - C_2\left(1 - \frac{R_o}{R_L}\right) = \frac{10}{(2\pi)(1.08 \times 10^8)300} - 13.2\left(1 - \frac{50}{300}\right)$$

$C_1 = 38.2$ pf

Input Matching. The curves of Figs. 25.14 and 25.15 show Re y_{ib} vs. bias at 108 mc. Figure 25.16 shows the equivalent input circuit. Figure 25.17 shows the input matching network circuit. Since X_{eq} is inductive and R_{eq} is 40 ohms, it was decided to resonate L_{eq} with C_3 and allow slight mismatch between R_g and R_{eq}. L_{eq} for the 2N1142 in the common-base configuration is 0.02 to 0.5 μh. Therefore, C_3 is chosen to vary from 9 to 180 pf.

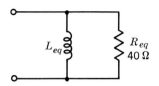

Fig. 25.16. Input equivalent circuit.

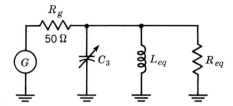

Fig. 25.17. Input matching network.

Construction and Testing. The networks were constructed of high-Q coils and capacitors. Each component was tested on the Boonton RX meter to be sure it exhibited the proper impedance at 108 mc. The complete amplifier schematic diagram is shown in Fig. 25.18.

The amplifier was built in a brass chassis. All components were measured and fitted so as to assure minimum lead length. The input was driven by a General Radio 1215-B unit oscillator. Power output was measured with an H.P. 430C power meter using a bolometer mount, with a General Radio 185.0-mc low-pass filter inserted between the output matching network and bolometer.

Comparison of Predicted and Experimental Results. The predicted results were based on an idealized situation in which the following effects were neglected:

1. Power loss due to r_c' (collector body resistance).
2. Matching network losses.
3. Harmonic generation.

The collector body resistance losses amount to approximately 20 mw. A conservative estimate of the a-c collector body resistance can be made by measuring the saturation voltage at a large value of collector current. For the 2N1142,

$$r_c' = \frac{V_{CE(sat)}}{I_C} \cong 30 \text{ ohms}$$

Thus the losses for the design example are

$$P_{ir'c} = \frac{I_p^2 r_c'}{4} \cong 20 \text{ mw}$$

The loss in the intrinsic base resistance, r_b, was found to be negligible.

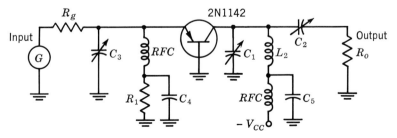

Fig. 25.18. 108-mc amplifier.

The matching network losses can be computed as

$$P_{lm} = 20 \log_{10} \left(1 - \frac{Q_1}{Q_{u1}}\right) \quad \text{db}$$

where Q_1 is the loaded Q of the matching network and Q_{u1} is the unloaded Q. For the design example,

$$P_{lm} = 20 \log_{10} (1 - {}^{10}\!/_{300}) = 0.25 \text{ db} \simeq 20 \text{ mw}$$

The output of the amplifier circuit was measured on an H.P. model 430C power meter with bolometer mount and found to be 285 mw. When a low-pass coaxial filter was inserted between the matching network and the bolometer, the output decreased to 270 mw. Thus, the harmonic content was 15 mw.

Table 25.1 lists the experimental results along with the necessary adjustment. The predicted result, shown in line 5, is based on an idealized situation in which the losses in the collector body resistance and matching network are neglected. When the measured power output is adjusted by adding lines 1, 2, and 3, line 4 is obtained. A comparison of line 4 and line 5 shows that when the measured result is adjusted to conform with the idealized situation, good agreement is obtained between measured and predicted values of R_F power output.

The measured d-c power input of the amplifier circuit was 512 mw compared to a predicted value of 478 mw. Thus, the intrinsic collector efficiency $N_{ic} = 310 \text{ mw}/512 \text{ mw} = 61\%$. *Intrinsic collector efficiency* is defined as the fundamental output power divided by the d-c input power if the collector body resistance is zero. The measured collector efficiency is $N_c = 270 \text{ mw}/512 \text{ mw} = 53\%$, compared to a predicted value of 68%. A major portion of the difference between the measured and predicted values of efficiency is due to the losses cited above, which are included in the calculation of intrinsic efficiency. The remaining difference is probably due to harmonics and losses in the auxiliary network such as power supplies, etc.

The total device dissipation is the d-c input power plus the a-c input power minus the a-c output power. For the design example,

A-c input power	= 43 mw
D-c input power	= 512 mw
Total input power	= 555 mw

The a-c output power at the transistor terminals is equal to

Fundamental power	= 270 mw
Harmonic generator loss	= 15 mw
Loss in matching network	= 20 mw
A-c output power	= 305 mw

Total input power	= 555 mw
A-c output power	= 305 mw
Total device dissipation	= 250 mw

The total device dissipation can be used to find the maximum allowable ambient

Table 25.1

1. Measured value, mw.. 270
2. Collector body resistance loss, mw....................................... 20
3. Matching network loss, mw... 20
4. Fundamental power generated in the intrinsic transistor, mw.............. 310
5. Predicted power output, mw.. 325
6. Harmonic generator loss, mw... 15

temperature. The thermal resistance for the 2N1142 is 0.1°C/mw with an infinite heat sink, and 0.25°/mw in free air. Under the operating conditions of the example, the maximum ambient in free air (with no heat sink) is 37°C, and 75°C with an infinite heat sink.

26

Remote-control System

This chapter describes a remote-control system that demonstrates the high-frequency capabilities of TI alloy mesa germanium transistors. Good remote-control performance may be achieved over a range of one mile; under ideal conditions with no obstruction or interference, range may be extended to over two miles.

The system components, a transmitter and a receiver, are described separately, and suggestions for adjusting the system for optimum performance are presented.

26.1. TRANSMITTER

Figure 26.1 is a block diagram of the transmitter which consists of an RF and an audio section. The RF section includes a crystal oscillator and a keyed power amplifier. A free-running multivibrator turns the power amplifier on and off at an audio-frequency rate.

Figure 26.2 is the transmitter schematic. The crystal oscillator, Q_3, is a common-base oscillator at the resonant frequency of Y_1. Feedback is from the collector to the emitter through the collector-emitter capacitance of Q_3. C_5 forms a voltage divider with this capacitance to provide the proper feedback level to sustain oscillation. R_6, R_7, and R_9 are bias resistors; R_8 is a decoupling resistor; C_4 is an RF bypass capacitor, while C_6 tunes the collector circuit to the 27.255-mc crystal frequency. Output is taken through a two-turn link at the cold end of L_1.

The power amplifier, Q_4, is operated as a driven common-emitter stage. R_{10} and R_{11} are bias resistors. The bias voltage on the base of Q_4 is varied at

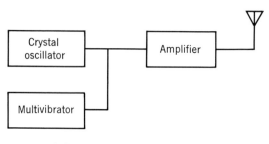

Fig. 26.1. Transmitter block diagram.

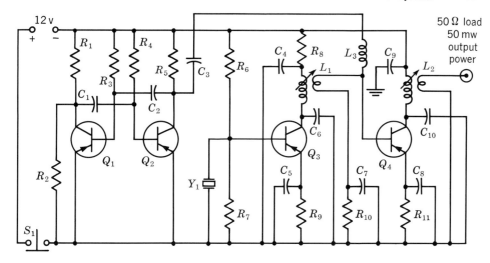

Parts List

Resistors	Kilohms	Watt
R_1	6.8	½
R_2	20	½
R_3, R_4	100	½
R_5	6.8	½
R_6	47	½
R_7	4.7	½
R_8, R_9	150 ohms	½
R_{10}	1	½
R_{11}	47 ohms	½

Miscellaneous
S_1 Push-button switch (normally open)
Y_1 27.255-mc crystal

Capacitors	
C_1, C_2	0.01-μf disk
C_3	0.1-μf disk
C_4, C_7, C_8, C_9	0.05-μf disk
C_5	56-pf disk
C_6, C_{10}	33-pf disk

Inductors
L_1, L_2 Adjustable RF coil (J. W. Miller
    4403 or equivalent).   Add 2
    turns of No. 24 enameled wire
    on cold end.
L_3 RF coil, 15 μh (Delevan 1537–40
    or equivalent).

Transistors	
Q_1, Q_2	2N1274
Q_3, Q_4	TI 395

Fig. 26.2.   27-mc transmitter.

an audio rate which keys the output stage. C_8 and C_9 are RF bypasses; C_{10} is the collector-tuning capacitor. Output is taken from a two-turn link wound on the cold end of L_2 to a 50-ohm antenna.

26.2. RECEIVER

As shown in the block diagram (Fig. 26.3), the receiver consists of a super-regenerative detector, quench filter, audio amplifier, audio filter, power detector, and relay. The receiver was designed for maximum performance consistent with simple circuitry.

Receiver operation is as follows: The incoming signal, a carrier in the 27-mc region modulated with an audio tone, is coupled into the collector circuit of Q_1 which acts as a superregenerative detector.

The detector operates as a self-quenched oscillator with audio taken across the collector load resistance. This stage is desirable for remote-control equipment

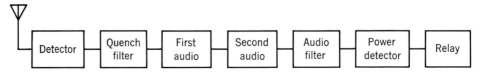

Fig. 26.3.   Receiver block diagram.

because of its high sensitivity.   The lack of selectivity can be tolerated since audio filtering is used.

Output from the detector consists of a supersonic (about 200-kc) quench signal and the modulation from the incoming signal.   This signal is applied to the quench filter which passes only the audio signal to the amplifier.   Without this filter, the quench signal would overload the audio stages, preventing their proper operation.

The audio signal from the quench filter is amplified in a two-stage tuned amplifier.   By requiring a particular audio tone as well as the proper RF signal, the amplifier discriminates against undesired signals.   How this selectivity is obtained will be discussed later in detail.

The amplified audio is detected and the resulting direct current used to operate the relay.   The relay contacts can be used to control other circuits as desired.

The receiver schematic diagram is shown in Fig. 26.4.   The incoming signal is coupled into the collector circuit of Q_1, through a two-turn link on the cold end of L_1.

L_1 and C_3 provide a tuned circuit for the superregenerative detector, Q_1, which is operated as a common-base self-quenched oscillator with R_4 and C_5 in an RC quench-determining network. L_4 isolates the emitter from RF ground; C_1 and C_2 are RF bypasses. R_4 is the d-c emitter resistance. C_2, L_2, and C_7 form a quench filter, while R_5 is a volume or sensitivity control.

Q_2 and Q_3 comprise a two-stage tuned audio amplifier. L_3 and C_{12} form a resonant tank circuit at 1,000 cps.   At all frequencies other than this resonant frequency, the collector of Q_3 is placed very near the a-c ground, thus reducing the gain of Q_3.   The stages are direct-coupled, with R_7 and R_9 providing a feedback d-c bias arrangement. C_{11} is an audio bypass while C_6, C_9, and C_{13} are coupling capacitors.

Coupled to Q_4 through T_1, the audio signal is rectified by the emitter-base diode and the amplified current is used to operate relay K_1. C_{14} bypasses the relay and smooths the pulsating direct current.   Contacts of K_1 may be used to actuate the necessary control equipment.

26.3.   ADJUSTMENT SUGGESTIONS

Observe the normal precautions for building high-frequency equipment.   Short leads and isolation of stages help eliminate unwanted feedback.   The receiver should be aligned in the order suggested below.

    I. Transmitter adjustment:
        A. Connect a 0- to 1.5-volt voltmeter across R_{10}.
        B. Adjust L_1 until maximum meter reading is obtained.   (Disconnect either end of L_3 to perform this adjustment.)

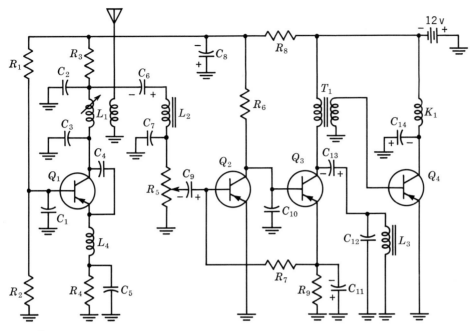

Parts List

Resistors	Kilohms	Watt
R_1	22	½
R_2	2.2	½
R_3, R_4	1	½
R_5	10	Potentiometer
R_6	2.7	½
R_7	10	½
R_8	270 ohms	½
R_9	150 ohms	½

Transistors

Q_1	2N2188
Q_2, Q_3, Q_4	2N1274

Capacitors

C_1	0.001-μf disk
C_2, C_7, C_{10}	0.05-μf disk
C_3	15-μf disk
C_4	18-pf disk
C_5, C_{12}	0.002-μf disk
C_6, C_9, C_{13}	5-μf electrolytic
C_8, C_{14}	100-μf electrolytic
C_{11}	40-μf electrolytic

Transformer

T_1 10–2 kilohms (Thordorson TR7 or equivalent)

Inductors

L_1 Adjustable RF coil (J. W. Miller 4403 or equivalent). Add 2 turns of No. 24 enameled wire on cold end.

L_2 30-mh choke (Bud CH 1228 or equivalent).

L_3 8.5 henrys (Stancor C1279 or equivalent).

L_4 RF coil, 15 μh (Delevan 1537–40 or equivalent).

Miscellaneous

K_1 Typical: Sigma 11F-2300-G/SIL or equivalent

Fig. 26.4. 27-mc receiver.

C. If a dummy load or RF power meter is available, connect to the output jack of transmitter. If a dummy load or RF power meter is not available, connect suitable antenna to the transmitter.

D. Connect a 0–1 volt voltmeter across R_{11}. Adjust L_2 for minimum meter reading. Readjust L_1 for maximum reading across R_{11}. A reading of 0.376 volt across R_{11} represents an input of approximately 92 mw.

    E. Reconnect L_3.

Note: Steps A through D must be performed with switch, S_1, closed.

II. RF section alignment:

    A. Connect suitable antenna to receiver.

    B. Set L_1 at mid-range.

    C. Set R_5 for maximum output.

    D. Connect an a-c VTVM (or oscilloscope) between collector of Q_3 and ground. (*Note:* If L_3C_{12} circuit has not been tuned to transmitter modulation frequency, disable it by disconnecting either end of C_{13}.)

    E. Turn on transmitter.

    F. Adjust L_1 for maximum VTVM reading. (Use the transmitter without an antenna or bottom cover as a signal source.)

III. Tuning L_3C_{12} audio filter:

To produce audio selectivity, a filter composed of L_3 and C_{12} provides a low-impedance path to ground for Q_3 at all frequencies other than 1,000 cps. For best gain and selectivity, L_3 and C_{12} must be tuned to match the modulation frequency of the transmitter. This is accomplished as follows:

    A. Complete RF alignment of receiver.

    B. Set R_5 at mid-range.

    C. Connect an a-c VTVM between collector of Q_3 and ground.

    D. Turn on transmitter.

    E. While observing VTVM reading, change value of C_{12} until a maximum reading is obtained.

IV. Audio gain adjustment:

Maximum setting of R_7 is dictated by noise output of the detector in a no-signal condition. Too high a setting will prevent the relay from dropping out.

    A. Current method:

        1. Complete RF alignment of receiver.

        2. Obtain value of dropout current for relay to be used.

        3. Insert a 0- to 5-ma milliammeter between relay and 12-volt battery.

        4. Increase audio gain control, R_5, until relay current is 0.5 ma less than dropout current.

        5. Lock R_5 in this position.

    B. Voltage method:

        1. Complete RF alignment of receiver.

        2. Connect a d-c voltmeter from collector of Q_4 to ground. (*Note:* Use voltmeter with at least 20,000 ohms/volt.)

        3. Adjust R_5 until the drop across the relay coil is equal to resistance of relay coil times dropout current minus 0.5 ma.

        4. Lock R_5 in this position.

Note: The current method is preferred to the voltage method.

If only a short range is desired, greater protection against accidental operation may be achieved as follows:

1. Complete RF alignment of receiver.
2. Complete tuning of L_3C_{12} audio filter.
3. Mount receiver's antenna in its permanent location.
4. Connect antenna to receiver.
5. Place transmitter at maximum range where operation is desired.
6. Turn on transmitter.
7. Adjust R_5 until relay just pulls in.
8. Lock R_5 in this position.

This setting may be considerably lower than if adjusted for maximum sensitivity; hence the greater protection.

26.4. PERFORMANCE

This circuit provides enough gain to operate many small-signal relays. The requirements for the relay are: (1) The value of pull-in current must not exceed 150 ma, and (2) the product of the pull-in current and the coil resistance must not exceed 12 volts. A typical relay is Sigma 11F-2300-G/SIL with a coil resistance of 2,300 ohms and a current of 4.6 ma.

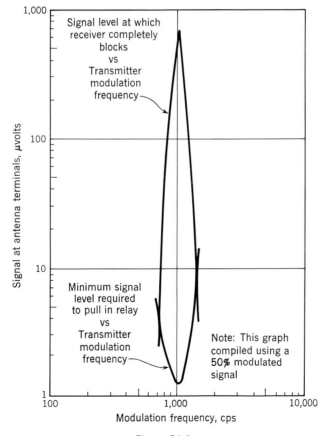

Figure 26.5

As shown in Fig. 26.5, the receiver sensitivity to the desired signal is 1.2 μv at the antenna terminals to energize the relay. At 750 cps, a signal level of 3.7 μv is required, and at 1,400 cps, 10 μv. Unmodulated carriers have no effect, regardless of strength. Because the level at which the receiver will block varies inversely with the modulation frequency deviation from 1,000 cps, further selectivity is obtained. In order for an unwanted RF signal to energize the relay, it must be amplitude-modulated between 750 and 1,400 cps, and produce a voltage on the antenna within the limits shown on the graph.

The total receiver current drain with a 12-volt battery is 9 ma with no signal input, and 14.5 ma when saturated. With the receiver properly aligned and no signal input, the following d-c voltages were measured at the transistor terminals. (All voltages are referred to ground and were measured with a VTVM.)

Transistor	V_B	V_C	V_E
Q_1	−0.94	−9.4	−1.38
Q_2	−0.3	−0.69	0
Q_3	−0.69	−11.8	−0.51
Q_4	−0	−12	0

Part **4**

Switching-mode Designs

27

Switching Design Considerations

The basic concept in switching circuitry is that of a discrete change of state. The change of state may take the form of a voltage change, a current change, or both. It may be used to perform logical operations as in a computer, or to transfer energy as in relay drivers and switching regulators.

Two static states are considered in transistor switching circuitry, the ON state and the OFF state. In saturated switching circuits, the ON state is marked by a very low collector voltage and relatively large collector current, and the OFF state is marked by a relatively high collector voltage and a very small collector current. The selection of components and supply voltages which allow this change of state will be called the *d-c design procedure*.

A transistor cannot change states in zero time. The time interval between initiation and completion of the switching action is a measure of switching speed. The rate at which a computer can do work is determined largely by the switching speed of its circuitry, and the efficiency of a power-switching circuit can be affected by switching speed. In some applications, a slow transistor with a high power rating can be replaced by a faster transistor with a lower power rating.

Efficiency of a computer circuit is difficult to define because information, power, and cost are measured in different units. The basic question is where to compromise between a fast, complex, high-power circuit and a relatively slow, simple, inexpensive low-power circuit.

27.1. WORST-CASE D-C DESIGN

One of the first steps in switching circuit design is the selection of circuit values to ensure turn-on and turn-off in the circuit. Separate equations relating circuit and transistor parameters can be written for the ON and OFF states, and two circuit parameters, such as the values of R_B and R_K in Fig. 27.1, can be selected as the dependent and independent variables, respectively.

A worst-case design may be accomplished by assuming that all transistor and component tolerances go to their worst-case extremes at one time. For example, in the flip-flop circuit of Fig. 27.1 the ON and OFF equations for Q_2 are:

369

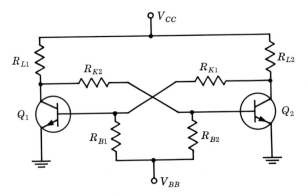

Fig. 27.1. Basic flip-flop.

ON: $\quad \underline{R}_B = \dfrac{\overline{V}_{BB} + \overline{V}_{BE(on)2}}{\dfrac{\underline{V}_{CC1} - \overline{R}_{L1}\overline{I}_{CBO1} - \overline{V}_{BE(on)2}}{\overline{R}_{K2} + \overline{R}_{L1}} - \dfrac{1}{\underline{h}_{FE2}}\left(\dfrac{\overline{V}_{CC2} - \underline{V}_{CE(sat)2}}{\underline{R}_{L2}} - \dfrac{\overline{V}_{BE(off)1} + \underline{V}_{CE(sat)2}}{\overline{R}_{K1}}\right)}$ (1)

OFF: $\quad \overline{R}_B = \dfrac{\underline{V}_{BB} - \overline{V}_{BE(off)2}}{\dfrac{\overline{V}_{BE(off)2} + \overline{V}_{CE(sat)1}}{\underline{R}_{K2}} + \overline{I}_{CBO2}}$ (2)

where the underlines indicate the minimum, and the overlines the maximum, specified values. Voltage and current magnitudes are used for simplicity in applying the equations to either NPN or PNP transistors. $V_{BE(off)}$ is normally a reverse-bias voltage. If a slight forward bias is used in the OFF state, the following substitution must be made in the OFF equation [Eq. (2)]:

$$V_{BE(off)2} \rightarrow -V_{BE(off)2}$$

Note that two distinct V_{CC} terms are contained in the ON equations. In most switching circuits with a single V_{CC} supply, the worst-case condition for turn-on is

$$\underline{V}_{CC1} = \overline{V}_{CC2} = \underline{V}_{CC}$$

In circuits with external d-c loads, $\underline{V}_{CC1}$ and $\overline{V}_{CC2}$ can be represented by Thévenin equivalent generators. In this case, both $\underline{V}_{CC1}$ and $\overline{V}_{CC2}$ should be used to ensure absolute worst-case conditions.

The transistor maximum and minimum parameter values are obtained from the data sheet. The resistor and power-supply maximum and minimum values are determined from the following relations:

$$\overline{X} = X_{(nominal)}\,(1 + \Delta) \tag{3}$$

and $$\underline{X} = X_{(nominal)}\,(1 - \Delta) \tag{4}$$

where Δ is the tolerance of X expressed as a decimal fraction. Temperature effects on resistors are sometimes ignored, assuming that the temperature change is compensated by a uniform drift of all resistors in the same direction. Temperature effects on transistors, however, must be considered. The following conditions usually exist at temperature extremes:

Low Temperature		High Temperature	
$V_{BE(on)}$	Maximum	I_{CBO}	Maximum
h_{FE}	Minimum	$V_{CE(sat)}$	Maximum
$V_{CE(sat)}$	Minimum		

Thus, turn-on worst case occurs at low temperature, and turn-off worst case occurs at high temperatures.

Equation (1) gives the minimum allowable value of R_B for turn-on, and Eq. (2) the maximum allowable value of R_B for turn-off. If several trial values of R_K are substituted in (1) and (2), the resulting values can be plotted as in Fig. 27.2. Combinations of R_B and R_K above the ON curve ensure that Q_2 will turn ON; combinations below the OFF curve ensure that Q_2 will turn OFF. Combinations above the ON curve and below the OFF curve ensure d-c stability in both the ON and OFF states.

The worst-case design procedure yields the most reliable individual circuit, but it greatly limits maximum fan-in and fan-out of logic stages. Since the probability of all components having worst-case values simultaneously is small, a statistical approach to d-c design may be used to increase fan-in and fan-out of logic stages.

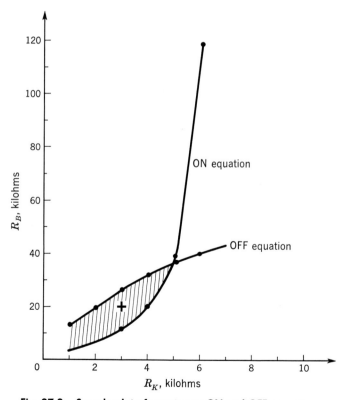

Fig. 27.2. Sample plot of worst-case ON and OFF equations.

The resulting reduction in the number of stages may increase the overall reliability of a computer. A special case of statistical design techniques is satisfactory for many applications—nominal values of resistance and supply voltage are used with worst-case values of transistor current gain and leakage currents. The yield of usable circuits is usually very high for this type of design. Statistical design is not discussed in detail here because of its complexity.

27.2. DESIGN EXAMPLE

Consider the circuit of Fig. 27.1. Assume the following circuit values and specifications:

Temperature range	−55 to +55°C
V_{CC}	−10 volts ±5%
V_{BB}	+10 volts ±5%
$V_{BE(off)}$	0.2 volt
R_{L1}, R_{L2}	1 kilohm ±5%
Transistor	PNP, germanium alloy
h_{FE} (at −55°C, $V_{CE} = -1$ volt, $I_C = -10$ ma)	10 min
$V_{BE(on)}$ (at −55°C, $I_B = -1$ ma, $I_C = -10$ ma)	−0.6 volt max
$V_{CE(sat)}$ (at +55°C, $I_B = -1$ ma, $I_C = -10$ ma)	−0.5 volt max
I_{CBO} (at +55°C, $V_{CE} = -10$ volts)	−100 μa max

The magnitudes of these worst-case values were substituted in Eqs. (1) and (2). Equations (3) and (4) were applied to the resulting values of $\bar{R}_B$ and $\underline{R}_B$ to obtain nominal values, which are plotted in Fig. 27.2. Any point within the shaded area would be a valid solution to the problem. The point $R_B = 20$ kilohms, $R_K = 3$ kilohms was chosen for maximum d-c stability. A point on the ON curve would result in minimum ON current, I_{B1}. A point on the OFF curve would result in minimum OFF bias.

D-c design equations for logic circuits become more complex than the simple equations shown here, but the same principles apply.

28

Digital Circuits

A multivibrator circuit uses two active devices with positive feedback in such a way that the two devices tend toward opposite states, one OFF, one ON. The bistable, astable, and monostable multivibrators are discussed below. The Schmitt trigger is also discussed here because of its similarity to multivibrators.

28.1. BISTABLE (FLIP-FLOP) MULTIVIBRATOR

The bistable multivibrator is characterized by its ability to maintain either of two possible states. It is widely used in counting circuits, shift registers, and memory circuits. The basic circuit is shown in Fig. 28.1.

To analyze the flip-flop operation, assume that Q_1 is ON and Q_2 is OFF. With Q_2 OFF, enough current flows from V_{CC} through R_{L2} and R_{K1} to forward-bias the base of Q_1 and saturate Q_1. The collector voltage of Q_1 is then $V_{CE(sat)}$. The R_{K2}, R_{B2} divider network holds the base of Q_2 reverse-biased, thus keeping Q_2 OFF. If a disturbance is introduced to start the turn-on of Q_2 or the turn-off of Q_1, regeneration can occur, and the opposite state (Q_2 ON, Q_1 OFF) will follow.

Design Procedure. The d-c design procedure is one of the first steps in the design. The philosophy of d-c design is explained in Chap. 27.

Before applying the ON-OFF design equations, certain other design decisions must be made. Because many of the design considerations are interrelated, there are very few concrete rules. The final design will be a compromise of the considerations presented below.

The collector saturation current,

$$I_{C(sat)} \cong \frac{V_{CC}}{R_L} \tag{1}$$

should be chosen considering the following factors:

1. The supply voltages V_{CC} and V_{BB} should be much larger than the transistor saturation voltages $V_{CE(sat)}$ and $V_{BE(on)}$, to minimize effects of variations in these voltages.

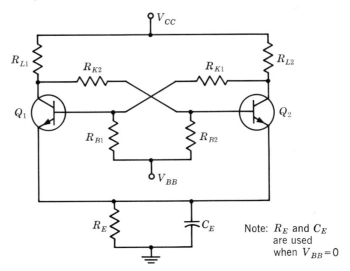

Fig. 28.1.   Basic flip-flop with emitter bias.

2. V_{CC} and R_L should be such that the load line does not cross any breakdown region on the collector characteristics.

3. Total circuit dissipation and transistor dissipation should be kept within limits.

4. The current gain, h_{FE}, varies with collector current in many transistors. $I_{C(sat)}$ should be such that h_{FE} is a reasonable value.

For maximum speed, the product $R_L C_{OB}$ should be much less than $1/2\pi f_T$, and R_L should be much greater than h_{ie}.   These two conflicting requirements are difficult to optimize analytically.   A propagation time test is described in Sec. 5.5. Propagation time can be measured on several trial circuits to determine the circuit for maximum speed.

After V_{CC}, V_{BB}, and R_L are chosen, values of R_K and R_B can be calculated.   The flip-flop d-c design equations are identical with Eqs. (1) and (2) of Chap. 27.

If the flip-flop drives external d-c loads to ground, substitution should be made for V_{CC} and R_L in Eq. (1) of Chap. 27:

$$\underline{V}_{CC1} \quad \text{should be replaced by} \quad \frac{V_{CC}\underline{R}_{X1}}{\overline{R}_{L1} + \underline{R}_{X1}} \tag{2}$$

$$\overline{R}_{L1} \quad \text{should be replaced by} \quad \frac{R_{X1}\overline{R}_{L1}}{\overline{R}_{L1} + \underline{R}_{X1}} \tag{3}$$

$$\overline{V}_{CC2} \quad \text{should be replaced by} \quad \frac{V_{CC}\overline{R}_{X2}}{\overline{R}_{X2} + \overline{R}_{L2}} \tag{4}$$

$$\underline{R}_{L2} \quad \text{should be replaced by} \quad \frac{\overline{R}_{X2}\underline{R}_{L2}}{\overline{R}_{X2} + \underline{R}_{L2}} \tag{5}$$

where R_{X1} and R_{X2} are the external loads on Q_1 and Q_2, respectively.

Self-bias. A single-supply flip-flop may be made by returning R_{B1} and R_{B2} to ground and using an external emitter impedance, R_E and C_E. A nominal value of emitter voltage (V_E) between 0.5 and 1.5 volts is commonly used. The approximate value of R_E is

$$R_E \cong \frac{V_E R_L}{V_{CC} - V_E} \tag{6}$$

In this case, $\underline{V}_{CC1}$, $\overline{V}_{CC2}$, and $\overline{V}_{BB}$ in the worst-case ON equation should be modified:

$$\underline{V}_{CC1} \quad \text{should be replaced by} \quad \underline{V}_{CC} - \overline{V}_{E2} \tag{7}$$

$$\overline{V}_{CC2} \quad \text{should be replaced by} \quad \underline{V}_{CC} - \overline{V}_{E2} \tag{8}$$

$$\overline{V}_{BB} \quad \text{should be replaced by} \quad \overline{V}_{E2} \tag{9}$$

where
$$\overline{V}_{E2} = \frac{(\underline{V}_{CC} - \underline{V}_{CE(sat)2})(\underline{h}_{FE2} + 1)\overline{R}_E}{\underline{h}_{FE2}R_{L2} + (\underline{h}_{FE2} + 1)\overline{R}_E} \tag{10}$$

and V_{E2} is the emitter voltage when Q_2 is ON.

Flip-flops are usually constructed symmetrically; this makes it necessary to analyze only one of the two transistors. The equations shown are written for Q_2. If an asymmetrical flip-flop is designed, it will be necessary to interchange the subscript numbers in the equations and analyze Q_1 separately.

If the first value of R_E substituted into the equations does not give a good d-c solution, a different value should be tried. The time constant $R_E C_E$ should be much greater than the transition period of the flip-flop. If $I_{C1(sat)} \neq I_{C2(sat)}$ in a single-supply flip-flop, R_E should be replaced by a zener diode to eliminate changes in V_E as the flip-flop changes states.

The counting flip-flop shown in Fig. 28.2 is formed by adding a steering network to the basic flip-flop. The trigger capacitors C_T charge and discharge in such

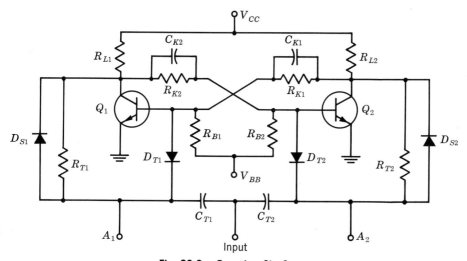

Fig. 28.2. Counting flip-flop.

a manner that the steering points A_1 and A_2 follow the collectors of Q_1 and Q_2, respectively. This action is such that the circuit is triggered with each negative excursion of the input signal. Assuming that the circuit has been in the state shown long enough for the steering network to be stabilized with Q_1 ON and Q_2 OFF, then the voltage at A_1 will be $V_{CE(sat)}$, and the voltage at A_2 will be $[R_K/(R_L + R_K)]V_{CC}$. Then diode D_{T2} has a large reverse bias, while D_{T1} has a small reverse bias. An incoming negative pulse will forward-bias D_{T1} and turn OFF Q_1, thereby turning ON Q_2. This process is repeated for opposite conditions when the next triggering pulse occurs.

Selection of Steering Network. All capacitances should be small to minimize RC time constants, but they should also be large enough to provide sufficient triggering and overdrive. C_K is chosen to provide overdrive during the turn-on period.

The speedup capacitor C_K reduces the transition time of the circuit by providing overdrive to the transistor being turned ON. C_T couples the trigger to the transistor being turned OFF. First-approximation values of C_T and C_K are given by

$$C_K = K \frac{Q_S}{V_{CC}} \tag{11}$$

and

$$C_T = K \frac{Q_B}{V_{CC}} \tag{12}$$

where Q_S is the stored base charge necessary for collector saturation, and Q_B is the total stored base charge. The constant, K, is an empirical safety factor; values of 1.5 to 2.0 are commonly used.

Equation (12) is a good approximation for the value of C_T when the rise time of the triggering pulse is short. However, if the triggering rise time is long, the value of C_T must satisfy the following inequality:

$$0.8C_T V_P \geqq K(I_{B1}t_r + Q_B) \tag{13}$$

where V_P is the trigger-pulse amplitude, I_{B1} is the base current supplied to the ON transistor, and t_r is the voltage rise time of the trigger pulse.

It may be necessary to optimize C_T and C_K experimentally for maximum speed. C_K may be optimized with the propagation time test of Sec. 5.5, and C_T can then be optimized in the actual flip-flop circuit. Storage time increases with temperature, making high temperature the *worst case* for triggering.

The time constant $R_K C_K$ should be such that

$$3R_K C_K < \tau \tag{14}$$

where τ is the period of the triggering signal.

R_T should be large to minimize loading, but $R_T C_T$ should be small enough to permit recovery of the steering circuit within a cycle. If a speedup diode is not used,

$$3R_T C_T < \frac{\tau}{2} \tag{15}$$

assuming $R_T \gg R_L$.

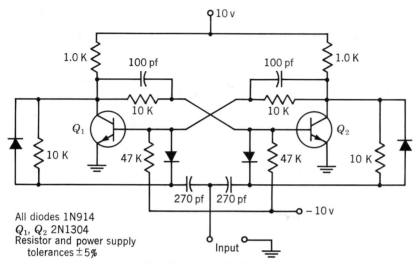

Fig. 28.3. 250-kc flip-flop.

If a speedup diode is used, $R_T C_T$ should be such that

$$0.7 R_T C_T < \frac{\tau}{2} \tag{16}$$

The diodes should have a recovery time in the same order of magnitude as the flip-flop transition time, and the diode capacitance should be much lower than the circuit capacitances.

Typical Design. The flip-flop circuit shown in Fig. 28.3 was designed to operate in the temperature range $-55°C < T_A < +55°C$ with an input frequency of 250 kc. Circuits from a typical production run of this circuit could be expected to operate at speeds considerably greater than 250 kc.

28.2. ASTABLE (FREE-RUNNING) MULTIVIBRATOR

The astable or free-running multivibrator has no stable state. It is commonly used as a square-wave generator. The basic astable multivibrator circuit is shown in Fig. 28.4. To analyze its operation assume that D_1 and D_2 are not connected into the circuit; i.e., the emitters of Q_1 and Q_2 are connected to ground. Also assume that Q_1 has just turned ON, and Q_2 has just turned OFF at $t = 0$. The voltage across C_2 is approximately V_{CC}, which makes $V_{BE2} = -V_{CC}$. The initial voltage across C_1 is approximately zero. The base end of C_1 is clamped to $V_{BE(on)}$ of Q_1. C_1 charges rapidly through R_{L2} to V_{CC}. The $R_{L2} C_1$ time constant causes the leading edge of the output wave to be rounded (see Fig. 28.5). Q_1 is held ON by the current from V_{BB} through R_{B1}. The collector end of C_2 is clamped to $V_{CE(sat)}$ of Q_1. C_2 begins to charge in such a way that V_{BE2} rises toward V_{BB}. When V_{BE2} reaches $V_{BE(on)2}$, Q_2 begins to turn ON; the resulting negative voltage excursion at the collector of Q_2 is coupled through C_1 to the base of Q_1, turning Q_1 OFF. The circuit at $t = \tau/2$ is now in the opposite state from that at $t = 0$. The reverse

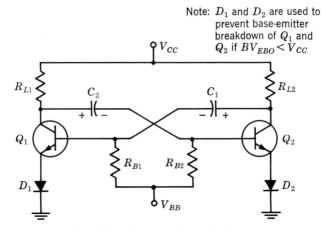

Note: D_1 and D_2 are used to prevent base-emitter breakdown of Q_1 and Q_2 if $BV_{EBO} < V_{CC}$

Fig. 28.4. Basic astable multivibrator.

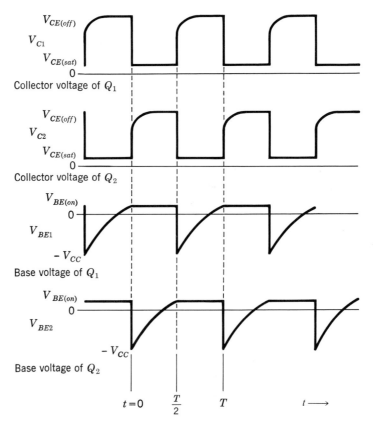

Fig. 28.5. Astable multivibrator waveforms.

process is repeated from $t = \tau/2$ to $t = \tau$; at $t = \tau$, the circuit has returned to its original state.

Design Procedure. The load resistors and the transistors are chosen, based on the same considerations as in the bistable multivibrator. R_B is chosen to ensure saturation of the transistor.

$$R_{B1} \leq h_{FE1} \frac{(V_{BB} - \overline{V}_{BE(on)})R_{L1}}{V_{CC} - V_{CE(sat)}} \tag{17}$$

If $BV_{EBO} < V_{CC}$, diodes should be used in the emitter leads as shown in Fig. 28.4. The reverse breakdown of the diode should be greater than $(V_{CC} - BV_{EBO})$.

The OFF time of each transistor is controlled by the time constant $R_B C$. The time constant and the OFF time are related by

$$R_{B1}C_1 = \frac{t_{OFF(1)}}{\ln[(V_{BB} + V_{CC} - V_{BE(on)})/(V_{BB} - V_{BE(on)})]} \tag{18}$$

If $V_{BB} = V_{CC}$, and $V_{CC} \gg V_{BE(on)}$, then

$$R_B C \cong \frac{t_{OFF}}{\ln 2} = 1.44 t_{OFF} \tag{19}$$

A variable V_{BB} can be used to control the frequency of the multivibrator, but in cases where a constant frequency is desired, a single supply is usually used for convenience and for better frequency stability with voltage changes. Equation (18) is reasonably correct at low frequencies if

$$I_{CBO} + I_{EBO} \ll \frac{V_{BB}}{R_B}$$

A higher frequency is affected by input capacitance and stored base charge. It is impractical to build a frequency-stable multivibrator if $CV_{CC} \cong Q_{SB}$.

If the multivibrator is constructed symmetrically, the duty cycle of the output will be 50%; lower duty cycles can be achieved by using different values of C. The multivibrator must not be made so nonsymmetrical that the waveform of the transistor with the short OFF time is limited by the $R_L C$ time constant. For example,

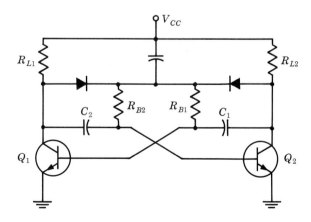

Fig. 28.6. Sure-starting astable multivibrator.

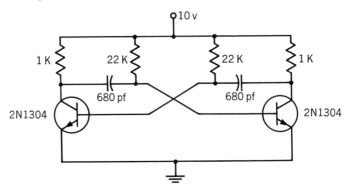

Fig. 28.7. 50-kc free-running multivibrator.

if Q_1 is to have a short OFF time, $3R_{L1}C_2 < t_{OFF1}$. If the supply voltages are applied slowly to the circuit of Fig. 28.4, both Q_1 and Q_2 may go into saturation and stay. This locked-up condition is less likely to occur when the supplies are switched ON sharply. The circuit shown in Fig. 28.6, however, will always start, regardless of how slowly V_{CC} is applied.

Typical Design. The circuit of Fig. 28.7 was designed using the transistor and load resistor of the bistable flip-flop of Fig. 28.3. The 2N1304 has a base-emitter breakdown voltage of -25 volts, making the emitter diodes unnecessary. This circuit oscillates at approximately 50 kc.

28.3. MONOSTABLE (ONE-SHOT) MULTIVIBRATOR

The monostable or one-shot multivibrator has one stable state. It is a hybrid between the bistable and astable multivibrators. Consider the circuit of Fig. 28.8. Q_2 is held ON by the base current through R_{B2}. Q_1 is held OFF by R_{K1}, R_{B1}, and $-V_{BB}$. If either transistor is triggered out of its stable state, regeneration can occur, and the astable state (Q_1 ON, Q_2 OFF) will exist for a time determined by $R_{B2}C$. Q_2 is held OFF as in the free-running multivibrator, and Q_1 is held ON as in the bistable multivibrator. After C has charged such that Q_2 begins to turn ON, Q_1 turns OFF and the cycle is complete.

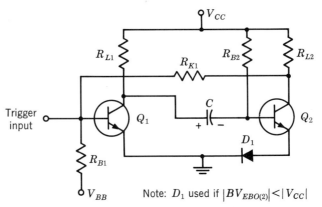

Note: D_1 used if $|BV_{EBO(2)}| < |V_{CC}|$

Fig. 28.8. Basic monostable multivibrator.

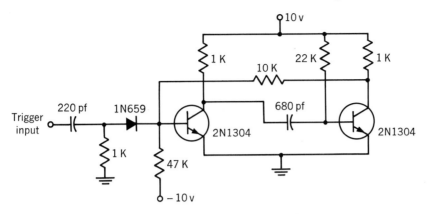

Fig. 28.9.   10-μsec monostable multivibrator.

Design Procedure. R_{L1}, R_{L2}, R_{K1}, R_{B1}, V_{CC}, V_{BB}, and Q_1 are selected as outlined for the bistable multivibrator. R_{B2}, C, and Q_2 are selected as outlined for the astable multivibrator. The diode is used only if $BV_{EBO(2)} < V_{CC}$. The OFF time of Q_2 is given by

$$t_{OFF} \cong R_{B2}C_2 \ln 2 = 0.7R_{B2}C_2$$

Triggering is usually accomplished at the base of Q_1.

Typical Design. Figure 28.9 shows a typical one-shot design. Values are taken from the circuits of Figs. 28.3 and 28.4 to form this circuit. Its output pulse width is approximately 10 μsec.

28.4. SCHMITT TRIGGER

The Schmitt trigger is a regenerative circuit which changes states abruptly when the input signal crosses specific d-c triggering levels. The use of the Schmitt trigger to produce a square wave from a sinusoidal input is a common application.

Consider the circuit of Fig. 28.10. If $v_{(in)}$ is zero, then Q_1 is OFF and Q_2 is ON.

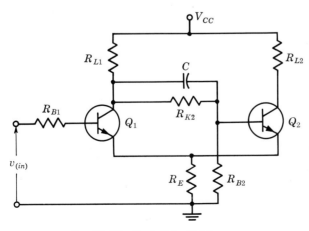

Fig. 28.10.   Basic Schmitt trigger.

With Q_2 ON, $V_E > 0$. If $v_{(in)}$ is allowed to rise to $(V_E + V_{BE1})$, Q_1 begins to conduct, lowering the collector voltage of Q_1 and raising V_E. These excursions will reduce the base current in Q_2 to the point that Q_2 comes out of saturation. The decrease in I_{C2} causes V_E to fall, which increases I_{B1}. Both transistors are active and the circuit is regenerative. The regeneration continues until Q_1 is ON and Q_2 is OFF. Note that V_E is now less than it was initially because $R_{L1} > R_{L2}$. Consequently, the *trip* point is also lowered. The two trip points are called the upper trip point, UTP, and the lower trip point, LTP.

This difference in trip points makes possible the *snap* action which reduces the effect of noise. When $v_{(in)}$ falls to the LTP, the reverse operation occurs, and the circuit returns to its initial state.

Design Procedure. The transistor type, the V_{CC}, and R_{L2} are selected considering the same factors outlined for the bistable flip-flop. V_{E2}, the emitter voltage when Q_2 is ON, should be much greater than the normal variations in $V_{BE(on)}$. V_{E1}, the emitter voltage when Q_1 is ON, should be less than V_{E2} by the desired difference in trip points. Neglecting the current in R_{B1}, the upper and lower trip points are:

$$\text{UTP} = V_{E2} + V_{BE1} \quad \text{and} \quad \text{LTP} = V_{E1} + V_{BE1}$$

Large differences in trip points tend to increase the regenerative action of the circuit.

Values of V_{E1} greater than 1 volt and differences in trip points of 0.5 volt are common. After selecting desired values of UTP and LTP, and hence V_{E1} and V_{E2}, R_E and R_{L1} are calculated by

$$R_E = \frac{V_{E2}R_{L2}}{V_{CC} - V_{E2}} \quad \text{and} \quad R_{L1} = \frac{(V_{CC} - V_{E1})R_E}{V_{E1}}$$

R_{K2} and R_{B2} are selected as outlined for the self-biased flip-flop, using Eqs. (1) of Chap. 27 and (11) through (15) of this chapter for the ON case, and Eqs. (2) of Chap. 27 and (14) and (15) of this chapter for the OFF case.

The external base resistor R_{B1} is used to limit base current in Q_1. R_{B1} should be

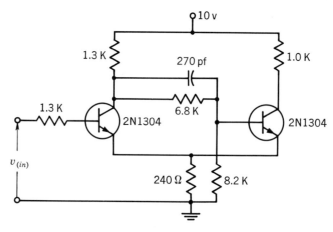

Fig. 28.11. Typical Schmitt trigger.

small and h_{FE1} large to minimize the voltage drop across R_{B1}, but R_{B1} should be much greater than R_E to minimize changes in V_{E1} when $V_{(in)}$ goes highly positive.

The output is usually taken from Q_2 because V_{E1} rises after $V_{(in)}$ becomes greater than the UTP, and this change shows up in the collector. V_{E2} does not change in this manner since $V_{(in)}$ is isolated by the OFF transistor, Q_1.

Typical Design. The circuit of Fig. 28.11 is a typical Schmitt trigger. The UTP = 2.2 volts and the LTP = 1.8 volts. It will perform well at frequencies of 100 kc or less. The 2N1304, with a minimum h_{FE} of 40, was selected to reduce the separation between $v_{(in)}$ and the trip points. The capacitor may be removed for low-frequency operation.

29

Logic Circuits

29.1. SATURATED TRANSISTOR LOGIC CIRCUITS

The transistor switch is widely used as the basic logic element in many control operations as well as in the arithmetic section of most digital computers. Six types of circuit configurations using the transistor as a switch are:

1. Transistor-resistor OR circuit.
2. Transistor-resistor AND circuit.
3. Transistor-resistor NOT (inverter) circuit.
4. Transistor-resistor NOR circuit.
5. Transistor-diode NOR circuit.
6. Transistor-diode NAND circuit.

The operation of each of the above circuits is discussed here, and design techniques for the NOR and NAND circuits are described. In order to describe operation of the individual circuits, a brief discussion will first be given of the binary number system, and of Boolean algebra and the manner in which it is applied to analysis and synthesis of control and computer systems.

The Binary Number System and Boolean Algebra. Generally, switching circuits have two stable states: ON or OFF, low voltage or high voltage, low current or high current. The decimal number system is incompatible with such circuits. It is desirable therefore to convert decimal numbers to binary numbers for manipulation within a computer or control circuit. Numbers are written in the decimal and binary systems in an identical manner. The decimal number system is easily understood because it is familiar, whereas a binary number system appears strange and complex.

To show the similarity of these number systems, consider first the manner in which the decimal number "one hundred and sixty-seven" is represented in the decimal system. It is written "167" and represents $(1 \times 10^2) + (6 \times 10^1) + (7 \times 10^0)$, which is equal to $100 + 60 + 7$, or 167. Each digit is multiplied by ten raised to a certain power. The value of the power of ten by which a digit is multiplied is determined by the position of the digit in the number. Thus, a digit in the first column (reading from right to left) is multiplied by 1, a digit in the second column is multiplied by 10, and a digit in the third column is multiplied by 100. This process is extended for higher-order digits.

The base of a number system is called its *radix*. The base or radix of the decimal system is 10, and of the binary system 2. The binary system uses only the digits 0 and 1 and is ideally suited to switching circuits. A binary number written as 101011, with the most significant bit to the extreme left, is interpreted as (1×2^5) + (0×2^4) + (1×2^3) + (0×2^2) + (1×2^1) + (1×2^0), which is equal to 32 + 0 + 8 + 0 + 2 + 1, or the decimal number 43. Rules for binary and decimal addition, subtraction, division, and multiplication are identical. Although more digits are required to express numerical values in the binary system than in the decimal system, the ease with which binary representations can be manipulated by electronic circuitry has led to almost exclusive use of some form of the binary system.

Boolean algebra is a type of mathematics used in conjunction with the binary number system. This algebra may be used to express the relationships between inputs and outputs of various circuits or systems. For example, consider the symbolic diagram of Fig. 29.1. Inputs A, B, and C are combined in such a manner that an output signal is present only if A *and* B *and* C are present; otherwise, there is no output.

Throughout this section, the following nomenclature is used in Boolean expressions: The word AND is understood when there is no symbol between letters; a plus symbol is defined as OR; the prefix NOT is added to a letter having a bar over it. An expression for the diagram of Fig. 29.1 can be written:

$$\text{Output} = ABC \qquad (1)$$

and is read "Output equals A and B and C." As in ordinary algebra, there are certain rules which govern manipulation of Boolean algebra expressions. If the above equation is expanded in accordance with the rules, many equivalent expressions can be written for the diagram of Fig. 29.1.

A relationship between inputs and outputs for the symbolic diagram of Fig. 29.2 is

$$\text{Output} = A + B + C \qquad (2)$$

and is read "Output equals A or B or C."

Figure 29.3 is a symbolic diagram having as a Boolean expression

$$\text{Output} = \bar{A} \qquad (3)$$

which is read "Output equals not A."

The equations which express relationships between inputs and outputs of the three symbolic diagrams are referred to as *logical expressions*. Circuits employed to realize these logical expressions are known as logic circuits. Logic circuits used to realize the symbolic diagrams of Figs. 29.1 through 29.3 are the AND, OR, and

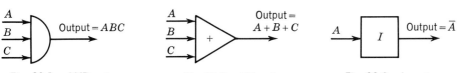

Fig. 29.1. AND gate.   **Fig. 29.2. OR gate.**   **Fig. 29.3. Inverter.**

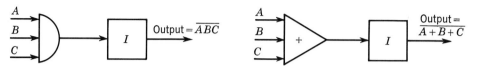

Fig. 29.4.   NAND gate.   **Fig. 29.5.   NOR gate.**

NOT (inverter) circuits, respectively.   These three logic circuits are the basic building blocks from which control and arithmetic operations are synthesized.   When the symbolic diagrams of Figs. 29.1 and 29.3 are combined as shown in Fig. 29.4, the relationship between inputs and outputs is

$$\text{Output} = \overline{ABC} \tag{4}$$

and is read "Output equals not the expression 'A and B and C.'"

When the symbolic diagrams of Figs. 29.2 and 29.3 are combined as shown in Fig. 29.5, the relation between inputs and outputs is

$$\text{Output} = \overline{A + B + C} \tag{5}$$

and is read "Output equals not the expression 'A or B or C.'"   If De Morgan's theorem is applied to expression (4), the result is

$$\text{Output} = \overline{A} + \overline{B} + \overline{C} \tag{6}$$

When both sides of expression (5) are negated, the result is

$$\overline{\text{Output}} = A + B + C \tag{7}$$

If the reference is inverted in either expression (6) or (7) (A substituted for $\overline{A}$, B

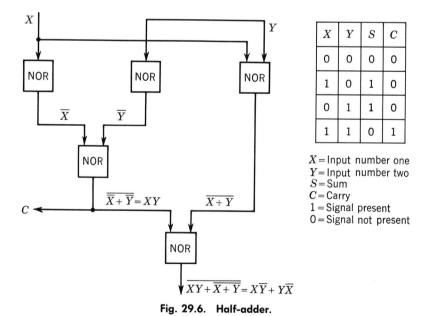

X	Y	S	C
0	0	0	0
1	0	1	0
0	1	1	0
1	1	0	1

X = Input number one
Y = Input number two
S = Sum
C = Carry
1 = Signal present
0 = Signal not present

Fig. 29.6.   Half-adder.

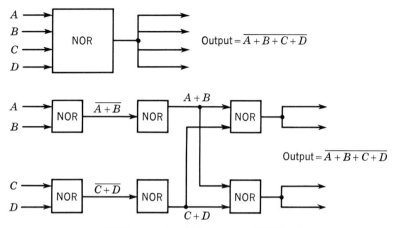

Fig. 29.7. Four-input, four-output NOR logic.

substituted for $\overline{B}$, etc), the expressions are identical. Therefore, a circuit which will perform either the NAND (negative AND) or the NOR (negative OR) function can be made to perform the other by reversing the reference levels of the signal voltages; hence these circuits are interchangeable. A NOR or a NAND circuit can serve to formulate any and all combinational logic functions. As an example, Fig. 29.6 shows how five NOR functions are combined to form a half-adder.

It would be ideal if logic circuits were not limited in their number of inputs and outputs. The importance of maximizing the number of inputs and outputs is illustrated in Fig. 29.7. Suppose that at some point in the system it is desired to take four separate inputs, perform a NOR function with them, and feed the output to four separate identical stages. The logic function is performed with one logic block, and hence one transistor which has a fan-in of four and a fan-out of four. In order to perform the same operation with a fan-in and fan-out of two, however, six logic blocks or six transistors are needed.

The discussion now proceeds to transistor logic circuits showing how the AND, OR, NOT, NOR, and NAND functions can be accomplished with the transistor switch.

Series and Parallel Transistor Logic. Figure 29.8 shows how logic functions may be realized using transistors in series. Figure 29.9 shows how the same logic functions can be accomplished using transistors in parallel. These methods of obtaining logic functions require one transistor for each input. Logic circuits accepting more than one input and supplying more than one output are often preferable.

Transistor-Resistor Logic NOR Circuit. Figure 29.10 shows a TRL circuit with M inputs and N outputs. A negative signal to any of the input resistors will cause the transistor to be in saturation, and the collector voltage will be near ground potential (binary 0). The collector voltage will be negative (binary 1) only when neither input A nor B nor C is negative. Because the OR and NOT functions are performed by the input resistor network and the transistor, respectively, the overall circuit is considered to be a NOR circuit. A logic expression for this circuit is

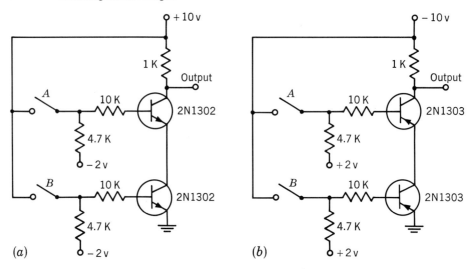

Gates using *NPN* and *PNP* transistors
and gate for normally open switches
or gate for normally closed switches
Note: Phase inversion of input

Fig. 29.8. Basic logic circuits using series transistors.

$$\text{Output} = \overline{A + B + C} \qquad (8)$$

The above equation can be rearranged to the form

$$\text{Output} = \overline{A}\,\overline{B}\,\overline{C} \qquad (9)$$

This latter expression for the TRL output shows that the circuit performs the AND operation on the inverse of each of the inputs.

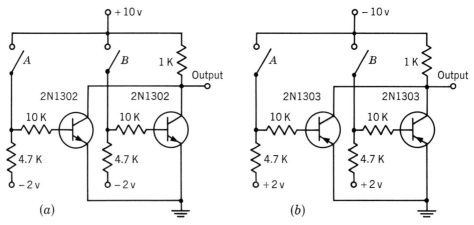

Gates using *NPN* and *PNP* transistors
or gate for normally open switches
and gate for normally closed switches
Note: Phase inversion of input

Fig. 29.9. Basic logic circuits using parallel transistors.

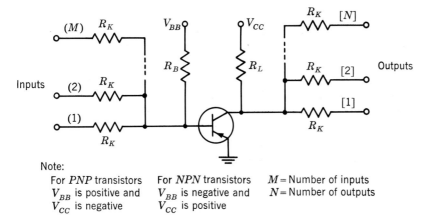

Note:

For *PNP* transistors	For *NPN* transistors	M = Number of inputs
V_{BB} is positive and	V_{BB} is negative and	N = Number of outputs
V_{CC} is negative	V_{CC} is positive	

Fig. 29.10. Basic NOR TRL circuit.

A TRL logic block is assumed to be driven by other identical TRL elements, and its outputs are to be used to drive additional TRL circuits having the same values of M, N, resistors, and voltages. Figure 29.11 shows a connection of TRL circuits.

Arbitrary selection of all voltage and resistance values for a TRL circuit will usually not give satisfactory operation. The worst-case method of designing a reliable circuit is described here. Figure 29.12 shows the conditions for minimum base drive to a TRL transistor. All input transistors but one are in saturation, and all resistances, voltages, and transistor parameters have simultaneously gone to their extreme values in the direction which would tend to prevent Q_1 from saturating. The equation shown with this figure is an expression for a minimum value of R_B in terms of all other circuit variables. A line over a variable indicates a maximum value and a line under a variable indicates a minimum value. M = inputs, and N = outputs. Any value of R_B greater than the value calculated from this equation will allow Q_1 to be in saturation when at least one input transistor is at cutoff.

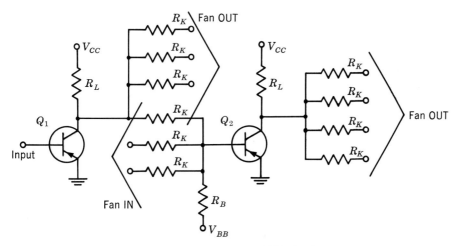

Fig. 29.11. Connection of TRL circuits.

Figure 29.13 shows a worst-case condition for maintaining Q_1 at cutoff. The equation presented with this figure determines the maximum value which R_B can have for reliable operation of the circuit.

All values on the right sides of the two worst-case equations (except for $\underline{R}_K$ and $\overline{R}_K$) are selected from collector current requirements, the expected range of saturation voltages, the resistance and voltage tolerances, the desired values of M and N, the maximum leakage currents, the reverse base-emitter voltage, and the anticipated minimum value of current gain. The minimum value of R_B is calculated for various nominal values of R_K by using the ON equation of Fig. 29.12. The maximum value of R_B is calculated in a similar manner by using the OFF equation shown with Fig. 29.13. Nominal values of R_B may be plotted for both cases by using the following relationships:

$$\overline{R}_B = R_{B(nominal)}(1 + \Delta R) \tag{10}$$

and

$$\underline{R}_B = R_{B(nominal)}(1 - \Delta R) \tag{11}$$

where Δ equals the tolerance expressed as a decimal fraction.

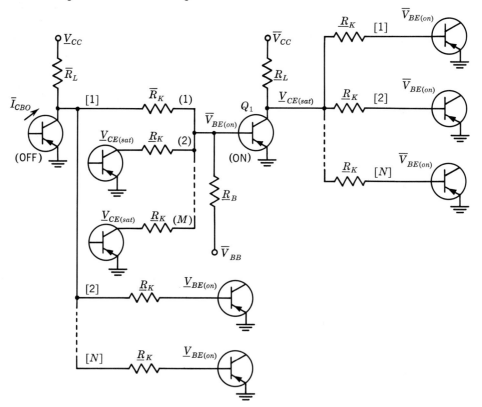

TRL ON equation (use magnitudes only):

$$\underline{R}_B = \cfrac{\overline{V}_{BB} + \overline{V}_{BE(on)}}{\cfrac{(M-1)(\underline{V}_{CE(sat)} - \overline{V}_{BE(on)})}{\underline{R}_K} + \cfrac{(\underline{V}_{CC} - \overline{I}_{CBO}\overline{R}_L - \overline{V}_{BE(on)})\underline{R}_K + (N-1)\overline{R}_L(\underline{V}_{BE(on)} - \overline{V}_{BE(on)})}{\overline{R}_L\underline{R}_K + \overline{R}_K\overline{R}_L(N-1) + \underline{R}_K\overline{R}_K} - \cfrac{1}{\underline{h}_{FE}}\left(\cfrac{\overline{V}_{CC} - \underline{V}_{CE(sat)}}{\underline{R}_L} + \cfrac{\overline{V}_{BE(on)} - \underline{V}_{CE(sat)}}{\underline{R}_K/N}\right)}$$

Fig. 29.12. TRL NOR circuit, ON condition.

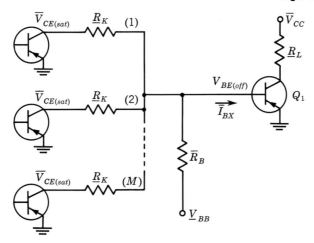

TRL OFF equation (use magnitudes only):

$$\underline{R}_B = \frac{\underline{V}_{BB} - V_{BE(off)}}{\dfrac{V_{BE(off)} + \overline{V}_{CE(sat)}}{\underline{R}_K/M} + \overline{I}_{BX}}$$

Fig. 29.13.   TRL NOR circuit, OFF condition.

There are general rules of thumb to be applied when choosing which valid solution to use. The theory behind this design procedure will permit the choice of any point lying on or between the two curves. However, by moving away from the boundaries, a safety factor is incorporated in the design; hence, reliability increases as the point chosen moves farther away from the boundaries of the area of solution. If speed is a prime consideration, it is best to choose a point where the values of the resistors are the smallest possible; the speed of the circuit increases as the point chosen moves toward the origin of the graph. If power dissipation is of prime importance, then a point is chosen where the values of the resistors are the largest possible; power dissipation decreases as the point chosen moves away from the origin of the graph.

All circuit parameters, in addition to transistor parameters, affect the area of solution. In general, large values of V_{BB} and V_{CC} increase the area of solution, but this means using high-impedance circuits (large values of R_L, R_B, and R_K). Thus, the operating speed may be reduced appreciably as supply voltages are increased. The area of solution becomes smaller as supply voltages decrease, and as N, M, or $V_{BE(off)}$ increases. In certain cases, the ON and OFF curves may not intersect. This means that no combination of R_B and R_K will allow the circuit to operate reliably under adverse conditions.

Transistor-Diode Logic NOR Circuit.   Diodes may be used in conjunction with transistors, as in Fig. 29.14, to perform the NOR function. This type of logic block is usually referred to as a TDL (transistor-diode logic) NOR circuit. Figures 29.15 and 29.16 show worst-case circuit conditions and equations for the ON and OFF states, respectively, of this type of logic block.

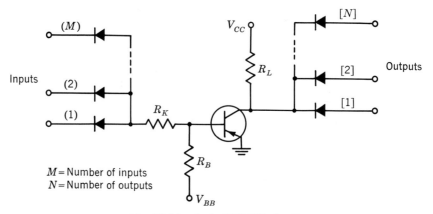

Fig. 29.14.   Basic NOR TDL circuit.

Transistor-Diode Logic NAND Circuit.   A second type of transistor-diode logic block, the TDL NAND circuit, is shown in Fig. 29.17.   Resistor R_L is a load resistor for the input transistors and, in conjunction with the input diodes, performs the AND operation on input signals.   The transistor inverts the output of the AND

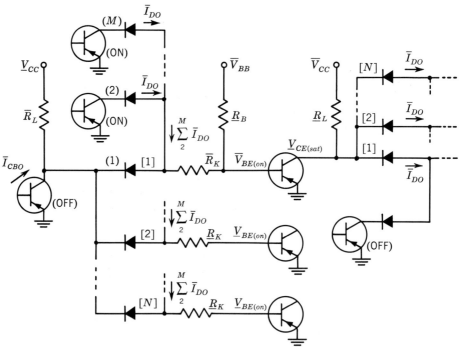

NOR TDL ON equation (use magnitudes only):

$$\underline{R}_B = \cfrac{\overline{V}_{BB} + \overline{V}_{BE(on)}}{\cfrac{(N-1)\overline{R}_L(\underline{V}_D + \underline{V}_{BE(on)} - \overline{V}_{BE(on)} - \overline{V}_D) + \underline{R}_K\{\underline{V}_{CC} - [\overline{I}_{CO} + N(M-1)\overline{I}_{DO}]\overline{R}_L\} - (\overline{V}_{BE(on)} + \overline{V}_D)\underline{R}_K}{\overline{R}_L\underline{R}_K + \overline{R}_K\overline{R}_L(N-1) + \overline{R}_K\underline{R}_K} - \cfrac{1}{\underline{h}_{FE}}\left(\cfrac{\overline{V}_{CC} - \underline{V}_{CE(sat)}}{\underline{R}_L} + N\overline{I}_{DO}\right)}$$

Fig. 29.15.   TDL NOR circuit, ON condition.

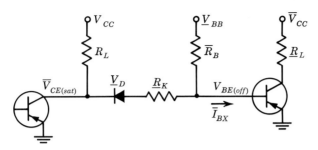

NOR TDL OFF equation (use magnitudes only):

$$\overline{R}_B = \frac{V_{BB} - V_{BE(off)}}{\dfrac{(V_{BE(off)} + \overline{V}_{CE(sat)} - \underline{V}_D)}{\underline{R}_K} + \overline{I}_{BX}}$$

$V_{BE(off)}$ is assumed to reverse-bias the transistor.

Fig. 29.16. TDL NOR circuit, OFF condition.

circuit and the complete circuit performs the NOT-AND (NAND) operation. A logical expression for the output of this circuit is

$$\text{Output} = \overline{ABC} \tag{12}$$

where A, B, and C are input levels to the diodes. Figures 29.18 and 29.19 show worst-case circuit conditions and equations for the ON and OFF states respectively, of this type of logic block.

Table 29.1 shows design parameters and circuit values for TRL NOR logic, TDL NOR logic, and TDL NAND logic. The circuits using silicon transistors were designed to operate over the range -55 to $125°C$. The circuits using germanium transistors were designed to operate over the range -10 to $+55°C$. For additional circuits see the "Texas Instruments Incorporated Computer Manual."

Speedup Capacitors. In saturated transistor logic circuits, storage time is generally the most significant component of propagation time (see Propagation

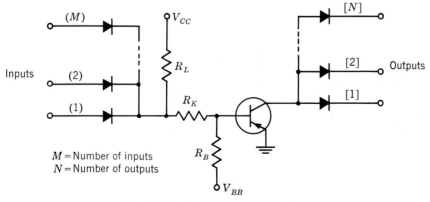

Fig. 29.17. Basic NAND TDL circuit.

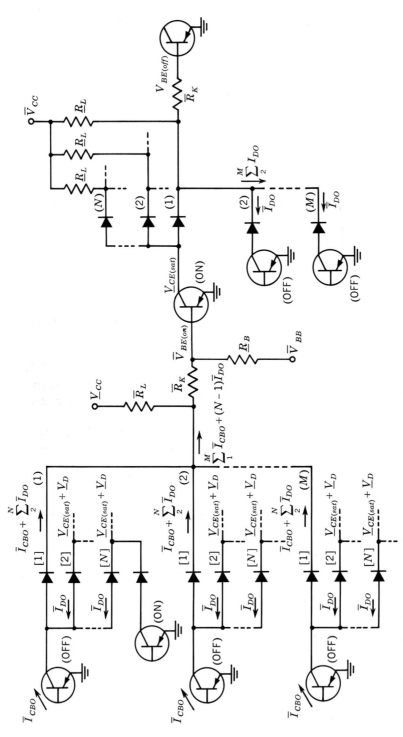

TDL ON equation (use magnitudes only):

$$\underline{R}_B = \frac{\dfrac{\underline{V}_{CC} - \overline{R}_L M[\overline{I}_{CBO} + (N-1)\overline{I}_{DO}] - \overline{V}_{BE(on)}}{\overline{R}_L + \overline{R}_K} - \dfrac{N}{\underline{h}_{FE}}\left[\dfrac{\overline{V}_{CC} - (\underline{V}_{CE(sat)} + \underline{V}_D)}{\overline{R}_L} + (M-1)\overline{I}_{DO} - \dfrac{(\underline{V}_{CE(sat)} + \underline{V}_D + V_{BE(off)})}{\overline{R}_K}\right]}{\overline{V}_{BB} + \overline{V}_{BE(on)}}$$

Fig. 29.18.   TDL NAND circuit, ON condition.

Table 29.1

Transistor type	Logic	Logic constants							Transistor constants						Diode constants			Circuit designs				
		V_{CC}	V_{BB}	I_C ma	R_L kilohms	$\% V$	$\% R$	$V_{BE(off)}$	h_{FE} min at $-55°C$	$V_{BE(on)}$ min	$V_{BE(on)}$ max	$V_{CE(sat)}$ min	$V_{CE(sat)}$ max	I_{CBO} max μa	V_D min	V_D max at $-55°C$	I_{DO} at T_{max}, μa	Max M	Max N	R_K for max M and N, kilohms	R_B for max M and N, kilohms	T_P,* msec
2N744	TRL NOR	10	10	10	1	2	5	0	20	0.87	1.1	0.15	0.33	10	...	...	...	2	3	2.7	30	33
	TDL NOR	10	10	10	1	2	5	0	20	0.87	1.1	0.15	0.33	10	0.15	0.9	10	10	6	1.2	47	23
	TDL NAND	10	10	10	1	2	5	0	20	0.87	1.1	0.15	0.33	10	0.15	0.9	10	4	5	3.0	27	14†
2N2412	TRL NOR	10	10	10	1	2	5	0	20	0.85	1.1	0.08	0.26	5	...	...	...	2	4	2.7	33	77
	TDL NOR	10	10	10	1	2	5	0	20	0.85	1.1	0.08	0.26	5	0.15	0.9	10	10	6	1.8	6.8	75
	TDL NAND	10	10	10	1	2	5	0	20	0.85	1.1	0.08	0.26	5	0.15	0.9	10	10	6	3.0	30	21‡
2N964	TRL NOR	5	5	10	0.5	2	5	0.1	27	0.36	0.56	0.08	0.2	15	...	...	...	2	3	2.0	15	37
	TDL NOR	5	5	10	0.5	2	5	0.1	27	0.36	0.56	0.08	0.2	15	0.28	0.8	1	10	8	1.2	47	26
	TDL NAND	5	5	10	0.5	2	5	0.1	27	0.36	0.56	0.08	0.2	15	0.28	0.8	1	5	3	2.0	7.5	11§
2N797	TRL NOR	5	5	10	0.5	2	5	0.1	32	0.36	0.51	0.07	0.15	10	...	...	...	2	4	2.0	16	43
	TDL NOR	5	5	10	0.5	2	5	0.1	32	0.36	0.51	0.07	0.15	10	0.28	0.8	1	10	9	1.0	43	35
	TDL NAND	5	5	10	0.5	2	5	0.1	32	0.36	0.51	0.07	0.15	10	0.28	0.8	1	10	5	2.7	12	15†

* Measured for $M = N = 3$ if obtainable.
† 33-pf speedup capacitor used.
‡ 47-pf speedup capacitor used.
§ 20-pf speedup capacitor used.

Germanium transistor temperature design range: -10 to $+55°C$.
Silicon transistor temperature design range: -55 to $+125°C$.
Silicon TRL temperature design range: 0 to $+125°C$.

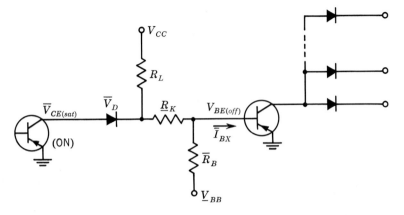

TDL OFF equation (use magnitudes only):

$$\overline{R}_B = \frac{\underline{V}_{BB} - V_{BE(off)}}{\dfrac{(\overline{V}_D + \overline{V}_{CE(sat)} + V_{BE(off)})}{\underline{R}_K} + \overline{I}_{BX}}$$

$V_{BE(off)}$ is assumed to reverse-bias the transistor.

Fig. 29.19.   TDL NAND circuit, OFF condition.

Time, Sec. 5.5). In the NAND circuit, speed can be greatly improved by shunting resistor R_K with a capacitor as shown in Fig. 29.20. The circuit applies constant-current drive to the transistor during the steady-state operation, but during the switching transient, the capacitor is essentially a low impedance and the drive approaches a voltage drive. The stored charge on the capacitor during saturation of the transistor should be only large enough to equal Q_{SB}, the stored base charge of the transistor. The capacitor should have a time constant which will permit it to recover sufficiently between incoming pulses. Making C_K too large defeats its purpose since this adds a time constant that may limit the maximum clock rate. The equivalent circuit and circuit time constant obtained the instant after the drive

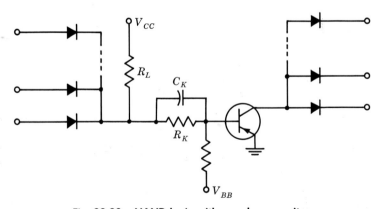

Fig. 29.20.   NAND logic with speedup capacitor.

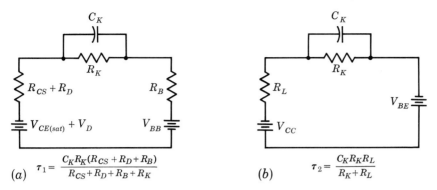

$$(a) \quad \tau_1 = \frac{C_K R_K (R_{CS} + R_D + R_B)}{R_{CS} + R_D + R_B + R_K}$$

$$(b) \quad \tau_2 = \frac{C_K R_K R_L}{R_K + R_L}$$

Fig. 29.21. Time constants added.

transistor is switched ON are shown in Fig. 29.21*a*, OFF in Fig. 29.21*b*. Again, care should be taken in selecting C_K to assure that both time constants are small enough to allow the capacitor to recover sufficiently during the ON and OFF intervals of the clock pulse.

Comparison of Logic Types. The designer of computer logic circuitry continually strives to handle more bits of information per second per dollar. The emphasis in a particular system will be on either or both of the above requirements. Component count in a circuit, component reliability, ease of manufacture, power dissipation, and maximum fan-in and/or fan-out are other factors affecting the choice of design.

Although each system must be evaluated after the basic objectives have been decided, some general statements can be made. These general comparisons apply to the circuits *without speedup* capacitors. When capacitors are used the speed is increased significantly, but in the TRL circuit severe cross talk or noise problems arise that present significant disadvantages outweighing the speed advantage.

TRL vs. TDL. When speed and maximum fan-in and fan-out are not of prime importance, TRL circuitry is commonly used in place of TDL circuitry because of its simplicity, low cost, and component reliability. The speed of TRL logic circuits is device-dependent up to the point where time constants of load resistors and capacitors limit the speed. Generally, a faster transistor gives faster logic circuits.

TDL NOR vs. TDL NAND. The main differences between TDL NOR and TDL NAND circuitry are in speed and maximum fan-in and fan-out capabilities. NAND circuitry is faster, whereas NOR circuitry is capable of higher fan-in and fan-out. Both these differences can be attributed to the way in which the diodes are used in the circuits. TDL NAND circuitry may be a bit more difficult to design, but its excellent speed performance outweighs this disadvantage. In some systems, the higher fan-in and/or fan-out of TDL NOR circuitry may be used to decrease the number of logic stages required. Therefore, if speed is not the primary concern, TDL NOR is more economical.

Circuitry Speed. The speed of logic circuits in general depends a great deal on the external circuitry. As with high-frequency techniques, low impedance (low resistance as well as low stray capacitance) is important. Thus, high-speed operation involves lower resistance, lower capacitance, and higher currents.

A significant advantage of the mesa transistor in logic circuits is that the important design-limiting parameter (transistor current gain) increases as current increases. Therefore, much faster propagation times can be obtained by operating at an increased current level. Although this carries a penalty of increased power dissipation, epitaxial devices with their lower internal voltage drops help reduce this problem. The epitaxial technique also provides higher current-carrying capability and lower device capacitance with the same mesa geometry.

29.2. COMPLEMENTARY LOGIC CIRCUITS

A PNP current mode switch is shown in Fig. 29.22a. Current generators at the emitter and collector supply constant currents of I_2 and I_1 as shown. With the base of Q_1 grounded, the current I_2 divides between Q_1 and Q_2. The base-to-emitter voltage drop of Q_1 and also Q_2 is approximately 0.2 volt. This causes the common-emitter point to be 0.2 volt positive with respect to ground. If a positive voltage greater than 0.2 volt is applied to the base of Q_1, the base-to-emitter diode of this transistor becomes reverse-biased, and the collector current drops to the value of the collector reverse current. I_2 then flows almost entirely through Q_2.

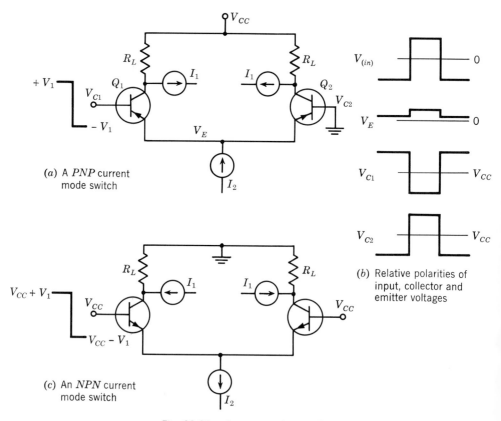

(a) A PNP current mode switch

(b) Relative polarities of input, collector and emitter voltages

(c) An NPN current mode switch

Fig. 29.22.   Current mode switches.

When a negative voltage greater than 0.2 volt is applied to the base of Q_1, this transistor conducts, and consequently Q_2 will turn OFF. I_2 then flows into the emitter of Q_1.

When Q_1 is OFF, the voltage at the collector is

$$V_{C1} = -V_{CC} - I_1 R_L \tag{13}$$

When conducting, the collector current of Q_1 is αI_2 where $\alpha = I_C/I_E$. A portion of I_2 supplies I_1, and what is left of I_2 flows through R_L. The collector voltage of Q_1 then becomes

$$V_{C1} = -V_{CC} + (\alpha I_2 - I_1) R_L \tag{14}$$

If I_1 is chosen to be $I_2/2$, then Eqs. (13) and (14) can be written as

$$V_{C1} \cong -V_{CC} - I_1 R_L \tag{15}$$

and

$$V_{C1} \cong -V_{CC} + I_1 R_L \tag{16}$$

The total voltage change at the collector of Q_1 is

$$V_C = 2(I_1 R_L) \tag{17}$$

The quantity I_2 may be relatively large. It is for this reason that the circuit of Fig. 29.22a is considered to be a current switch. Relative polarities of input voltage, emitter voltage, and collector voltages are shown in Fig. 29.22b.

Since nonsaturated switches operate at higher speeds than saturated switches, it is necessary to keep the current mode switch out of saturation. The emitters of Q_1 and Q_2 are near ground potential while the collector potentials vary by about $(-V_{CC} \pm I_1 R_L)$. By choosing $-V_{CC}$ sufficiently large, saturation may be avoided.

It should be noted that two outputs are available, one at each collector; the computer designer derives added flexibility from this complementary output. The input signal at the base of Q_1 is given as plus and minus with respect to ground, whereas the output varies plus and minus about V_{CC} (see Fig. 29.22b).

A second current mode switch using NPN transistors is shown in Fig. 29.22c. This circuit requires an input signal which goes plus and minus with respect to V_{CC}, and gives an output which varies plus and minus with respect to ground, i.e., the exact complement of the circuit of Fig. 29.22a. Thus, a logic chain would use alternating types of current mode switches. It should be noted that current mode switching can be accomplished using only one polarity of transistor if some means is available to reestablish the proper d-c level between each successive stage of logic.

In general, nonsaturating switches operate at a higher dissipation level than saturating switches because of the higher collector-to-emitter voltage when the switch is in the ON condition; thus, when choosing a transistor for a current-mode switch, the maximum power dissipation becomes an important factor.

D-C Analysis. Figure 29.22a indicates that three constant-current generators are required. To obtain such a generator, a large resistance can be placed in series with a d-c voltage as shown in Fig. 29.23. If the external resistance R_X connected between points A and B of Fig. 29.23 is much smaller than the resistor, R_S, the current from V will be essentially independent of the value of R_X. The circuit of Fig. 29.22 can be closely approximated by the circuit shown in Fig. 29.24. From

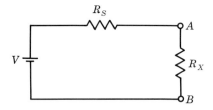

Fig. 29.23. Constant current is achieved by use of relatively large R_S compared to load R_X.

Fig. 29.24, with the transistor removed, the collector circuit current generators are

$$I_1 = \frac{-V_{CC} + V_1}{R_1} \quad \text{if } R_1 \gg R_L \tag{18}$$

Also, since either Q_1 or Q_2 is conducting, R_2 is connected at point C to provide a low-impedance path to ground. Thus,

$$I_2 = \frac{V_2}{R_2} \quad \text{if } V_2 \gg V_{BE} \tag{19}$$

Overall system design considerations usually determine the voltage swing required and the impedance level; hence, I_1 and R_L will probably be predetermined. If arbitrary supply voltages are used, I_2 is determined by the values of α and I_1, while resistors R_1 and R_2 can be obtained from Eqs. (18) and (19).

Consider the following design example for a current mode switch. The circuit will be identical with that of Fig. 29.24. The collector voltage of Q_2 is to be -5.5 volts when the input is negative and -6.5 volts when the input is positive, i.e., a voltage swing of 1.0 volt. Since the collector voltage is 6.0 ± 0.5 volts, $-V_{CC}$ is chosen to be -6 volts. Values of $-V_1$ and V_2 are chosen to be -45 and $+45$ volts, respectively. If R_L is 50 ohms, then I_1 is 10 ma. Assuming $\alpha = 0.98$, I_2 must then be approximately $2 \times I_1 = 20$ ma. R_1 is calculated from Eq. (18) and is 3,900 ohms. R_2 is calculated from Eq. (19) and is 2,200 ohms.

To show that the currents are substantially at their design values, the magnitude of all currents will be calculated for the condition in which Q_1 is conducting and Q_2 is cut off. The circuits in Fig. 29.25a and b are simplified equivalents of the

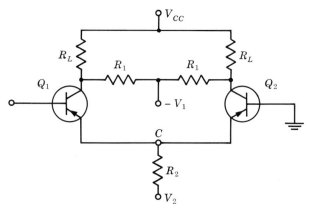

Fig. 29.24. Circuit approximating Fig. 29.22.

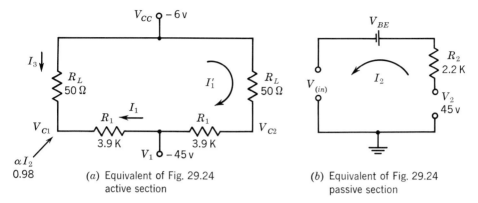

(a) Equivalent of Fig. 29.24
active section

(b) Equivalent of Fig. 29.24
passive section

Figure 29.25

circuit of Fig. 29.22 under these operating conditions. V_{BE} and α are assumed to be 0.2 volt and 0.98, respectively. From Fig. 29.25b,

$$I_2 = \frac{V_2 - V_{BE} + V_{(in)}}{R_2} \tag{20}$$

If $V_{(in)} = 0.5$ volt,

$$I_2 = \frac{45 - 0.2 + 0.5}{2,200} = 20.5 \text{ ma} \tag{21}$$

The reverse current of the emitter-base junction of Q_2 has been neglected since it is much smaller than I_2. The collector current of Q_1 is approximately αI_E. Using Fig. 29.25a and neglecting the reverse currents, the collector voltage of Q_1 is

$$V_{C1} = \alpha I_2 \frac{R_1 R_L}{R_1 + R_L} + \frac{V_1 R_L}{R_1 + R_L} + \frac{V_{CC} R_1}{R_1 + R_L} \tag{22}$$

Since $R_L \ll R_1$,

$$V_{C1} = \alpha I_2 R_L + \frac{V_1 R_L}{R_1} + V_{CC} \tag{23}$$

Using the values given in Fig. 29.25a,

$$V_{C1} \cong -5.58 \qquad I_1 \cong -10.1 \text{ ma} \qquad I_3 \cong 8.3 \text{ ma}$$

The voltage at the collector of Q_2 is

$$V_{C2} = \frac{V_1 - V_{CC}}{R_1 + R_L} R_L + V_{CC} \tag{24}$$

and since $R_L \ll R_1$, then

$$V_{C2} = \frac{V_1 R_L}{R_1} + V_{CC} \tag{25}$$

Using the values given in Fig. 29.25b,

$$V_{C2} = -6.58 \text{ volts} \qquad \text{and} \qquad I_1 = 9.9 \text{ ma}$$

These calculations show that the output voltage swing is 1.0 volt, which is sufficient to drive an NPN current mode switch.

Transient Analysis. The analysis of switching times proceeds in the following manner: the transistors together with the external elements are replaced by an equivalent network, which is an approximate high-frequency equivalent circuit, representing the current mode switch when the output current is a function of the input current. This network is then modified to represent the transistor circuit during the interval when an input signal has been applied, but before the output current has begun to change.

Figure 29.26 shows typical input- and output-current waveforms for a transistor switch. The delay, rise, storage, and fall times are shown.

The output-current rise time is calculated. Figure 29.27 shows the current mode switch of Fig. 29.24 with the resistors and voltage sources in the collector circuit replaced by their Thévenin equivalents, and the constant-current generator in the emitter circuit neglected because of its large internal resistance. In the following analysis, it is assumed that the internal impedance of both transistors is identical.

Looking to the right of A in Fig. 29.27, the input impedance of the grounded-base transistor can be shown to be

$$Z_{(in)} = Z_e + r_b(1 - \alpha) \tag{26}$$

where Z_e is the emitter impedance, r_b is the base resistance, and α is short-circuit current gain in the grounded-base configuration. The input impedance of Q_1 is

$$Z_{(in)} = r_b + \frac{Z_e}{1 - \alpha} + \frac{Z_{(ext)}}{1 - \alpha} \tag{27}$$

where $Z_{(ext)}$ is the impedance in the emitter circuit of Q_1, and is equal to $Z_{(in)}$ of Eq. (26). Substitution of Eq. (26) into Eq. (27) for $Z_{(ext)}$ gives

$$Z_{(in)} = 2\left(r_b + \frac{Z_e}{1 - \alpha}\right) \tag{28}$$

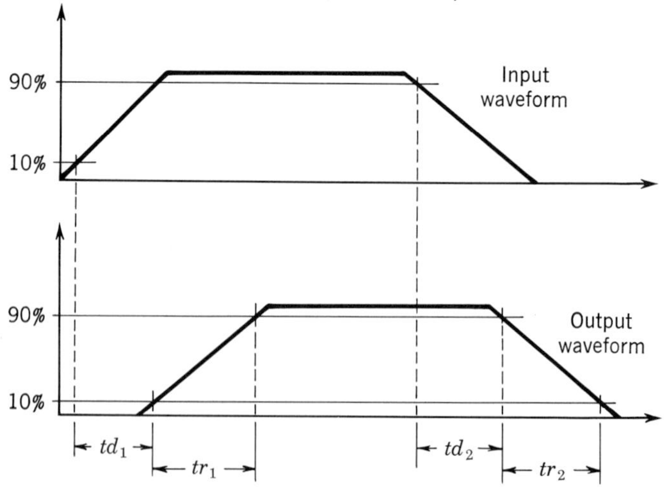

Fig. 29.26. Typical input and output waveforms for a transistor switch.

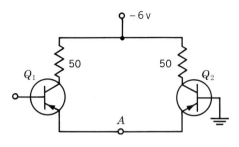

Fig. 29.27. Current mode switch of Fig. 29.24 using Thévenin equivalents.

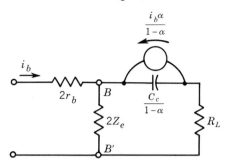

Fig. 29.28.   Composite equivalent circuit.

A composite equivalent circuit can be drawn as in Fig. 29.28. The base current is

$$i_b = \frac{E_{(in)}}{Z_{(in)}} = \frac{E_{(in)}}{2[r_b + Z_e/(1 - \alpha)]} \tag{29}$$

That portion of the circuit to the right of BB' can be presented as shown in Fig. 29.29. Because R_L is small compared to the reactance of $C_c/(1 - \alpha)$, even at high frequencies the current through R_L is

$$i_o = \frac{i_b \alpha}{1 - \alpha} \tag{30}$$

where i_b is the base current. Substitution of Eq. (29) into Eq. (30) yields

$$i_o = \frac{E_{(in)} \alpha}{2[r_b + Z/(1 - \alpha)](1 - \alpha)} \tag{31}$$

The parameter α is frequency-dependent and can be approximated by

$$\alpha = \frac{\alpha_o}{1 + jf/f\alpha} \tag{32}$$

where α_o = low-frequency small-signal current gain
f = frequency at which α is to be calculated
f_α = alpha cutoff frequency

The impedance Z_e is also a function of frequency and is, to a close approximation,

$$Z_e = \frac{r_e}{1 + jf/f_\alpha} \tag{33}$$

Fig. 29.29.   Portion of Fig. 29.28 equivalent circuit to right of BB' can be represented thus.

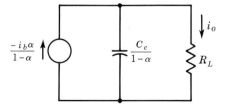

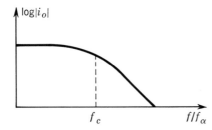

Fig. 29.30. Load current vs. frequency, for equivalent circuit of Fig. 29.29.

where r_e is the emitter junction resistance. Substitution of Eqs. (32) and (33) into Eq. (31) gives, after rearrangement of terms,

$$i_o = \frac{\alpha_o E_{(in)}}{2r_b(1 - \alpha_o) + 2r_e + j2r_b f/f_\alpha} \tag{34}$$

Figure 29.30 shows a plot of i_o vs. frequency. The current gain of the circuit is down 3 db at the frequency f_c. This frequency can be determined by equating the real and imaginary terms of the denominator of Eq. (34) and solving for frequency. Thus,

$$f = f_c = f_\alpha \left[(1 - \alpha_o) + \frac{r_e}{r_b} \right] \tag{35}$$

The following measurements were made on a Texas Instruments 2N1305 transistor: $f_\alpha = 6.6$ mc, $\alpha_o = 0.994$, and $r_b = 105$ ohms. From the relation

$$r_e \cong \frac{kT}{qI_E}$$

where k = Boltzmann's constant
T = absolute temperature
q = electronic charge
I_E = emitter current

r_e is calculated to be 2.6 ohms, using an average I_E of 10 ma. Substitution of these values into Eq. (35) gives $f_c = 0.204$ mc.

From Eq. (34), the d-c or maximum value of i_o is calculated to be 77 ma for $E_{(in)} = 0.5$ volt. The RL circuit of Fig. 29.31 can be selected so that its frequency response is the same as that shown in Fig. 29.30. If the maximum value of input current to this circuit is adjusted to be 77 ma, an expression for current through the RL circuit may be written:

$$i_o = 77(1 - e^{-t/\tau}) \tag{36}$$

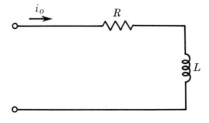

Fig. 29.31. RL circuit to give curve shown in Fig. 29.30.

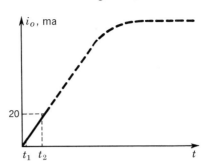

Fig. 29.32. Curve resulting from Eq. (36).

where $\tau = L/R$ and is the circuit time constant. The impedance of this circuit is

$$Z = R + j\omega L \tag{37}$$

and to have a frequency cutoff at $f_c = 0.204$ mc, the real and imaginary terms of Eq. (37) must be equal at this frequency. Solving for L/R under this condition yields

$$\frac{L}{R} = \tau = \frac{1}{\omega} = 7.81 \times 10^{-7} \text{ sec}$$

The output-current rise time of the current mode switch may now be calculated. Although the collector current rises toward 77 ma, it is limited to a maximum value of 20 ma because of the constant-current generator in the emitter circuit. Equation (36) gives the magnitude of i_o after the output current has begun to flow. This equation is used to calculate t_1 and t_2 (Fig. 29.32), which correspond to collector currents of 2 and 18 ma, respectively. These times are found to be $t_1 = 20.8$ mμsec and $t_2 = 208$ mμsec. Thus, $t_r = t_2 - t_1 = 187$ mμsec.

The current mode switch of Fig. 29.24 was breadboarded, using the resistor and voltage values selected in the example. A square-wave voltage, with a rise time of 20 mμsec, varying above and below zero volts by 0.5 volt, was applied to the input of Q_1. With Q_1 and Q_2 having the parameters given for the 2N1305 transistor, the rise time of the output current was measured to be 180 mμsec.

Delay time is divided into two parts. Figure 29.33 shows the input circuit of a transistor when it is biased in the reverse direction. C_{TE} is a depletion-layer capacitance between the emitter and base. When the transistor is reverse-biased, this capacitor is charged to a reverse polarity. Sufficient charge must be supplied by the input current to discharge the capacitor. The time required to discharge this capacitor, after the input has risen to its 10% value, is the first portion of the delay time.

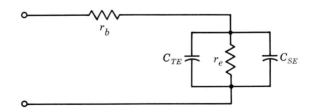

Fig. 29.33. Input circuit of transistor when biased in reverse direction.

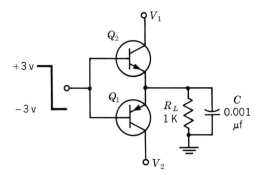

Fig. 29.34. Complementary emitter-follower circuit.

The remaining portion of the delay time is the time required for the output current to change from its initial value to 10% of its final value. This time has previously been calculated at t_1 and is 20.8 mμsec. The measured delay time of the circuit of Fig. 29.24 was 40 mμsec.

The second delay time t_{d2} and fall time t_{r2} are calculated, using the same equivalent circuit of Fig. 29.28. For this reason, t_{d2} and t_{r2} have the same values as t_{d1} and t_{r1}, respectively.

Complementary Emitter-Follower. A complementary emitter-follower is shown in Fig. 29.34. Q_1 and Q_2 are PNP and NPN transistors, respectively, and have nearly identical electrical characteristics. The advantage of a complementary emitter-follower over the conventional type can be seen with the aid of Fig. 29.35. This shows an emitter-follower driving a capacitive load.

A negative input to the base of Q_1 causes conduction, and C is charged with the polarity as shown. The charging path of C is through the forward resistance of the base-emitter diode of Q_1. This resistance is of the order of only a few ohms, and C will charge rapidly. Removal of the negative drive at the base causes Q_1 to stop conducting, and C must then discharge through R. If R is larger than the resistance in the charging path, the output-voltage waveform of Q_2 will have a longer fall time than rise time.

Figure 29.36 shows how the output waveform is distorted. To reduce the fall time of the output waveform, a circuit is required which will present a low-impedance path for the discharge of C. The complementary emitter-follower of Fig. 29.34 provides this low-impedance path. Q_1 of Fig. 29.34 is the same as in Fig. 29.35.

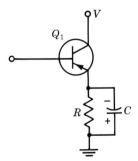

Fig. 29.35. Emitter-follower driving a capacitive load.

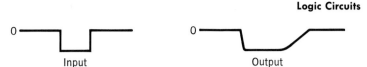

Fig. 29.36. Waveforms for circuit of Fig. 29.35. Note distortion in output waveform.

A negative input at the base connection causes Q_1 to conduct, and C is charged to a voltage which is almost equal to the input voltage. When the input goes positive, the emitter of Q_1 is negative with respect to its base. Q_2 conducts, and C discharges through the base-emitter diode of Q_2. This reduces the fall time of the output waveform and gives a symmetrical waveshape.

The biasing arrangement for the complementary emitter-follower of Fig. 29.34 is easily determined. For the output-voltage swing to have approximately the same magnitude as the input-voltage swing, the collector voltages for the PNP and NPN transistors will be chosen as -3 and $+3$ volts, respectively.

Transient Analysis. The complementary emitter-follower shown in Fig. 29.34 can be analyzed to ascertain the transient response in the following manner. If it is assumed that both NPN and PNP units have identical characteristics, then only one of the two transistors need be considered. When an ordinary emitter-follower is changed from the ON to the OFF condition, any capacitive load must discharge through the resistance of the biasing network, and hence produce a relatively long transition time. As an example, the circuit of Fig. 29.34 has a rise time of 80 mμsec and a fall time of 2.5 μsec when the NPN transistor is removed. If the NPN unit is included, the fall time is the same as the rise time.

It is obvious that one of the transistors is responsible for the rise and the other for the fall; hence, the transient analysis will consider a single transistor driving the load as shown in Fig. 29.35. If the equivalent circuit of Fig. 29.37 is used, current i_2 can be written as

$$i_2 = \frac{e_{(in)}Z_c}{Z_c(Z_e + Z_L) + r_b[Z_e + Z_L + Z_c(1 - \alpha)]} \tag{38}$$

and the voltage gain is

$$\frac{e_o}{e_{(in)}} = \frac{Z_L}{Z_e + Z_L + (r_b/Z_c)[Z_L + Z_e + Z_c(1 - \alpha)]} \tag{39}$$

Since $Z_c = 1/j\omega C_c$ at high frequencies and in the frequency range of interest,

$$\omega r_b C_c \ll 1$$

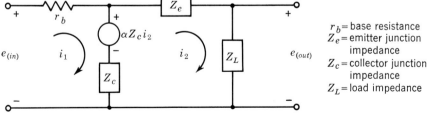

r_b = base resistance
Z_e = emitter junction impedance
Z_c = collector junction impedance
Z_L = load impedance

Fig. 29.37. Equivalent circuit for transient analysis.

where ω is radian frequency.   Equation (39) may now be written as

$$\frac{e_o}{e_{(in)}} = \frac{Z_L}{Z_e + r_b(1 - \alpha) + Z_L} \tag{40}$$

The terms of Eq. (40) as a function of frequency are as follows:

$$Z_e = \frac{r_e}{1 + p/\omega_\alpha} \qquad Z_L = \frac{R_L}{1 + R_L C_L p} \qquad \alpha = \frac{\alpha_o}{1 + p/\omega_\alpha} \tag{41}$$

where $r_e \cong kT/qI_E$
$\qquad p$ = complex frequency
$\qquad \omega_\alpha$ = alpha cutoff frequency expressed in radians
$\qquad R_L$ = load resistance
$\qquad C_L$ = load capacitance
$\qquad \alpha_o$ = low-frequency value of α

Substituting Eq. (41) into Eq. (40) yields

$$\frac{e_o}{e_{(in)}} = \frac{R_L}{R_L + r_e + r_b(1 - \alpha_o)}$$

$$\times \frac{(1 + p/\omega_\alpha)}{1 + \left\{ \dfrac{R_L C_L[r_e + r_b(1 - \alpha_o)] + (R_L + r_b)/\omega_\alpha}{R_L + r_e + r_b(1 - \alpha_o)} \right\} p + \dfrac{r_b R_L C_L p^2}{\omega_\alpha[R_L + r_e + r_b(1 - \alpha_o)]}} \tag{42}$$

If $R_L \gg r_e + r_b(1 - \alpha_o)$, Eq. (42) can be written

$$\frac{e_o}{e_{(in)}} = \frac{(1 + p/\omega_\alpha)}{1 + \{[r_e + r_b(1 - \alpha_o)]C_L + (R_L + r_b)/R_L\omega_\alpha\} p + r_b C_L p^2/\omega_\alpha} \tag{43}$$

Complementary transistors having the following characteristics were used in the circuit of Fig. 29.34: $\omega_\alpha = 2 \times 6 \times 10^6$ radians/sec; $\alpha_o = 0.99$; $r_b = 60$ ohms; $r_e = 10$ ohms.

These transistor parameters were measured at an average bias condition of $R_L = 1{,}000$ ohms, $C_L = 0.001$ μf.

By using the measured parameters given above, the rise time can be calculated as 75 mμsec.   The value determined experimentally was 80 mμsec, which shows good agreement with the calculated value.

30

Transistorized Timers

Timing can be accomplished by a variety of methods—mechanical, thermal, chemical, electronic, or a combination of these. Regardless of the method, a timer depends upon a time base either generated internally or applied from an external source. The spring-driven clock, for example, generates its own time base, whereas the ordinary electric clock uses an external time base—the period of the a-c line voltage. The first consideration in the design of transistorized timers is the generation of a suitable time base.

30.1. RC TIME-BASE GENERATORS

Analysis of a Theoretical Circuit. The time base for a simple low-cost circuit may be established by the use of a resistor, a capacitor, and a sensing network as shown in Fig. 30.1. Ignoring the loading of the sensing network, the time, t, for capacitor C to charge to voltage V_C in the simple timing circuit is

$$t = RC \ln \frac{V_B}{V_B - V_C} \tag{1}$$

The accuracy of a time base derived from the circuit is dependent on the stability of the RC product, of V_B, and of the sensing network. The change in the time base produced by an incremental change in the RC product with all other variables held constant is

$$\Delta t = \Delta RC \ln \frac{V_B}{V_B - V_C} \tag{2}$$

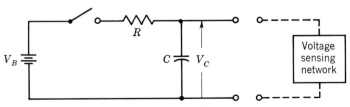

Fig. 30.1. Theoretical RC timing circuit.

where Δt = incremental change in t, and ΔRC = incremental change in the RC product.

The equation shows that a percentage change in the RC product will produce an equal percentage change in the time base.

The error in the time base produced by an incremental change in the source voltage V_B while all other parameters are held constant is

$$\Delta t = -\Delta V_B \frac{V_C RC}{V_B(V_B - V_C)} \tag{3}$$

where ΔV_B = incremental change in V_B. The error in the time base produced by an incremental change in V_C with all other parameters held constant is

$$\Delta t = \Delta V_C \frac{RC}{V_B - V_C} \tag{4}$$

where ΔV_C = incremental change in capacitor voltage. Mathematically, the percentage error resulting from an incremental change in V_C is a minimum when $V_C = 63\%$ of V_B.

The accuracy of a practical RC timing circuit will depend on well-regulated source voltages, small tolerances on resistors and capacitors or proper compensation for changes in these components, and a stable sensing circuit.

Analysis of a Transistorized Circuit. A practical timing circuit is shown in Fig. 30.2. The sensing circuit is designed to supply current to R_L when

$$V_C = V_Z + V_{BE(on)} \tag{5}$$

where V_C = voltage across the capacitor
  V_Z = zener voltage of D_1
  $V_{BE(on)}$ = base-emitter ON voltage of transistor Q_1

The time t' for the RC circuit to charge to the voltage which operates Q_1 is

$$t' = R'C \ln \frac{V'_B - I_{CBO}R'}{V'_B - I_{CBO}R' - V_Z - V_{BE(on)}} \tag{6}$$

where $\qquad R' = \dfrac{RR_s}{R + R_s} \qquad V'_B = V_B \dfrac{R_s}{R + R_s}$

and I_{CBO} = collector-base reverse current of Q_1 with the emitter open-circuited, and $V_{BE(on)}$ = base-emitter ON voltage of Q_1. All variables in Eq. (6) are dependent on temperature; therefore, an exact equation for t' is not practical because of its complexity. A better approach to the problem is to design the circuit to be as stable as possible with existing components, then compensate for variations in specific parameters over the operating temperature range.

In this circuit, as in all circuits where a transistor is to be operated as a saturated switch, two cases must be considered: the ON case and the OFF case. The circuit should be so designed that the transistor will saturate at the lowest operating temperature, and to ensure that the transistor will be held OFF at the highest temperature.

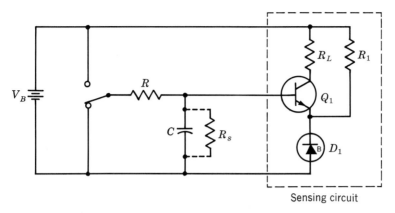

Fig. 30.2. Transistorized RC timing circuit.

A technique which will meet these requirements requires a d-c analysis of the equivalent circuit for both the ON and the OFF states of the transistor. The following considerations should be made in the design of the sensing network.

For the ON case, the collector current of Q_1 is

$$I_C = \frac{V_B - V_{CE(sat)} - V_Z}{R_L} \tag{7}$$

where $V_{CE(sat)}$ = collector-emitter saturation voltage. The maximum base current required to saturate the device is

$$I_{B(max)} = \frac{I_C}{h_{FE(min)}} = \frac{V_B - V_{CE(sat)} - V_Z}{h_{FE(min)}R_L} \tag{8}$$

where $h_{FE(min)}$ = minimum current gain of the device. The available base current is

$$I_B = \frac{V_B R_s - (V_Z + V_{BE(on)})(R + R_s)}{R R_s} \tag{9}$$

Thus, $h_{FE(min)}$ must be chosen so that

$$I_B \geqq I_{B(max)} \tag{10}$$

Collector power dissipation during the ON time is

$$P_{C(on)} = I_C V_{CE(sat)} \tag{11}$$

This equation may be used to determine the collector dissipation rating when

$$T_{ON} \gg \theta_{J\text{-}C} C_{J\text{-}C} \gg T_{SW} \tag{12}$$

where T_{ON} = ON time
   T_{SW} = time to switch the transistor from OFF to ON states
   $\theta_{J\text{-}C} C_{J\text{-}C}$ = junction thermal time constant

For large values of R and C, the time required to switch the transistor may be long compared to the thermal time constant of the transistor. Thus, the collector dissipation rating for this case should be determined from the equation

$$P_C = \frac{(V_B - V_Z)^2}{4R_L} \tag{13}$$

During the OFF time, the collector-emitter and emitter-base voltage-breakdown ratings must not be exceeded. The collector reverse current I_{CBO} should be small compared to the capacitor-charging current.

The zener diode D_1 should be selected with the following characteristics:

1. Voltage rating large compared to $V_{BE(on)}$.
2. Low dynamic impedance.
3. Adequate power rating when Q_1 is saturated.
4. Temperature coefficient which cancels that of the base-emitter junction (approximately 2 mv/C°).

If the timer circuit is to be operated over a wide temperature range, the temperature coefficients of all components should be considered. As noted in Eq. (6), components in the RC network will affect the stability of the time base. Resistor R has a temperature coefficient which causes the time base to vary with temperature. Fixed-composition resistors change with voltage as well as with temperature; the total change can be as much as $\pm 35\%$ from 25 to 105°C. Some 1% carbon resistors change 5% for a 100 C° temperature change.

Both capacitance and shunt resistance of capacitor C must be considered. For temperatures approaching 200°C, Teflon* capacitors at present are the most suitable. Since the shunt resistance is very high (1×10^9 megohm-μf product), these capacitors allow a wider range of charging currents for varying time delays. The Teflon temperature curve shows a negative coefficient of 100 ppm/C°. A typical Mylar* capacitor has a high shunt resistance (6×10^4 megohm-μf product), and is operational up to 125°C. The capacitance-vs.-temperature curve flattens near 25°C, then increases rapidly with temperature above 65°C.

Very often in analyzing a transistorized timer, the sensing network is automatically considered to be the major cause of instability. The above considerations, however, indicate that the major source of error may often be attributed to other factors; however, parameter variations of the transistor in the sensing network should not be ignored when considering the factors which might affect the stability of the time base.

The circuit of Fig. 30.2 may be temperature-compensated if desired. To obtain the required accuracy, it may be necessary to compensate for both the change in the RC product and the change in I_{CBO}. As a rule, the capacitor-charging current is made much larger than the leakage current I_{CBO}, making the effect of I_{CBO} negligible. Opposite temperature coefficients of V_Z and $V_{BE(on)}$ may eliminate the need for compensation in the emitter of Q_1. However, if the turn-on voltage $V_Z + V_{BE(on)}$ varies with temperature, compensation may be effected by using a thermistor or *sensistor*† resistor.

---

* Trademark of Du Pont.
† Trademark of Texas Instruments.

The temperature coefficient of each component in the timing circuit has a definite thermal time constant. Even though the circuit may be perfectly compensated for gradual temperature changes, the time base may vary with fast changes in temperature. Good heat-sinking techniques will minimize this problem.

30.2. DESIGN EXAMPLES

One-shot Multivibrator Timer. Considering economy, simplicity, and ease of assembly, a simple two-transistor monostable multivibrator makes a very good timer. For example, the timer circuit in Fig. 30.3, having an accuracy of $\pm10\%$ from -20 to $+60°C$, is designed to switch a 4-ma load with a 12-volt supply.

The output is -12 volts for periods of 1 to 5 sec, and is adjustable between these values. The circuit operates as follows: When power is applied, Q_1 is normally OFF and Q_2 normally ON. C_1 will charge with polarity as shown. Operating PB_1 causes Q_1 to conduct. Q_2 turns off since D_1 is reverse-biased, owing to the charge on C_1. Base drive for Q_1 now flows through R_4 from the collector of Q_2, which is at approximately -12 volts. The output voltage appearing at the collector of Q_2 remains until the charge on C_1 reverses, owing to the charging path through R_2 and R_3. Q_2 will turn ON, removing the base drive from Q_1, and the circuit will remain in this state until PB_1 is operated again.

Free-running, Dual-output Timer. The circuit of Fig. 30.4 has dual outputs, each of which may be controlled separately. The operation may be described as

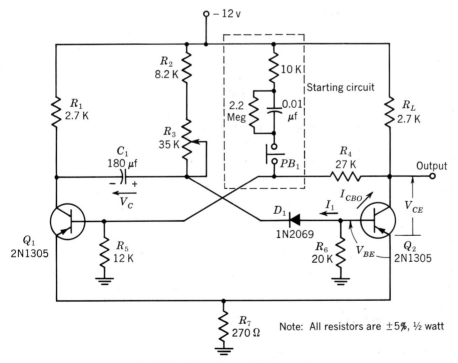

Fig. 30.3. One-shot multivibrator timer.

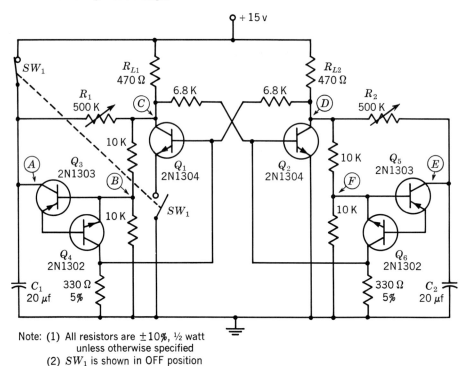

Note: (1) All resistors are ±10%, ½ watt
           unless otherwise specified
       (2) SW_1 is shown in OFF position
       (3) R_{L1} or R_{L2} can be replaced with a 500 Ω
           relay coil and 1N2069 diode in parallel

Fig. 30.4. Free-running, dual-output timer.

follows: When V_{CC} is applied with SW_1 (emitter leg) open, C_1 will charge, raising the potential at A above the potential at B, causing conduction in Q_3 and Q_4. This will turn Q_1 ON when SW_1 is closed. Closing SW_1 opens the direct V_{CC} supply to C_1. Q_1 now conducts, dropping the potential at point C to nearly ground level, and removes the charging source from C_1. When Q_1 turns ON, Q_2 turns OFF, raising the potential of point D from nearly ground to approximately V_{CC}. Hence C_2 commences to charge, and when point E rises to a greater potential than point F, transistors Q_5 and Q_6 conduct. This turns Q_2 ON and Q_1 OFF, and commences the charging cycle on C_1. If SW_1 is opened (emitter leg opened and V_{CC} supply to C_1 closed), C_1 will charge almost instantaneously, enabling the circuit to start a new cycle. The OFF time of Q_1 and Q_2 may be varied by adjusting R_1 and R_2, respectively.

A temperature check of this circuit showed an error of 3% over a range of 25 to 55°C, and a 10% error from -20 to $+25$°C. Most of this error was due to the difference in the firing point of the PNP-NPN "hook" combination. This type of repeating timer will give excellent results with a stable power-supply voltage and a constant ambient temperature. A typical accuracy of 0.1% may be expected with these conditions.

Bootstrap Timer. A bootstrap timer is shown in Fig. 30.5. Transistors Q_1 and Q_2 comprise a one-shot multivibrator with Q_1 normally ON and Q_2 normally OFF.

C_1 will charge through R_1 and D_1 toward 24 volts. The voltage on C_1 will be "followed" by the Darlington circuit, composed of Q_3 and Q_4. The voltage across the 4.7-kilohm resistor in the emitter of Q_4 will approximate that of C_1 and change at the same rate. This change will be coupled to the junction of R_1 and D_1 through a 10-μf capacitor. This type of feedback allows R_1 and C_1 to *see* almost the same charging voltage during the timing cycle. The result is a nearly linear output-voltage rise across the emitter resistor of Q_4. The length of the time cycle is set by controlling the emitter voltage of Q_5. This voltage must always be some value less than V_{CC}. When the sawtooth voltage applied to the base of Q_5 exceeds the emitter voltage, Q_5 will saturate. A negative pulse will be generated by the network connected to the collector of Q_5, and will be applied to the base of Q_1. When Q_1 turns OFF, Q_2 will turn ON and discharge C_1. When the one-shot multivibrator returns to its original stage, the timing cycle will begin again.

Overall accuracy of this circuit, from -50 to $+50°C$, is 3%. Counter circuits to give longer time cycles can easily be utilized for production-line control, acid-bath timers, photographic timers, and many other monotonous jobs which are repeated sequentially day after day.

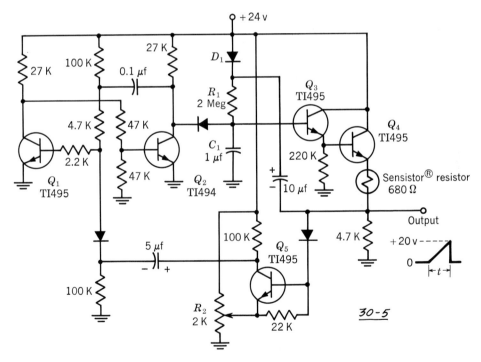

Note: (1) All resistors are ±5%, ½ watt unless otherwise specified
     (2) C_1 is a Teflon® dielectric capacitor
     (3) The temperature coefficient of R_1 is ±2 ppm/°C
     (4) R_2 sets the value of t
     (5) All diodes 1N2069

Fig. 30.5. Bootstrap timer.

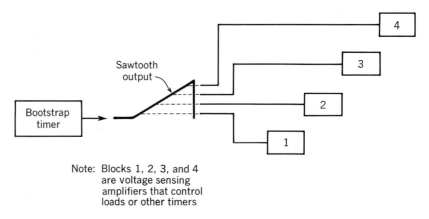

Note: Blocks 1, 2, 3, and 4
are voltage sensing
amplifiers that control
loads or other timers

Fig. 30.6.   Sequential bootstrap timer.

Sequential Timer.   The block diagram of a sequential bootstrap timer is shown in Fig. 30.6.   Four sequential events can be set to occur in order until all four are completed.   All four will turn OFF together, and the cycle will be repeated.   The order in which each event will occur is determined by the voltage level of the sawtooth waveform.   Blocks 1, 2, 3, and 4 may also represent timers whose outputs will perform functions of different time lengths, a feature often required for repeat-job operations.

Decade Timer.   Figure 30.7 shows a timer using digital methods, with a selection capability of 0.1 to 99.9 sec in 0.1-sec increments.   This timer makes use of the 60-cps line frequency for a time base.   The three decade counters, A, B, and C, have selective outputs which provide for operation of a relay or other devices when the three decades reach the time preset by the three switches, SW_2, SW_3, and SW_4.   The principal advantage of this timer over other types is that the accuracy depends on the stability of the 60-cps line frequency instead of on the circuit parameters.

An *oven-controlled* tuning-fork oscillator, running at 60 cps, could supply the input to this type of counter and afford the same accuracy.   Addition of more decade counters will provide extended time ranges with the same accuracy throughout the entire range.

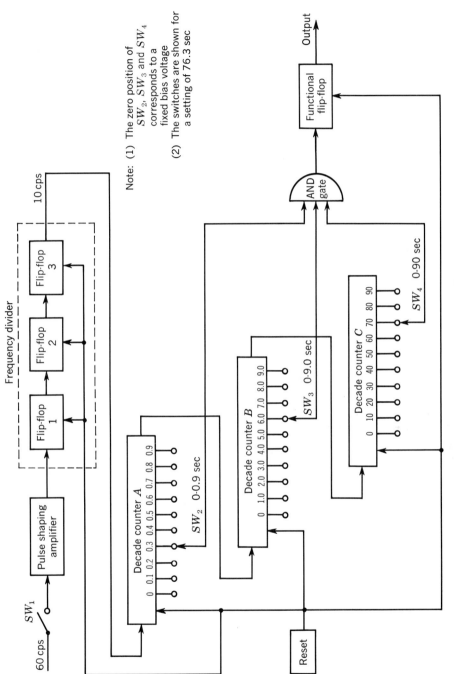

Fig. 30.7. Decade timer.

Note: (1) The zero position of SW_2, SW_3 and SW_4 corresponds to a fixed bias voltage

(2) The switches are shown for a setting of 76.3 sec

417

31

High-level Switching

Because of their efficiency and reliability, transistor switches are ideally suited to the manipulation and control of large amounts of power.

31.1. POWER DISSIPATION

In a practical switching circuit, the average power dissipated in the transistor is much less than the peak dissipation. Consequently, relatively large currents and voltages can be handled without exceeding the rated dissipation of the transistor. However, the voltages should be limited to a safe value below the breakdown voltage, and the current should stay within the maximum current specified for the transistor. At all times, the average power dissipation must be below the rated dissipation at the maximum ambient temperature.

An expression for the average power dissipated in a transistor switch can be derived from the idealized current and voltage waveforms of Fig. 31.1. The assumptions made are:

1. Power dissipated in the base is negligible.
2. Rise time and fall time are equal.
3. Storage time and delay times are negligible; i.e., the ON and OFF times are equal.

Even using these simplifying assumptions, the resulting equation is helpful in illustrating which of the transistor electrical quantities are most important for power-dissipation considerations.

$$P \text{ (average dissipation)} = \frac{1}{\tau} \int_0^{T_{ON}} V_{CE(sat)} I_p \, dt + \int_{T_{ON}}^{T_{ON}+T_{SW}} \left(I_p - I_p \frac{t}{T_{SW}} \right) \left(V_p \frac{t}{T_{SW}} \right) dt$$

$$+ \int_{T_{ON}+T_{SW}}^{\tau - T_{SW}} V_p I_{CO} \, dt + \int_{\tau - T_{SW}}^{\tau} \left(V_p - V_p \frac{t}{T_{SW}} \right) \left(I_p \frac{t}{T_{SW}} \, dt \right) \quad (1)$$

$$P \text{ (average dissipation)} = \underbrace{\frac{V_{CE(sat)} I_p T_{ON}}{\tau}}_{\text{ON}} + \underbrace{\frac{V_p I_{CO} T_{OFF}}{\tau}}_{\text{OFF}} + \underbrace{\frac{I_p V_p T_{SW}}{3\tau}}_{\text{Switching}} \quad (2)$$

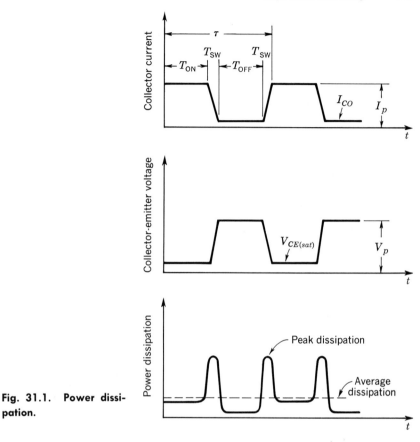

Fig. 31.1. Power dissipation.

This equation illustrates the importance of fast switching and low saturation voltage for efficient switching.

31.2. LOAD-LINE ANALYSIS

An important consideration in achieving maximum reliability in a high-level switch is the transistor's load line. The load line, or *VI curve* as it is sometimes called, is the locus of the transistor's operating points. A simple method of observing a load line is shown in Fig. 31.2. The vertical plates of an oscilloscope are connected across a small resistor inserted in the collector circuit. It should be noninductive, and its resistance should be much smaller than any other impedance in series with the transistor. The horizontal plates are connected to the collector and emitter terminals. The resulting trace shows the current and voltage that the transistor is handling as it functions in the circuit. The peak power dissipated by the transistor during switching can be determined by taking the peak product of the currents and voltages which occur simultaneously. If a determination of the average power dissipated is desired, the necessary time relationship can be obtained by modulating the trace with a time-mark generator.

In many high-level switching applications the load is inductive or transformer-coupled, and, consequently, problems inherent in inductive switching are en-

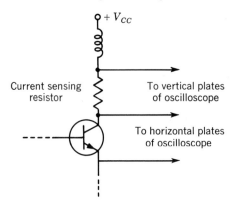

Fig. 31.2. Measurement of load line.

countered. A load line for a single-ended switch with an inductive load is shown in Fig. 31.3. The voltage induced in the inductance at turn-off adds to the supply voltage to form a collector-to-emitter voltage spike. This voltage could exceed the applicable collector-to-emitter voltage breakdown of the transistor, BV_{CEX}.

Another equally important possibility is that the transistor would experience a secondary voltage breakdown, because of the large current and voltage appearing simultaneously during turn-off. That is, the maximum allowable collector-to-emitter voltage is determined by the load line as well as by the rated BV_{CEX}. From voltage considerations alone, the maximum collector-emitter voltage could safely approach BV_{CEX}. But consideration of the load line (i.e., simultaneous current and voltage variations) often reveals that the maximum voltage must be restricted to something less than BV_{CEX}, especially if the load is inductive. Limiting the maximum collector-to-emitter voltage to the BV_{CES} rating (rather than to BV_{CEX}) often affords a safety factor for resistive and slightly inductive loads. However, even this may not be conservative enough for a high-level switching circuit with an inductive load line similar to that shown in Fig. 31.3. In every instance, it is

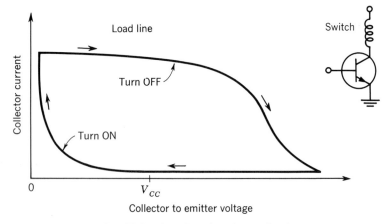

Fig. 31.3. Switch with inductive load.

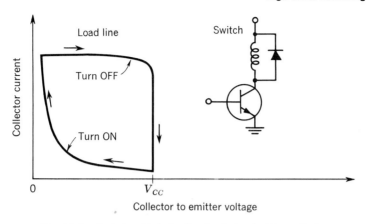

Fig. 31.4. Switch with inductive load shunted by a diode.

advisable to switch the transistor operating point through the region of high dissipation as rapidly as possible.

The most common method of protecting the transistor from the energy stored in the inductance of an inductively loaded single-ended switch is shown in Fig. 31.4. The diode limits the voltage across the transistor during turn-off to the supply voltage.

Further improvement in shaping of the load line can be achieved in many instances by shunting the diode with a small capacitor, as shown in Fig. 31.5. The capacitor voltage opposes the supply voltage during turn-off, thus allowing the current through the transistor to drop without a sudden voltage rise across the transistor. For some designs, the diode may become unnecessary.

Double-ended (push-pull) switches with inductive loads can also have their load lines shaped. A small capacitor connected from collector to collector, as shown in Fig. 31.6, is usually very effective in suppressing collector-to-emitter voltage spikes.

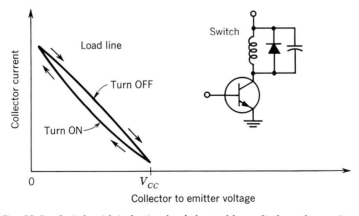

Fig. 31.5. Switch with inductive load shunted by a diode and capacitor.

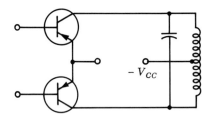

Fig. 31.6. Capacitor spike suppression.

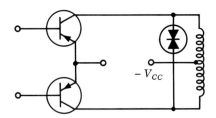

Fig. 31.7. Breakdown-diode spike suppression.

If the voltage spikes are exceptionally severe or fast switching time is of prime importance, it is best to replace the capacitor with a double-anode breakdown diode as shown in Fig. 31.7.

The sections following are representative of high-level switching applications.

BIBLIOGRAPHY

Newell, A. F.: An Introduction to the Use of Transistors in Inductive Circuits, *Mullard Tech. Communs.,* vol. 4, no. 35, pp. 157–160, November, 1958.

32

Light Flashers

Transistor-operated flashers are now replacing flare pots and mechanically operated flashers for reasons of reliability, safety, compactness, and efficiency.

Figure 32.1 shows a multivibrator flasher which drives two lamps alternately. Such a flasher has been used in aircraft applications. The design of the astable multivibrator is discussed in Sec. 28.2.

The construction barricade flasher is the most common flasher application at present. Some transistorized flashers run as long as 60 days on a single battery, whereas a flare pot must be refilled every few days. The barricade flasher must be inexpensive and efficient, usually driving a single lamp at 1 cps at a 15% duty cycle. A typical design of this type is shown in Fig. 32.2. To explain its operation, assume that the switch S_1 has just closed. Base current then flows through R_2 into Q_1. The collector current of Q_1 is the base current of Q_2. The resulting collector current in Q_2 divides between the lamp and the feedback path (R_1C_1). The feedback current adds to the base current of Q_1, and the resulting regeneration saturates Q_2, causing the lamp to burn at full brilliance. The feedback current decays exponentially, owing to the R_1C_1 time constant. The flasher begins to turn off when this current decays to a value that will not sustain saturation of Q_2. As Q_2 comes out of saturation, the voltage change is fed back to the base of Q_1 through the (R_1,C_1) path. Regeneration occurs again, causing both transistors to turn off rapidly.

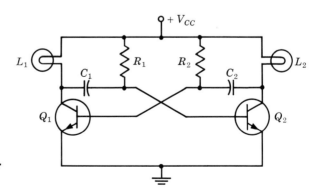

Fig. 32.1. Astable multivibrator light flasher.

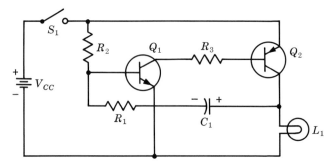

Fig. 32.2.   Low-current flasher.

The charge on C_1 is such that the base of Q_1 is made negative. C_1 begins to charge toward V_{CC} through R_1 and R_2.   When the base voltage of Q_1 reaches $V_{BE(on)1}$, Q_1 begins to turn ON, starting a new cycle.

The base current I_{B1} in Q_1 comprises two components: a static component, I_0, and a dynamic component, i_d, as shown in Fig. 32.3. I_0 and i_d are given by

$$I_0 \cong \frac{V_{CC} - V_{BE1}}{R_2} + I_{CBO} \tag{1}$$

and

$$i_d \cong \frac{V_{CC}}{R_1} \epsilon^{-t/R_1 C_1} \tag{2}$$

Therefore,

$$i_{B1} = I_0 + i_d \tag{3}$$

The operation of this flasher is very dependent upon the h_{FE} of both Q_1 and Q_2. To ensure starting and to prevent *lockup* in the ON state, both transistors should be in the active region when the feedback path (R_1,C_1) is open, and the closed-loop gain must be greater than unity.   An open-loop lamp current between 20 and 80% of the full-load lamp current, I_L, has been found to be satisfactory for a typical 5-volt 90-ma flasher lamp such as the GE 1850.   Then the static base current in Q_1 must be

$$I_0 \geqq \frac{0.2I_L}{h_{FE1}h_{FE2}} \tag{4}$$

and

$$I_0 \leqq \frac{0.8I_L}{h_{FE1}h_{FE2}} \tag{5}$$

The loop gain is

$$A_L \cong \frac{h_{FE1}h_{FE2}R_L}{h_{ie1} + R_1 + R_L} > 1 \tag{6}$$

where R_L = lamp resistance measured at $0.2I_L$, and h_{ie1} = input resistance of Q_1 measured with $i_{B1} = I_0$.   The flasher turns OFF when i_{B1} decays to a value ($I_{(off)}$) which will not sustain saturation of Q_2, that is, when

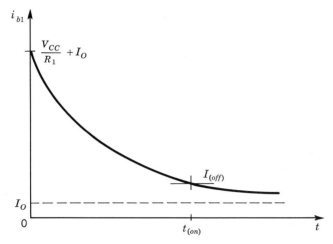

Fig. 32.3. Base current in Q_1.

$$I_{(off)} = \frac{I_L}{h_{FE1}h_{FE2}} \qquad (7)$$

Since

$$I_{(off)} \cong \frac{V_{CC}}{R_1} \epsilon^{-t_{ON}/R_1C_1} + I_O \qquad (8)$$

then

$$t_{ON} \cong R_1C_1 \ln \frac{V_{CC}}{R_1(I_{(off)} - I_O)} \qquad (9)$$

Assuming $R_2 \gg R_1$, the OFF time is

$$t_{OFF} \cong 0.7R_2C_1 \qquad (10)$$

This condition is illustrated in Fig. 32.3. When $t = t_{ON}$, i_{B1} has decayed to $I_{(off)}$. $I_{(off)}$ varies with h_{FE1} and h_{FE2}. I_{B1} should decay to $I_{(off)}$ within two time constants for reasonable ON time stability.

R_3 is chosen small enough to allow Q_2 to saturate when Q_1 is saturated,

$$R_3 < \frac{(V_{CC} - V_{BE(on)2} - V_{CE(sat)1})h_{fe}}{I_L} \qquad (11)$$

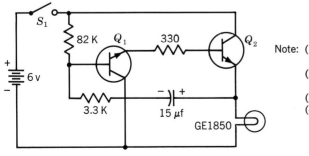

Note: (1) $Q_1 - $ 2N1302 inverted
configuration; $Q_2 - $ 2N1374
(2) $h_{FE1} \times h_{FE2}$ selected to be
between 500 and 1,000
(3) Typical ON time 0.2 sec
(4) Typical OFF time 0.8 sec

Fig. 32.4. Low-current flasher.

and R_3 must be large enough to prevent excessive collector currents in Q_1 and Q_2.

Figure 32.4 illustrates a typical flasher design. Q_1 is operated in the inverted configuration for lower h_{FE} and lower leakage current. Inverted h_{FE} of the 2N1302 can be expected to be between 5 and 20. Normal h_{FE} of the 2N1374 is specified to be between 50 and 150. Q_1 and Q_2 must be selected such that the $h_{FE1}h_{FE2}$ product satisfies Eqs. (4) to (6). An $h_{FE1}h_{FE2}$ product between 500 and 1,000 works well in this flasher.

The switch S_1 can be replaced with a solar-cell switch to turn off the flasher automatically in daytime; such an arrangement will roughly double battery life in unattended locations.

33

Blocking Oscillators

The blocking oscillator is a common type of relaxation oscillator. There are two major modes of operation: the astable or free-running mode, and the monostable or triggered mode. In computer circuitry, the blocking oscillator is often used as a pulse generator.

33.1. COMMON EMITTER

The circuit shown in Fig. 33.1 is a basic blocking oscillator in the common-emitter configuration. Upon application of a negative trigger pulse to the base, the collector current will start to rise. The collector voltage will rise toward $V_{CE(sat)}$, and a pulse will be coupled to the feedback winding. Since the feedback voltage is $180°$ out of phase with the primary voltage, a negative-going pulse will be coupled to the base, thereby turning the transistor ON and driving it into saturation. When the current in the transformer builds up to the point where the transistor cannot remain saturated, the feedback voltage will decrease, and the transistor will turn OFF. The back voltage that will be present at the collector when the field of the primary winding starts to collapse may exceed the BV_{CBO} rating of the transistor; consequently, a diode is connected across the primary winding to prevent voltage breakdown of the transistor.

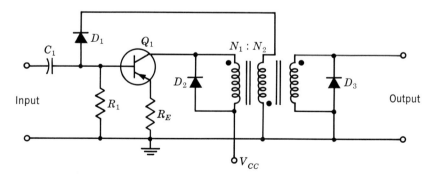

Fig. 33.1. Common-emitter triggered blocking oscillator.

427

Ignoring the load current and the current through R_1, the collector and base currents as a function of time are given by the following equations:

$$i_C \cong \frac{V_{CC}}{r}\left[1 - \left(1 - \frac{r}{n^2 r_b}\right)\epsilon^{-(rt/L_m)}\right] \qquad (1)$$

and
$$i_B \cong \frac{-V_{CC}}{r_b r}r_2\left[1 - \left(1 + \frac{r}{nr_2}\right)\epsilon^{-(rt/L_m)}\right] \qquad (2)$$

where $r = r_1 + r_2$
    r_1 = d-c resistance of the transformer primary plus R_{CS} (collector saturation resistance)
    $r_2 = r_e$ (saturated emitter resistance) plus R_E (external emitter resistance)
    r_b = base resistance
    $n = N_1/N_2$ = turns ratio
    L_m = magnetizing inductance

When the collector current is approximately $h_{FE}i_B$, the transistor will turn OFF. Using Eqs. (1) and (2), the pulse width, t_w, is

$$t_w \cong \frac{L_m}{r}\ln\frac{1 - r/n^2 r_b + (h_{FE}r_2/r_b)(1 + r/nr_2)}{1 + h_{FE}r_2/r_b} \qquad (3)$$

If $h_{FE}(r_e + R_E) \gg r_b$, then

$$t_w \cong \frac{L_m}{r}\ln\left(1 + \frac{r}{nr_2}\right) \qquad (4)$$

Thus, the effect of circuit parameters on pulse width can easily be determined from Eq. (4). Conversely, the magnetizing inductance necessary for a given pulse width can easily be computed. For example, assume

    $t_w = 1$ μsec
    $r_1 = 2$ ohms
    $r_2 = 2.7$ ohms
    $n = 5/1$

Therefore,

$$L_m = \frac{(1 \times 10^{-6})(4.7)}{\ln[1 + 4.7/(5)(2.7)]} = 15.7 \text{ μh}$$

The maximum collector current can be determined by substituting Eq. (3) into Eq. (1), thus:

$$i_{C(max)} = \frac{V_{CC}(1 + r/nr_b)h_{FE}(r_2/r_b)}{nr_2[1 - r/n^2 r_b + h_{FE}(r_2/r_b)(1 + r/nr_2)]} \qquad (5)$$

Assuming h_{FE} is large,

$$i_{C(max)} = \frac{V_{CC}}{nr_2 + r} \qquad (6)$$

33.2. COMMON BASE

The *saturated* common-base-type blocking oscillator is similar in operation to the saturated common-emitter type; therefore, the following discussion covers the common-base *nonsaturating*-type blocking oscillator. This is often used when fast response is desired.

Figure 33.2 illustrates the common-base nonsaturating blocking oscillator. When the transistor is triggered by a negative pulse, current will start to rise in the collector. The pulse coupled to the emitter will be in phase with the pulse at the collector. The negative pulse fed back to the emitter will aid the turn-on current, causing the transistor to be driven toward $V_{CE(sat)}$. However, the collector voltage will not reach $V_{CE(sat)}$ but will be clamped to a voltage level, V_1, which is above $V_{CE(sat)}$, thereby achieving nonsaturated operation of the blocking oscillator. There will be a constant voltage, V_2, across the magnetizing inductance, L_m. Since the current through the inductance builds up linearly, the current through D_1 will decrease at a linear rate. When the current through the diode ceases, the voltage V_2 will start to decrease, owing to the rising current required by L_m. D_1 will become reverse-biased, and the collector voltage will start to rise, causing the transistor to start turning OFF.

The magnetizing inductance L_m will discharge through D_2. The capacitor, being charged during the pulse, will cause the emitter-base junction to be reverse-biased. The transistor will not conduct until a new triggering pulse is applied.

Immediately after the transistor has turned ON, V_2 is present across the primary of the transformer, and very little current flows through the magnetizing inductance. The emitter current is

$$i_e = \frac{-V_2}{n[r_e + r_b(1 - \alpha_o)]} \tag{7}$$

The current through the primary of the transformer is

$$I_1 = \alpha_o i_e + i_{D1} = \frac{-V_2}{n^2}\left[\frac{1}{r_e + r_b(1 - \alpha_o)} + \frac{1}{R_L}\right] \tag{8}$$

From Eqs. (7) and (8),

$$i_{D1} = \frac{-V_2}{n^2}\left[\frac{1 - \alpha_o n}{r_e + r_b(1 - \alpha_o)} + \frac{1}{R_L}\right] \tag{9}$$

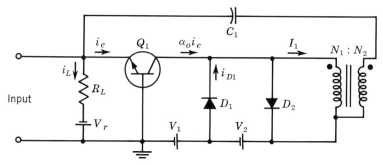

Fig. 33.2. Common-base nonsaturating triggered blocking oscillator.

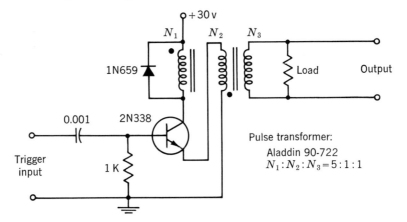

Fig. 33.3.   Common-base blocking oscillator.

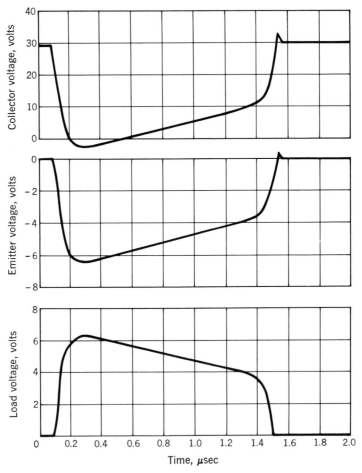

Fig. 33.4.   Blocking-oscillator waveforms with 1,000-ohm load.

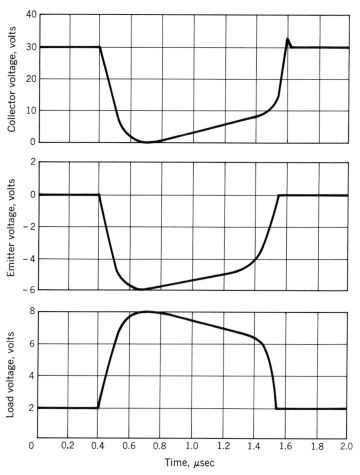

Fig. 33.5. Blocking-oscillator waveforms with 100-ohm load.

When the current in the magnetizing inductance builds up to i_{D1} in Eq. (9), the diode current will be zero, and the transistor will begin to turn OFF. Since the current in the magnetizing inductance increases linearly with time, the pulse width is

$$t_w = \frac{L_m i_{D1}}{V_2} = \frac{L_m}{n^2} \left[\frac{\alpha_o n - 1}{r_e + r_b(1 - \alpha_o)} - \frac{1}{R_L} \right] \tag{10}$$

The value of L_m necessary for a 1-μsec pulse is calculated in the following example; assume:

$r_e = 2.7$ ohms
$r_b = 50$ ohms
$R_L = 100$ ohms
$n = \frac{5}{1}$
$\alpha_o = 0.98$

Then,

$$L_m = \frac{(1 \times 10^{-6})(25)}{\dfrac{(5)(0.98) - 1}{2.7 + 50(1 - 0.98)} - \dfrac{1}{100}} = 24 \ \mu\text{h}$$

The circuit in Fig. 33.3 is a second common-base blocking oscillator, using a 2N338. The effect of loading is displayed in Figs. 33.4 and 33.5, which show the voltage waveforms for 1,000- and 100-ohm loads, respectively.

BIBLIOGRAPHY

Linvill, J. C., and J. F. Gibbons: "Transistors and Active Elements," pp. 492–498, McGraw-Hill Book Company, Inc., New York, 1961.

34

D-C Converters

Electronic equipment often requires, for its operation, a d-c voltage different from the available d-c power source. The circuit used to convert direct current from one level to another efficiently is called a d-c power converter.

The most simple and efficient power converters usually contain two power transistors and a special transformer, so connected that a regenerative switching action exists between the two transistors. The transformer, a vital part of the system, has a core material with a hysteresis curve approaching a square loop. The output is an almost perfect square wave, and, when rectified, the resultant voltage contains very little ripple.

34.1. THEORY OF OPERATION

The basic circuit for a converter is shown in Fig. 34.1a. Its output is magnetically coupled to its input through a *square core* transformer which has a characteristic hysteresis curve as shown in Fig. 34.1b.

To begin the explanation of its operation, assume that the circuit is oscillating. If transistor Q_1 is conducting, the supply voltage is dropped across the transformer primary, N_1, and the rate of flux change is linear, as indicated by the equation

$$\frac{d\theta}{dt} = \frac{V_{CC}}{N_1 \times 10^{-8}} \tag{1}$$

where $d\theta/dt$ = change of flux in core with respect to time, webers/sec

V_{CC} = supply voltage, volts

N_1 = one-half the total number of turns on the primary, i.e., from one end to center tap

[Equation (1) ignores the saturation voltage of the transistor and the resistive drop in N_1 in order to simplify the explanation.] This changing flux in the core will then induce a voltage in the other coils, with polarity as shown by the dots and magnitude proportional to the turns ratio. Therefore, transistor Q_1 is biased ON with a negative base voltage and transistor Q_2 is OFF with a positive voltage. Curves 2 and 4 of Fig. 34.1c show the collector and base voltages of transistor Q_1.

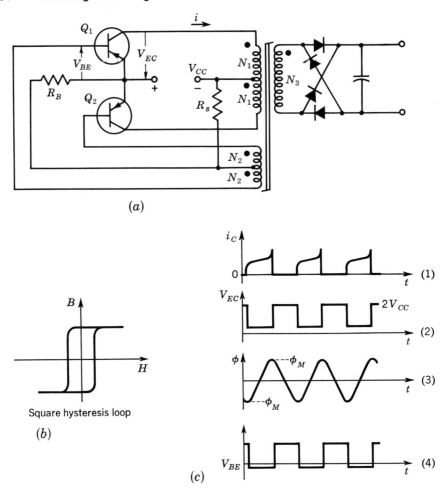

Fig. 34.1. A typical converter.

Curve 3 shows that flux change is linear as indicated by Eq. (1). When the core approaches saturation, the induced voltages are reduced, and the base drive is therefore reduced. Since transistor Q_1 is turning OFF, the induced voltage across N_1 is reversed. This causes a reversal of bias, and transistor Q_2 is turned ON as transistor Q_1 is turned OFF. The cycle then continues. It should be noted from Fig. 34.1a that when transistor Q_1 is conducting, N_1 of transistor Q_2 has an induced voltage of such polarity as to add to the supply voltage. Therefore, twice the supply voltage appears across each transistor during its OFF time.

The current waveform of the inverter can be explained by the transformer equivalent circuit as given in Fig. 34.2. Figure 34.2b is an approximate equivalent of 34.2a as seen from the input terminals, where R_1 is the effective primary resistance and R_2 is the effective secondary and load resistance referred to the primary. Depending on the sum of R_1 and R_2, the current will rise instantly, as shown by curve 1 of Fig. 34.1c. Then, by the equation

$$\frac{di}{dt} = \frac{V}{L} \tag{2}$$

the current will increase at a constant rate. The current spike at the end of the waveform is due to core saturation since inductance approaches zero. The current will tend to rise to a value governed by the current gain of the transistor.

34.2. TRANSFORMER CONSIDERATIONS

The basic equation describing converter operation as derived from Eq. (1) is

$$V = 4B_m f N_1 SA \times 10^{-8} \tag{3}$$

where V = peak square-wave voltage impressed across saturation-core primary winding N_1, volts

B_m = maximum flux density of saturating core, gauss

f = frequency of oscillation, cps

N_1 = number of primary turns on saturating core carrying load current for the ON transistor (i.e., from collector end to center tap)

A = cross-sectional area of saturating core, cm²

S = stacking factor of core

Thus, it becomes apparent that in the basic converter, i.e., the single-transformer configuration, the transformer performs two functions. Not only does it perform the standard function of transformation of power, but it determines the frequency of oscillation as well. The function of the transistors is simply to switch the d-c supply from one-half of the center-tapped primary to the other, thus permitting the resulting square-wave a-c voltage to be transformed to the secondary.

The design of the transformer involves the same considerations as that of a standard transformer with respect to amount and type of insulation, wire size, and window area necessary for windings. Equation (3) is of fundamental importance in determining the relationship among the core size, frequency, and supply voltage.

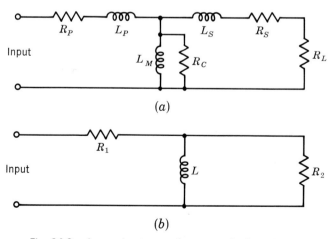

Fig. 34.2. Approximate transformer equivalent circuits.

34.3. TRANSISTOR CONSIDERATIONS

The transistors for a particular converter must satisfy two basic requirements. They should have a useful h_{FE} at a current level determined by the maximum value of the primary load current, and they must be capable of withstanding the maximum voltage applied to the collector-to-emitter terminals. As previously mentioned, this voltage will be approximately twice the supply voltage (if no voltage spikes are present), and will appear across the OFF transistor terminals. Generally speaking, it is best to limit this maximum collector-emitter voltage to less than the BV_{CES} rating of the transistor.

34.4. STARTING

The most common type of starting circuit is the resistive voltage-divider type such as shown in Fig. 34.1. A slight forward bias is applied to both transistors through the starting resistor R_S. The required magnitude of R_S is primarily a function of the load and the h_{FE} of the transistors. The worst case for starting will occur with heavy loads and at low temperatures, where h_{FE} is minimum. A filter capacitor on the secondary requires a heavy surge of current during starting as it charges up. Because this initial heavy load can make starting difficult, filter capacitors should be as small as possible.

The value of starting resistance is generally best determined by trial and error, but an approximate value can be determined from

$$V_1 = \frac{V_{CC}R_B}{R_S + R_B} \tag{4}$$

where $V_1 \cong 0.3$ for germanium transistors, and $V_1 \cong 0.5$ for silicon transistors.

To reduce losses, a diode can be used instead of R_B, being placed so that base current can flow in the forward direction. The value of R_S can be increased since the diode appears as an open circuit until the oscillations begin.

34.5. CIRCUIT CONFIGURATIONS

The most frequently used circuits are the common-emitter configuration shown in Fig. 34.1 and the common-collector autotransformer configuration shown in Fig. 34.3.

The common-collector autotransformer configuration has this advantage over the common-emitter configuration: The cases of the transistors can be mounted directly on a common heat sink without using insulating washers. A disadvantage is the need for additional base and starting resistors.

The dual-transformer configuration shown in Fig. 34.4 has many advantages over the single-transformer configuration. A comparison of the typical collector currents of both configurations at no load and full load, illustrated in Figs. 34.5 and 34.6, reveals one of them: Since the output transformer of the two-transformer configuration does not saturate, its magnetizing current is never large.

In the single-transformer converter, once the transformer saturates, the collector

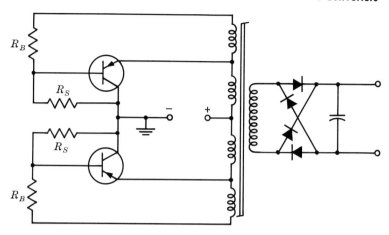

Fig. 34.3. Common-collector autotransformer configuration.

current increases until it tends to exceed $h_{FE}I_B$, i.e., pulls the ON transistor out of saturation. Conservative design is usually based upon the minimum value of h_{FE}, i.e.,

$$I'_L \leqq h_{FE(min)} I_B \tag{5}$$

where I'_L = maximum load current reflected to the primary. Since many transistors exhibit a 3:1 h_{FE} spread, it would be possible for the actual peak collector current to be three times greater than the maximum reflected load current in those transistors with a high h_{FE}.

The dual-transformer configuration differs from the conventional converter in that switching is determined by the small saturating tape-wound toroidal transformer, while the larger nonsaturating power transformer handles the feedback and output power transformation. Since the output transformer does not saturate, switching is not determined by the increasing magnetizing current *pulling* the ON transistor out of saturation. Instead, the ON transistor is pulled out of saturation by the decrease in base current which occurs when the toroidal transformer saturates. As the core reaches saturation, the increasing magnetizing current causes

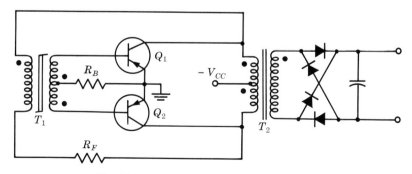

Fig. 34.4. Basic dual-transformer converter.

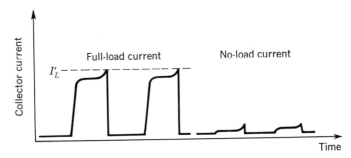

Fig. 34.5. Dual-transformer converter: typical collector currents.

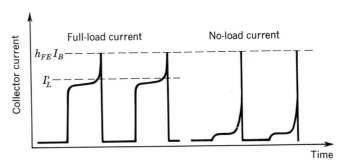

Fig. 34.6. Single-transformer converter: typical collector currents.

an additional voltage drop across the feedback resistor R_F. Thus the primary of the saturated transformer has less voltage dropped across it, effecting the decrease in secondary or base-drive voltage.

34.6. PRACTICAL CIRCUITS

Figures 34.7 to 34.9 and Table 34.1 provide circuit diagrams and parts lists for the following eight converters which are typical, practical circuits:

Converter output rating, watts	Voltage input	Voltage output	Transistor type
15	12	300	2N1038
30	12	300	2N1042
55	12	100	2N456
100	12	300	2N511
150	12	500	2N512
200	12	300	2N513
250	12	500	2N514
500	28	300	2N514A

Performance Characteristics. Figures 34.10 through 34.17 show plots of output voltage, output power, frequency, and efficiency vs. load current for the eight different converters. The output-voltage regulation is seen to be less than 7%

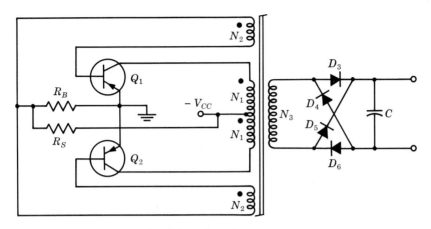

Fig. 34.7. Type A converter.

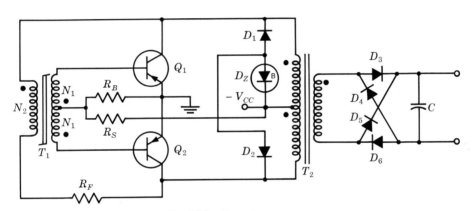

Fig. 34.8. Type B converter.

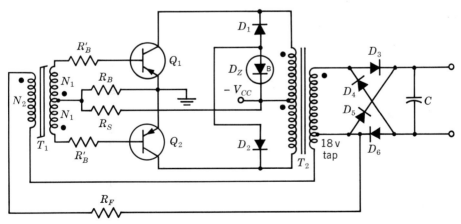

Fig. 34.9. Type C 500-watt converter.

Table 34.1. Parts List for Figs. 34.7 to 34.9

Type of circuit	Transistors Q_1, Q_2	Transformer T_1	Transformer T_2	N_1, turns AWG	N_2, turns AWG	N_3, turns AWG	R_B or R_B', ohms	R_S, ohms	R_F, ohms	Zener diode, D_Z	Diodes D_1, D_2	Diodes D_3, D_4, D_5, D_6	C, μf	Rating, watts
A	2N1038	Arnold 5772D2	.....	70 No. 18	20 No. 30	1,800 No. 30	15	1,200	.....	.....	.....	1N2071	2	15
A	2N1042	Magnetics 500172A	.....	78 No. 16	30 No. 29	2,000 No. 29	15	1,500	.....	.....	.....	1N2071	4	30
A	2N456	Magnetics 500352A	.....	29 No. 17	6 No. 24	275 No. 24	5	180	.....	.....	.....	1N2071	6	55
B	2N511	Magnetics 500942A	TI 440402-1	48 No. 24	.....	185 No. 28	2	100	5	1N1817	1N2069	1N2071	10	100
B	2N512	Magnetics 501812A	TI 440404-1	48 No. 22	.....	185 No. 26	2	75	10	1N1817	1N2069	1N2071	20	150
B	2N513	Magnetics 500262A	TI 440406-1	35 No. 20	.....	140 No. 26	1	75	5	1N1817	1N2069	1N2071	20	200
B	2N514	Magnetics 500262A	TI 440408-1	35 No. 20	.....	140 No. 24	1	75	5	1N1817	1N2069	1N2071	30	250
C	2N514A	Arnold 5233D2	TI 440413-1	35 No. 20	.....	140 No. 24	$R_B = \frac{1}{2}$ $R_B' = \frac{1}{2}$	75	10	1N1825	1N2069	1N1126	40	500

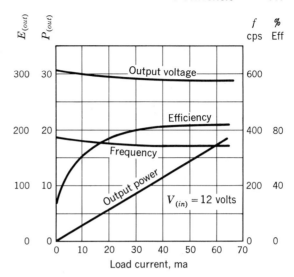

Fig. 34.10. 15-watt converter.

from one-half to rated load. The output power is almost a straight-line function of load current, as one would expect. The frequency of the 15-, 30-, and 55-watt converters decreases slightly under load. The frequency of the two-transformer converters remains almost constant under load.

The efficiency of all the converters is greater than 80% at rated load. The output ripple on all converters is less than 4% at rated load.

All these circuits are conservatively rated. In particular, the 500-watt converter has attained an output power of 700 watts on an intermittent basis.

Design Information. The step-by-step design for the 200-watt dual-transformer converter is given; the procedure may be followed in designing similar circuits.

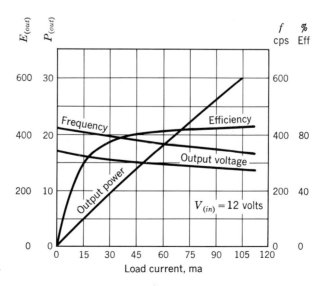

Fig. 34.11. 30-watt converter.

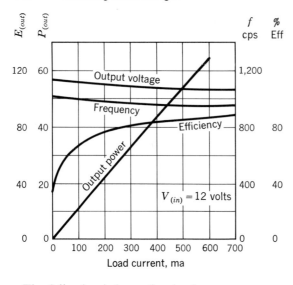

Fig. 34.12.   55-watt converter.

The following information is given:

Output power, P_o = 200 watts.
Supply voltage, V_{CC} = 12 volts.
Output voltage, V_o = 300 volts.
Core = Orthonol® toroid.
Frequency = 400 cps.
Circuit configuration = common emitter, i.e., type B converter.

A converter efficiency of 80% is assumed.   The necessary input power is

$$P_{(in)} = \frac{P_o}{\eta} = \frac{200}{0.8} = 250 \text{ watts} \tag{6}$$

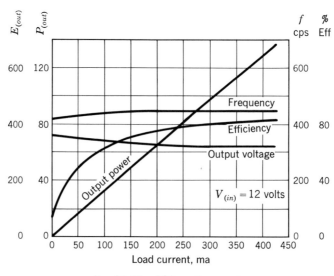

Fig. 34.13.   100-watt converter.

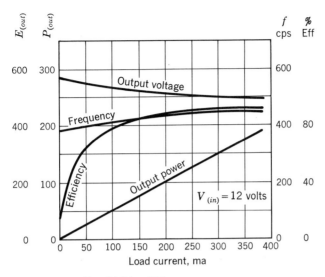

Fig. 34.14. 150-watt converter.

where $P_{(in)}$ = input power
P_o = output power
η = efficiency

The collector current of each transistor is given by

$$I_C = \frac{P_{(in)}}{V_{CC}} = \frac{250}{12} = 20.8 \text{ amp} \tag{7}$$

where V_{CC} = supply voltage. The 2N513 transistor is selected on the basis of maximum collector current and maximum collector breakdown voltages. Each

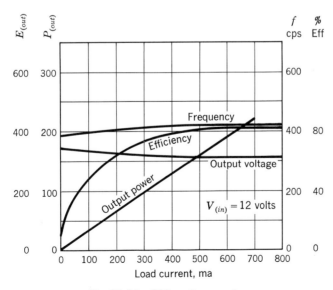

Fig. 34.15. 200-watt converter.

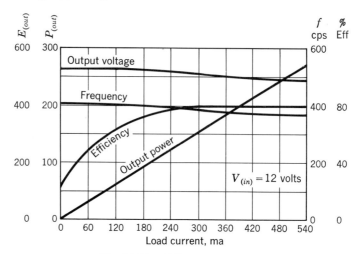

Fig. 34.16.   250-watt converter.

transistor, during its OFF time, is subjected to approximately twice the supply voltage. The base current of each transistor is

$$I_B = \frac{I_C}{h_{FE(min)}} = \frac{20.8}{20} = 1.04 \text{ amp} \tag{8}$$

where I_B = base current, and $h_{FE(min)}$ = minimum short-circuit current gain at specified I_C. From the data sheet for the 2N513, the maximum base-to-emitter voltage is 2 volts. The base-drive voltage is made equal to twice the maximum base-to-emitter voltage, to reduce the effect of variation in V_{BE} among transistors.

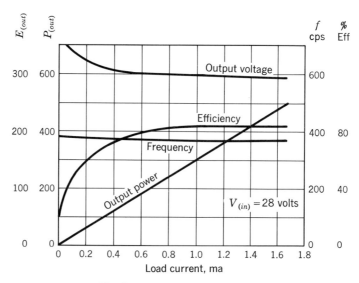

Fig. 34.17.   500-watt converter.

The power required by the base drive is given by

$$P_D = V_D I_B = 4(1.04) = 4.16 \text{ watts} \qquad (9)$$

where P_D = drive power, and V_D = drive voltage. A 90% efficiency is assumed for the drive transformer. Therefore, the power supplied to the primary of the drive transformer is

$$P_2 = \frac{P_D}{0.9} = \frac{4.15}{0.9} = 4.6 \text{ watts} \qquad (10)$$

The turns ratio for the drive transformer is chosen as 4:1. This sets the primary voltage of the drive transformer at 16 volts. The primary current of the drive transformer is given by

$$I_2 = \frac{P_2}{V_2} = \frac{4.6}{16} = 288 \text{ ma} \qquad (11)$$

Next, the wire sizes for the primary and secondary turns are chosen, based on 1,000 cir mils/amp:

N_2 (primary) AWG No. 26 (320 cir mils).
N_1 (secondary) AWG No. 20 (1,197 cir mils).

Selection of the toroidal core for the drive transformer is next. One method is to determine the necessary WA product from known and estimated factors and, use this product for core selection. WA is the product of the core window area, W, and the core cross-sectional area, A. It is frequently listed in the manufacturer's catalog of core data.

A necessary step in this procedure is to estimate the ratio of total wire area to the core window area. This ratio is the K factor, which for this particular design can be expressed as

$$K = \frac{N_2 A_{W2} + 2N_1 A_{W1}}{W} = \frac{N_2 A_{W2} + \frac{1}{2}N_2 A_{W2}}{W} \qquad (12)$$

where K = ratio of total wire area to core window area
  A_W = area of single strand of wire, cir mils
  W = area of core window, cir mils

The K factor is estimated to be 0.2 to assure ease in winding the core. Separating the known and unknown quantities in Eq. (12) results in

$$\frac{N_2}{W} = \frac{K}{A_{W2} + \frac{1}{2}A_{W1}} \qquad (13)$$

Since the only unknowns in the basic transformer expression of Eq. (3) are the number of primary turns N_2 and the area of the core A, Eqs. (3) and (13) can be solved simultaneously for the product of W and A:

$$WA = \frac{V(A_{W2} + \frac{1}{2}A_{W1})}{K4B_m f \times 10^{-8}} = \frac{(16)(919)}{(0.2)(4)(14,000)(400) \times 10^{-3}} \qquad (14)$$

$$WA = 328,000$$

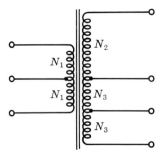

Fig. 34.18. Schematic diagram
of transformer.

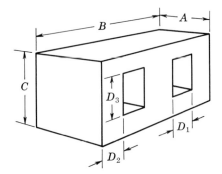

Fig. 34.19. Transformer core.

For the required *WA* product, a Magnetics 50026-2A core is chosen. The area is seen to be 0.514 cm². N_2 is calculated to be 140 turns, using Eq. (3). N_1 is found to be 35 turns. The number of primary and secondary turns and size of the wire are then determined. The *K* factor is checked; the actual *K* factor is slightly less than 0.2.

The design is completed with the determination of R_B, R_S, R_F, and the power transformer. The base resistor R_B is chosen to drop approximately half of the 4 volts supplied. The starting resistor R_S is made as large as possible to keep losses to a minimum and still assure reliable starting. The feedback resistor R_F is chosen to give 16 volts across the primary of the drive transformer at rated load.

The core loss in the 200-watt power transformer at rated load is calculated to be 10 watts. The primary and secondary winding losses are approximately 2 watts each. The input impedance of the transformer is made equal to approximately 40 times the load resistance. Figures 34.18 and 34.19 in conjunction with Table 34.1 give power transformer information.

BIBLIOGRAPHY

Jensen, J. L.: An Improved Square-wave Oscillator Circuit, *IRE Trans.,* vol. CT-4, no. 3, pp. 276–279, September, 1957.
Nowicki, J. R.: New High Power DC Converter Circuits, *Mullard Tech. Pub.,* vol. 5, no. 43, pp. 104–114, April, 1961.

35

Inverters

An inverter as defined here provides an a-c output from a d-c supply. In the simplest transistor inverters, the a-c output is a square wave. Many kinds of equipment will operate satisfactorily on a square-wave voltage, but in some instances a filter on the secondary is necessary in order to suppress objectionable harmonics. The fundamental harmonic content of a square wave is the maximum value of the square wave divided by 1.11. Thus, if a 115-volt rms sine wave is needed, the transformer output should be 128 volts plus filter drops.

In a converter, the exact value of frequency of oscillation and its change with load and input-voltage variations are not usually important. In an inverter, however, these considerations may be quite important. The frequency of oscillation of most common circuits is set by a saturating-core oscillator, and is dependent upon voltage as shown by the basic converter and inverter equation,

$$E = 4B_m f N_1 S A \times 10^{-8} \tag{1}$$

where E = peak square-wave voltage impressed across one-half the total center-tapped primary winding, volts

B_m = maximum flux density of the saturating core, gauss

f = frequency of oscillation, cps

N_1 = one-half the number of total primary turns on the saturating core

A = cross-sectional area of the saturating core, cm²

S = stacking factor of the core

Equation (1) shows that frequency is dependent on voltage since all other values are constant for a particular core. Therefore, the frequency can be controlled by controlling the input voltage. The transformer equivalent circuit of Fig. 34.2b (d-c converters) indicates that frequency may be controlled by controlling the induced voltage, which is given by the equation

$$E_i = \frac{E_A R_2}{R_1 + R_2} \tag{2}$$

where E_i = induced voltage, and E_A = applied voltage to the transformer. Ideally, R_1 should be zero or very small with respect to R_2. One method of minimizing

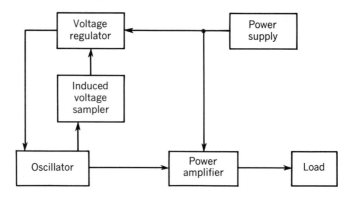

Fig. 35.1.   Block diagram of 60-cycle power inverter.

the difference between applied and induced voltage is to use large wire on the primary so that E_i approaches E_A in Eq. (2).   But this does not compensate for the change in transistor saturation voltage with current, which will cause a variation in frequency with load.   If the input voltage is regulated, the frequency can be controlled to about $\pm 2\%$ by using extra-large wire in the primary of the saturating-core transformer.

35.1.   FREQUENCY STABILITY

If closer frequency control is required, it is evident that a method of measuring the induced-voltage variation must be used, so that compensation can be obtained by adjusting the oscillator supply voltage.   Figure 35.1 shows a block diagram of the frequency-stable power inverter.   The frequency of operation of the saturating-core oscillator is dependent on the induced voltage of the oscillator transformer. This induced voltage is detected by a sensing circuit which varies the output voltage of the regulator to keep the transformer-induced voltage constant, and therefore stabilizes the frequency.   The oscillator is transformer-coupled to the power ampli-fier, which supplies power to the load.   Only the oscillator requires regulated supply voltage; hence, the power amplifier is connected directly to the power supply.

Saturating-core Oscillator.   The oscillator is an inverter using a saturating transformer.   Its circuit is identical with the basic converter circuit (without the rectifiers) shown in Fig. 34.1a.

Induced-voltage-sensing Circuit.   The sensing circuit is connected (as shown in Fig. 35.2) to each primary coil of the oscillator during the OFF cycle.   The

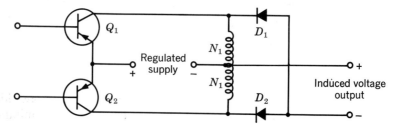

Fig. 35.2.   Induced-voltage-sensing circuit.

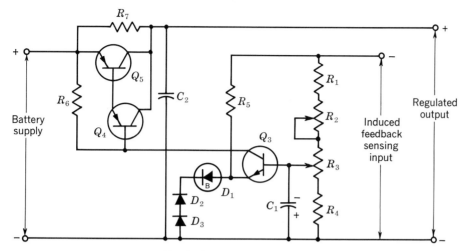

Fig. 35.3. Inverter regulator.

voltage seen by the sensing circuit is almost identical with the true induced voltage because of the high-impedance input circuit of the regulator.

Voltage Regulator.   The regulator circuit is shown in Fig. 35.3.   The induced voltage is negative with respect to the negative terminal of the supply and drives the base of Q_3.   If the induced voltage decreases, the drive to Q_3 is increased by the ratio of the reference voltage at the emitter to the voltage applied at the base. The series regulator Q_5 therefore increases the voltage fed to the saturating-core oscillator.   Consequently, the induced voltage will increase to approximately the initial value.

The diodes D_2 and D_3 provide temperature compensation for the avalanche diode D_1 and the transistor Q_3.   The capacitor C_1 decreases the high-frequency response of the regulator amplifier. R_7 provides sufficient regulator output voltage to initiate oscillations when power is initially applied.

35.2. POWER AMPLIFIER

The power amplifier as shown in Fig. 35.4 is driven by the oscillator and is supplied with power directly from the power supply.   If regulated output voltage is a requirement, a transistor regulator may be inserted between the supply and this amplifier.

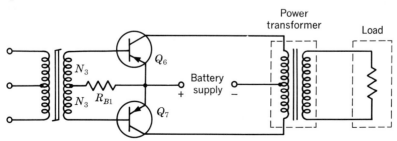

Fig. 35.4. Driven power amplifier.

The power transformer is wound with sufficient turns to provide square-wave output voltage at the frequency concerned. Peak current in the power transistor will be the peak reflected load current. Magnetizing current should be small since this transformer core is never saturated.

35.3. DESIGN PROCEDURE FOR 200 WATTS AT 60 CYCLES

A specific example will be used to explain the design procedure for the inverter circuit as outlined above. Assume the output to be a 60-cps 200-watt 115-volt square wave. The load is assumed to be resistive with no reactive component (most tape recorders, television sets, etc., are highly resistive). The input is a 12.6-volt automobile battery. The complete circuit diagram is shown in Fig. 35.5.

The Driven Power Amplifier. The power transformer must have sufficient core area to avoid saturation and high transistor currents, as discussed previously. The usual efficiency of this type of transformer should be in the order of 90%. A transformer design for this application is given in Fig. 35.6. If efficiency is 90%, 220 watts will be required at the transformer input.

Allowing for the power-transistor saturation voltage and transformer-primary resistance drop, the input to the primary of the transformer would be a square wave having a peak amplitude of approximately 11.5 volts. The transformer turns ratio is then

$$\frac{N_2}{N_1} = \frac{E_2}{E_1} = \frac{115}{11.5} \tag{3}$$

The peak primary current is

$$I_P = \frac{P_{(in)}}{E_1} = \frac{220}{11.5} = 19.1 \text{ amp} \tag{4}$$

For the transformer load, the voltage across the transistor during its OFF period is twice the supply voltage. These two requirements necessitate a 20-amp transistor with a BV_{CEX} rating of over 30 volts. The 2N513A and 2N514A units meet both requirements, but the 2N514A will be used in this application since it has a higher minimum h_{FE}. A base current of 1 amp will be required since this unit has a guaranteed minimum current gain of 20 at 25 amp. Typical V_{BE} is 0.5 to 1.0 volt; therefore, the induced voltage of N_3 will be 2 volts to take care of possible variations. R_{B1} should be a 1-ohm 5-watt noninductive resistor to assure sufficient overdrive for low saturation voltage. The efficiency of the whole system is governed almost entirely by power losses due to saturation, switching time, and the power transformer.

The Saturating-core Oscillator. Most important in the oscillator design is the saturating-core transformer. The core should have: (1) a square BH characteristic for frequency stability with load variations, (2) a saturation flux density, B_M, such that neither the number of turns nor the cross-sectional area has to be excessive, and (3) low losses at the frequency used (this is a function of the material and the lamination thickness, both of which are functions of the area enclosed by the BH curve). A tape-wound core of 50:50 nickel-iron (saturation flux density ≅ 14,500

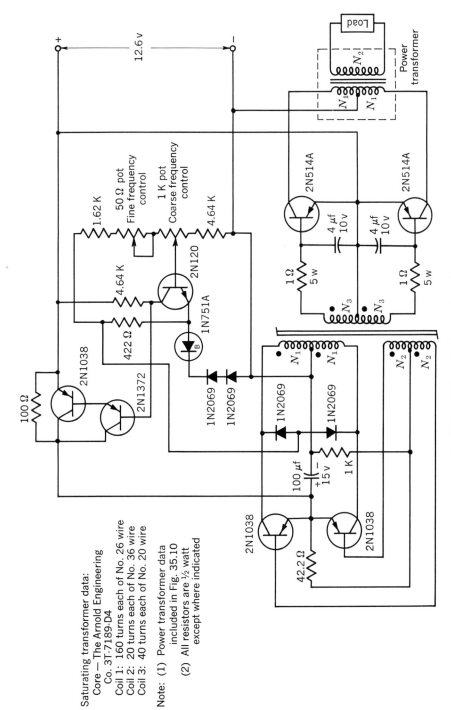

Saturating transformer data:

Core — The Arnold Engineering
    Co. 3T-7189-D4

Coil 1: 160 turns each of No. 26 wire
Coil 2: 20 turns each of No. 36 wire
Coil 3: 40 turns each of No. 20 wire

Note: (1) Power transformer data
        included in Fig. 35.10
    (2) All resistors are $\frac{1}{2}$ watt
        except where indicated

Fig. 35.5. 200-watt 60-cycle inverter.

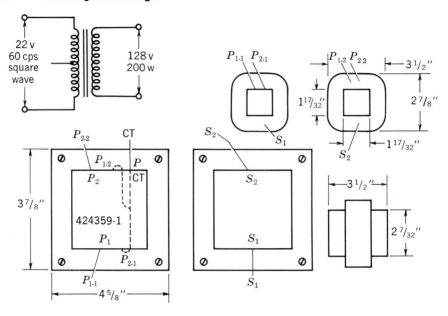

Specification	Winding	
	Primary	Secondary
Tube........................	1¹⁷⁄₃₂ by 1¹⁷⁄₃₂ in., 04 FK	Over primary
Wire size....................	No. 13 FX	No. 20 FX
Turns.......................	36 bifilar	468 ± 4
Taps........................	Bifilar	
Turns/layer.................	12	52
Length: winding/coil.........	1²³⁄₃₂–2⁷⁄₃₂ in.	1²⁷⁄₃₂–2⁷⁄₃₂ in.
Paper.......................	0–1–0, 0.007 kraft	0–1–0, 0.005 kraft
Wrapper....................	1 layer, 0.010 kraft	1 layer, 0.005 kraft
Anchor.....................	⅜-in. no. 27	¼-in. no. 27
Saddle......................	....	No. 27 tape
Lead........................	Self	Self
Lead length.................	6 in.	6 in.
Lead anchor.................	⅜-in. no. 27	¼-in. no. 27
Final wrap..................	1 layer, 0.005 GK	
Laminations.................	EI-13, 0.014 Silectron®	
Stack.......................	1 by 1 by 1½ in.	
Secure laminations...........	Through bolts	
Finish......................	Varnish-impregnated	

Insulation resistance

10,000 megohms minimum at 500 volts d-c between windings and from each winding to core.

D-c resistance

Terminals	Resistance (*maximum*), ohms
P_1, P_2	0.12
S_1, S_2	4.0

Fig. 35.6. Transformer, power output 200 watts.

gauss and 0.004-in.-thick laminations) is adequate for the 60-cps frequency. When using a tape-wound core, the gross core area must be multiplied by a stacking factor to obtain the actual core area. Core size is a function of the cross-sectional area, as shown by Eq. (1), and the area necessary to accommodate the windings. The core size for the 200-watt inverter shown in this chapter was not optimized. The availability of a usable core dictated this particular choice. The core constants are:

$B_M = 14,500$ gauss.
Gross area $= 1.61$ cm^2.
$f = 60$ cps.
Stacking factor $= 0.9$.
Window diameter $= 1.15$ in.

The voltage applied to the saturating-core transformer is assumed to be 8 volts. This value permits 4 volts to be dropped across the voltage regulator with a supply voltage of 12 volts, thus assuring reliable regulation.

From Eq. (1), N_1 may be determined as

$$N_1 = \frac{8}{(4)(14,500)(60)(1.61)(0.9)(10^{-8})} = 159 \text{ turns} \tag{5}$$

The voltage induced in the oscillator base-drive windings, N_2, should be in the order of 1 volt. Therefore,

$$N_2 = N_1 \frac{E_2}{E_1} = 160 \times \frac{1}{8} = 20 \text{ turns} \tag{6}$$

and, further,

$$N_3 = N_1 \frac{E_3}{E_1} = 160 \times \frac{2}{8} = 40 \text{ turns} \tag{7}$$

The maximum current in the base circuit of the power stage will not exceed 2 amp unless the regulator output exceeds 10 volts. Therefore, the maximum primary current will be

$$I_1 = \frac{N_3}{N_1} I_3 = \frac{40}{160} \times 2 = 0.5 \text{ amp} \tag{8}$$

The transistor for this application must be capable of carrying a collector current of 0.5 amp and should have a BV_{CEX} rating of over 20 volts. The 2N1038 more than meets these requirements. Since it has a minimum current gain of 20 at $+25°C$, a base current of 25 ma is sufficient. (For low-temperature operation this must be increased to allow for a decrease in current gain.)

Wire size is calculated on the basis of 1,000 cir mils/amp. Since the duty cycle is 50% for each winding, the minimum wire sizes are as follows:

$$A_{N1} = 0.5 \times \frac{1,000}{2} = 250 \text{ cir mils} \tag{9}$$

$$A_{N2} = 0.025 \times \frac{1,000}{2} = 12.5 \text{ cir mils} \tag{10}$$

$$A_{N3} = 2 \times \frac{1,000}{2} = 1,000 \text{ cir mils} \tag{11}$$

The AWG wire sizes are selected as 26, 36, and 20, respectively. Size 36 is larger than necessary, but is selected for ease of handling. The total area of wire then is

$$A_W = 2N_1 A_{26} + 2N_2 A_{36} + 2N_3 A_{20} = 200,000 \text{ cir mils} \tag{12}$$

The available winding area in circular mils is

$$A_A = (\text{ID})^2 = 1,320,000 \text{ cir mils} \tag{13}$$

Thus
$$\frac{A_W}{A_A} = 0.152 \tag{14}$$

Equation (14) indicates that the core size is excessive. It could be reduced until the result of this calculation is about 0.4. These windings should be bifilar-wound to increase coupling and thereby reduce voltage spikes due to current interruption in the leakage inductances.

Figure 35.7 shows an equivalent circuit of the emitter-base bias circuit. Before oscillations start, the induced voltage across N_2 is zero; therefore, the 1-volt potentials shown do not exist. The voltage across R_{B2} is then

$$E_{RB} = \frac{8 \times 40}{1,000 + 40} = 0.3 \text{ volt} \tag{15}$$

This bias is enough to cause both transistors to begin conducting. Because of the strong positive feedback provided by the base-drive windings, any slight disturbance in the collector currents becomes amplified until one transistor is driven into saturation. This condition persists until the core saturates and the base drive fails. Then the saturated transistor turns OFF, and the cycle repeats with the opposite transistor. To calculate base bias current after the circuit is running, Fig. 35.7 is drawn for one condition of base voltages, i.e., when transistor 1 is ON and transistor 2 is OFF. If $V_{BE} = 0.4$ volt for transistor 1, $I_1 = 8.6$ ma, and $I_2 = -15$ ma to provide the necessary base-drive current, $I_{B1} = 23.6$ ma. Transistor 2 as shown has a reverse bias of 1.6 volts, and is therefore turned OFF.

The Voltage Regulator. The direct current to the oscillator will be 0.5 to 0.7 amp; thus, a 2N1038 can be used as the series regulator Q_5, as shown in Fig. 35.3.

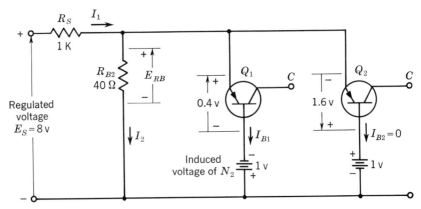

Fig. 35.7. Equivalent oscillator bias circuit.

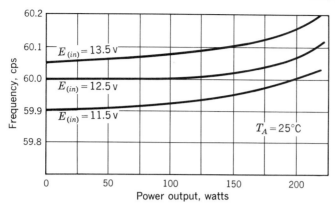

Fig. 35.8.   Frequency vs. power output with input voltage constant.

Since the 2N1038 has a minimum current gain of 20, the required base current will be 35 ma, which can be provided by a 2N1372. The minimum current gain of the 2N1372 is 30; therefore, its maximum base current will be 1.2 ma. A 2N120 silicon transistor was selected for Q_3 to minimize change in regulator output voltage with temperature. The 2N120 has a minimum current gain of 76; therefore, 16 μa base current will be required.

The induced voltage from the sensing circuit shown in Fig. 35.2 will be approximately 7.5 volts when the 0.5-volt drop across the sensing diodes is taken into account. D_1 is a 1N751A avalanche diode, which has a nominal reference voltage of 5.1 volts, and R_5 was selected to provide approximately 4 ma of diode current. Temperature compensation of the regulator was accomplished by connecting a pair of 1N2069 silicon diodes, D_2 and D_3, in series with D_1. C_1 was found to be unnecessary after the 4-μf despiking capacitors were connected from base to emitter of the two 2N514A transistors in Fig. 35.5.

Test Results and Data for the 200-watt 60-cycle Inverter. Figure 35.8 shows experimental data for frequency variation vs. changes in load at different constant input voltages. The maximum frequency variation for a change of load from 0 to 200 watts and a voltage change of 11.5 to 13.5 volts is less than 0.5%.

The curves swing upward as the output power is increased, owing to the increase in base-to-emitter voltage of the 2N514A transistors. Thus, the base current decreases and results in less load on the saturating-core oscillator. For typical installations, the input voltage to the inverter will decrease as the load is increased; therefore, the frequency will vary less with power output than indicated by Fig. 35.10.

The variation of frequency with temperature is shown in Fig. 35.9 for no-load and full-load conditions. For various transistors used in the inverter circuit, the per cent frequency deviation was approximately the same as indicated by Fig. 35.9; however, the shape of the curves in each case was different.

Figure 35.10 shows efficiency plotted against output power. An interesting point is that the efficiency is about 86% at 200 watts. The efficiency of the transformer at these powers was around 90%. This means that the power transformer was a major factor in circuit efficiency. The no-load input power was 8.5 watts.

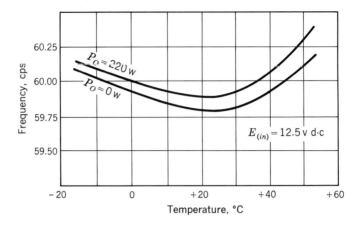

Fig. 35.9.   Frequency vs. temperature for no-load and full-load conditions.

For a 12-hr period, during which supply voltage may have varied only slightly, maximum frequency variation was less than 0.1%.

35.4.   ADDITIONAL CIRCUITS

Figure 35.11 shows a circuit for a 100-watt 60-cps inverter. It was not as thoroughly tested as the 200-watt circuit. Slightly more frequency change with temperature may be expected since the sensing-input transistor (2N1302) is germanium.

Figure 35.12 shows a low-power 60-cycle inverter designed to drive a timer. This circuit does not include the sensing circuit, but instead makes the primary oscillator windings large enough to reduce the effect of the primary resistance. The timer represented an almost constant load except for variations in supply voltage. For supply-voltage variations between 11.5 and 14.5 volts, the maximum frequency variation was $\pm 1\%$.

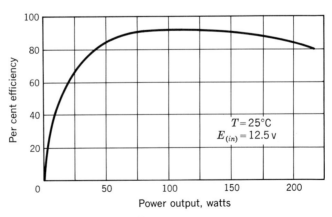

Fig. 35.10.   Efficiency vs. power output.

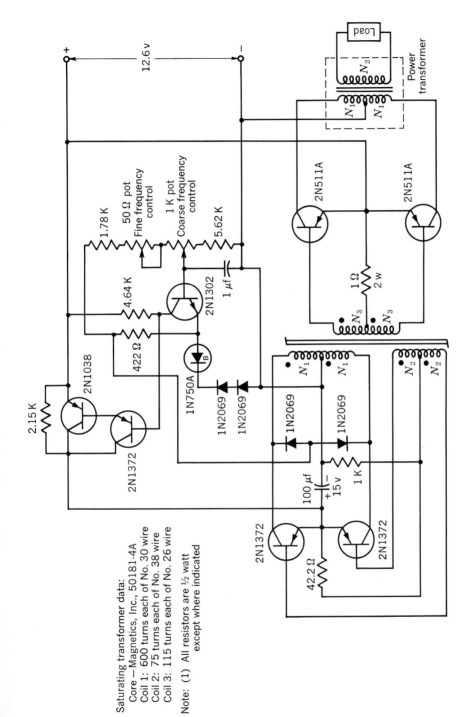

Fig. 35.11. 100-watt 60-cycle inverter.

457

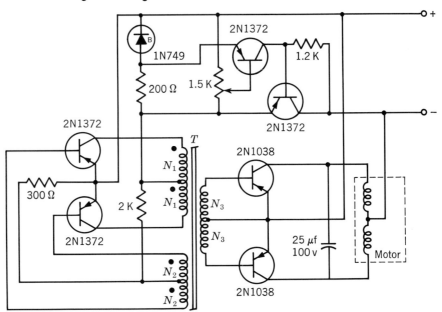

Transformer data:
Core — Magnetics, Inc., 50076-4A
Coil 1: 1,100 turns each of No. 36 wire

Coil 2: 130 turns each of No. 36 wire
Coil 3: 200 turns each of No. 36 wire

Note: All resistors are ½ watt

Fig. 35.12.   20-watt 60-cycle inverter.

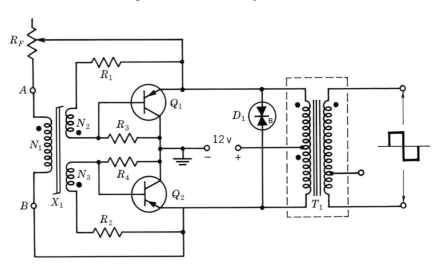

Parts List

Q_1, Q_2—2N514
D_1—1N1823 (27-volt double-anode clipper)
R_F—20-ohm 5-watt rheostat
R_1, R_2—1 ohm, 5 watts
R_3, R_4—150 ohms, 1 watt

X_1—Tape-wound toroid, 5320-D4 Arnold Engineering Co., or 5000-4A Magnetics, Inc.
N_1—316 turns, #24 heavy Formvar
N_2, N_3—79 turns, #22 heavy Formvar
T_1—Texas Instruments transformer #440401 or equivalent

Fig. 35.13.   250-watt 60-cycle dual-transformer inverter.

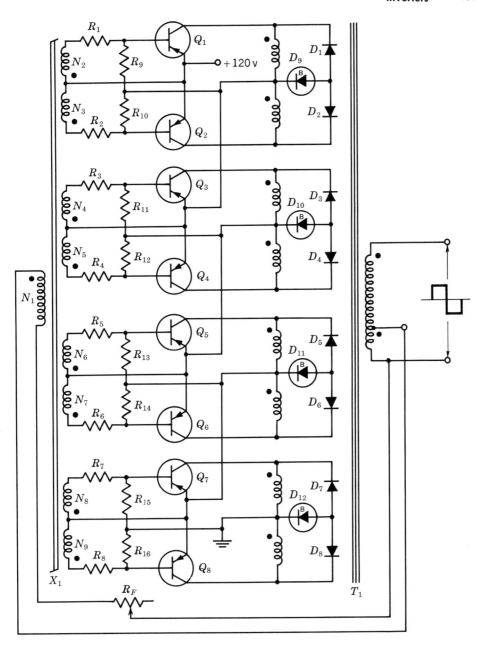

Parts List

Q_1 through Q_8—2N458A
D_1 through D_8—1N2069
D_9 through D_{12}—1N1825R
R_1 through R_8—5 ohms, 1 watt
R_9 through R_{16}—910 ohms, 1 watt
R_F—25-ohm 5-watt rheostat

T_1—Texas Instruments transformer #440220 or equivalent
X_1—Tapewound toroidal core, 51425-4A Magnetics Inc., or 5772-D4 Arnold Co.
N_1—448 turns, #22 heavy Formvar
N_2 through N_9—112 turns, #28 heavy Formvar

Fig. 35.14. 400-watt 60-cycle dual-transformer inverter.

The dual-transformer configuration is an especially useful inverter circuit. Two power inverters using this configuration are illustrated in Figs. 35.13 and 35.14. The inverter in Fig. 35.13 operates from a 12-volt d-c supply and provides a 60-cycle 130-volt square-wave output to a 250-watt load. Performance characteristics are illustrated in Fig. 35.15. An inverter designed to operate from a 120-volt d-c supply and capable of over 400 watts output is illustrated in Fig. 35.14. Input voltage is divided equally across the four series primaries, subjecting each transistor to only 60 volts in the OFF condition. Output voltage is a 60-cycle 140-volt square wave. Operating characteristics are illustrated in Fig. 35.16.

The output transformers (T_1 in each instance) were designed by the transformer engineering department of Texas Instruments.* These transformers were designed for maximum efficiency and minimum sag in the output square wave. To this end, size and weight considerations were sacrificed, making these transformers larger than many commercial transformers with similar power ratings. The output transformers of the 250- and 400-watt inverters weigh 22 lb each. If size and weight are of prime importance, almost any 60-cycle output transformer should operate satisfactorily if it does not saturate and if it can handle the required power.

Several advantages of this dual-transformer configuration were discussed in Chap. 34, D-C Converters. Another important advantage when used in an inverter is the ease with which the frequency of oscillation can be adjusted. The frequency vs. load-current curves shown in Figs. 35.15 and 35.16 cover one particular value of R_F. Frequency can be adjusted to exactly 60 cps for any value of load current by varying this resistance. On the other hand, a single-transformer configuration offers

---

* Information concerning these transformers can be obtained by contacting the transformer engineering department of Texas Instruments Incorporated, Box 6015, Dallas 22, Tex.

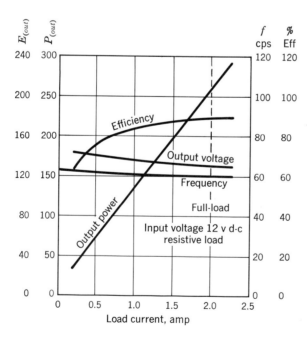

Fig. 35.15. 250-watt inverter operating characteristics.

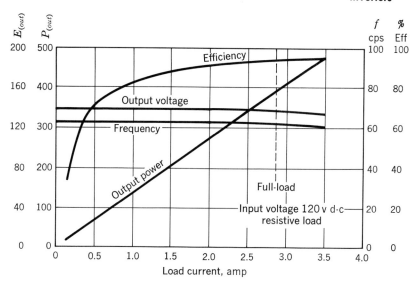

Fig. 35.16.   400-watt inverter operating characteristics.

no method of frequency adjustment other than varying the d-c supply voltage, and in most instances this is impractical.

An additional modification will provide a constant-frequency output for a limited variation of the supply voltage. The addition of a double-anode breakdown diode across the primary (from point A to point B in Fig. 35.13) of the small saturating drive transformer will provide the constant voltage necessary for a fixed frequency. Note that the feedback resistor will act as the series dropping element necessary for a simple regulator of this type. This particular inverter would require modification of the toroidal core transformer to permit a large voltage drop across the series resistor, R_F.

BIBLIOGRAPHY

Bright, Pittman, and Royer: Transistors as "On-Off" Switches in Saturable-core Circuits, *Elec. Mfg.,* December, 1954.

Card, W. H.: Transistor-oscillator Induction-motor Drive, *Communs. and Electronics,* no. 38, pp. 531–535, September, 1958.

Feth, G. C.: Core-reset Functions in Magnetic-amplifier Analysis, parts I and II, *Communs. and Electronics,* no. 38, pp. 503–519, September, 1958.

Hurley, R. B.: "Junction Transistor Electronics," pp. 189–320, John Wiley & Sons, Inc., New York, 1958.

Jensen, J. L.: An Improved Square-wave Oscillator Circuit, *IRE Trans.,* vol. CT-4, pp. 276–279, September, 1957.

Lohr, J. F.: Transistorized Static Inverter Design, *Electronic Design,* pp. 58–61, April 16, 1958.

Lowry, H. R.: Transistorized Regulated Power Supplies, parts I and II, *Electronic Design,* vol. 4, pp. 38–41, February 15, 1956; pp. 32–35, March 1, 1956.

Middlebook, R. D.: Design of Transistor Regulated Power Supplies, *Proc. IRE,* vol. 45, pp. 1502–1509, November, 1957.

Sherr, S., and P. M. Levey: Design Considerations for Semiconductor-regulated Power Supplies, *Electronic Design,* vol. 4, pp. 22–24, July 15, 1956.

Smyth, R. R., and M. G. Shorr: Transistorized Power Sources for D-C to A-C and D-C to D-C Conversion, *Electronic Design,* November 15, 1956.

Swartz, Seymour: "Selected Semiconductor Circuits Handbook," part 9, pp. 1–46, John Wiley & Sons, Inc., New York, 1960.

Thomas, Donald R.: Transistorized Power Converters, Device-Circuit Notes, Semiconductor-components Division, file A-59-1, Texas Instruments, Inc., Dallas.

Uchrin, G. C., and W. O. Taylor: A New Self-excited Square Wave Oscillator, *Proc. IRE,* vol. 43, p. 99, January, 1955.

Wasserman, Reuben: Self-excited Transistor D-C–A-C Converter Design, *Electronic Design,* pp. 78–81, April 13, 1960.

36

Switching-mode Voltage Regulators

The primary advantage of a switching regulator over a conventional regulator is that relatively low power is dissipated in the series regulating transistor. Consequently, the full current capabilities of the transistor can be used with minor emphasis given to its thermal characteristics.

A comparison of the power dissipation in the series regulating transistor of conventional and switching regulators is given in the following example: A 2N1907 is used as the series regulating transistor in both regulators, and the regulated output is 20 volts d-c at 5 amp with an input of 45 volts d-c. The 2N1907 collector dissipation is 125 watts in the conventional regulator, but it is only 8 watts (or less) in the switching regulator. Complete calculations for determining the collector dissipation in the 2N1907 switching transistor are given in Sec. 36.5.

The advantages of the switching regulator over conventional series regulators may be summarized as follows:

1. Higher efficiency, hence lower power dissipation and smaller physical size.
2. Use of fewer, more economical transistors.
3. High power-output capabilities.

36.1. CIRCUIT ANALYSIS

A block diagram of a switching regulator is shown in Fig. 36.1. The regulated output voltage is applied to the d-c controlled multivibrator which generates pulses whose duty cycle depends upon the difference in voltage between the d-c reference and the regulated output. The multivibrator pulses are applied to a switching driver which operates the series transistor switch. A low-pass filter is used to integrate the pulses at the output of the series switch. Ripple voltage from the unregulated d-c supply is filtered by modulation of the switching duty cycle; however, the switching frequency must be much greater than the ripple frequency.

36.2. D-C CONTROLLED MULTIVIBRATOR

One possible circuit for the basic multivibrator is shown in Fig. 36.2. The d-c reference voltage, $V_{(ref)}$, is applied to the base of Q_2 through a voltage divider. The regulated output voltage is applied to the base of Q_1. Transistors Q_1 and Q_2 are

463

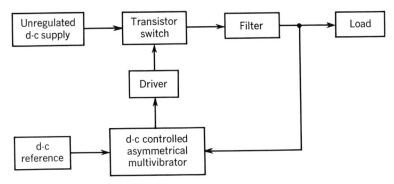

Fig. 36.1.   Block diagram of switching regulator.

connected as a differential amplifier, which drives another differential amplifier composed of Q_5 and Q_6. The collector currents of Q_5 and Q_6 provide the charging currents for C_1 and C_2, respectively. The duty cycle depends upon I_{C5} and I_{C6}, and will change when the voltage at the base of Q_1 is changed. Degeneration is provided in the emitter circuits of Q_5 and Q_6 to make I_{C5} and I_{C6} less dependent on the h_{FE} of each transistor.

The waveforms for the case in which the collector currents of Q_5 and Q_6 are equal are shown in Fig. 36.3. The period is

$$T = t_1 + t_2 \tag{1}$$

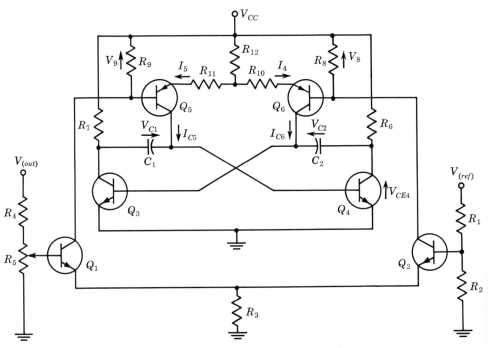

Fig. 36.2.   D-c controlled asymmetrical multivibrator.

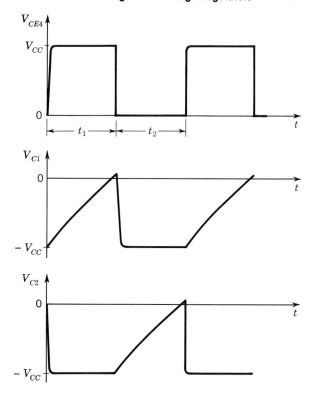

Fig. 36.3. Multivibrator
voltage waveform.

Neglecting the rise and fall times of V_{CE4}, the duty cycle is

$$\tau = \frac{t_1}{t_1 + t_2} \tag{2}$$

The relationship between charging current and capacitance of the timing circuit
may be determined from the equation

$$V_c = \frac{1}{C} \int i_c \, dt \tag{3}$$

where V_c = voltage across the capacitor, and i_c = charging current. The collector
currents of both Q_5 and Q_6 are assumed to be reasonably constant during the
positive charging periods of C_1 and C_2. Therefore, Eq. (3) may be written for these
periods as follows:

$$t_1 = \frac{V_{CC} C_1}{I_{C5}} \tag{4}$$

and

$$t_2 = \frac{V_{CC} C_2}{I_{C6}} \tag{5}$$

where I_{C5} and I_{C6} are the collector currents of Q_5 and Q_6, respectively, and V_{CC} =
supply voltage. When a load, R_L, is connected to the collector of Q_4, V_{CC} in Eq.
(5) must be replaced by $V_{CC}[R_L/(R_6 + R_L)]$. The equation which shows how a

change in τ is related to the difference between regulated output voltage, $V_{(out)}$, and reference voltage, $V_{(ref)}$, is derived as follows:

$$V_{B1} = V_{(out)} K_1 \tag{6}$$

and

$$V_{B2} = V_{(ref)} K_2 \tag{7}$$

where K_1 and K_2 are the voltage-divider ratios in the base circuits of Q_1 and Q_2, respectively. Since Q_1 and Q_2 are connected as a differential amplifier,

$$V_9 - V_8 = A(V_{B1} - V_{B2}) \tag{8}$$

where A = voltage gain of the differential amplifier. For a symmetrical differential amplifier,

$$\Delta V_9 = -\Delta V_8 \tag{9}$$

Thus,

$$\Delta V_9 = \frac{\Delta(V_{B1} - V_{B2})A}{2} \tag{10}$$

and

$$\Delta V_8 = \frac{-\Delta(V_{B1} - V_{B2})A}{2} \tag{11}$$

If R_{10} and R_{11} are equal, and the change in voltage across each is large compared to ΔV_{BE5} and ΔV_{BE6}, then

$$I_{C5} + I_{C6} = I_o \tag{12}$$

where I_o is a constant. Thus,

$$\Delta I_{C5} = \frac{\Delta(V_{B1} - V_{B2})A}{2R_{11}} \tag{13}$$

and

$$\Delta I_{C6} = \frac{-\Delta(V_{B1} - V_{B2})A}{2R_{10}} \tag{14}$$

Assuming $C_1 = C_2$, and $R_L \gg R_6$,

$$\tau = \frac{I_{C6}}{I_{C5} + I_{C6}} = \frac{I_{C6}}{I_o} \tag{15}$$

Thus,

$$\Delta\tau = \frac{\Delta I_{C6}}{I_o} = \frac{-\Delta(V_{(out)} K_1 - V_{(ref)} K_2)A}{2I_o R_{10}} \tag{16}$$

The equations which show how frequency varies with duty cycle are given as follows:

$$T = t_1 + t_2 = V_{CC} C_1 \left(\frac{1}{I_{C5}} + \frac{1}{I_{C6}} \right) \tag{17}$$

and

$$f = \frac{1}{T} = \frac{I_{C5} I_{C6}}{V_{CC} C_1 (I_{C5} + I_{C6})} \tag{18}$$

Substituting Eqs. (12) and (15) into (18),

$$f = \frac{(\tau - \tau^2) I_o}{V_{CC} C_1} \tag{19}$$

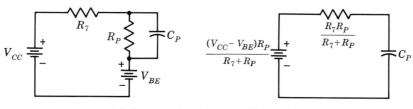

(a) Charging circuits during ON time of Q_4

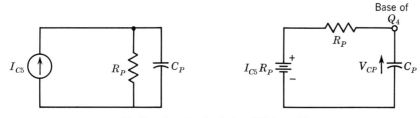

(b) Charging circuits during OFF time of Q_4

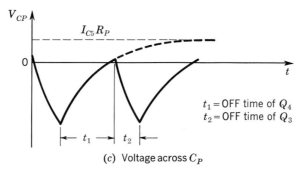

$t_1 =$ OFF time of Q_4
$t_2 =$ OFF time of Q_3

(c) Voltage across C_P

Fig. 36.4. Approximate equivalent charging circuits of C_P.

As an example of the change in f for a given change in duty cycle, assume that the frequency at which $\tau = 0.5$ is f_o. If τ is changed to 0.15 or 0.85, then

$$f = 0.51 f_o$$

To decrease the change in frequency when low or high duty cycles are approached, C_1 can be replaced by a parallel combination of a resistor, R_p, and a capacitor, C_p. The value of R_p is arbitrary; however, good frequency stability has been obtained by choosing R_p such that the sum of R_7 and R_p can saturate Q_4 when both I_{C5} and I_{C6} are zero. The value of C_p can be obtained by referring to the equivalent circuits in Fig. 36.4.

36.3. DRIVER CIRCUIT

The driver circuit may be analyzed by referring to Fig. 36.5. The driver transistors Q_7 and Q_8 are operated as switches, and are saturated when driven with the positive pulses from the multivibrator. The value of R_{18} must be chosen such that Q_9 will be saturated when $E_{(in)}$ is minimum. The maximum collector current of

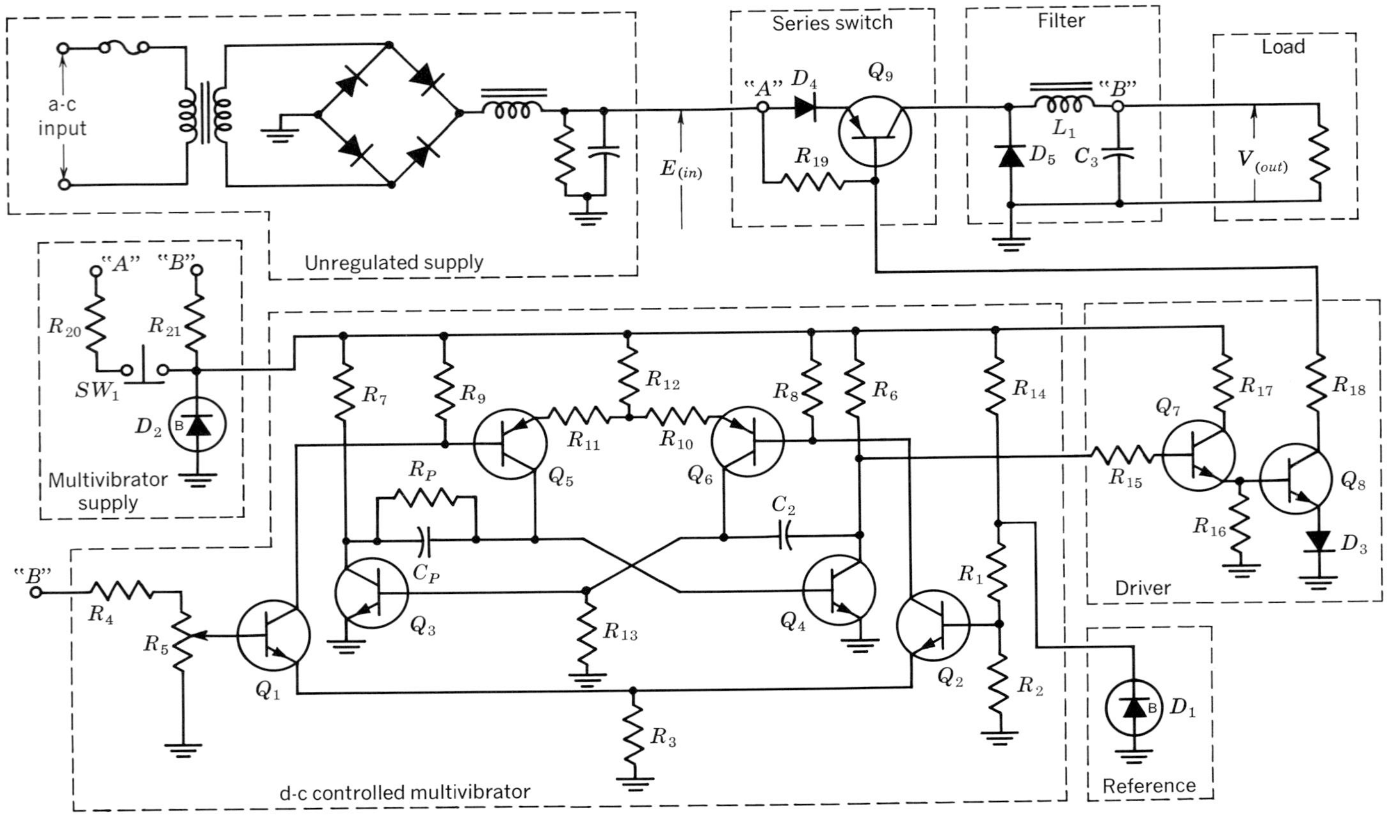

Fig. 36.5. 100-watt switching regulator.

Labels in figure: Load, Filter, Series switch, Unregulated supply, Driver, Reference, d-c controlled multivibrator, Multivibrator supply, a-c input, $V_{(out)}$, $E_{(in)}$, "A", "B", SW_1

Parts List

Resistors*	Kilohms		Resistors*	Kilohms		Resistors*	Kilohms
R_p	4.7		R_8, R_9	10		R_{17}	270 ohms
R_1	1.8		R_{10}, R_{11}	2.2		R_{18}	110 ohms, 20 watts
R_2, R_3	3.3		R_{12}	4.7		R_{19}	33 ohms
R_4	3.0		R_{13}	47		R_{20}	200 ohms, 10 watts
R_5	1.0		R_{14}	680 ohms		R_{21}	82 ohms, 2 watts
R_6	470 ohms		R_{15}	2.0			
R_7	2.2		R_{16}	680 ohms			

Transistors		Diodes and rectifiers		Capacitors	μf
Q_1, Q_2, Q_3, Q_4	2N1304	D_1	1N751	C_p	0.02
Q_5, Q_6	2N1305	D_2	1N2499	C_2	0.001
Q_7	2N1302	D_3	1N2069	C_3	1,000
Q_8	2N1720	D_4	1N1581		
Q_9	2N1907	D_5	XR-78	Inductor	
				L_1	10 mh

* All resistors ±5%, ½ watt, unless otherwise specified.

Q_8 occurs when $E_{(in)}$ is maximum; therefore, the collector current rating of Q_8 must be determined for this condition. The value of R_{15} must be chosen such that Q_7 and Q_8 are saturated when the collector current of Q_8 is maximum. The collector-to-emitter voltage rating of Q_8 must be greater than the maximum value of $E_{(in)}$.

The approximate equation for the collector power dissipation in the driver transistor Q_8 can be determined by assuming the current and voltage waveforms are as shown in Fig. 36.6. When the transistor is OFF, the energy, ϵ, dissipated is

$$\epsilon_{C1} = T_{OFF} V_{CE(off)} I_{C(off)} \tag{20}$$

During the ON time,

$$\epsilon_{C2} = T_{ON} V_{CE(sat)} I_C \tag{21}$$

Neglecting $I_{C(off)}$, the collector current and collector-to-emitter voltage during the switching interval may be written as follows:

$$i_C = I_C \frac{t}{T_{SW}} \tag{22}$$

and

$$V_{CE} = V_{CE(off)} - [V_{CE(off)} - V_{CE(sat)}] \frac{t}{T_{SW}} \tag{23}$$

The energy dissipated during one switching interval is

$$\epsilon_{C3} = \int_0^{T_{SW}} i_C V_{CE} \, dt \tag{24}$$

After integration and grouping of terms, Eq. (24) becomes

$$\epsilon_{C3} = \frac{T_{SW} I_C}{6} (V_{CE(off)} + 2V_{CE(sat)}) \tag{25}$$

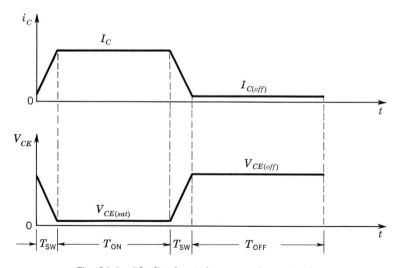

Fig. 36.6. Idealized switching waveforms for Q_8.

Thus, the total collector power dissipation is

$$P_{C8} = \frac{T_{OFF}}{T} V_{CE(off)} I_{C(off)} + \frac{T_{ON}}{T} V_{CE(sat)} I_C + \frac{T_{SW}}{T} \frac{I_C}{3} \left(V_{CE(off)} + 2 V_{CE(sat)} \right) \quad (26)$$

where T = period of waveform
T_{ON} = ON time of transistor
T_{OFF} = OFF time of transistor
T_{SW} = switching interval
$V_{CE(sat)}$ = collector-to-emitter saturation voltage
$V_{CE(off)}$ = collector-to-emitter voltage during OFF time
I_C = collector current during ON time
$I_{C(off)}$ = collector current during OFF time

36.4. SERIES SWITCHING CIRCUIT

Assuming that the power dissipation in Q_9 (Fig. 36.5) is low, the maximum collector current rating may be utilized by choosing L_1 such that the collector current is reasonably constant during the conduction time of Q_9. The voltage across L_1 during this time is

$$V_{L1} = E_{(in)} - V_{(out)} = L_1 \frac{dI_{C9}}{dt} \quad (27)$$

where $E_{(in)}$ = d-c input voltage
$V_{(out)}$ = regulated output voltage
I_{C9} = collector current of Q_9 during ON time

The ripple voltage across C_3 is much less than V_{L1}, assuming

$$C_3 \gg \frac{1}{\omega^2 L_1} \quad (28)$$

where ω = switching frequency in radians per second. Thus,

$$\frac{dI_{C9}}{dt} = K \quad (29)$$

during the ON time of Q_9, and

$$L_1 = \frac{\Delta t (E_{(in)} - V_{(out)})}{\Delta I_{C9}} \quad (30)$$

where $\Delta t = T_{ON}$ = ON time of Q_9. Equation (30) may be used to determine L_1 such that $\Delta I_{C9} \ll I_{C9}$ during the ON time. Therefore,

$$I_{C9} \cong I_L \quad (31)$$

where I_L is the direct load current. Thus, the maximum load current a switching regulator can deliver is approximately equal to the maximum collector current rating of the series switching transistor.

The equation that relates duty cycle to the input and output voltages of the regulator is derived as follows: Assume that Eq. (30) is satisfied such that $\Delta I_{C9} \ll I_{C9}$ during T_{ON}. Neglecting the circuit losses, the average power, P, transferred from the d-c supply to the load is

$$\bar{P} = E_{(in)}I_{C9}\tau \tag{32}$$

where $\tau = $ switching duty cycle. The load power may also be expressed by the equation

$$\bar{P} = I_L V_{(out)} \tag{33}$$

Substituting Eqs. (31) and (33) into (32) yields

$$\tau = \frac{V_{(out)}}{E_{(in)}} \tag{34}$$

where

$$E_{(in)} \geqq V_{(out)}$$

The collector dissipation for the series switching transistor Q_9 can be determined by referring to the waveforms shown in Fig. 36.7.

Dissipations during the OFF and ON times are given by Eqs. (20) and (21), respectively. During the switching interval, D_5 and L_1 will cause the collector voltage to switch much faster than the collector current. Thus, the approximate equation for V_{CE} during this interval is

$$V_{CE} \cong V_{CE(off)} \tag{35}$$

Neglecting $I_{C(off)}$, the collector current during the switching interval is

$$i_C = I_C \frac{t}{T_{SW}} \tag{36}$$

The energy dissipated during the switching interval is

$$\epsilon_{C3} = \int_0^{T_{SW}} i_C V_{CE} \, dt \tag{37}$$

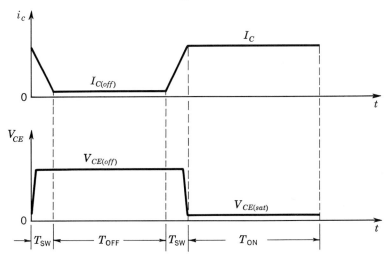

Fig. 36.7. Idealized switching waveforms for Q_9.

After integration, Eq. (37) becomes

$$\epsilon_C = \frac{T_{SW} V_{CE(off)} I_C}{2} \tag{38}$$

Thus, the total collector power dissipation is

$$P_{C9} = \frac{T_{OFF}}{T} V_{CE(off)} I_{C(off)} + \frac{T_{ON}}{T} V_{CE(sat)} I_C + \frac{T_{SW}}{T} V_{CE(off)} I_C \tag{39}$$

During the OFF time of Q_9, D_4 and R_{19} minimize the collector leakage current. The diode D_5 transfers the stored energy in L_1 to the load during this time, and must have a peak current rating equal to the maximum collector current of Q_9. Since D_5 conducts when Q_9 is OFF, the collector-to-emitter voltage rating of Q_9 must be greater than the maximum value of input voltage, $E_{(in)}$.

Other Design Considerations. *Temperature Compensation.* Since differential amplifiers are used to control the multivibrator, the regulator will exhibit good temperature stability if the avalanche diode D_1 has a temperature coefficient near zero, and the resistors R_1, R_2, R_4, and R_5 have temperature coefficients that are nearly equal. The value of D_1 and the corresponding current necessary to approach a zero temperature coefficient can be determined by referring to the data sheets for Texas Instruments voltage-regulator diodes.

Short-circuit Protection. The regulator will exhibit short-circuit protection if Q_9 is turned OFF immediately after a short, and remains OFF until the short is removed. This may be accomplished by removing the multivibrator supply voltage during the short-circuit condition. The starting resistor R_{20} is connected to point A through a start button SW_1 so that it is normally disconnected from the circuit except during starting of the regulator. When a short occurs, the multivibrator supply voltage will go to zero, and remain there until the short is removed and the start button is pushed.

Transient Suppression. A positive-voltage transient will appear at the output of the regulator when the load current is suddenly decreased, and will be maximum when the load current is switched from full to no load. Neglecting the losses in the output filter and the current in R_{21}, the maximum voltage that will appear at the output is

$$V_{O(max)} = \sqrt{V_{(out)}^2 + \frac{L_1 I_{L(max)}^2}{C_3}} \tag{40}$$

Thus, the L_1/C_3 ratio should be minimized within practical limits to reduce the output-voltage transient.

A low inductance-to-capacitance ratio should also be chosen for the filter of the unregulated supply in Fig. 36.5 to reduce the supply-voltage transient resulting from a sudden change in load current. If the ratio is not low enough, the output of the unregulated supply can momentarily drop below the regulated voltage when the load current is suddenly increased, and the regulator may begin oscillating with the unregulated supply.

To prevent an output-voltage transient from occurring when starting the regulator, SW_1 should be closed before the a-c input voltage is applied to the rectifying

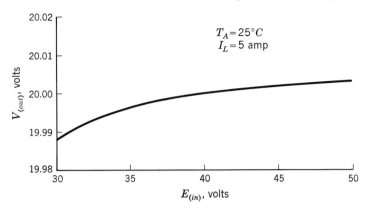

Fig. 36.8.   Output voltage vs. d-c input voltage.

circuit.   Assuming that the response time of the regulator is short compared to the unregulated supply filter, regulation will begin before the output of the unregulated supply is appreciably larger than the regulated voltage.

36.5.   DESIGN EXAMPLE

A 100-watt switching regulator has been built, using the circuit and list of recommended components in Fig. 36.5, to meet the following specifications:

$V_{(out)}$ = 20 volts.
I_L = 0 to 5 amp.
$E_{(in)}$ = 40 ± 10 volts.
Input frequency to the unregulated supply = 60 cps.
Operating temperature = −25 to 50°C.
$R_0 \leq$ 0.02 ohms.
Overall voltage regulation $\leq$ ±0.2 volt.

Circuit Performance.   *Series-switch Power Dissipation.*   The maximum collector dissipation in the series switching transistor Q_9 in Fig. 36.5 occurs when the

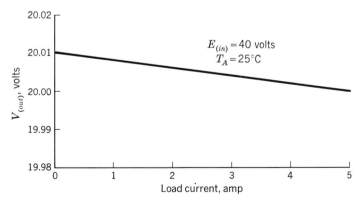

Fig. 36.9.   Output voltage vs. load current.

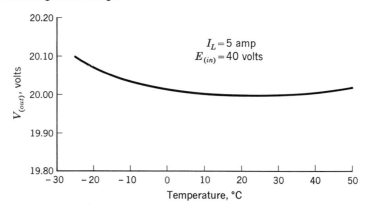

Fig. 36.10.   Output voltage vs. temperature.

load current and a-c input voltage to the rectifying circuit are maximum.   The values used in Eq. (39) for these conditions are as follows:

$$T = 100 \ \mu sec \qquad T_{ON} = 44 \ \mu sec \qquad T_{OFF} = 52 \ \mu sec \qquad T_{SW} = 2 \ \mu sec$$

$$V_{CE(sat)} = 1 \ \text{volt} \qquad V_{CE(off)} = 45 \ \text{volts}$$

$$I_{C(off)} = I_{CBO} = 50 \ \text{ma} \qquad I_C = 5 \ \text{amp}$$

Thus, $$P_{C9} = 1.17 + 2.20 + 4.50 = 7.87 \ \text{watts}$$

The 10-kc switching frequency will result in more power dissipation than a lower frequency, as indicated by the third term of Eq. (39).   This frequency was chosen, however, to minimize the size of the output filter.

Regulation Characteristics.   Typical regulation curves for the switching regulator are shown in Figs. 36.8 to 36.10.

The average values for regulation factor F, output resistance R_0, and regulation temperature coefficient K_T are 0.0007, 0.002 ohm, and 0.0011 volt/C°, respectively. From these values, the regulator performance can be determined from the regulation equation:

$$\Delta V_{(out)} = F \ \Delta E_{(in)} + R_0 \ \Delta I_L + K_T \ \Delta T$$

The values of $\Delta E_{(in)}$, ΔI_L, and ΔT are specified as 20 volts, 5 amp, and 75 C°, respectively.   Thus,

$$\Delta V_{(out)} = 0.11 \ \text{volt}$$

37

Switching-mode Motor Control

37.1. ADVANTAGES OF SWITCHING-MODE CONTROL

A series d-c motor is used in applications where variable-speed operation and high starting torque are required; various techniques are available for speed control of a d-c motor in such applications. Each of these techniques is based on a common principle: regulating the speed of the motor by controlling the input power to the motor.

The most common method of controlling the speed of a series motor is to use a variable resistor inserted in series with the motor. This method is particularly applicable when the available power supply consists of a constant-voltage source, such as a storage battery. The power supplied is divided between the motor and the series resistor, with the resulting disadvantage that the system is inefficient when the power loss in the rheostat is high. Another disadvantage is that the potential drop across the resistance will cause poor speed regulation with respect to varying loads.

A more desirable method of speed control involves the use of a periodically operated switch, inserted in place of the series rheostat. The continual opening and closing of the switch regulates the input to the motor; variation of the time duration of the ON and OFF positions of the switch provides a control of the speed of the motor. Figure 37.1 shows the time relationship between the OFF and ON positions of such a switch for various settings of motor speed. One of the main advantages of this system is an efficient utilization of the available power; the switch has very high impedance when open and very low impedance when closed.

The speed regulation of a system using a switch as a speed-control element is an improvement over that of a system using a series resistance control, since potential drop across the switch varies negligibly with load current.

37.2. CIRCUIT EXAMPLE

Figure 37.2 is a block diagram of a transistorized switching circuit. This system was designed to control the speed of a 20-amp 24-volt d-c series motor with peak starting currents up to 100 amp. The power-switch stage of the circuit con-

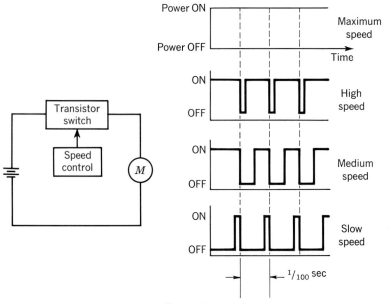

Figure 37.1

trols the power delivered to the motor, while the driver stage serves as a current amplifier, furnishing sufficient current to drive the power switch. The automatic drive-control stage controls the power level of the driver stage under varying load conditions, so that a high system efficiency can be maintained. The required ON-OFF cycling operation of the driver stage and the duty cycle of the power switch are controlled by a variable resistor in the multivibrator. The multivibrator also establishes the period of the switching cycle.

Figure 37.3 is a complete schematic diagram of the speed-control system. A rectifier and a capacitor are placed in parallel across the motor, to minimize the possibility of damage to the power transistors when they switch off the heavily inductive motor load. Without the rectifier and the capacitor a high voltage would

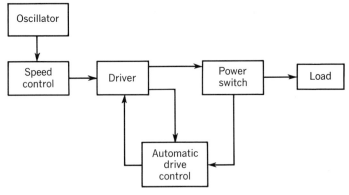

Fig. 37.2. Block diagram.

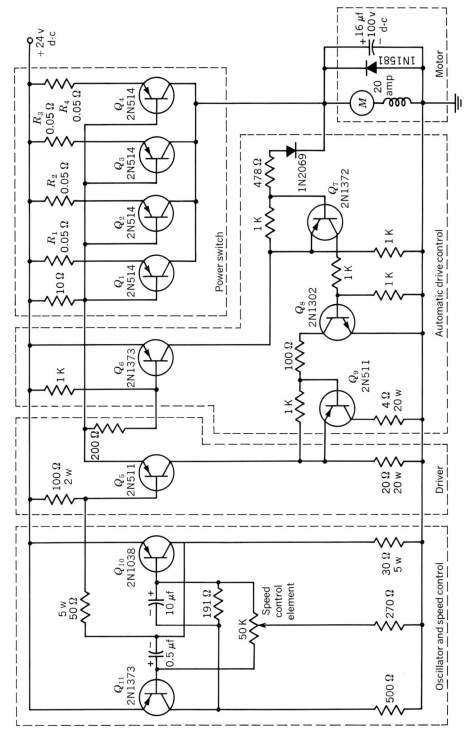

Fig. 37.3. Complete schematic diagram of speed-control system.

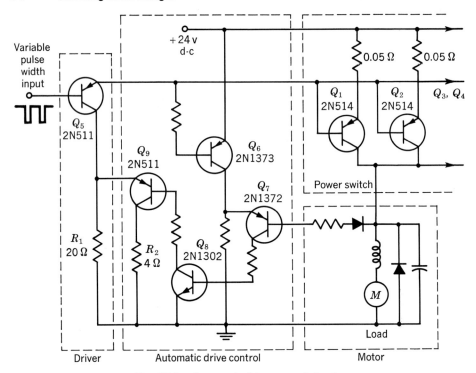

Fig. 37.4. Automatic drive-control circuit.

appear across the power-switch stage during turn-off, because of the reverse voltage induced in the motor windings when the current is interrupted.

The power-switch stage of the circuit consists of four parallel 2N514 transistors. Four transistors were necessary because the current required by the motor in a starting or stalled condition approaches 100 amp; 2N514 transistors can carry an absolute maximum collector current of 25 amp. Special precautions must be taken to assure an equal division of current among the four power-switch transistors. Emitter resistors provide compensation for variations in $V_{CE(sat)}$, h_{FE}, and forward transfer admittance (Y_{FE}). The resistor values are a compromise between efficiency and current distribution of the paralleled transistors. Increasing these values reduces the circuit efficiency, but provides better equalization of collector currents.

A factor to be considered when transistors are used in switching circuits is that the transistors must remain in a saturated state while handling large currents, in order to keep the transistor power dissipation to a minimum. If a saturated condition is to be maintained over a wide range of collector current variations, the base current must be sufficiently large to accommodate the largest anticipated value of I_C in conjunction with the lowest value of h_{FE}. If I_B is too small to keep the transistor in a saturated state, the resulting increase in power dissipation could exceed the transistor's power rating. However, if I_B is maintained at a value corresponding to the largest anticipated value of $I_{C(max)}/h_{FE(min)}$, the driver stage is inefficient when only moderate values of I_C are required (normal operation of the motor).

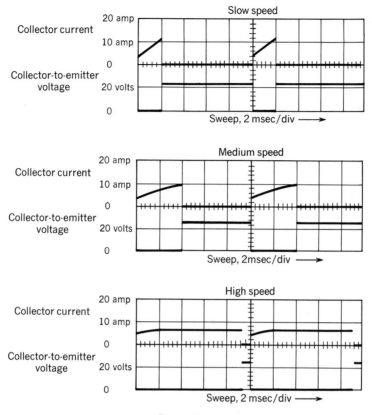

Figure 37.5

Provision should be made for automatic variation in I_B when I_C is varied. This is accomplished in the speed-control system by an automatic drive-control circuit (see Fig. 37.4). The automatic drive-control stage, represented by Q_6, Q_7, Q_8, and Q_9, senses any difference in V_{CE} of Q_6 and the power-switch transistors. If the paralleled 2N514 transistors in the power-switch stage are not in saturation during any portion of the ON cycle of operation, the base voltage of Q_7 will become negative with respect to its emitter voltage, and the transistors Q_8 and Q_9 will begin to conduct. This conduction will cause more base current to flow into the power-switch stage of the circuit, driving that stage back into saturation.

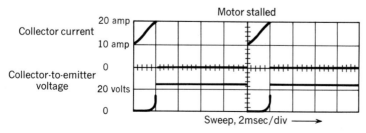

Figure 37.6

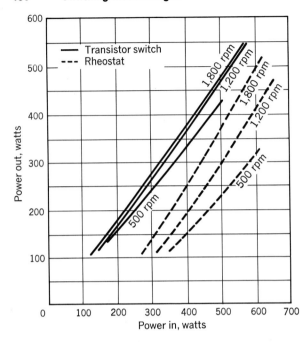

Fig. 37.7. Control element: power out vs. power in (speed = constant).

Figure 37.5 shows oscilloscope waveforms of the collector voltage and current for the power-switch stage of the circuit under various conditions of motor speed at an intermediate load. Figure 37.6 represents the collector current and voltage waveforms of a single transistor in the power switch under a stalled condition of motor operation, with the automatic drive-control stage removed. The waveforms shown in Fig. 37.6 indicate that the instantaneous power dissipated in the transistor at the end of the ON cycle is 240 watts. Automatic drive control is a necessity if this high dissipation is to be avoided.

Switching action of the system is provided by a multivibrator (Q_{10} and Q_{11}), which holds the driver stage either in full saturation or completely OFF. Thus, the driver stage of the system is operated at a low power-dissipation level.

The circuit component which controls the ratio of OFF and ON time for the power switch is the 50-kilohm variable resistor in the multivibrator. The extreme settings of the variable resistor will cause the switching action to cease, and the power switch will be either full ON or OFF. Intermediate settings will establish the pulse width and, therefore, the percentage of ON time for the power switch. Operating frequency of the multivibrator is approximately 100 cps.

Figure 37.7 is a comparison of power out vs. power in for three different speed settings of the control element. These curves indicate that the transistorized switch is much more efficient than the series rheostat for speed control.

The circuit was designed to function at 24 volts, and to supply a current which approached 100 amp. With minor modifications, it is flexible enough to work in applications requiring lower or higher power. Current-switching capacity of the circuit is limited only by the number of transistors paralleled in the power-switch stage and the maximum current-carrying capacity of each of the transistors.

38

Switching-mode Servo Amplifier

A common servo amplifier consists of a number of cascaded linear amplifier stages with a class B push-pull output stage supplying power to the control winding of a two-phase servo motor. Better efficiency can be achieved by replacing such an amplifier with one which operates in a switching mode.

One approach to a switching amplifier is to employ pulse-duration modulation (PDM). With this method, the input signal is used to control the pulse duration of a relatively constant repetition-rate pulse signal. The repetition rate of the pulse signal is much higher than the signal frequency, permitting the PDM signal to be filtered at the output, and thereby recovering the amplifier signal frequency. The amount of output power is a function of the power-switching capabilities of the output transistors and the duty cycle of the modulated pulse train.

A practical switching servo amplifier is shown in block form in Fig. 38.1, with waveshapes shown in Fig. 38.2. The actual circuit is shown in Fig. 38.3. The input signal controls the current sources in the free-running multivibrator, thus

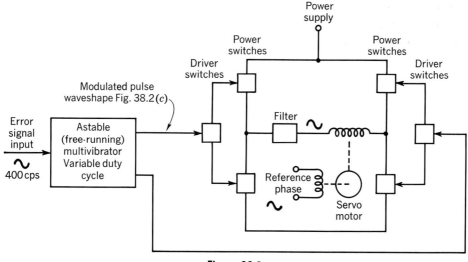

Figure 38.1

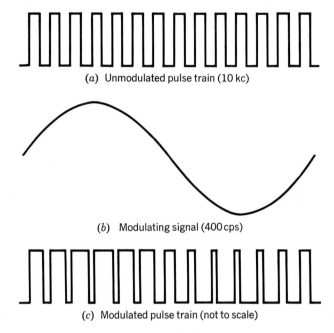

(*a*) Unmodulated pulse train (10 kc)

(*b*) Modulating signal (400 cps)

(*c*) Modulated pulse train (not to scale)

Figure 38.2

achieving PDM. The driver and power complementary transistor switches complete the circuit.

This method, while particularly useful for single-frequency applications, can also be used for varying-frequency input signals. However, this approach makes the pulse repetition rate somewhat dependent on the duty cycle. It may therefore be difficult to achieve a large separation between the pulse-train repetition rate and a varying-frequency signal.

The pulse repetition rate for this circuit is approximately 10 kc; this was a compromise between the desirable high frequency dictated by filter considerations and the low frequency required by switching considerations.

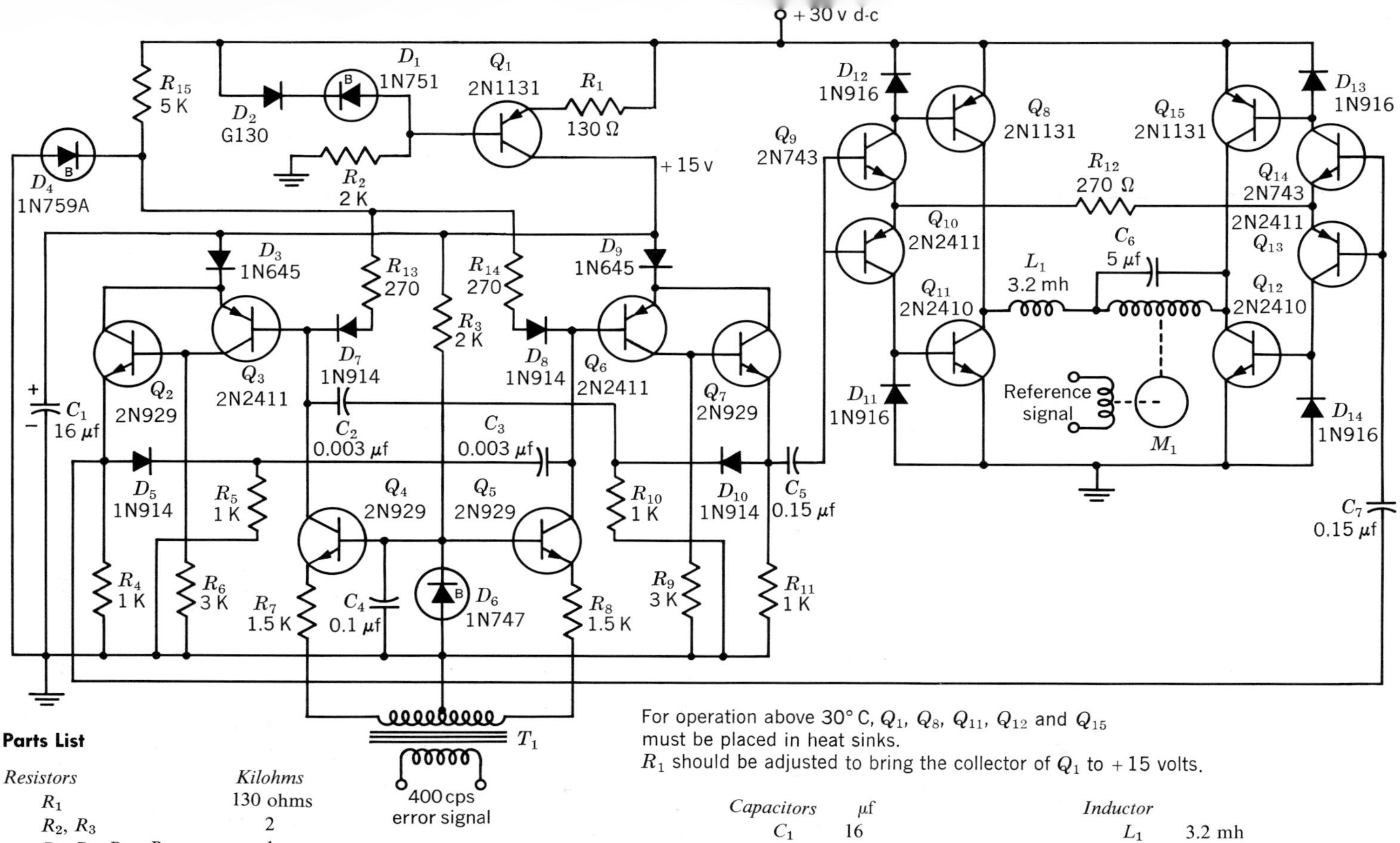

Figure 38.3

Parts List

Resistors

	Kilohms	
R_1	130 ohms	
R_2, R_3	2	
R_4, R_5, R_{10}, R_{11}	1	
R_6, R_9	3	
R_7, R_8	1.5	
R_{12}, R_{13}, R_{14}	270 ohms	
R_{15}	5	

Transistors

Q_1, Q_8, Q_{15}	2N1131
Q_2, Q_4, Q_5, Q_7	2N929
Q_3, Q_6, Q_{10}, Q_{13}	2N2411
Q_9, Q_{14}	2N743
Q_{11}, Q_{12}	2N2410

For operation above 30° C, Q_1, Q_8, Q_{11}, Q_{12} and Q_{15} must be placed in heat sinks.
R_1 should be adjusted to bring the collector of Q_1 to $+15$ volts.

Capacitors

		μf
C_1		16
C_2, C_3		0.003
C_4		0.1
C_5, C_7		0.15
C_6		5

Diodes

D_1	1N751
D_2	G130
D_3, D_9	1N645
D_4	1N759A
D_5, D_7, D_8, D_{10}	1N914
D_6	1N747
$D_{11}, D_{12}, D_{13}, D_{14}$	1N916

Inductor

L_1	3.2 mh

Miscellaneous

M_1	John Oster Manufacturing Co. type 11-5101-03

Transformer

T_1	Step-down 117–12.6-volt

483

39

Digital Servo System

The digital servo system described here demonstrates the application of transistorized circuitry to machine tool control, air-navigation computing systems, and radar. A simple and highly accurate method of positioning a mechanical object, using numerical input information, is to employ a digital servomechanism. Digital systems (often referred to as *sampled data control systems*) are gaining wide acceptance.

39.1. ANALOG VS. DIGITAL SERVOMECHANISMS

A digital servo employs digital means to compare input and output. The difference between the two numbers is a number which must be converted to a form suitable for driving the mechanical element until the digital error is reduced to zero. The digital information pertaining to the output position is obtained from some form of encoder.

In an analog system, a voltage proportional to the desired input quantity is compared with a voltage obtained from the output transducer, which is typically a potentiometer or a synchro. Thus, if the input information is obtained from a punched card or tape reader, intermediate conversion is required to change the input signal to analog form.

A good linearity for a servo potentiometer is 0.01%; in other words, the shaft can be positioned to an accuracy of 2 minutes of arc. A synchro can position a shaft to an accuracy of better than 1 minute of arc. A 19-bit shaft encoder can position a shaft within 2 seconds of the desired position. Thus, the accuracy of a digital system is potentially much greater than that of an analog system.

Of course, when dealing with this magnitude of error, noise becomes of paramount importance because of the low level of the error signal. In an analog system the error signal, being so small, usually picks up some 60-cps noise as well as noise due to the transducer, making it difficult to differentiate the error signal from the noise. The standard technique for overcoming this is to shape the frequency response suitably at the expense of transient response. In the digital system, only two levels of error signal can occur—one or zero (or typically, 20 or 0 volts).

39.2. DESCRIPTION OF SYSTEM

A block diagram of the system is shown in Fig. 39.1. The binary input consists of a series of switches, each switch representing a particular significant digit. The digital shaft encoder is a Datex C711 type, coded in Gray code. The output from the encoder is converted into natural binary code and compared with the binary input. The difference between input and output numbers results in the digital error signal, which is converted into an analog signal. This is chopped by the modulator into a phase-sensitive 60-cps voltage, the phase depending on which way the motor has to turn in order to reduce the digital error. The modulator output is amplified to drive a two-phase 3-watt Diehl motor (type FPE-25L-107-13). The tachometer is mounted integrally with the motor and is used to damp the system. The speed reducer is a 25:1 precision gear train made by Motion Control Incorporated.

39.3. SHAFT-POSITION ENCODER

The shaft encoder is of the disk type, shown pictorially in Fig. 39.2. The dark areas shown are connected through the disk to a face plate on the back of the disk. A voltage is applied to the back face by a brush, and the digital output is obtained from the fixed brushes B_0 to B_3. The disk is mounted on a shaft so that a digital output ranging from 0000 to 1111, corresponding to the shaft position, is obtained.

The disk shown is coded in binary code, but most practical disks are coded in a reflected binary code such as Gray code. The reason for this is the large angular

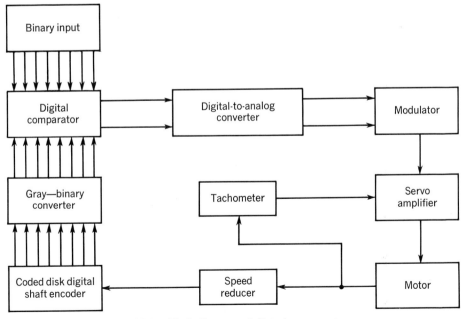

Fig. 39.1. Block diagram of digital servo system.

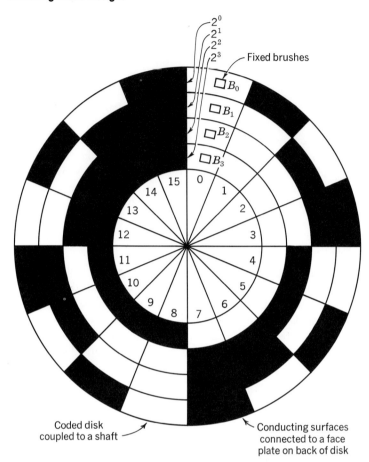

Fig. 39.2. Binary-coded disk.

error that can occur if there is any brush misalignment. Consider the shaft in position 1111, and assume that brush B_3 is advanced one sector. It will then read 0111, which corresponds to a position 180°, or eight sectors, away. The reason such a large error can occur, using binary code, is that between successive numbers more than one digit can change.

In the Gray code, only one digit changes between successive numbers. A comparison of binary and Gray codes is shown in Fig. 39.3. Considering a Gray-coded disk in position 15, and brush B_3 advanced one sector, the output is now 0000, which corresponds to position 0, or just one sector error.

The encoder used had 10 bits resolution; thus the servo was capable of positioning the shaft to an accuracy of $360°/2^{10} = 0.352°$. Only 8 bits were used for this demonstration because backlash in the gear train made the stabilization of the system difficult using 10 bits.

39.4. GRAY-TO-BINARY CONVERTER

Figure 39.4 gives the rules for converting Gray code to binary code, and the form of the conversion logic. The truth table was derived from the rules, and the Boolean expression for the logic obtained from it. NOR logic was used because this promised the simplest and cheapest system. Consequently, the Boolean expression was converted from a sum of products to a product of sums in order to obtain the least number of NOR elements to perform the logic. The basic NOR element used, and the resultant NOR logic circuit for one digit, is shown in Fig. 39.5.

39.5. BINARY COMPARATOR

The binary comparator compares the binary input with the binary number corresponding to the output position. It consists of a number of modules, one for each digit to be compared. Each module compares an input digit with the corresponding digit from the Gray-to-binary converter.

When the input digits are the same, the two outputs from each module are "one." In cases of inequality, one output will be a "one" and the other "zero," depending on which way the motor has to turn. This is illustrated in Fig. 39.6 by the truth table from which the binary comparator module is derived. The number of NOR elements used could be reduced if the output were zero when equality of inputs existed. However, this corresponds to the output transistors being in the saturated condition, and therefore the output voltages to the *DA* converter would vary considerably from device to device, causing an error output voltage from the modulator at null. If the outputs are "one" when equality exists, the output transistors are

Decimal	Binary	Gray
0	0 0 0 0	0 0 0 0
1	0 0 0 1	0 0 0 1
2	0 0 1 0	0 0 1 1
3	0 0 1 1	0 0 1 0
4	0 1 0 0	0 1 1 0
5	0 1 0 1	0 1 1 1
6	0 1 1 0	0 1 0 1
7	0 1 1 1	0 1 0 0
8	1 0 0 0	1 1 0 0
9	1 0 0 1	1 1 0 1
10	1 0 1 0	1 1 1 1
11	1 0 1 1	1 1 1 0
12	1 1 0 0	1 0 1 0
13	1 1 0 1	1 0 1 1
14	1 1 1 0	1 0 0 1
15	1 1 1 1	1 0 0 0

Fig. 39.3. Comparison of Gray and binary code representations of decimal digits 0 to 15.

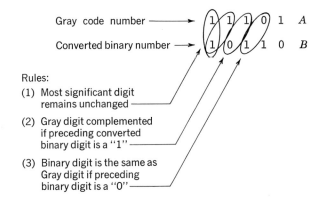

Rules:

(1) Most significant digit remains unchanged

(2) Gray digit complemented if preceding converted binary digit is a "1"

(3) Binary digit is the same as Gray digit if preceding binary digit is a "0"

Form of conversion logic:

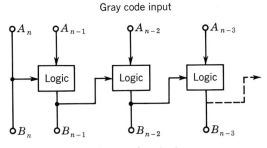

Truth table for logic:	A_{n-m}	B_{n-m+1}	B_{n-m}
	0	0	0
	0	1	1
	1	0	1
	1	1	0

$$B_{n-m} = A'_{n-m} B_{n-m+1} + A_{n-m} B'_{n-m+1}$$
$$= (A'_{n-m} + B'_{n-m+1})(A_{n-m} + B_{n-m+1})$$

Fig. 39.4. Conversion of Gray code to binary.

cut off, and the input voltages to the *DA* converter are equal, regardless of device characteristics.

39.6. DIGITAL-TO-ANALOG CONVERTER AND MODULATOR

The digital-to-analog converter converts the digital output of the binary comparator into two analog currents, the magnitude of each depending on which way the motor has to turn. The modulator subtracts these two currents, giving a phase-sensitive 60-cps square-wave output signal. The circuit is shown in Fig. 39.7. The *DA* converter consists of weighted resistors connected from each output of the binary comparator to the modulator, the weight of the resistor depending on the

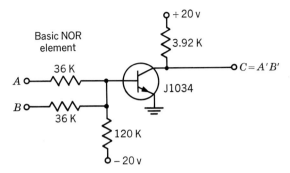

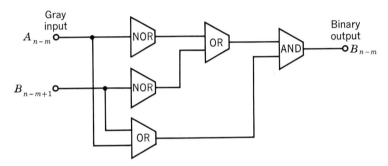

$$B_{n-m} = (A'_{n-m} + B'_{n-m+1})(A_{n-m} + B_{n-m+1})$$

Fig. 39.5. Gray-to-binary converter module.

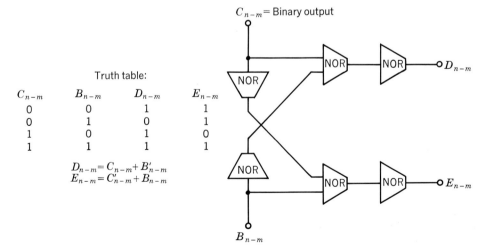

Truth table:

C_{n-m}	B_{n-m}	D_{n-m}	E_{n-m}
0	0	1	1
0	1	0	1
1	0	1	0
1	1	1	1

$$D_{n-m} = C_{n-m} + B'_{n-m}$$
$$E_{n-m} = C'_{n-m} + B_{n-m}$$

Fig. 39.6. Binary comparator module.

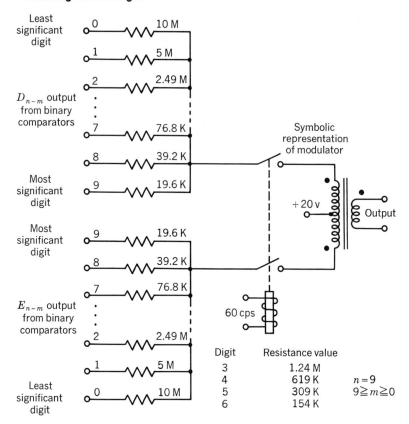

Fig. 39.7.   Digital-to-analog converter.

significance of the digit.   For example, if the only difference between input and output occurs in comparing the least significant digit (LSD), the digitizer will have to travel only one increment equal to $360°/2^8$.   Consequently, the input voltage to the motor must be just sufficient to cause it to move one increment.   However, if the difference between input and output occurs in comparing the most significant digit (MSD), the digitizer will have to rotate 180°, and the input voltage to the motor must be sufficient to drive it at full speed until the error is zero.   The resistance values are such, therefore, that for an LSD error, one unit of current will be driven into the modulator; for the next LSD error, two units of current; for the next, four; and so on up to the eighth digit or the MSD, in which 28 units of current will be driven into the modulator.   The process of demodulation is illustrated in Fig. 39.8, for a five-bit linear digitizer.   The desired position corresponds to the binary input, and this is compared with each increment as the error is reduced, using the truth table in Fig. 39.6.   The modulator output is proportional to the difference ($D_{n-m} - E_{n-m}$); the error reduces in steplike fashion, one unit of current at a time, until it is zero.

The actual circuit diagram of the modulator is shown in Fig. 39.9.   The input swing to the modulator is 20 volts, and since the transistors are used in the reversed connection to reduce the offset voltage, it is necessary that the transistors have a BV_{EBO} rating greater than 20 volts. This requirement is fulfilled by the Texas Instruments Limited alloy junction 2S302. Potentiometers between the transistors are used to compensate for the variation of offset voltage between transistors. The modulator had to be driven from the 115-volt 60-cps supply in order to maintain a precise phase relationship with the two-phase motor. Two zener diodes back to back are used as shown, to produce an approximate square-wave drive to switch the transistors ON and OFF.

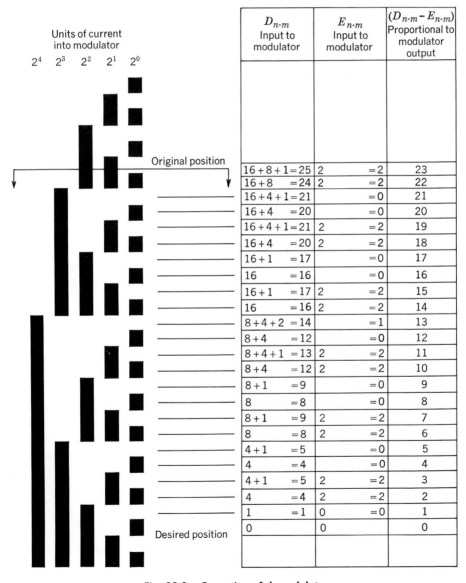

Units of current into modulator 2^4 2^3 2^2 2^1 2^0	$D_{n\text{-}m}$ Input to modulator	$E_{n\text{-}m}$ Input to modulator	$(D_{n\text{-}m} - E_{n\text{-}m})$ Proportional to modulator output
Original position	$16+8+1=25$	2 $=2$	23
	$16+8\ \ \ =24$	2 $=2$	22
	$16+4+1=21$	$=0$	21
	$16+4\ \ \ =20$	$=0$	20
	$16+4+1=21$	2 $=2$	19
	$16+4\ \ \ =20$	2 $=2$	18
	$16+1\ \ \ =17$	$=0$	17
	$16\ \ \ \ \ \ =16$	$=0$	16
	$16+1\ \ \ =17$	2 $=2$	15
	$16\ \ \ \ \ \ =16$	2 $=2$	14
	$8+4+2\ =14$	$=1$	13
	$8+4\ \ \ \ =12$	$=0$	12
	$8+4+1\ =13$	2 $=2$	11
	$8+4\ \ \ \ =12$	2 $=2$	10
	$8+1\ \ \ \ =9$	$=0$	9
	$8\ \ \ \ \ \ \ =8$	$=0$	8
	$8+1\ \ \ \ =9$	2 $=2$	7
	$8\ \ \ \ \ \ \ =8$	2 $=2$	6
	$4+1\ \ \ \ =5$	$=0$	5
	$4\ \ \ \ \ \ \ =4$	$=0$	4
	$4+1\ \ \ \ =5$	2 $=2$	3
	$4\ \ \ \ \ \ \ =4$	2 $=2$	2
	$1\ \ \ \ \ \ \ =1$	0 $=0$	1
Desired position	0	0	0

Fig. 39.8. Operation of demodulator.

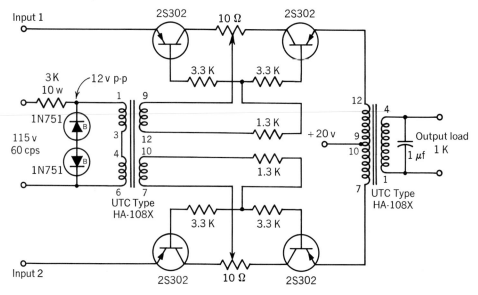

Fig. 39.9. Modulator.

Although high-quality transformers are used, some differentiation of the output waveform occurs. This is due to the direct current flowing in the primary of the transformer, causing a reduction in the primary inductance, to the high source impedance, and to the low operating frequency. The switching transients are damped by means of a 1-μf capacitor across the output.

The modulator gives a 2.4-mv peak-to-peak output signal for a 2-μa input signal on one side, and 1.1 volts peak to peak for 1-ma input signal on one side. The first corresponds to an LSD error, and the latter to an MSD error.

39.7. SERVO AMPLIFIERS

The preamplifier is shown in Fig. 39.10; it is a conventional operational type. It is used to sum the modulator and tachometer outputs. It has adjustable overall d-c feedback to ensure that when the amplifier is overloaded, equal clipping will occur, and the squared output will have equal mark-space ratio. This is to ensure that for a large error full torque will be obtained from the motor.

The power amplifier of Fig. 39.11 is used to drive the 3-watt split-phase motor. The motor is tuned with a 4-μf capacitor to make the load appear more resistive. Feedback is used to lower the output impedance, principally to improve the transient response of the motor.

39.8. SYSTEM STABILIZATION

The chief factors affecting the stability of the system are the frequency response of the motor and amplifier combination, the mechanical response of the motor, tachometer and digitizer, and backlash in the gear reducer. Backlash has the same effect as introducing a lag into the system, and its presence is generally observed

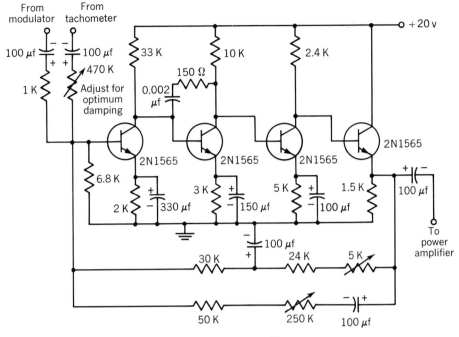

Fig. 39.10.   Preamplifier.

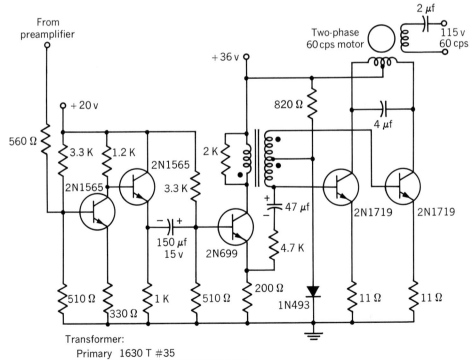

Transformer:
   Primary   1630 T #35
   Secondary   1020 T #29 Bifilar wound
   Laminations   EI 75 SL14 5 x 5 interleaved

Fig. 39.11.   Power amplifier.

as a low-amplitude high-frequency oscillation. It is, of course, imperative that the magnitude of the backlash be much less than the resolution of the servo.

The error signal from the modulator is a staircase function; consequently, the damping of the system must be such that the system is able to come to a standstill within one increment of digitizer movement. The stability of the system is adjusted by means of gain adjustment and tachometer feedback. The gain of the amplifier must be such that when there is error in the LSD only, there will be sufficient output to overcome the friction in the motor and cause motion in the output shaft. Tachometer feedback has the same effect as friction damping, without the power loss and steady-state error associated with friction damping. The gain over and above that previously mentioned was adjusted for optimum transient response of the system.

CONCLUSIONS

A simple digital servomechanism has been discussed which is capable of being adapted to an actual machine system. The digital-computer section of the system consists of NOR logic, which is flexible enough to enable use of the least expensive

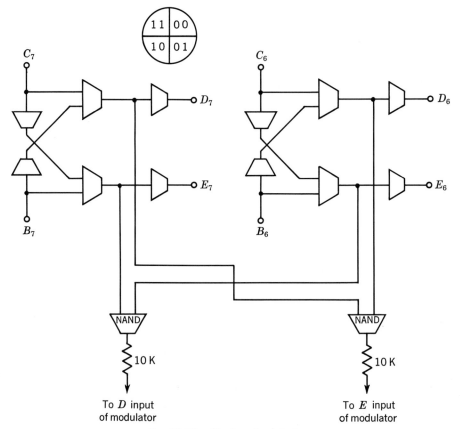

Fig. 39.12.   Short-route detector.

silicon transistors. The present system has a resolution capability of 1½°. The system is capable of positioning the shaft to a resolution of ⅓°, however, by utilizing all 10 bits, which is possible with a better gear train.

The output shaft position is indicated by a pointer on a binary-coded 90° quadrant scale. Because of the output-position indication system used, the output shaft cannot rotate more than 360°. Therefore, if the shaft is positioned 1° from reference, it will take the long route to get to 359°. This may be overcome by the addition of two NAND gates as shown in Fig. 39.12.

When the output shaft is in sector 00 and the desired position is in sector 11, then the input to the modulator from the NAND gate must be sufficient to overcome the actual signal and force the motor in the opposite direction. This can be achieved by making the weighted resistor equal to half the MSD weighted resistor. Thus, if the actual position is 1°, and the desired position is 359°, the error signal that would make the motor turn in the long-route direction will be just under twice the MSD input current. The output from the appropriate NAND circuit will be twice the MSD current, making the motor turn in the short-route direction.

APPENDIX

Field-effect Transistors

A.1 INTRODUCTION

Conventional transistors exhibit inherently low (but not zero) input impedances except when operating at very small currents. In the early years of transistor circuit design this characteristic, plus the current-oriented amplification requirements, appeared as major restrictions to the engineers who had originally worked with vacuum tubes. Time has proved that many of these objections existed only in the designer's mind, and they vanished as he learned to work with the device.

Nonetheless, there are applications where nothing but a high input impedance will do. In these cases, conventional transistor circuitry is often awkward or impossible to design. The development of the field-effect transistor (FET) was prompted by this need. However, the FET offers additional advantages which may encourage wide acceptance:

1. FETs do not depend upon minority carriers, thus their radiation resistance is good.
2. FETs are free from certain sources of noise that occur in common transistor action. At least one type of FET now in production exhibits a 3-db spot noise figure at 10 cps.
3. The power gain of the FET far exceeds that of common transistors at audio frequencies.
4. The power gain of the FET tends to increase with the current capability, so that power FETs show considerable promise.

A.2 THEORY OF OPERATION

A unipolar FET can be regarded as a structure containing a semiconductor current path whose resistance is modulated by the application of a transverse electric field.

For the sake of simplicity, consider a bar of semiconductor silicon crystal having length L, width W, thickness T, excess impurity concentration P, and ohmic (non-rectifying) contacts at each end, as shown in Fig. A.1.

497

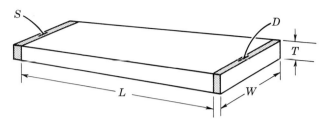

Figure A.1

The approximate bar resistance R_o between terminals S and D is

$$R_o \cong \frac{L}{(q\mu)PWT} \tag{1}$$

where q = electron charge
μ = majority carrier mobility

The factor $q\mu P$ in the denominator of Eq. (1) is the conductivity σ of the semiconductor material. A more complete expression for conductivity is

$$\sigma = q(n\mu_n + p\mu_p) \tag{2}$$

where σ = conductivity
n = electron density
μ_n = mobility of electrons
p = hole density
μ_p = mobility of holes

In this discussion we will assume that $P \gg N$ for a P-type crystal. It will be more convenient to talk about conductance G_o rather than resistance R_o:

$$G_o = \frac{1}{R_o} = \sigma \frac{WT}{L} \cong \frac{(q\mu)PWT}{L} \tag{3}$$

If we assume that the width and length of the bar in Fig. A.1 are fixed, Eq. (3) shows that the conductance can be decreased by removing some of the current carriers from the crystal or by decreasing the effective thickness T. The FET uses the depletion regions of back-biased PN junctions to control this conductive thickness.

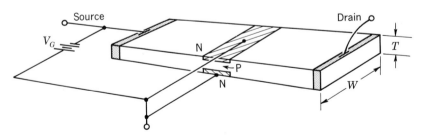

Figure A.2

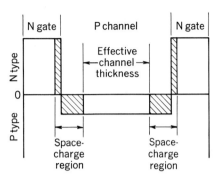

Figure A.3

Figure A.2 shows a P-type bar of silicon which has had N-type impurities introduced into opposite sides, creating PN junctions. We are interested in conductance of the P-type channel between the two N-type gate regions. Assume that any current flow between the source and drain contacts is restricted to the P-type channel. The conductance of this channel (at very low currents) is given by Eq. (3). Consider what happens to this conductance when the gate is made positive with respect to the source; that is, when a *reverse bias* is applied to the gate-to-channel PN junction.

Figure A.3 shows a representative plot of the net impurity concentration through a cross section of the bar at a given junction bias voltage. Since the charges stored on each side of the junction must be the same, the space charge will be extended farther in the purer region. It is assumed that the concentration in the N regions is uniform, the concentration in the P region is uniform, and the junction transitions are abrupt. As indicated in Fig. A.3, there will exist at each gate-channel junction a *space-charge* region, from which all free charge carriers have been removed, leaving only the nuclei and bound electrons. The width of these space-charge regions is a function of the junction potential and the impurity concentration.

Applying a reverse voltage to the gate-channel junction will cause the conductance of the channel to decrease because of a widening of the space-charge regions. Thus the conductance of the channel is an inverse function of the gate-to-channel voltage. In other words, the transverse electric *field* introduced into the channel by the gate has an *effect* on the channel conductance; hence the term *field effect*.

Now let us see what happens as the drain-to-source voltage is increased. Referring to Fig. A.4, assume that the source and gate contacts are grounded. Also assume that all parts of the gate are at ground potential (this is a reasonable assumption, since the gate current is normally very small). Now, when we apply a negative voltage V_D to the drain, a current will flow from the source through the channel to the drain. Space-charge regions will be set up as indicated by the shaded area in Fig. A.4. The current will then be confined to the neutral P-type channel between the space-charge regions.

Because of the IR drop along the channel, the reverse bias on the gate-channel junction will not be uniform along the length of the channel. The greater the distance from the source, the stronger the reverse bias on the junction; this causes the space charges to assume a wedge shape. Now we may explore in some detail the behavior of such a structure.

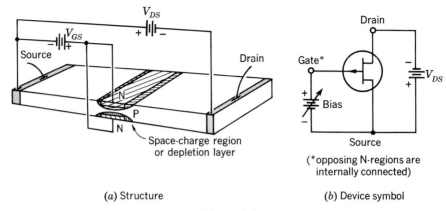

(a) Structure   (b) Device symbol

(*opposing N-regions are internally connected)

Figure A.4

A.3 DEVICE CHARACTERISTICS

Static Characteristics. *Gate Cutoff Current.* By connecting the drain to the source and reverse-biasing the gate-channel diode, a measure of the d-c input impedance and an indication of the quality of the diode can be obtained. A circuit for the measurement of this gate cutoff current I_{GSS} is shown in Fig. A.5. The voltage used in this measurement is 10 volts, the gate being positive with respect to the channel for a P-channel device. If this voltage were increased in magnitude, a voltage would be reached at which the gate-channel diode would break down. Figure A.6 shows the typical exponential variation of I_{GSS} with temperature for a silicon device. It can be seen that d-c values of short-circuit input impedance are in the thousands of megohms near 0°C.

Breakdown Voltages. In order to better understand the breakdown-voltage terminology, consider the typical drain characteristics presented in Fig. A.7 for the 2N2499. These are curves of drain current I_D as a function of drain voltage V_{DS} for the common-source configuration with gate-to-source voltage V_{GS} as a parameter. It will be noted that the gate bias voltage is of polarity opposite to that of the drain supply voltage*; hence, for ordinary bias conditions, a greater potential difference exists across the gate-drain diode than exists across the gate-source

---

* These devices can be operated with a few tenths of a volt forward bias, provided the gate-source diode is not turned on.

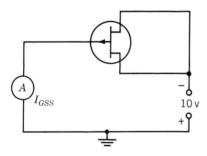

Figure A.5

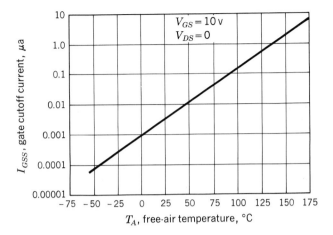

Figure A.6

diode. This implies that gate-drain diode breakdown will occur before gate-source diode breakdown. By disconnecting the source from the drain in Fig. A.5 and applying a current source of -10 μa to the drain, the drain-gate breakdown voltage BV_{DGO} can be determined under the conditions stated on the specification sheet. The smallest voltage specified for the three types of units mentioned above is -20 volts.

Since the point at which the source is connected to the channel is physically removed from the drain connection, the source can be connected to the gate in the above measurement without appreciably changing the value of the breakdown voltage. This connection yields BV_{DSS} breakdown voltage from drain to source with the gate shorted to the source. A typical value of BV_{DSS} may be seen at the break on the $V_{GS} = 0$ curve.

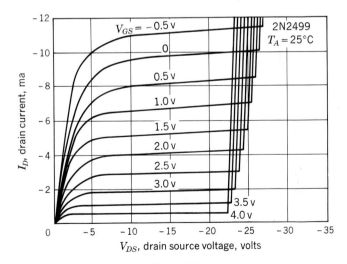

Figure A.7

The break in the drain characteristic curves may be seen to occur at lower drain voltages as the gate voltage is increased; that is, the drain-gate breakdown voltage is almost constant and independent of drain-source current. Equation (4) states the relationship suggested above.

$$BV_{DG} = BV_{DSX} + V_{GS} \cong \text{constant} \tag{4}$$

where the subscript X denotes the value of BV_{DS} for a particular value of V_{GS}. Substituting BV_{DGO} for the constant, Eq. (4) becomes

$$BV_{DSX} = BV_{DGO} - V_{GS} \tag{5}$$

Using the specified minimum BV_{DGO} and values of gate voltage, a curve can be plotted on the drain characteristic as suggested in Fig. A.8. In the area to the right of this curve, breakdown is likely to occur. The useful area on the drain characteristic is therefore between this curve and one of the characteristic curves for slightly forward gate bias. Signals on the gate which cause the gate-source diode to go into forward conduction are clipped because of the sudden drop in input impedance, but the drain current is not severely affected. If the signal causes the drain-gate diode to break down, the signal is again clipped by conduction between the drain and the gate.

Channel Pinch-off. As the magnitude of the drain voltage is increased from zero, the drain current is at first strongly dependent on drain voltage. However, as the voltage is increased further, the increasing size of the depletion layer pinches off

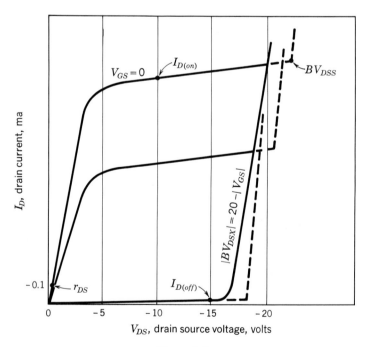

Figure A.8

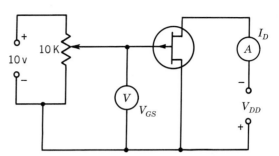

Figure A.9

current flow in the channel, and practically no further increase in drain current occurs until the breakdown voltage is reached. When a reverse bias is applied to the gate, the channel IR drop necessary to produce pinch-off will occur at a lower value of drain current, since the gate bias now supplies a part of this voltage. A pinch-off voltage may be defined as the drain-source voltage which separates the *triode region* from the *pentode region* for a given gate bias voltage; but to describe this point adequately on a smooth curve, the slope of the (drain) output characteristic line must be defined at the point of measurement.

While pinch-off voltage can adequately be described in this fashion, such a procedure is cumbersome in a large-scale production testing facility. The pinch-off parameter may also be described as the gate-source voltage required to reduce the drain current to a specified value, or it may be described in terms of drain current for specified gate and drain voltages. This last definition is used with the circuit of Fig. A.9 to measure $I_{D(off)}$. Location of the point of measurement on the drain characteristic is indicated in Fig. A.8.

Also indicated in Fig. A.8 is the point of measurement of the drain current with zero gate bias. Because of the magnitude of this current, it is called the ON current, $I_{D(on)}$. It is measured in the pinched-off region. By applying a forward bias to the gate-source diode, higher current than $I_{D(on)}$ can be realized, although the input impedance drops rapidly as the gate-source diode nears forward conduction. In the region extending a few tenths of a volt from each side of the $V_{GS} = 0$ line, the characteristic in the pinched-off region is symmetrical and linear about zero. This feature of the silicon FET allows small-signal operation with zero bias.

Variation of $I_{D(on)}$ with temperature is indicated in Fig. A.10 for the 2N2499. It is an inverse function of temperature between -50 and $125°C$. Preliminary investigations indicate that at lower temperatures $I_{D(on)}$ reaches a maximum and then decreases. With the device submerged in liquid nitrogen, the shapes of the characteristic curves are about the same as at room temperature.

Low-level Operation. Location of the point of measurement of the static drain-source resistance r_{DS} is shown near the origin on Fig. A.8. This parameter is indicative of the low-level switching capabilities of the device. Except for the condition of forward gate bias, r_{DS} represents the lowest drain-source resistance. If the drain-source voltage is maintained below pinch-off, the device can be used as a voltage-variable resistor.

Small Signal Characteristics. An important characteristic of the small-signal input admittance and reverse transfer admittance is their almost linear increase in

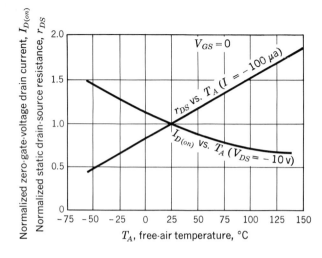

Figure A.10

magnitude with frequency. Both admittances are reactive from 10 cps to 100 mc. In Figs. A.11, A.12, A.13, and A.14 the typical variations of the input admittance and the reverse transfer admittance with frequency are shown. Figure A.11 shows that the magnitude of the input admittance begins to increase at about 1 cps. In Fig. A.12 the reverse transfer admittance begins to increase at about 50 cps. Above these frequencies, a comparison of Figs. A.11 and A.12 with Figs. A.13 and A.14, respectively, shows the real parts to be very small compared with the magnitudes of the admittances. The input admittance and the reverse transfer admittance are shown in Figs. A.15 and A.16 for frequencies up to 100 mc. The real

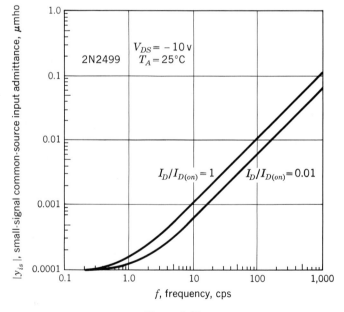

Figure A.11

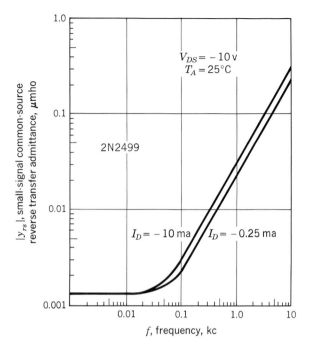

Figure A.12

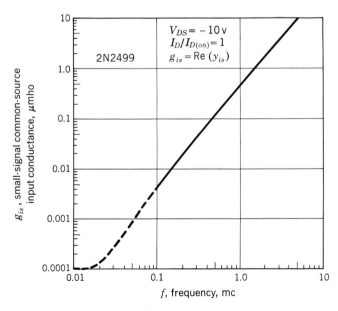

Figure A.13

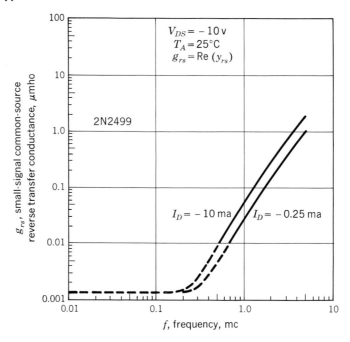

Figure A.14

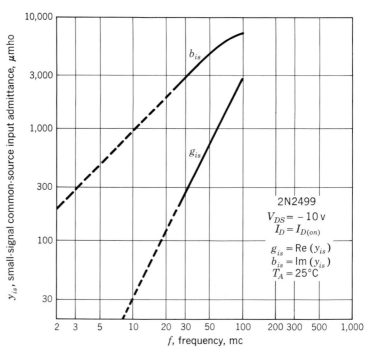

Figure A.15

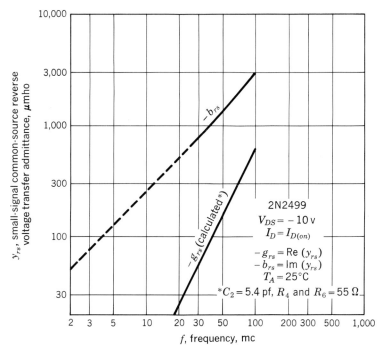

Figure A.16

and imaginary parts of these two parameters roughly correspond to the real parts and the magnitudes of the four preceding figures.

The forward transfer admittance is virtually constant and real from direct current to 20 mc. Above 50 mc the real part drops very rapidly, but the imaginary part maintains the magnitude. This is shown in Fig. A.17. Transit time in the channel material is a possible cause of the rapid drop in the real part.

The output admittance is resistive up to about 1 mc. Between 1 and 5 mc the reactive part grows larger than the real part; between 5 and 100 mc the reactive part is dominant. Figure A.18 shows extrapolations into this transition region from data taken at higher frequencies.

Figure A.19 presents an example of the geometry employed in fabricating the 2N2499 silicon FET, which utilizes advanced gaseous diffusion and photolithographic techniques of the type required to produce superior high-frequency bipolar transistors. Germanium FETs are made at Texas Instruments Inc. by a modification of the same alloy process used to fabricate ultra-reliable computer transistors.

Whatever the process, the functional structure of the FET can be reduced to that shown in Fig. A.20. This figure suggests an equivalent circuit which will represent the FET. We will develop this circuit for the 2N2499.

Because of the linear nature of the relationship of the terminal and transfer admittances with frequency, an equivalent circuit can be used to represent the 2N2499 from direct current to about 100 mc. The equivalent circuit is shown in Fig. A.21. Location of the lumped constants has been taken directly from the rep-

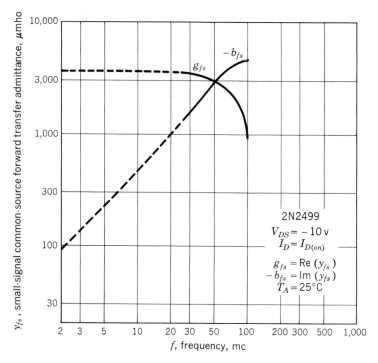

Figure A.17

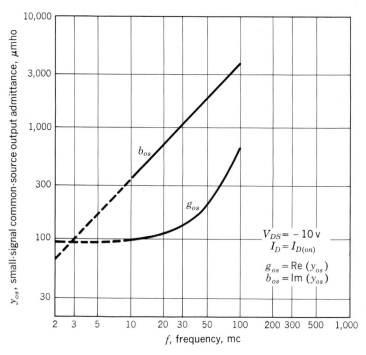

Figure A.18

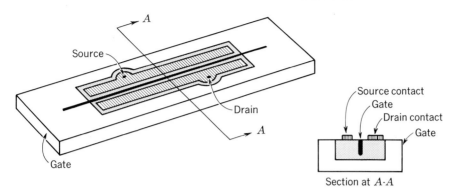

Section at A-A

Figure A.19

resentation in Fig. A.20. It is assumed that the gate current is divided between two branches at the ohmic contact, each branch current being required to flow through a bulk resistance in the gate, the space-charge layer, and a bulk resistance in the drain or source. The space-charge layer is represented by a capacitor in parallel with a leakage resistance. Joining the drain and source bulk resistances is a current generator in parallel with the differential channel resistance in the pinch-off region. The voltage which activates the current generator has been assumed to be the voltage across the gate-source capacitor. The internal d-c transconductance is g_m'. Because of internal feedback in the bulk resistance of the source R_5 the external d-c transconductance is

$$g_m = \frac{g_m'}{1 + g_m' R_5} \tag{6}$$

Large differences in magnitude exist among the resistances of Fig. A.21. Their order is as follows: $R_1, R_2 \gg r_D \gg R_3, R_4, R_5, R_6$. The approximate magnitudes are

$$R_1, R_2 \cong 10^{10} \text{ ohms}$$
$$R_3 + R_5 \cong 150 \text{ to } 200 \text{ ohms}$$
$$R_4 + R_6 \cong 50 \text{ to } 60 \text{ ohms}$$

In Fig. A.22 are shown the real parts of the forward transfer admittance and the output admittance as functions of drain current. The higher drain currents provide higher forward transfer admittance but lower output impedance. Figures A.23, A.24, and A.25 show the effects of bias current and voltage on the capacitive components of the four admittances. The input capacitance C_{is} is approximately equal to the parallel combination of C_1 and C_2 in the equivalent circuit. The output capacitance C_{os} and the reverse transfer capacitance C_{rs} are very nearly equal to C_2.

Noise Characteristics. Noise figure is defined as the amount of degradation suffered by the signal-to-noise power ratio in passing through a system. The nature of noise figure has been discussed in Chap. 21. To recapitulate, for the FET,

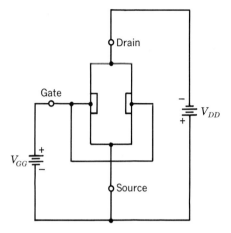

Drain

Gate

V_{DD}

V_{GG}

Source

Figure A.20

$$F = 10 \log \frac{E_{(on)}{}^2}{A_v{}^2(4\ KTBR_g)} \tag{7}$$

where $A_v = E_{os}/E_g$, the voltage gain measured at signal levels far above the noise
level

$K = $ Boltzmann's constant, 1.38×10^{-23} joule/$°$K

$T = $ temperature of R in $°$K $= °$C $+ 273$

$B = $ equivalent rectangular bandwidth of the system, cps

$R_g = $ resistance of the signal source impedance, ohms

$E_g = $ the signal source equivalent Thévenin voltage generator

$E_{os} = $ the output voltage of the FET

$E_{(on)}$ is the output noise voltage produced by R_g and system noise when $E_g = 0$.

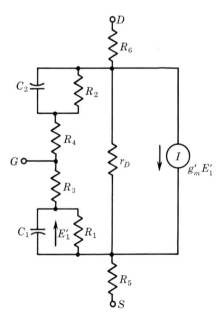

Figure A.21

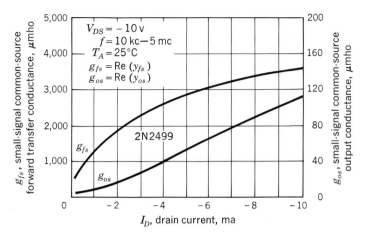

Figure A.22

All terms in Eq. (7) can be measured, and noise figure for a system can be computed. If the gain of the first stage of the system is high, noise generated by succeeding stages will be negligible at the output and the noise figure of the first stage may be considered the noise figure of the system. Figure A.26 shows the basic system used and its external equipment.

For the narrow-band noise-figure measurements, it is necessary to measure the equivalent rectangular bandwidth B, the gain G, and the output noise $E_{(on)}$, with $E_g = 0$. When gain measurements are made, the output should be monitored with an oscilloscope to check for the presence of clipping or pickup, e.g., 60 cycles. The generator output should be kept low enough to prevent clipping, and the test circuit should be placed in a well-shielded enclosure to prevent unwanted pickup. The frequency of the generator must be set at the center frequency of the filter.

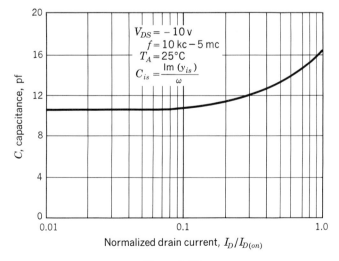

Figure A.23

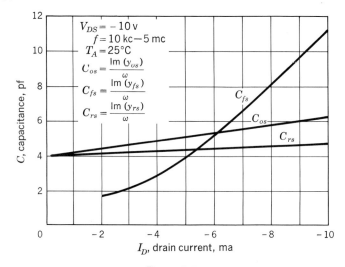

Figure A.24

For the Krohn-Hite filter, minimum pass bandwidth is obtained by setting the high and low cutoff frequencies equal.

According to Fig. A.27, the break point of the $1/f$ region is less than 100 cps. This is about half an order of magnitude lower than most transistors. The 1-megohm source resistance shown in Fig. A.27 is not optimum at all frequencies. At lower frequencies the optimum source resistance is higher; e.g., at 10 cps the

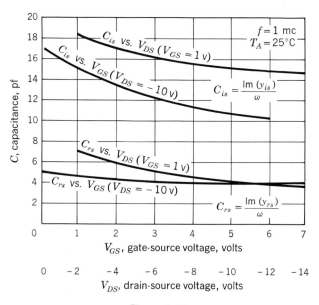

Figure A.25

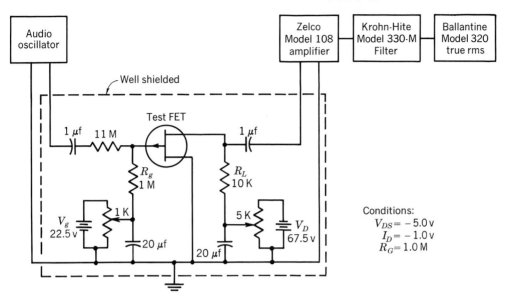

Figure A.26

optimum source resistance is about 10 megohms. Figure A.28 shows the optimum R_g and optimum NF of the 2N2500 vs. frequency. Figure A.29 shows that, contrary to operation with other transistors, noise figure is independent of operating current for the FET. Although noise figure is proportional to voltage, the change is slight over a normal operating range.

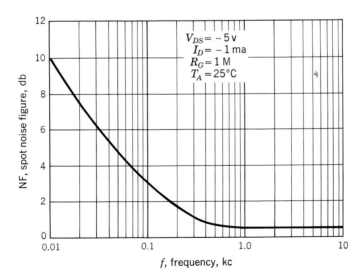

Figure A.27

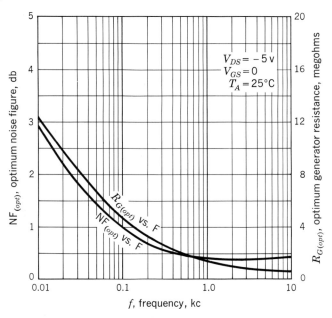

Figure A.28

A.4 BIAS DESIGN CONSIDERATIONS

The 2N2497, 8, 9 data sheet gives two sets of curves to assist the designer in setting the bias operating point.   Figure A.30 shows the gate-source voltage required to bias a field effect with a given $I_{D(on)}$ to the desired drain current.   This curve is most useful in fixed bias design, d-c amplifier design, and other design work where the gate bias voltage is needed.   The curves in Fig. A.31 are re-

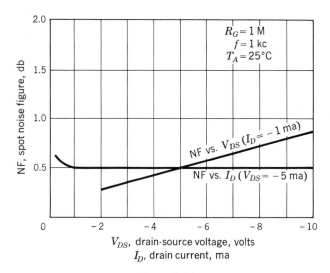

Figure A.29

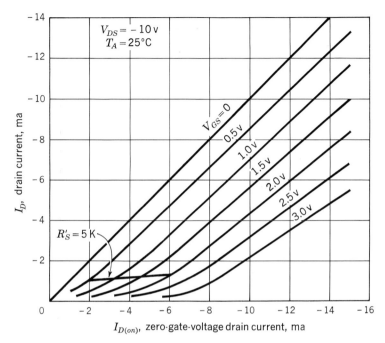

Figure A.30

lated to the curves in Fig. A.30 by the equation $R_s = V_{GS}/I_D$. These curves are given specifically for the purpose of determining the value of source resistance needed for self-biasing (circuit shown in Fig. A.31).

To illustrate the use of these curves, a bias example for each FET type has been worked up and the results are shown in Fig. A.31. Since the procedure used is not completely obvious, a detailed explanation of the 2N2498 example follows.

The easiest way to stabilize drain current with a three-to-one $I_{D(on)}$ variation for each device type is to use self-biasing. To achieve tolerable stability, the drain current I_D should be selected about half the minimum $I_{D(on)}$. In this example, -1.25 ma was selected for I_D. The value of source resistance R_s was taken from the second set of curves at the intersection of $I_D = -1.25$ ma and $I_{D(on)} = -4.0$ ma, the center value for the 2N2498. Thus, $R_s = 1$ kilohm will give a symmetrical change in I_D over the $I_{D(on)}$ range for the 2N2498. To find this change in I_D on Fig. A.31, follow the $R_s = 1$ kilohm curve to $I_{D(on)} = -2$ ma and -6 ma; the respective values of I_D are -0.75 ma and -1.75 ma. This gives a change of 0.5 ma in each direction, or a 40 per cent change of design center. This amount of operating-point stability is usually good enough for the average small-signal stage; Fig. A.32 suggests a method for achieving greater stability where desired.

Considerable increase in stability can be achieved without loss in device dynamic operating range by fixed-biasing the gate of circuit A and compensating for this by adding resistance R to R_s as shown in circuit B. Five volts was selected as a reasonable value to bias the gate. However, any value can be selected from the device standpoint, since both the gate and source are changed by the same amount

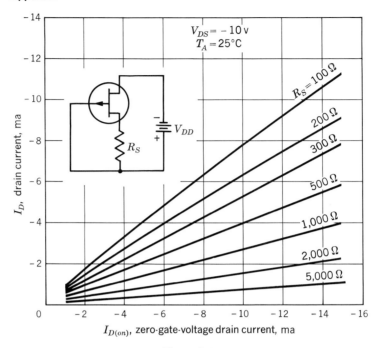

Figure A.31

to keep V_{GS} constant; therefore the device is no closer to breakdown than before. The value of R is determined by V_G/I_D, or -5 volts $\div$ -1.25 ma $= 4$ kilohms for the example. This gives a new $R_s' = 5$ kilohms. To find the increase in stability, R_s' is plotted on Fig. A.30 through the operating point as follows: symmetrical points are found on the V_{GS} curves (for 0.5 volt and 2.0 volts) by dividing the

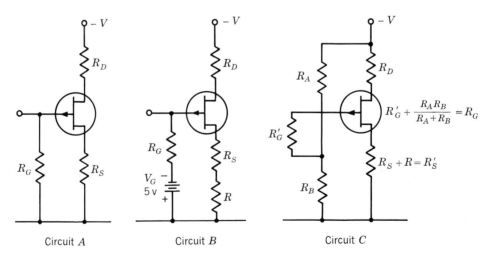

Figure A.32

Table A.1

FET type	I_D design center, ma	R_S, kilohms	R'_S, kilohms
2N2497	−0.5	2.00	12.0
2N2498	−1.25	1.00	5.0
2N2499	−4.00	0.53	1.8

differences between these voltages and the operating point V_{GS} (or 1.25 volts) by 5 kilohms.

$$\frac{1.25 - 0.5}{5 \text{ kilohms}} = \frac{2.0 - 1.25}{5 \text{ kilohms}} = \frac{0.75}{5 \text{ kilohms}} = 0.15 \text{ ma}$$

Thus, the point on the 0.5-volt curve is $I_D = -1.25 + 0.15 = -1.10$ ma, and on the 2.0-volt curve it is $I_D = -1.25 - 0.15 = -1.4$ ma, as shown on Fig. A.30. Since these points are almost the exact values of the new I_D for the -2 ma and -6 ma $I_{D(on)}$ devices, the drain current can be considered to change ± 0.15 ma, or ± 12 per cent from design center. Thus, the stability is considerably improved, I_D change being one-third that of the first case.

This analysis has shown no effects of temperature, but there are two other curves on the 2N2497, 2N2498, 2N2499 data sheet that can be used in combination with the biasing curves to determine the effects of temperature: gate cutoff current vs. temperature, and normalized $I_{D(on)}$ vs. temperature. Comparison of these curves shows that the temperature coefficient of I_{GSS} is the usual positive-log type for diode saturation current. They only tend to compensate, since the drop

Table A.2

$I_{D(on)}$, ma	V_{GS}, volts*	I_D, ma†	I_D, ma§	Per cent variation of I_D above and below design center I_D due to max and min $I_{D(on)}$	
				Circuit A	Circuit B or C
1	0.5	−0.35	−0.47		
2	1.0	−0.50	−0.50	±30%	± 6%
3	1.5	−0.65	−0.53		
2	0.4	−0.75	−1.10		
4	1.25	−1.25	−1.25	±40%	±12%
6	2.00	−1.75	−1.40		
5	0.4	−2.15	−3.2		
10	2.12	−4.00	−4.0	±45%	±19%
12	2.75	−4.60			
15	3.7	−5.80	−4.7		

* Value of V_{GS} for design center I_D in Table A.1.
† Value of I_D for R_S in Table A.1.
§ Value of I_D for R'_S in Table A.1.

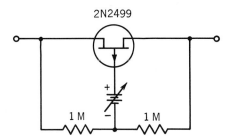

Figure A.33

in the gate resistor biases the unit ON and the $I_{D(on)}$ decreases, turning it OFF for the same changes in temperature. The temperature effect on $I_{D(on)}$ can be added to the bias stability determination by adding its variation to the ends of the normal device $I_{D(on)}$ range and then applying it to the biasing curves.

A.5 APPLICATIONS

Potential applications for the FET are virtually limitless. The typical applications presented here were selected merely to suggest its great flexibility.

Voltage-controlled Current Source. Figure A.7 showed the variation of drain current vs. gate voltage. At any given gate voltage, an increase in drain voltage beyond pinch-off will cause very little change in drain current. The device is a constant current source in this region, with drain current depending on gate voltage.

Voltage-variable Resistor. When biased with drain-source voltage below pinch-off, the FET can act as a voltage-variable resistor. The circuit of Fig. A.33 illustrates this type of application.

Timers. Figure A.34 is a circuit for a linear scale timer. The time cycle T is described by the equation $T = R_1C$, if $R_2 \ll R_1$. The potentiometer R_2 compensates for capacitor and transistor transfer tolerances. For extended time cycles, the capacitor should be a high quality Mylar® or polystyrene type.

The operation of the timer circuit in Fig. A.35 is similar to that of a one-shot multivibrator. Q_3 is normally ON, and C_1 is charged to $V_{CC} - V_{D1} - V_{BE(3)} - V_{GS(2)}$ with polarity as shown. When S_1 is pushed, Q_2 and Q_3 turn OFF. Q_3 re-

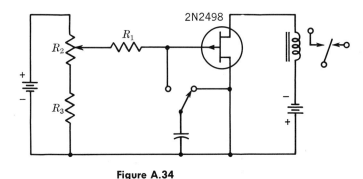

Figure A.34

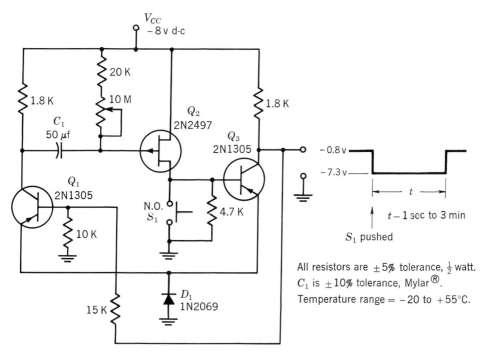

Figure A.35

mains OFF until the charge on C_1 decreases to the point where Q_2 is turned ON sufficiently to cause Q_3 to conduct.

A-C Amplifier.   The amplifier in Fig. A.36 demonstrates how FETs may be used to obtain very high input impedance without sacrificing bandwidth or low noise performance.   Input impedance is 30 megohms shunted by 8 pf.   Amplifier voltage gain is 40 db ± 0.5 db from -55 to $+125°$C.

The high input impedance is obtained by bootstrapping Q_1.   Considerable increase in stability is achieved without loss in dynamic operating range by fixed-biasing the gate of Q_1 and compensating for this by adding resistance to the source of Q_1.   By using this type of bias, a 3-to-1 change in $I_{D(on)}$ as guaranteed by the 2N2498 will produce about $\pm 12\%$ change in drain current from the design center.

Wide bandwidth is obtained by operating Q_2 grounded base to reduce the Miller capacity of the field effect at high frequencies.   By using a field effect for Q_3, it is possible to use a large load resistor for Q_2 to obtain a large voltage gain from Q_2. Figure A.37 shows the frequency response of the amplifier.

The low noise characteristics of the amplifier vs. generator resistance are shown in Fig. A.38.   The broadband noise figure of the amplifier is less than 3 db over a generator resistance range of 50 kilohms to 5 megohms.

Simple D-C Millivoltmeter.   FETs are semiconductors and, therefore, their electrical characteristics are temperature sensitive.   Thus, in direct-coupled d-c amplifiers they perform best in differential connections.   However, FETs differ significantly from transistors in that the input current is only a few nanoamps,

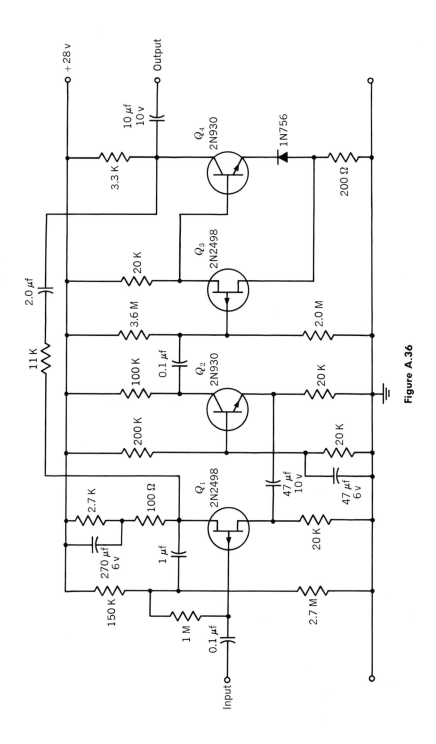

Figure A.36

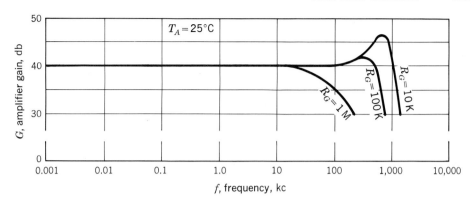

Figure A.37

being all diode saturation current, and it is therefore independent of the drain current. This makes possible low-drift amplifier performance for megohm sources. An example of this performance is given by the simple meter amplifier shown in Fig. A.39.

The differential amplifier is made up of a pair of simple two-stage feedback amplifiers with an approximate voltage gain of 3. The operating conditions of the field effect are $V_{DS} = 10$ volts and $I_D = 1$ ma. These conditions were selected to give a forward transconductance of 1,000 to 1,500 μmhos and an output impedance greater than 50 kilohms. A PNP-transistor constant-current source is used to improve operating conditions stability of FETs with $I_{D(on)}$ ranging from 1 to 6 ma and to improve the common-mode rejection ratio. When used as a d-c millivolt-meter, the circuit has an input sensitivity of 20 megohms per volt with a common-mode rejection ratio of 1,000 to 1.

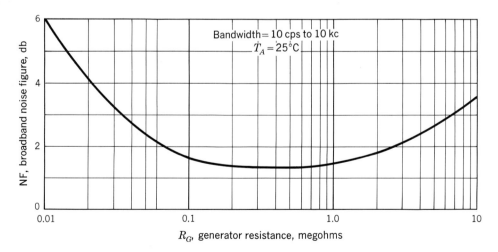

Figure A.38

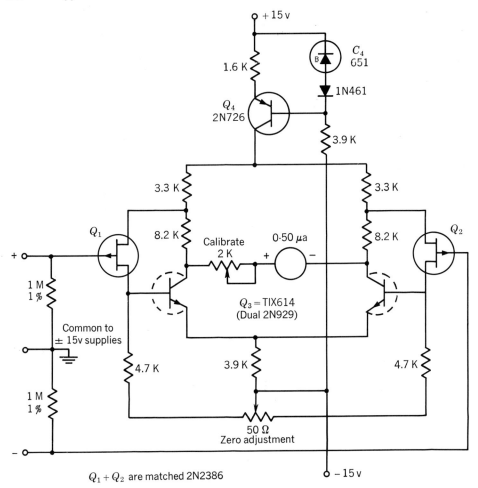

Figure A.39

Reasonably good temperature characteristics are achieved by matching the FETs as shown in the following table:

Parameter		Test Conditions	Min	Max	Units	Per cent match
$I_{D(on)}$	zero-gate-voltage drain current	$V_{DS} = -10$ v $V_{GS} = 0$	-1	-6	ma	10
V_{PO}	pinch-off voltage	$V_{DS} = -10$ v $I_D = 10$ μa	2	6	volts	10
I_{GSS}	gate cutoff current	$V_{GS} = 10$ v $V_{DS} = 0$ v		10	na	10

Temperature data from -25 to $+50°$C were taken for this circuit with matched FETs and 1-megohm gate resistors as shown. The output change was found to be linear, giving an equivalent input voltage drift of 0.175 mv per C°. This drift is lower than can reasonably be achieved with very tightly matched dual transistors under the same conditions, i.e., 1-megohm base resistors.